Elementary Coordination Chemistry

PRENTICE-HALL INTERNATIONAL SERIES IN CHEMISTRY

PRENTICE-HALL, INC.
PRENTICE-HALL INTERNATIONAL, INC., UNITED KINGDOM AND EIRE
PRENTICE-HALL OF CANADA, LTD., CANADA

J. S. Griffith:

THE IRREDUCIBLE TENSOR METHOD FOR
MOLECULAR SYMMETRY GROUPS

J. H. Hildebrand and R. L. Scott:

REGULAR SOLUTIONS

E. K. Hyde, I. Perlman, and G. T. Seaborg:

THE NUCLEAR PROPERTIES OF THE HEAVY ELEMENTS
Volume I: Systematics of Nuclear Structure and Radioactivity

E. K. Hyde, I. Perlman, and G. T. Seaborg:

THE NUCLEAR PROPERTIES OF THE HEAVY ELEMENTS
Volume II: Detailed Radioactivity Properties

E. K. Hyde:

THE NUCLEAR PROPERTIES OF THE HEAVY ELEMENTS
Volume III: Fission Phenomena

M. Jones:

ELEMENTARY COORDINATION CHEMISTRY

ELEMENTARY COORDINATION CHEMISTRY

R. W. Kiser:

INTRODUCTION TO MASS SPECTROMETRY
AND ITS APPLICATIONS

W. T. Simpson:

THEORIES OF ELECTRONS IN MOLECULES

PRENTICE-HALL INTERNATIONAL, INC., *London*
PRENTICE-HALL OF AUSTRALIA, PTY., LTD., *Sydney*
PRENTICE-HALL OF CANADA, LTD., *Toronto*
PRENTICE-HALL OF INDIA (PRIVATE) LTD., *New Delhi*
PRENTICE-HALL OF JAPAN, INC., *Tokyo*

Elementary Coordination Chemistry

MARK M. JONES

Professor of Inorganic Chemistry
Vanderbilt University

PRENTICE-HALL, INC.

Englewood Cliffs, N. J.

Current printing (last digit):

11   10   9   8   7   6   5   4   3   2

Library of Congress Catalog No. 64–21751
Printed in the United States of America
25392C

Preface

The purpose of this book is to provide an elementary introduction to that vast and fascinating fund of information which is covered by the term "coordination chemistry."

I hope that this book will provide a satisfactory introduction to coordination chemistry for chemists. It should also be of use to workers in other fields such as biology, medicine, or physics, who are interested in applications of these compounds. An effort has been made to provide a sufficiently detailed discussion of elementary aspects for the independent reader; the bibliographies provide an entry into more specialized works for those with interests in a more detailed treatment than presented here.

As with any book of this type, there is a far reaching and difficultly delineated dependence upon the standard works in the field. Among the more important of these are Bailar's "Chemistry of the Coordination Compounds," Basolo and Pearson's "Mechanisms of Inorganic Reactions," Grinberg's "Einführung in die Chemie der Komplexverbindungen," Martell and Calvin's "Chemistry of the Metal Chelate Compounds," Pascal's "Traite de Chimie Minerale," Lewis and Wilkin's "Modern Coordination Chemistry," Sidgwick's "The Chemical Elements and Their Compounds," the "Handbuchs" of Gmelin and Abegg, and last in listing, but first in importance, Werner's "Neuere Anschauungen."

The plan of the book includes numerous exercises at the ends of many of the chapters. The purpose of these is to focus attention on the detailed application of general principles to specific cases. I hope that these may be useful when the book is used as a text.

I wish to acknowledge with thanks the assistance which has been furnished by students in my courses who have read a rough draft and pointed out errors and inconsistencies. I owe a debt of thanks to those members of the Vanderbilt faculty who have read parts of the manuscript; these include Professors A. W. Ingersoll, S. P. Colowick, E. L. Lippert, Jr., L. J. Schaad, and R. V. Dilts, who commented on various parts. I wish especially to thank Professor

K. Keith Innes, who read the greater part of the manuscript and furnished innumerable improvements. Financial support for the preparation of part of the manuscript was provided by the Natural Sciences Committee of Vanderbilt University. Needless to say, I accept complete responsibility for any errors and gaucheries of speech or thought which remain after so many friends have exhausted themselves in trying to weed them out.

MARK M. JONES
Nashville, Tennessee

Contents

CHAPTER **4.** TYPICAL COMPLEXES OF THE
VARIOUS ELEMENTS   64

CHAPTER **5.** THE NATURE OF BONDING IN
COORDINATION COMPOUNDS   125

CHAPTER **6.** SOME GENERAL ASPECTS OF THE
BEHAVIOR OF COMPLEXES   173

CHAPTER 7. DETERMINATION OF THE STRUCTURES OF COORDINATION COMPOUNDS   234

CHAPTER **9.** SOME TYPES OF COORDINATION
                COMPOUNDS OF SPECIAL INTEREST   343

CHAPTER **10.** SOME APPLICATIONS OF COORDINATION
                 COMPOUNDS: 376

Elementary Coordination Chemistry

1

Introduction

SCOPE

One of the most surprising aspects of coordination compounds is the very unobtrusive manner in which they occur in numerous systems of chemical and biological importance. The name "complex compounds" suggests esoteric knowledge of a rather impractical sort to most ears, yet these materials are the key to the very breath of every human being. They are also an integral part of the complicated system of reactions by which plants remove carbon dioxide from the atmosphere for use in their growth processes. It is in their multifarious uses that we find our interests most directly affected.

An understanding of the chemical principles underlying the behavior of these compounds requires all of the theoretical chemistry that we can muster. In describing these systems we shall find it necessary to use many disciplines foreign to the field of inorganic chemistry proper. In many respects the field of coordination chemistry constitutes an area roughly analogous to that of organic chemistry, but with more of its fundamental problems unsolved. Inorganic stereochemistry, much of which is concerned with coordination compounds, is a field of considerably greater diversity than organic stereochemistry as central atoms with as many as eight or ten atoms bonded to them are encountered. All in all, we shall find the field to be one which is characterized by a bewildering, and at times chaotic, variety. This variety we hope ultimately to fit together into a coherent and meaningful pattern; only parts of this pattern are apparent at the present time.

Under the heading of "coordination compound" or "complex compound" (which terms are frequently but not always used interchangeably) will be included all those combinations of two or more atoms, ions or molecules which arise as the result of the formation of a bond by the sharing of a pair of electrons *originally associated with only one of the components* and which further possess some identifiable physical or chemical characteristics of a distinct species. Thus these will be systems where one of the constituents is a Lewis acid and the other(s) will act as Lewis bases. The Lewis bases will commonly be referred to as *ligands*. We will also consider a number of substances which do not fit neatly into this category. For the most part we will center our attention on those combinations of a central metallic cation (Lewis acid) with one or more molecules of a Lewis base or different Lewis bases in which the resultant species has physical and chemical properties quite different from those of its constituents. Within this rather hazy framework will be found species with a rather wide range of stabilities. Some possess such a transitory existence that they are barely detectable by the most subtle and sensitive methods of probing matter. Others are found which are among the most stable molecules known, capable of being sublimed at 800° C![1]

One might reasonably ask why this group of compounds should be singled out for special study. There are several kinds of answers to such a question but some of a rather practical nature are:

1. These compounds are formed by so many elements that any comprehensive chemical study must include them and any comprehensive chemical theory must explain their existence and behavior.

2. Their applications are more numerous than might be expected and new applications are being discovered each year.

3. Many chemical phenomena are exhibited to a superlative degree by these compounds (e.g., molecular rotation of polarized light and catalysis of oxygen transfer).

4. They are of vital importance in biological systems. Living matter utilizes both very stable complexes and rather unstable ones as catalysts for chemical processes.

DEVELOPMENTS PRIOR TO THE WORK OF ALFRED WERNER. It is very difficult to determine the date of the preparation of the first coordination compound. There are two reasons for this. First, some coordination compounds are found in nature and second, some practical processes known from antiquity make use of complexes, though usually poorly defined ones (a few dyes are an exception). The chemistry of complexes may be said to have originated in 1704 with the discovery of Prussian blue by Diesbach, a color maker. He told the details of his discovery to the chemist Dippel who investigated the preparation and published his results.[2] This material was prepared by heating equal parts

[1] Copper phthalocyanine: E. A. Lawton, *J. Phys. Chem.* **62**, 384 (1958).

[2] See R. Abegg, editor, *Handbuch der Anorganischen Chemie*, IV, 3, 2, Teil B, 465–469, S. Hirzel, Leipzig (1935).

of cream of tartar and saltpeter with oxblood (or animal flesh). The product was then dissolved in water, treated with green vitriol and alum, and finally hydrochloric acid to obtain the desired blue pigment. This material, called Prussian blue, has a structure which has only recently been elucidated. It is more conveniently prepared by the addition of ferric salts to solutions of soluble ferrocyanides.

After this, one may cite the investigation of the products of oxidation of ammoniacal cobalt solutions by Tassaert.[3] In the years that followed, a large amount of effort was expended on studies of the complexes of chromium, cobalt, nickel, iron, and the platinum metals. Much of this older work is reviewed in the standard works on inorganic chemistry such as the major writings of Gmelin, Dammer, and Abegg, and the texts of Pascal, Mellor, and Friend. It is generally considered that the first reliable work on the composition of the cobalt(III) ammines was begun by F. A. Genth at Marburg about 1847.[4] Following this a number of workers began a systematic study of the compositions and reactions of complexes. Names such as Cleve, Woolcott Gibbs, Blomstrand, Marignac, and Fremy are today almost forgotten; yet their work and the work of their lesser known contemporaries served as a foundation for all later theories and experiments in this field.

By 1870 a great deal of information on these complexes had been gathered and it is from this date that the work of Sophus Mads Jorgensen[5] assumes importance. Jorgensen, a professor at Copenhagen, methodized much of this field by the preparation and careful characterization of a great number of complex compounds. In this way he was able to establish the existence of several instances of isomerism, even though his explanation of the nature of the isomerism was erroneous.

As a result of the increase in activity, a great mass of experimental information of high accuracy had accumulated by 1890. However, there was no really satisfactory theoretical framework into which the information could be fitted nor was there any indication that a general system could be developed from the structural ideas then current in the field. By and large, the purely empirical viewpoint prevailed among the chief investigators of these compounds. This was soon to suffer a drastic change during the years in which the impact of Alfred Werner's ideas and experimental prowess dominated this field of study.

THE WORK OF ALFRED WERNER. At the beginning of Alfred Werner's work in this field, Jorgensen was its acknowledged master. Werner himself did not hesitate to concede his indebtedness to Jorgensen's careful experimental results. In 1890 the enormous mass of experimental data which had accumu-

---

[3] Tassaert, *Annales de Chimie*, (1) **28**, 106–107 (1799).

[4] Published as a preliminary notice in 1851. The work was completed by Genth in collaboration with Woolcott Gibbs and is reprinted in the *American Journal of Science*, (2) **23**, 234, 319 (1857); **24**, 86 (1857).

[5] G. B. Kauffman, *J. Chem. Educ.* **36**, 521 (1959); *Chymia* **6**, 180 (1960).

lated appeared to be completely chaotic to most chemists. The principal theory available for its interpretation was that of Blomstrand. This theory, which was accepted and extended by Jorgensen, considered that long chains of NH_3 groups were present in the ammines (ammonia complexes). Typical structural formulae may be seen in those presented by Jorgensen[6] for what are now named dichlorotetramminecobalt(III) chloride and the product of its reaction with water, dichloroaquotriamminecobalt(III) chloride:

$$
\begin{array}{c}
\mathrm{Cl} \\
\diagup \\
\mathrm{Co-Cl} \qquad\qquad + H_2O \quad\rightarrow \\
\diagdown \\
NH_3 \cdot NH_3 \cdot NH_3 \cdot NH_3 \cdot Cl
\end{array}
\qquad
\begin{array}{c}
\mathrm{Cl} \\
\diagup \\
\mathrm{Co-Cl} \qquad\qquad + NH_3 \\
\diagdown \qquad\qquad H \\
NH_3 \cdot NH_3 \cdot NH_3 OCl \\
\qquad\qquad H
\end{array}
$$

The chief objection to this theory was the fact that an able exponent of it could *explain* the occurrence of certain kinds of isomerism in complexes but could not successfully *predict* such behavior.

This whole field was then changed practically overnight by the genius of Alfred Werner. The anecdotes that relate how this occurred are of some interest. Werner had been concerned with a number of aspects of valence theory and had presented some of these in outline in his article "Beitrage zur Theorie der Affinitat."[7] As his interest turned away from the problems of organic stereochemistry and toward those of inorganic stereochemistry he began to develop the germ of structural theory for coordination compounds. N. Bjerrum[8] has related the following account of the manner in which this theory assumed its final form. At this time (1892) Werner was an assistant professor and a professorship was soon to be open at Zurich when Hantzsch was called to Leipzig. Werner (whose account was repeated by Bjerrum) was told by Hantzsch that he could be promoted to succeed Hantzsch if his ideas on complexes became more widely known. Hantzsch was convinced of their great importance and told Werner to write a paper in which this was made evident, especially those parts of it dealing with sixfold coordinate compounds. Werner then went into a room with a box of cigars, paper, and pen and did not leave the room until the box of cigars was gone and the paper was written. The paper was published the following year.[9] A somewhat different version is given by both Pfeiffer[10] and Berl.[11] According to both, Werner had been thinking about this problem for some time and, one morning at two he awoke with its entire

[6] S. M. Jorgensen, *Zeit. anorg. Chem.* **11**, 448 (1885); **14**, 417 (1897).

[7] A. Werner, *Vierteljahresschrift der Zuricher Naturforschenden Gesellschaft* **36**, 1 (1891).

[8] N. Bjerrum, *Proceedings of the Symposium on Coordination Compounds*, Danish Chemical Society, Copenhagen (1954), pp. 14–15.

[9] A. Werner, *Zeit. anorg. Chem.* **3**, 267–330 (1893).

[10] P. Pfeiffer, *J. Chem. Educ.* **5**, 1090–1098 (1928); *Ber.* **53A**, 9–11 (1920).

[11] E. Běrl, *J. Chem. Educ.* **19**, 153 (1942).

solution in his mind. He then got up and wrote until five to complete his theory. As a result he was promoted to a full professorship in 1895.[12] Regardless of the exact manner in which the ideas assumed their final form, subsequent events in this field have substantiated the validity of the theory which was developed and Werner himself spent the next twenty years of his life working toward this end.

In outline, Werner showed that a systematic structural chemistry of coordination compounds could be built up from the following assumptions: first, that the valencies of a metal atom may fall into primary and secondary types and second, that a constant number of directly attached atoms or groups must be arranged in a definite, fixed geometrical pattern about a central metal atom.

Werner proposed that a metallic ion, such as Co^{+3}, has two kinds of valencies which we may call principal (ionic) and auxiliary (coordinate) valencies. In the immediate neighborhood of the central ion there will be a number (usually but not invariably a fixed number) of groups which are bonded directly to the central atom and retained with greater or lesser tenacity by it. In addition to these coordinated groups (in the "inner sphere") there are present ions of charge opposite to that of the complex ion which are required to form an electrically neutral solid. Since anions as well as neutral molecules are commonly found in the coordination sphere the actual number and charge type of these other lattice ions (in the "outer sphere") will be determined by the requirement of electrical neutrality. When such a species is dissolved in water, the groups (anions or neutral molecules) in the inner or coordination sphere will tend to remain bonded to the central atom while the remaining species required to build up the neutral lattice (spoken of as the species in the outer sphere) will behave as independent particles in solution (e.g., they will conduct an electrical current, affect the colligative properties, etc.). Furthermore, the arrangement of the coordinated groups about the central ion is restricted to a relatively small number of rather highly symmetrical patterns. Thus, six groups will be arranged octahedrally about the central ion in complex species such as $Co(NH_3)_6^{+3}$, $Ir(NH_3)_6^{+3}$, $Cr(NCS)_6^{-3}$, $PtCl_6^{-4}$, $Rh(CN)_6^{-3}$, FeF_6^{-3}, and literally thousands of other complexes of the same coordination type.

When a coordinating molecule such as ethylenediamine ($H_2NCH_2CH_2NH_2$ abbreviated as "en") is present in an ion such as $Co(en)_3^{+3}$ the coordinated nitrogen atoms are again arranged at the apices of an octahedron. Such molecules, which contain two or more coordinating groups, are now called *chelating agents* or *chelons*. They usually, but not invariably, give rise to complexes with the same stereochemical disposition of ligand atoms as is found for complexes of the same central ion with simpler ligands such as NH_3 or CN^-. When four groups are found coordinated to a given central atom, two of the many possible arrangements are found to be used almost exclusively. These are the square planar arrangement of ligands such as is found in the com-

---

[12] According to Pfeiffer he succeeded Viktor Merz. Hantzsch left Zurich in 1893 to go to Wurzburg as Emil Fischer's successor.

plexes of Pd(II), Cu(II), Pt(II), and many other transition metal ions and the tetrahedral arrangement, examples of which may be seen in the complexes of Zn(II), Be(II), B(III), and many other nontransition metal ions as well as a few transition metal ions. These types are illustrated in Figure 1.

Trans–dichlorodiammine– Tetramminecopper(II) ion   Tetramminezinc(II) ion
platinum(II)

Fig. 1   Structures of *trans*-dichlorodiammineplatinum(II), the tetrammine-copper(II) ion, and the tetramminezinc(II) ion.

The opposition to Werner's theory was initially very extensive; it was accepted by Jorgensen only years later. The consequences of these ideas were far-reaching and implied that certain definite types of behavior would be observed in compounds of previously unknown types. Practically all of the stereochemical implications of Werner's ideas have been proven in detail. His treatment of isomerism in coordination compounds is still the basis for this subject, though our present knowledge of the intimate details of structure naturally extends beyond the meager information available to him.

From the publication of this theory in 1893 until the continued onslaughts of arteriosclerosis caused his mind to be deranged (i.e., for over twenty years), Werner worked out its numerous consequences in a series of brilliant experimental studies. Among the consequences, by far the most impressive are those dealing with the optical isomerism of coordination compounds. As a result of the octahedral structure of complexes such as $Cr(en)_3^{+3}$, $[Co(en)_2(NO_2)_2]^+$, and $[Co(en)_2(NH_3)(Cl)]^{+2}$, they are not superposable upon their mirror images. When a compound is superposable upon its mirror image every atom can be brought into the same relative position in both structures. When such superposability of a compound and its mirror image is not possible the result is enantiomorphs or optical isomers of the sort familiar from organic chemistry, e.g., *d*- and *l*-tartaric acid. Werner's resolution of $[Co(en)_2(NH_3)(Cl)]^{+2}$ via its +-bromcamphor-π-sulfonate in 1911 was the first such successful attempt (the experimental work was done by V. King). It was followed by numerous other resolutions and a full realization that here indeed was a powerful argument for the essential validity of Werner's theoretical postulates.

Many other aspects of Werner's work will be considered later; they are an inextricable and important part of every phase of coordination chemistry. In all, Werner published over two hundred papers and supervised over one hundred and fifty doctoral theses. Many of these contain important experimental evidence bearing on the extension of the coordination theory to an unbelievably wide range of topics. It is odd that no full scale biography of this man exists, though there are a few sketches of his life and work.[13]

DEVELOPMENTS SINCE THE INITIAL WORK OF ALFRED WERNER. Following the publication of Werner's theory the study of coordination compounds took a new and more resolute direction. It attracted numerous adherents throughout the world. A number of alternative theories appeared, but none of them has stood the test of time. The work of later investigators has refined our knowledge of the structure of complexes without destroying the grand design due to Werner.

Werner was fortunate in having a number of able contemporaries who accepted his structural ideas and used them as a guide in the detailed development of various parts of this field. These include P. Pfeiffer, L. A. Tschugaev, and H. Ley, who developed the field of inner complex salts and chelates. In 1905 Tschugaev discovered the reaction of nickel(II) and dimethylglyoxime so commonly used in analytical work and Ley gave the correct interpretation of the reaction of copper(II) and glycine in this same year (this was independently proposed by G. Bruni). The work of G. Bodlander, N. Bjerrum, and others on the stability constants of complexes began shortly after 1893 and gained new momentum from the work of J. Bjerrum, I. Leden, and G. Schwarzenbach in the late 1930's and early 1940's. The stereochemical aspects of coordination theory were extended especially by F. M. Jaeger and F. G. Mann during the 1920's and early 1930's, while the systematic exploitation of the coordination chemistry of the platinum metals was carried out by a large group of Russian chemists of whom the most prominent are I. I. Tscherniaev and A. A. Grinberg. Early work on the catalytic properties of complexes may be seen in the work of Y. Shibata and K. Shibata while the related problems involving biochemically interesting coordination compounds were attacked by F. Haurowitz, O. Warburg, F. J. W. Roughton, and others. Studies of the stabilization of unusual oxidation states were carried out by P. Ray while numerous applications of coordination compounds in analytical chemistry and the theoretical principles underlying their mode of action were examined by F. Feigl, W. Prodinger, J. Yoe, and many others. The preparative aspects of the field were not neglected either, as may be seen in the example of the work of Delepine (especially on iridium complexes) and Dubsky (polynuclear complexes).

[13] Pfeiffer, loc. cit.; Berl, loc. cit.; G. T. Morgan, *J. Chem. Soc.* **117**, 1639 (1920); P. Pfeiffer, *Angew. Chem.* **33**, 37 (1920); J. Lifschitz, *Zeit. Elektrochem.* **26**, 514 (1920); P. Karrer, *Helv. Chim. Acta* **3**, 196 (1920); idem, C. Matschoss *Manner der Technik* (1925), p. 290; idem, *Schweizerische Chemikerzeitung*, p. 73 (1920); W. Klemm, *Zeit. anorg. Chem.* **248**, 314 (1941).

The theoretical aspects of bonding in these compounds were soon cast into a more definite form. In a way Werner was one of the last major chemical theorists who worked essentially in independence of the continuing developments in physics. A simple electrostatic theory was proposed by Kossel and many calculations on a similar basis were carried out with encouraging results by Magnus and Garrick. At an early date (1909), measurements on the thermodynamic properties of complexes were undertaken by A. B. Lamb.

While electrons were not very commonly considered to be of importance chemically when Werner proposed his theory, it is a tribute to his insight that N. V. Sidgwick was able to incorporate most of the structures given by Werner into the Lewis picture of electron pair bonds without difficulty. Perkins and Sidgwick developed the concept of the coordinate bond by proposing that the ligand species shared a pair of electrons with the central atom to form an electron pair bond of the same general nature as was found in classical covalent compounds. The compounds which Werner studied were mostly ones which possessed considerable stability and in many respects were analogous to organic compounds. In recent years studies on less stable materials have become especially prominent and these are also found to fit very neatly into the general scheme proposed by Werner.

No cursory examination can do justice to the work in this field in the last quarter century and to single out names would lead to invidious comparisons which would serve no useful purpose. Suffice it to say that coordination chemistry has grown throughout these years and continues to expand in both breadth and depth. The later chapters in this book have as their purpose the discussion of many features of this development.

2

Nomenclature and Types of Coordinating Agents

NOMENCLATURE

NOMENCLATURE PROBLEMS. The problem of devising suitable names for complex compounds is a very serious one for which only a partial solution is presently available. Names for most of the simple compounds may be written using the I.U.P.A.C. rules but anyone who wishes to be able to read the literature in this field must be aware of the nomenclature difficulties peculiar to it and familiar with the several systems of nomenclature, some of which are no longer in use. It is of interest to note that the most recent reference works in this field use slightly different systems of nomenclature. It is possible to use any of the variants on the basic I.U.P.A.C. system without being unintelligible to workers versed in the other methods. Initially, two of the obsolete systems will be considered since these are extensively used in the older literature. Subsequently the "modern" system and its variants will be examined in some detail.

One of the first attempts at a systematic nomenclature was by Fremy. Fremy used names based on the colors of the compounds as described by Chevreul's color system. As might be imagined, this was not altogether satisfactory. In several cases, however, it led to common names which have been retained and may still be seen in the journal literature. Some of these names are given below with their structural equivalents.

STEM	EXAMPLE
luteo- (yellow)	luteocobaltic chloride, $[Co(NH_3)_6]Cl_3$; also used for other hexammines
rhodo- (shade of red)	rhodo-chromic chloride, $[(NH_3)_5Cr—OH—Cr(NH_3)_5]Cl_5 \cdot H_2O$

erythro- (carmine red)	erythro-chromic bromide

$$[(NH_3)_5Cr\text{—}O\text{—}Cr(NH_3)_5]Br_4 \cdot H_2O$$
$$|$$
$$HBr$$

purpureo- (purplish-red)	purpureocobaltic chloride, $[Co(NH_3)_5Cl]Cl_2$; also used for other halopentammines
praseo- (green)	praseocobaltic chloride
	trans-$[Co(NH_3)_4Cl_2]Cl \cdot H_2O$
roseo- (red)	roseocobaltic chloride $[Co(NH_3)_5(H_2O)]Cl_3$
flavo- (brown)	flavocobaltic nitrate *cis-*$[Co(NH_3)_4(NO_2)_2](NO_3)$
croceo- (yellowish)	croceocobaltic nitrate *trans-*$[Co(NH_3)_4(NO_2)_2](NO_3)$
violeo- (violet)	violeocobaltic chloride *cis-*$[Co(NH_3)_4Cl_2]Cl \cdot \frac{1}{2}H_2O$
xantho- (golden yellow)	xanthocobaltic nitrite $[Co(NH_3)_5(NO_2)](NO_2)_2 \cdot 2H_2O$

Similar listings may be found in several of the common reference works in this field.[1]

With the introduction of stereochemical ideas into this field by Werner, the inadequacy of previous systems was obvious. Werner therefore developed a system of nomenclature which is used in much of the literature of the first half of the present century. It also forms the basis for the modern systems of nomenclature which have improved upon many of the detailed rules by making them simpler but no less specific. The rules devised by Werner may be summarized as follows:

1. A vowel or vowel-consonant combination is suffixed to the name of the metal to indicate its oxidation state in the complex:

-a-	univalent		*-an-*	pentavalent
-o-	bivalent		*-on-*	hexavalent
-i-	tervalent		*-in-*	heptavalent
-e-	tetravalent		*-en-*	octavalent

In this system $HgCl_2$ is mercurochloride. This rule is not used for neutral complexes, in which the name of the metal is used without modification.

2. The cation is named first and then the anion.

3. In naming a complex, the groups bonded to the central atom are given before the name of the central atom.

The bonded groups are named in the following order: negative, neutral, positive. Within each of the charge classes the groups are named alphabetically with the exception of water (*aquo-*) which is the first of the neutral groups to be designated and ammonia ((*ammine-*) which is the last. The alphabetical ordering of the negative ligands is not always followed.

---

[1] G. Urbain and A. Senechal, *Introduction a la Chimie des Complexes*, Librairie Scientifique, A. Hermann et Fils, Paris (1913), pp. 127–133; J. C. Bailar, Jr., *The Chemistry of the Coordination Compounds*, Reinhold Publishing Corp., New York (1956), p. 98. Bailar also presents a very useful list (p. 97) of the formulas corresponding to the salts named for individuals, which are often cited in the literature.

4. When a complex is an anion, its name ends in *-ate.*

5. The prefix μ is used to designate bridging groups (such as the -OH in rhodo-chromic chloride) in polynuclear complexes. Werner did not use this means of designating bridging OH groups as these had the special suffix *-ol.*

6. The names of the ligands are indicated as follows: (a) negative ligands are named by suffixing *-o* to the stem. Thus *chloro-, bromo-, cyano, fluoro-, sulfato-, hydroxo-, oxalato-,* etc. (b) neutral ligands are named in much the same manner, thus $C_2H_4(NH_2)_2$ is *ethylenediamine-,* C_5H_5N is *pyridine-,* and no suffix is usually added to the name of the ligand itself. Two exceptions to this are NH_3 which is called *ammine* and H_2O which is called *aquo.*

7. The number of each species of attached groups is indicated by the appropriate prefix: *di-, tri-, tetra-, penta-, hexa-, hepta-, octa-,* etc., but no prefix is used when but a single group of a given type is present.

EXAMPLES OF WERNER'S NOMENCLATURE

$Na_3[Fe(CN)_6]$	sodium hexacyanoferriate
$K_2[MnF_6]$	potassium hexafluoromanganeate
$[Cr(NH_3)_6](NO_3)_3$	hexamminechrominitrate
$[Co(en)_2Cl(NO_2)]Br$	chloronitrodiethylenediamine-cobaltibromide
$[Cr(H_2NCONH_2)_6]Br_3$	hexaureachromibromide
$[Co(NO_2)_3(NH_3)_3]$	trinitrotriamminecobalt

The enormous advantages which resulted from the introduction of this systematic nomenclature were immediately apparent in the literature of the period. Later, the rules of Werner served as the basis for the I.U.P.A.C. rules for naming coordination compounds. The most recent set of these rules was issued in 1959. The following rules are by no means all-inclusive but serve as a rather adequate basis for naming most of the coordination compounds which will be encountered.

1. In naming complex compounds the cation is named first and then the anion.

2. In naming the constituents of the complex, the ligands are named first and then the central metal species. In writing the formulas of complexes, the central atom is written first and then the ligands.

3. The oxidation state of the central atom is indicated by a Roman numeral in parentheses which follows the name of the complex cation or anion. This may be omitted in some cases where the amounts of the various constituents are given in words, e.g., $Ca(PCl_6)_2$ is calcium bis(hexachlorophosphate) under the rules for naming simple compounds.

4. Prefixes such as *cis-, trans- d,* or *l* etc., are to be used where necessary.

5. Names of complex anions have the characteristic ending *-ate.* Names of complex cations or neutral complexes have no differentiating ending.

6. In naming the ligands; the anionic ligands are named first, then the neutral ligands, and finally the cationic ligands.

7. The anionic ligands are named in the following order: H^-, O^{2-}, OH^-, other simple monatomic anionic ligands, polyatomic anionic ligands, and finally organic anions. In naming the other monatomic anionic ligands the order is the same as that used for naming the binary compounds of the non-metals, namely: B, Si, C, Sb, As, P, N, Te, Se, S, At, I, Br, Cl, F. In naming the polyatomic anionic ligands the order is that of the increasing number of atoms in the ligand. Where two ligands have the same number of atoms, the order is that of decreasing atomic number of the central species in the ligand, e.g., CrO_4^{-2} first then SO_4^{-2}. In naming the organic ligands the order is the alphabetical one.

8. Neutral ligands are named in the following order:

first: H_2O (aquo), then NH_3 (ammine)

second: other neutral coordinated ligands in the order in which the coordinated atom falls in the series:

B, Si, C, Sb, As, P, N, H, Te, Se, S, At, I, Br, Cl, O, F

third: neutral organic ligands in alphabetical order.

9. In naming ligands, the ending *-o* is suffixed in most cases (exception: NH_3 is ammine). If the name ends in *-ide, -ite,* or *-ate* the endings used are *-ido, -ito,* and *-ato,* respectively. For some ligands custom has firmly established other names. Some of these are:

F^-	*fluoro-*	OH^-	*hydroxo-* (sometimes *hydroxy-*)
Cl^-	*chloro-*	O_2^{2-}	*peroxo-*
Br^-	*bromo-*	S^{2-}	*thio-* or *sulfido-*
I^-	*iodo-*	HS^-	*thiolo-*
O^{2-}	*oxo-*	CN^-	*cyano-*
SCN^-	*thiocyanato-* (but German *rhodanato-* sometimes seen)		

10. When the complex is an anion the metal name used is to be derived from the Latin name in some cases. Thus, plumbate, argentate, ferrate, aurate, cuprate, etc., but never hydrargyrate or stibnate.

11. When anions derived from hydrocarbons are present the ending *-o* is omitted and the organic name for the radical corresponding to the ligand species is used. Thus $Na[BH_4]$ is sodium tetrahydridoborate but $Na[B(C_6H_5)_4]$ is sodium tetraphenylborate.

12. When groups may be coordinated through different atoms the different structures are named using either (a) special names such as *thiocyanato-* for -SCN and *isothiocyanato-* for -NCS or *nitro-* for $-NO_2$ and *nitrito-* for -ONO or (b) the symbol of the element at which coordination takes place is written after the ligand name. For example, *thiooxalato-S* for a thiooxalate group coordinated through sulfur and *thiooxalato-O* for a *thiooxalate* group coordinated through oxygen.

13. For polynuclear complexes, the symbol μ is prefixed to the bridging groups. When there are several bridging groups of the same kind these are to be written *di-μ*, *tri-μ*, etc. For more complicated compounds of this class the terms *cis-*, *trans-*, *sym-*, and *asym-*, are to be used as prefixes where they are useful. If a bridging group binds more than two central atoms, the number of central atoms bridged by a given ligand is to be written as a subscript after the letter μ, e.g., as μ_3.

Examples of the use of these rules follow. It will be seen that several minor variations occur in the new systematic names when these are compared with the ones given earlier. The choice of the Greek numerical prefixes is to some extent a matter of personal taste but the present trend seems to be toward a more liberal use of *bis-*, *tris-*, *tetrakis-*, *pentakis-*, *hexakis-*, etc., when naming complexes containing complicated ligands. In this case the numerical prefix is to be followed by the name of the coordinated species in parentheses. This practice is to be commended as one which eliminates much confusion in naming complexes which contain organic ligands with long names even when these are monodentate.

$K_2[OsNCl_5]$ potassium nitridopentachloroosmate(VI)

$[Co(NH_2)_2(NH_3)_4]OC_2H_5$ diamidotetramminecobalt(III)ethylate

$Na_3[Ag(S_2O_3)_2]$ sodium bis(thiosulfato)argentate(I)

$[Fe(CN)_2(CH_3NC)_4]$ dicyanotetrakis(methylisocyanide)iron(II)

$[Ru(HSO_3)_2(NH_3)_4]$ bis(hydrogensulfito)tetrammineruthenium(II)

$NH_4[Cr(SCN)_4(NH_3)_2]$ ammonium tetrathiocyanatodiamminechromate(III)

$K[AgF_4]$ potassium tetrafluoroargentate(III)

$K_2[NiF_6]$ potassium hexafluoroniccolate(IV) but American usage calls this potassium hexafluoronickelate(IV) also

$K[CrOF_4]$ potassium oxotetrafluorochromate(V)

$Cu(C_5H_7O_2)_2$ bis(acetylacetonate)copper(II) or bis(2,4-pentanedionato)copper(II) but usage in the United States includes the names bis(2,4-pentanediono)copper(II), as well as bis(2,4-pentanedione)copper(II)

bis(4-fluorosalicylaldehydato)-copper(II)

cis-$[PtCl_2(P(C_2H_5)_3)_2]$ *cis*-dichlorobis(triethylphosphine)platinum(II)

$[Fe(dipyr)_3]Cl_3$ tris(dipyridyl)iron(III) chloride. Dipyr is the abbreviation for α,α'-dipyridyl

$[Co(en)_3]_2(SO_4)_3$ tris(ethylenediamine)cobalt(III) sulfate

$[Zn(H_2NCH_2CH(NH_2)CH_2NH_2)_2]I_2$ bis(1,2,3-triaminopropane)zinc iodide

$Na_2[Fe(CN)_5(NO)]$ disodium pentacyanonitrosylferrate(III). The NO group is considered to be a neutral ligand except where the charge on the central metal ion is known. When the composition is completely specified, as in the name given, the charge on the central metal ion *may* be omitted

$HCo(CO)_4$ hydrogen tetracarbonylcobalt(-I)

$Na[Co(CO)_4]$ sodium tetracarbonylcobaltate(-I)

[Ni(CO)$_2$(P(C$_6$H$_5$)$_3$)$_2$]   dicarbonylbis(triphenylphosphine)nickel(O)

[Fe(en)$_3$][Fe(CO)$_4$]   tris(ethylenediamine)iron(II) tetracarbonylferrate(-II)

[Mn$_2$(CO)$_{10}$]   decacarbonyldimanganese or bis(pentacarbonylmanganese)

Fe(C$_5$H$_5$)$_2$ bis(cyclopentadienyl)iron(II)

[Fe(C$_5$H$_5$)$_2$]Cl   bis(cyclopentadienyl)iron(III)chloride

K[SbCl$_5$(C$_6$H$_5$)]   potassium pentachloro(phenyl)antimonate(V). This name introduces the separation of organic groups from the rest of the name by parentheses
when only one such group is present. This will be found to be convenient in avoiding confusion with the corresponding compounds containing substituted organic
groups, e.g., chlorophenyl radicals

potassium bis(thiooxalato-S,S)niccolate(II)

dichloro(N,N dimethylaminoethylaminoethyl-
sulfide-N′,S)platinum(II)

K$_2$[Pt(NO$_2$)$_4$]   potassium tetranitroplatinate(II)

[Co(NO$_2$)$_3$(NH$_3$)$_3$]   trinitrotriamminecobalt(III)

[Co(NCS)(NH$_3$)$_5$]Cl$_2$ isothiocyanatopentamminecobalt(III) chloride

[(NH$_3$)$_5$Cr-OH-Cr(NH$_3$)$_5$]Cl$_5$ μ-hydroxo-bis(pentamminechromium(III))chloride,
alternatively pentamminechromium(III)-μ-hydroxopentamminechromium(III)

sym-trans-di-μ-chlorodichlorobis(triethylarsine)diplatinum(II)

Fe$_2$(CO)$_9$ tri-μ-carbonylbis(tricarbonyliron(O))

[Be$_4$O(CH$_3$COO)$_6$] μ_4-oxo-hexa-μ-acetatotetraberyllium(II). The common name of
this compound is basic beryllium acetate; its structure is given in Figure 2(a). It consists of a central oxygen surrounded tetrahedrally by four Be^{+2} ions, with an acetato
bridging group joining each apical beryllium with its three neighbors

[CuI(As(C$_2$H$_5$)$_3$)]$_4$ tetra-μ_3-iodo-tetrakis(triethylarsine)copper(I). The structure is
given in Figure 2(b). It consists of a tetrahedron of copper atoms with an iodine on
each face of the tetrahedron. The arsenic is coordinated to the copper in such a
manner that it completes a coordination tetrahedron surrounding the copper

From examples such as these last few, it is obvious that the correct naming
of a compound is predicated on a knowledge of its structure. In cases where
this is not known it is probably preferable to give the empirical formula. As a
general rule the empirical formula and the structural units of which the complex is composed (where these are known) will be preferable to a name of dubi-

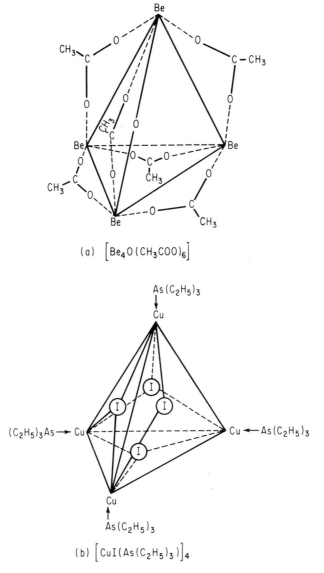

(a) $\left[Be_4O(CH_3COO)_6\right]$

(b) $\left[CuI(As(C_2H_5)_3)\right]_4$

Fig. 2 Structures of: (a) [Be₄O(CH₃COO)₆]; and (b) [CuI(As(C₂H₅)₃]₄.

ous validity. In cases of doubt reference to the I.U.P.A.C. rules is to be recommended.[2]

There are a number of problems which arise in the naming of coordination compounds which do not have generally accepted answers. Many of these have been discussed by W. C. Fernelius and his co-workers.[3] Fernelius' system is widely used and taught in the United States. It is *not* merely an extension of the *present* I.U.P.A.C. system, but allows alternative schemes for naming some compounds. Some of the important differences are:

1. In naming a sequence of coordinated groups the order is negative, neutral, positive, but within each group the ordering is alphabetical.

2. Coordinated hydrogen salts are named as acids by dropping the word hydrogen and replacing the suffix *-ate* by *-ic*.

3. The names of positively charged ligands end in the suffix *-ium*.

Unfortunately the new I.U.P.A.C. system has adopted the suggestions of Fernelius only in part, thus placing approval on a mixed and still inadequate system of nomenclature. When very intricate structures are to be named the difficulties become obvious. The greatest shortcoming is probably that there is no accepted method of naming geometrical isomers which are not *cis-* or *trans-* isomers.

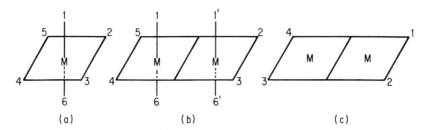

Fig. 3   Numbering system used in F. Basolo and R. G. Pearson, "Mechanisms of Inorganic Reactions," John Wiley & Sons, Inc., 1958 (Reproduced by permission of the publisher).

When naming octahedral complexes a numbering system originally used by Werner and outlined by Basolo and Pearson[4] is often advantageous.

[2] W. P. Jorissen, *et al.*, *J. Amer. Chem. Soc.* **63**, 889 (1941); K. A. Jensen *et. al.*, *Ber.* **92**, XLVII (1959); H. A. Bassett *et al.*, *J. Amer. Chem. Soc.* **82**, 5523 (1960). The nomenclature system used by Chemical Abstracts differs from this in some details. It may be found in *Chemical Abstracts* **39**, 5869 (1945); **46**, 12407 (1952).

[3] W. C. Fernelius, *Chem. Eng. News* **26**, 161 (1948); *Advances in Chemistry Series* **8**, 9 (1953); W. C. Fernelius, E. M. Larsen, L. E. Marchi, and C. L. Rollinson, *Chem. Eng. News* **26**, 520 (1948).

[4] F. Basolo and R. G. Pearson, *Mechanisms of Inorganic Reactions*, John Wiley & Sons, Inc., New York (1958), pp. 27–28.

The numbering of octahedral positions for mononuclear and binuclear complexes and for binuclear planar complexes is shown in Figure 3. Unfortunately the use of the primed and unprimed numbers for coordination positions of the same atom is sufficiently unusual to be misleading as well as hard to use in more complicated cases. This system, however, can be extended to most of the cases of structural isomerism which are found for mononuclear and binuclear complexes.

Anyone reading the literature today must bear in mind that no single system of nomenclature for coordination compounds is universally accepted. In general, the older I.U.P.A.C. rules (of 1941) are followed but with variations of at least three types to cover compounds not explicitly cited in the original committee report. In most cases the structures can nevertheless be reconstructed rather readily from the names.

TYPES OF COORDINATING AGENTS

In principle, any Lewis base (or molecule possessing one or more sites which can function as Lewis bases) can coordinate to a metallic ion or atom acting as a Lewis acid. In practice the variety of coordinating agents is very great with examples of almost every conceivable donor atom being found. The great chemical differences of a specific sort which are found make it impossible to arrange donor atoms in any absolute listing of the order of the tendency to form a coordinate bond. Some ions or atoms show a preference for one type of donor and some for another and the preference may vary with the oxidation state of the central atom. Thus chromium(III) forms very stable bonds with oxygen donors while platinum(IV) forms very weak bonds with the same donors. Just as there is no absolute scale of Lewis acidity, there is no absolute scale of coordinating ability for ligands. Many of the trends will appear later in the discussion of the complexes formed by the specific ions. A review of the varying donor specificity for the common ions has been presented.[5]

It seems necessary to concede that almost any pair of electrons not involved in a single bond may conceivably be used by its parent molecule for the formation of a coordinate bond with an appropriate Lewis acid. It is convenient to consider the most commonly encountered donor atoms group by group in the periodic table. These donor atoms usually are found in the far right-hand side of the periodic table.

GROUP VIII. In spite of earlier claims that the inert gas atoms could act as donor atoms toward Lewis acids such as boron trifluoride, later work has failed to confirm the existence of any of these compounds; there is no evidence at present that the inert gas atoms can act as donor atoms in the usual meaning of the term.

[5] S. Ahrland, J. Chatt, and N. R. Davies, *Quarterly Reviews* **12**, 265 (1958).

GROUP VII. The halide ions all form complexes with metal ions. Customarily, only one pair of electrons is donated by a halide ion or atom. This is not an absolute rule, however, as two pairs of electrons are frequently shared in polynuclear complexes containing bridging halide ions, e.g., in $W_2Cl_9^{3-}$, Al_2Cl_6, Fe_2Cl_6, etc. More rarely three pairs will be shared as in $[CuI(As(C_2H_5)_3)_3]_4$. There are two stability sequences for the halide complexes. In one, the fluoro complexes are the most stable, followed by the other halide ions arranged in order of increasing atomic number. This order, $F^- > Cl^- > Br^- > I^- > At^-$, is the order expected on the basis of simple electrostatic considerations and is commonly found for the halide complexes of small, highly charged cations with inert gas electronic structures. In the second sequence this order is reversed and the stability of the complexes decreases in the order $I^- > Br^- > Cl^- > F^-$. Ions whose complexes exhibit this type of behavior include Hg^{+2}, Cu^{+2}, and, in general, ions with an outer shell of 18 electrons. Since this is the order of the polarizability of the halide ions it is no surprise that the ions for which this holds are among the most strongly polarizing ones. While it is possible that a variety of species derived from the halogens may act as donors (e.g., polyhalide ions), there is little information available on such species.

GROUP VI. The elements in this group furnish the donor atoms for a large number of both simple and complicated ligands. Oxygen, sulfur, selenium, and tellurium, when in the -2 oxidation state, coordinate with great readiness with many cations and other Lewis acids. Oxygen in practically any of the oxides seems able to share a pair of electrons if the appropriate acceptor species is present. Water, ethers, alcohols, acid anions (both inorganic and organic), ketones, nitro compounds, and phenols are all capable of acting as donor molecules by sharing a pair of electrons on an oxygen atom.[6] Sulfide ion and its derivatives, simple and complicated, and the corresponding derivatives of selenium and tellurium are also good coordinating agents (see refs. 5, 6). Less commonly, these elements share more than one pair of electrons with Lewis acids.

GROUP V. The elements of Group V exhibit donor properties in several oxidation states, though examples of coordinating agents in which these elements are in the -3 oxidation state are by far the most numerous. Some examples of coordinating agents derived from each of these elements are listed below. Bismuth shows very little tendency to share a pair of electrons when it is present in organic derivatives or bismuthine.

---

[6] A nearly complete collection of the literature on these compounds up to 1927 may be found in P. Pfeiffer, *Organische Molekülverbindungen*, F. Enke, Stuttgart 2nd ed. (1927), p. 24 ff. See also, I. Lindqvist, *Inorganic Adduct Molecules of Oxo Compounds*, Academic Press, Inc., New York (1963).

Nitrogen	*Phosphorus*	*Arsenic*	*Antimony*	*Bismuth*
ammonia	phosphines	arsines	stibines	bismuthines
amines	PF_3	$AsCl_3$	$SbCl_3$	
cyanides	PCl_3			
nitric oxide	PBr_3			
hydrazine	$P(SCN)_3$			
azo compounds				
hydroxylamine				
nitrite				

GROUP IV. With the exception of carbon in its multiple bonded forms, the elements in Group IV have been little studied as donor atoms. Thus carbon monoxide is well characterized as a donor species in which a pair of electrons on the carbon atom is shared. The physical properties of the other monoxides are such that the analogies with carbon have not been demonstrated in this respect. Of the monoxides, carbon monoxide is the only one which is gaseous and easily studied as a donor. The others are relatively high melting solids which are not soluble in solvents without chemical change. Other organic compounds in which π electrons on a carbon atom or in a skeleton of carbon atoms exhibit donor properties include the isonitriles, ethylenic and acetylenic linkages, and of course, aromatic systems. Few, if any of the analogous compounds of the heavier elements in this family appear to have been studied as donor groups.

GROUPS III, II, and I. The elements in these groups give rise to species which function primarily as Lewis acids even though sometimes very weak ones.

VARIETIES OF LIGAND STRUCTURES

Given the large number of possible donor atoms it comes as no surprise that the types of ligand structures which have been studied are very numerous. The incorporation of the donor atoms into organic molecules gives rise to organic ligands whose structures cover a wide range of types and sizes. The most widely investigated of these organic ligands are those which contain two or more donor atoms per molecule. Such molecules are commonly called *chelating agents* and the resulting complexes are called *metal chelate compounds* or often are simply referred to as *chelates*. It is in no small part due to the *applications* of this type of compound that an expanded interest in coordination chemistry has arisen since 1945. Some examples of this type of coordinating agent are listed below. When a coordinating agent has anionic and neutral donor groups in equal numbers (usually one of each) it forms neutral complexes with any ion whose coordination number is equal to twice its charge. The resultant complexes are spoken of as inner complex salts and usually have solubility and volatility properties similar to those of organic molecules. They are widely used as insoluble precipitates in gravimetric analysis and for the solvent extraction of metals from aqueous solutions.

SOME TYPICAL CHELATING AGENTS[7]

$H_2NCH_2CH_2NH_2$ ethylenediamine

$$HOOCCH_2 \diagdown \qquad \diagup CH_2COOH$$
$$NCH_2CH_2N \qquad \text{ethylenediaminetetraacetic acid}$$
$$HOOCCH_2 \diagup \qquad \diagdown CH_2COOH$$

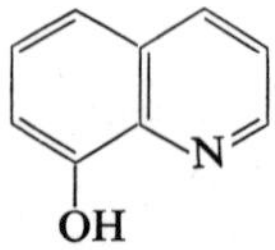

8-hydroxyquinoline or "oxine"

$CH_3C{=}NOH$
$CH_3C{=}NOH$ dimethylglyoxime

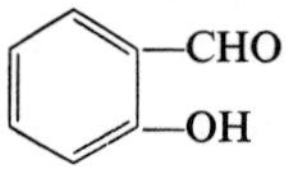

salicylaldehyde

$HN{=}C{-}C{=}NH$
$\quad HS \quad SH$ dithiooxamide or rubeanic acid

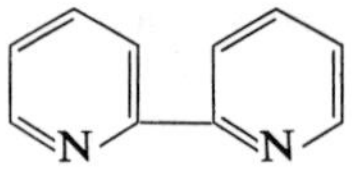

α,α'-dipyridyl

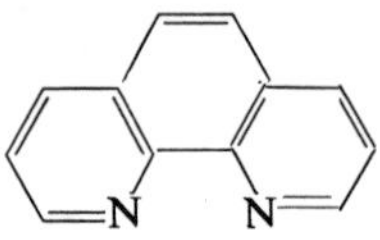

orthophenanthroline

$CH_2{-}CH{-}CH_2$ 2,3-dimercaptopropanol-1
$OH \quad SH \quad SH$ (British Anti-Lewisite or BAL)

---

[7] See also, H. Diehl, *Chem. Revs.* **21**, 39 (1937).

EXERCISES

1. Name the following complexes:

(a) $[Co(N_3)(NH_3)_5]SO_4$

(b) $LiAlH_4$

(c) $K_5[V(CN)_5(NO)]\cdot H_2O$

(d)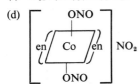

(e)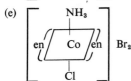

(f)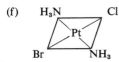

(g)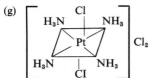

(h) $[Cr(H_2O)_5F][SiF_6]$

(i) $[Cr(H_2O)_4Br_2]Br\cdot 2H_2O$

(j) $Na[Os(O)_3N]$

(k) $[Cr(en)(C_2O_4)(H_2O)(OH)]$

(l) $K_2[VF_3(O)(H_2O)]$

(m) $K_6[Th(CO_3)_5]\cdot 1OH_2O$

(n) $(NH_4)_3[SbCl_6]$

(o) $[Cr(en)_3](SO_4)_3$

(p) $K_3[W(CN)_8]$

(q) $(NH_4)[SbCl_6]$

(r) $K_2[U(SO_4)_3]\cdot 2H_2O$

(s) $(NH_4)_2[ReOCl_5]$

(t) $K_3[Re(O_2)(CN)_4]$

(u)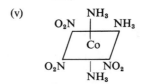

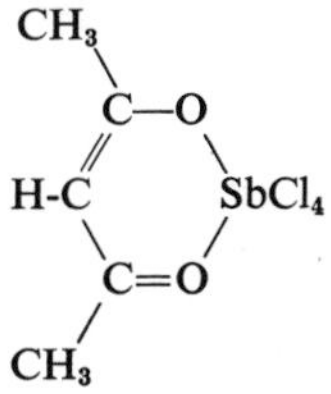

(v)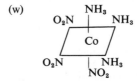

(w)

(x) $[Pt(SC(NH_2)_2)_2(NH_3)_2]Cl_2$

(y) $[Pt(P(OH)_3)_2(NH_2C_6H_5)_2]Br_2$

(z) $[IrBr_4(PCl_3)_2]$

2. Write the correct systematic name and draw the structure of the complexes whose common names are given below. Those with which you are unfamiliar may be found in reference works such as *Handbook of Chemistry and Physics* or *The Merck Index*.

sodium ferrocyanide   chloroauric acid

sodium ferricyanide   chromic nitrate hexahydrate

sodium cobaltinitrite   potassium antimonyl tartarate

sodium nitroprusside   cryolite

chloroplatinic acid   sodium fluosilicate

         gold sodium thiosulfate

3. Give the systematic names for the following polynuclear complexes:

$[(NH_3)_5Cr-OH-Cr(NH_3)_5]Cl_5$

$\{Co[(HO)_2Co(NH_3)_4]_3\}\,(SO_4)_3$

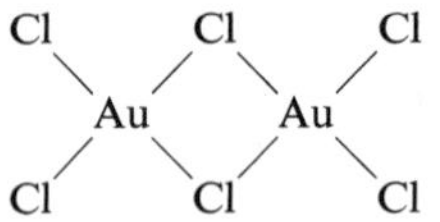

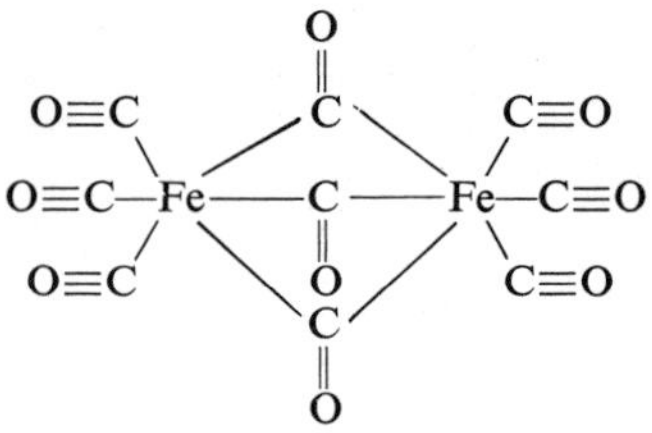

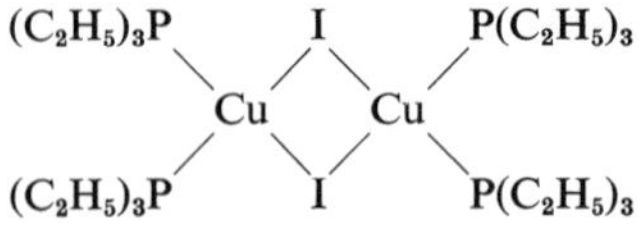

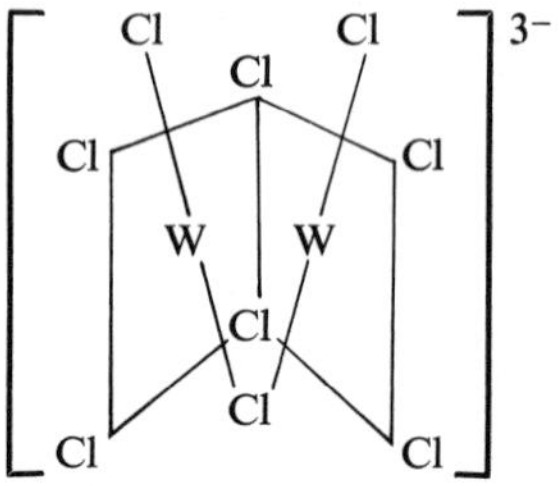

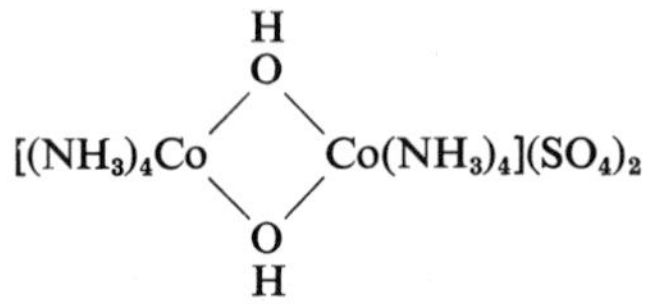

4. Draw the structures of the compounds named below:
   (a) Tetramminecopper(II) sulfate
   (b) *trans*-dichlorobis(ethylenediamine)cobalt(III) chloride
   (c) Carbonatotetramminecobalt(III) nitrate
   (d) Bis(ethylenediamine)cobalt(III)di-μ-hydroxo-bis(ethylenediamine)cobalt(III) hydrogen sulfate
   (e) Tris(ethylenediamine)cobalt(III) hexacyanochromate(III)
   (f) Tetracarbonyl(orthophenanthroline)chromium(O)
   (g) Silver *trans*-tetranitrodiamminecobaltate(III)

3

Some Aspects of Descriptive Coordination Chemistry

Most chemists are so familiar with the reaction of cupric ion and ammonia in aqueous solution that they come to the erroneous conclusion that complexes can always be prepared by mixing suitable solutions of the metal salt and the ligand. While such a procedure does work in the case of most readily formed complex species, the complexes so formed are also the most readily destroyed. When we consider those complexes which are stable even in strongly acidic environments or which can be prepared in geometrically isomeric forms, the necessary preparative methods are often quite different. More important, the reactions by which such complexes are prepared are usually slow and show gross similarities to the reactions involving stable covalent bonds so thoroughly studied in organic chemistry. Since these are the most difficult complexes to prepare, it is with reactions of this second class that we shall concern ourselves initially. Of these, one of the commonest is the oxidation of cobaltous ion in ammoniacal solutions.

THE OXIDATION OF AMMONIACAL SOLUTIONS OF COBALTOUS SALTS

When a solution of a cobalt(II) salt is made strongly ammoniacal it is found to be very susceptible to the action of oxidizing agents such as air, hydrogen peroxide, nitrites, hypochlorites, chlorates, and halogens. The originally brown solution turns ultimately to a purple-red and contains a mixture of various cobalt(III) ammine complexes including $Co(NH_3)_6^{+3}$, $[Co(NH_3)_5(H_2O)]^{+3}$, and in the presence of chlorides $[Co(NH_3)_5Cl]^{+2}$. The separation and characterization of the complexes present in this mixture was the starting point of much of our knowledge of complexes. The conditions under which the oxidation is carried out determine which products are obtained. In the reaction using chlorides noted above, the chloropentammine and the aquopentammine are the initial products and these are slowly converted to the hexammine in the presence of an excess of ammonia. An elegant preparative method for $Co(NH_3)_6^{+3}$ salts is based upon the discovery of J. Bjerrum that decolorizing charcoal is a catalyst for the equilibrium between the aquopentammine and the hexammine.[1] In the presence of the catalyst and an excess of ammonia practically all of the aquopentammine is converted to hexammine:

$$[Co(NH_3)_5(H_2O)]^{+3} + NH_3 \xrightarrow[\text{charcoal}]{\text{decolorizing}} Co(NH_3)_6^{+3} + H_2O$$

This appears to be a phenomenon of some generality, as activated charcoal is a catalyst for other reactions involving Co—N bonds in cobalt(III) complexes; an example of this may be seen[2] in the catalytic racemization of $Co(en)_3^{+3}$. By carrying out this oxidation in the presence of charcoal and an excess of ammonia and ammonium chloride, the yellow-orange salt, $[Co(NH_3)_6]Cl_3$ can be obtained. An analogous procedure (i.e., oxidation of a basic solution of a cobaltous salt) can be used for the preparation of similar compounds such as $[Co(en)_3]Cl_3$, the required modification being the substitution of ethylenediamine for ammonia. These compounds have rather similar yellow colors, a fact responsible for the trivial name "luteocobaltic chloride" for the hexamminecobalt(III) chloride.

By introducing slight modifications into this procedure, a fair number of closely related cobalt(III) complexes can be prepared. When the oxidation of ammoniacal cobaltous nitrate is carried out in the presence of a large amount of ammonium carbonate, the carbonatotetramminecobalt(III) ion is produced. When the resulting solution is carefully evaporated with the addition of small amounts of ammonium carbonate, the salt $[Co(NH_3)_4CO_3]NO_3 \cdot \frac{1}{2}H_2O$ can be obtained. This compound is of importance because the easily replaceable carbonato group must occupy two adjacent (*cis-*)positions of the coordination octahedron. It thus forms a starting material of known structure which can be used in some (but not all) cases for the preparation of *cis-*isomers. The limitations of this reaction may be seen in its reactions with hydrochloric acid. When an aqueous solution of this compound is treated with hydrochloric acid, the *trans-*aquochlorotetramminecobalt(III) ion is formed unless the acid is concentrated *and* the temperature is kept very low. Under these latter conditions

[1] J. Bjerrum and J. P. McReynolds, *Inorganic Syntheses* II, 216 (1946). The use of elevated pressures was studied by R. Jouan, *J. Chim. Phys.* **56**, 277 (1959).

[2] D. Sen and W. C. Fernelius, *J. Inorg. Nuclear Chem.* **10**, 269 (1959). F. M. Dwyer and A. M. Sargeson, *Nature* **187**, 1022 (1960) present a different interpretation of this phenomenon.

the carbonato complex can be converted directly to the *cis*-dichloro-tetram-minecobalt(III) chloride. The use of an alcoholic solution of the acid has been recommended to prevent the formation of the *trans*-form.[3] This loss of the original arrangement is common for simple ammines[4] but does not always occur in the corresponding ethylenediamine compounds. The conversion of the carbonatotetrammine to the chloropentammine is carried out as follows:[5]

$$[Co(NH_3)_4(CO_3)]^+ \xrightarrow[\text{HCl}]{\substack{\text{dil.}\\\text{aqueous}}} [Co(NH_3)_4(Cl)(H_2O)]^{+2} \xrightarrow[\text{NH}_3]{\text{aqueous}}$$

$$[Co(NH_3)_5(H_2O)]^{+3} \xrightarrow[\text{HCl}]{\text{aqueous}} [Co(NH_3)_5Cl]Cl_2$$

Preparations of typical salts of the ions mentioned above and many related ones as well may be found in the standard inorganic laboratory manuals.[6]

In the course of the oxidation of ammoniacal cobaltous solutions, poly-nuclear complexes are often obtained. This important type of complex is present during the early stages of the oxidation when bridging peroxo groups are formed by the taking up of atmospheric oxygen. These peroxo bridged complexes sometimes can be obtained pure.[7] The following reaction is probably the first step in such oxidation processes:

$$Co^{+2} + NH_3 + NH_4NO_3 + O_2 \rightarrow$$

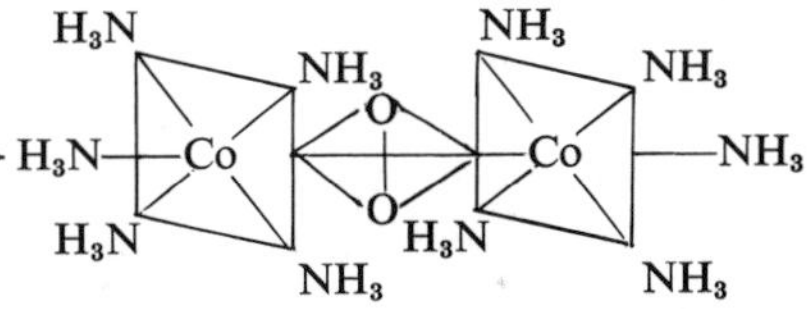

Several salts of this cation were prepared and characterized by Werner and Mylius (loc. cit.). The nitrate explodes when heated to 200°. If such an oxidation is carried out in the presence of an anion other than perchlorate, the anion may be found in the mononuclear complex which is the ultimate product of

[3] J. C. Bailar, Jr., *The Chemistry of the Coordination Compounds*, Reinhold Publishing Corp., New York (1956), p. 279.

[4] A. Werner, *Ber.* **40**, 4817 (1908).

[5] H. Biltz and W. Biltz, *Laboratory Methods of Inorganic Chemistry*, translated by W. T. Hall and A. A. Blanchard, John Wiley & Sons, Inc., New York, 2nd ed. (1928), p. 172.

[6] H. Biltz and W. Biltz, loc, cit.; L. Vanino, *Handbuch der Praparativen Chemie*, F. Enke, Stuttgart, 2nd ed. (1921), Vol. I, *Anorganischer Teil*; W. Palmer, *Experimental Inorganic Chemistry*, Cambridge University Press, London (1954); H. Grubitsch, *Anorganischeprä-parative Chemie*, Springer-Verlag, Vienna (1950); H. Hecht, *Praparative Anorganische Chemie*, Springer-Verlag, Berlin (1951); (edited) *Inorganic Syntheses*, McGraw-Hill, Inc., New York (1940), Vol. I; G. Brauer, *Handbuch der Praparativen Anorganischen Chemie*, F. Enke, Stuttgart, 2nd ed. (1960).

[7] S. M. Jorgensen, *Zeit, anorg. Chem.* **5**, 185 (1894); A. Werner and A. Mylius, *ibid.*, **16**, 252 (1898). C. Brosset and N. Vannerberg, *Nature*, **190**, 714 (1961).

the reaction. Thus, $[Co(NH_3)_5Br]^{+2}$ can be obtained by the further oxidation of an ammoniacal solution of cobaltous bromide.

ISOMERISM IN COBALT(III) COMPLEXES

The complexes of cobalt(III) are sufficiently stable so that they may occur in separable isomeric forms. One example is the *cis*- and *trans*-type such as is found with $[Co(en)_2(NH_3)Cl]Cl_2$. Since the six-coordinated groups are arranged about the central cobalt atoms at the apices of an octahedron, two geometrical isomers can be written for the ion as follows:

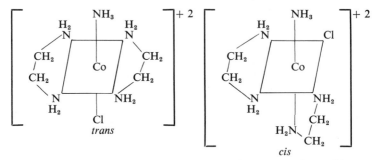

occurs in two enantiomorphic
forms

Jorgensen[8] obtained one of these compounds by evaporating a mixture of what is now known to be *trans*-dichlorobis(ethylenediamine)cobalt(III) chloride with the required amount of aqueous ammonia. Werner[9] prepared another isomer by treating *trans*-chloroisothiocyanatobis(ethylenediamine)-cobalt(III) chloride with hydrogen peroxide. Since the oxidation of the isothiocyanato group to the ammine group occurs without breaking the Co—N bond, the compound which was prepared by Werner must be the *trans*-isomer and that prepared by Jorgensen the *cis*-isomer, as shown in Figure 4. The salt prepared by Jorgensen was resolved by Werner into its enantiomorphs and hence, proven to have the *cis*-configuration.

Optical isomers like those with *cis*-$[Co(en)_2(NH_3)Cl]^{+2}$ have been characterized and resolved for a large number of cobalt complexes. Such isomers occur when the mirror image of a given structure is *not* superposable on the original structure. When such isomers are separated it is found that their solutions possess the power of rotating the plane of polarized light. Furthermore, the rotation produced by a solution of one complex is equal in magnitude but opposite in sign to the rotation produced by the same length of a solution of the same concentration of the other complex. Werner's octahedral structure for the cobalt(III) complexes predicted that (a) a *cis*- and a *trans*-isomer would be

[8] S. M. Jorgensen, *J. prakt. Chem.* (2) **41**, 453 (1890).
[9] A. Werner, *Ann.* **386**, 55, 170 (1912).

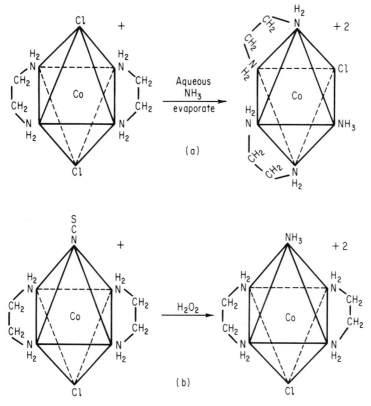

Fig. 4 The preparation of: (a) *cis-* and (b) *trans-* [Co(en)$_2$(NH$_3$)Cl]$^{+2}$.

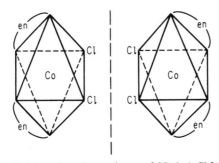

Fig. 5 The mirror image forms of [Co(en)$_2$Cl$_2$]$^+$.

possible for complexes of the type [Co(en)$_2$X$_2$] and (b) the *cis*-isomer should be resolvable into two nonsuperposable mirror image forms. These mirror image forms are illustrated in Figure 5. This prediction has been confirmed for numerous compounds of this type. Some of the reactions by which these compounds are produced are given in the following scheme.[10] Those compounds which have been separated into enantiomorphic forms are marked "resolved."

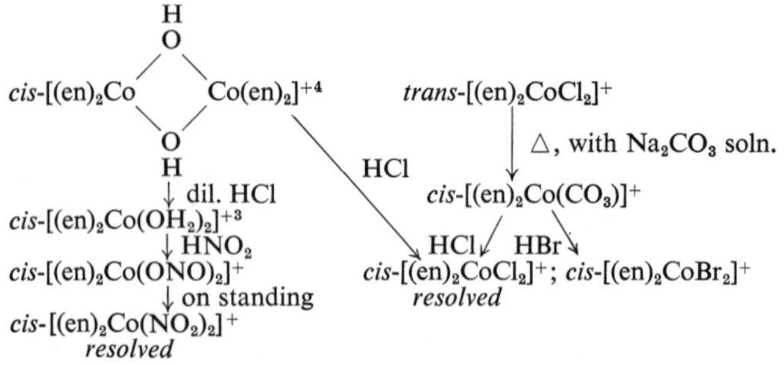

$$
\begin{array}{c}
\text{H} \\
\text{O}
\end{array}
$$

cis-[(en)$_2$Co $\diagup$ $\diagdown$ Co(en)$_2$]$^{+4}$ *trans*-[(en)$_2$CoCl$_2$]$^+$

$$
\begin{array}{c}
\text{O} \\
\text{H}
\end{array}
$$

$\downarrow$ dil. HCl   HCl $\quad$ $\triangle$, with Na$_2$CO$_3$ soln.

cis-[(en)$_2$Co(OH$_2$)$_2$]$^{+3}$ $\qquad\qquad$ *cis*-[(en)$_2$Co(CO$_3$)]$^+$

$\downarrow$ HNO$_2$

cis-[(en)$_2$Co(ONO)$_2$]$^+$ $\qquad$ HCl $\diagup$ HBr $\diagdown$

$\downarrow$ on standing $\qquad$ *cis*-[(en)$_2$CoCl$_2$]$^+$; *cis*-[(en)$_2$CoBr$_2$]$^+$

cis-[(en)$_2$Co(NO$_2$)$_2$]$^+$ $\qquad\qquad$ *resolved*

resolved

One of the assumptions in the structural work given above is that *cis*-positions on the coordination sphere must be occupied when a chelating agent is present which can form a four-, five-, six-, or seven-membered ring. Thus the carbonato group, when functioning as a bidentate chelating agent must occupy *cis*-positions. The same is true also for oxalato, sulfito, and malonato ions as well as compounds such as ethylenediamine. If the successive coordinating groups of a chelating agent are sufficiently far apart it is apparently possible that they may occupy *trans*-positions and some examples of this are claimed in the literature.[11]

It is worthwhile to consider just how the enantiomorphic forms of ions such as [Co(en)$_2$Cl$_2$]$^+$ can be separated in a state of reasonable purity. Although there are several possible methods for the resolution of enantiomorphs, the most generally successful method is through the formation and separation of diastereoisomeric derivatives. The physical properties of diastereoisomers are often very different and these differences, especially solubility differences, will usually be great enough to allow at least a partial separation. Diastereoisomeric salts are salts in which the same optically active ion (cation or anion) is combined with the different enantiomorphic ions (anions or cations), thus:

$$
\left\{ \begin{array}{c} d\,\text{M} \\ + \\ l\,\text{M} \end{array} \right\} + l\,\text{A} \longrightarrow \left. \begin{array}{c} d\,\text{M}\,l\,\text{A} \\ + \\ \underbrace{l\,\text{M}\,l\,\text{A}} \end{array} \right\} \text{ have different physical properties}
$$

$\uparrow$ $\qquad\qquad\qquad$ $\uparrow$

racemic mixture $\qquad$ pair of diastereoisomers
(inactive)

Here, d M and l M are the dextrorotatory and the levorotatory forms of an ion M (which has a nonsuperposable mirror image) and l A is a levorotatory anion. The formation of the two diastereoisomers d M l A and l M l A then

[10] Adapted from P. Pfeiffer, "Komplexchemie" in K. Freudenberg, *Stereochemie*, F. Deuticke, Leipzig and Vienna (1932), p. 1279. Many such schemes may be found in the books and papers of both Werner and Pfeiffer.

[11] N. Schlesinger, *Ber.* **58**, 1877 (1925).

occurs on mixture. The diastereoisomers are not mirror isomers and hence, like geometrical isomers, they have different physical properties. Usually fractional crystallization of the solution containing the two diastereoisomers will result in the early separation of the least soluble of the two and the more soluble form will concentrate in the mother liquor. Subsequently, treatment of the fractions with some reagent which forms a very insoluble precipitate with *l* A will allow the separation of the *d* M and *l* M from the diastereoisomer and their preparation in a state of greater or lesser purity.

A typical example of such a resolution may be seen in the separation[12] of the optical isomers of *cis*-[Co(en)$_2$Cl$_2$]$^+$. This resolution is effected through the formation of diastereoisomeric salts with the optically active anion *d*-α-bromocamphor-π-sulfonate. The reaction sequence is as follows:

$$\text{in } H_2O \text{ at } 15°$$

dl-cis-[Co(en)$_2$Cl$_2$]Cl + NH$_4$(C$_{10}$H$_{14}$SO$_4$Br) $\longrightarrow$
ammonium *d*-α-
bromcamphor-
π-sulfonate

l-cis-[Co(en)$_2$Cl$_2$]*d*(C$_{10}$H$_{14}$SO$_4$Br) (as a precipitate) + NH$_4$Cl
↓
grind in a mortar at 0° with HCl
↓
l-cis-[Co(en)$_2$Cl$_2$]Cl + solution containing the *d*-α-bromcamphor-π-sulfonate

In some cases the *d* and *l* forms of a complex are readily interconvertible. When this is the case three possibilities may arise:

1. The ready conversion may prevent the successful resolution of the complex. Any sample of one of the enantiomorphs which is momentarily separated rapidly changes to a racemic mixture. This is very common and *prevents* resolution. Examples of this are provided by trisoxalatoaluminate (Al(C$_2$O$_4$)$_3^{-3}$) and other labile complexes.

2. The conversion of one form to another may occur in the presence of a resolving agent and the transformation then may proceed in only one direction under conditions induced by the prevailing asymmetric influence of the resolving agent. When this is the case it is possible for the solubility of one of the diastereoisomers to be so much less than that of the other that the solid obtained on addition of the resolving agent may contain essentially *all* of the complex in the form of a diastereoisomer of only one of the two possible enantiomorphic forms. The name for this type of process is *second order asymmetric transformation*. An example is the resolution of tris(catecholato)-arsenate(V) with either cinchonine or quinine.

3. If the transformation occurs only in the presence of a catalyst the continuous separation of the least soluble of a pair of diastereoisomers can be used

[12] J. C. Bailar, Jr., *Inorganic Syntheses*, McGraw-Hill, Inc., New York (1946), II, p. 224.

to obtain more than half of a given racemate in the form of the diastereoisomer of one of the enantiomorphic forms. An example of this may be seen in the resolution of tris(ethylenediamine)cobalt(III) ion in the presence of Co(II). Co(II) in neutral or basic solution catalyzes the racemization of the more soluble form and the least soluble form is removed as it is generated.[13]

PREPARATION OF SOME PLATINUM COMPLEXES[10, 14]

Platinum forms complexes of several different types but the most commonly encountered examples fall into one of the following two classes:

1. The four-coordinated, square planar complexes of Pt(II).

2. The six-coordinated, octahedral complexes of Pt(IV).

Both of these types possess sufficient structural stability to be studied from a stereochemical point of view, and the geometrical and optical isomers (of Pt(IV)) are generally *not* very readily interconvertible.

Platinum dissolves in aqua regia and evaporation of the solution yields chloroplatinic acid, H_2PtCl_6, which is the compound of platinum most frequently encountered in commerce. When chloroplatinic acid is heated to $300°$, platinum tetrachloride, $PtCl_4$, is formed, and at temperatures still more elevated platinum dichloride, $PtCl_2$, becomes the chief product *if* the conditions are carefully controlled. These compounds of platinum are unlike typical salts in that they never give rise to simple monatomic platinum ions in aqueous solution; the species in such solutions are *always* complex. They can be used conveniently as starting materials for the preparation of numerous other complexes.

A few of the reactions of platinum dichloride illustrate the great complex forming tendency of Pt(II). As is found with other species, Pt(II) forms more stable bonds with some donor atoms than with others. Stable bonds are formed with ligand groups bonded through sulfur, carbon, and the halogens other than fluorine. Less stable bonds are formed with nitrogen and still less stable bonds with oxygen. Some typical complex forming reactions involving platinum dichloride are:

$$PtCl_2 + 4KCN \rightarrow K_2[Pt(CN)_4] + 2KCl$$

$$PtCl_2 + 2CH_3CN \xrightarrow{\text{slowly}} [PtCl_2(CH_3CN)_2]$$

$$PtCl_2 + 2C_6H_5CN \xrightarrow[60-70°]{\text{very slowly}} [PtCl_2(C_6H_5CN)_2]$$

[13] D. H. Busch, *J. Amer. Chem. Soc.* **77**, 2747 (1955). A similar racemization occurs in the presence of active carbon: B. Douglas, *ibid.*, **76**, 1020 (1954).

[14] N. V. Sidgwick, *The Chemical Elements and Their Compounds*, Oxford University Press, London (1950), pp. 1578–1628.

$$PtCl_2 + 2C_6H_5NC \xrightarrow[\substack{\text{reaction in} \\ \text{ether solution}}]{\text{immediate}} [PtCl_2(C_6H_5NC)_2]$$

$$PtCl_2 + 4NH_3 \rightarrow [Pt(NH_3)_4]Cl_2$$

$$PtCl_2 + 2KCl \rightarrow K_2[PtCl_4]$$

All of the four-coordinate platinum(II) compounds possess a square planar arrangement of the bonds between the platinum and the ligands. This was suggested by Werner[13] and was conclusively proven by Mills and Quibell[14] by the resolution of the cation:

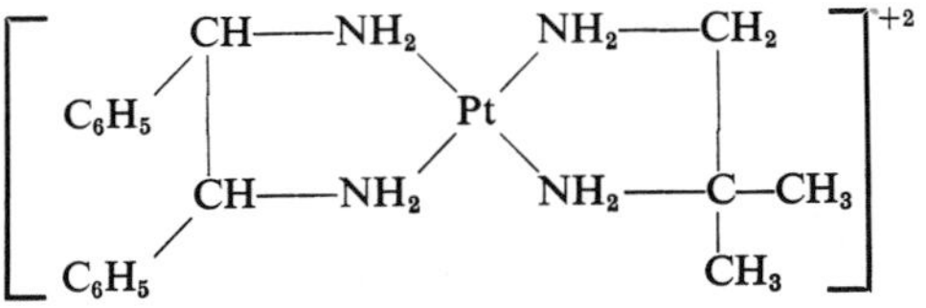

The synthesis of this cation was effected by the following series of reactions:

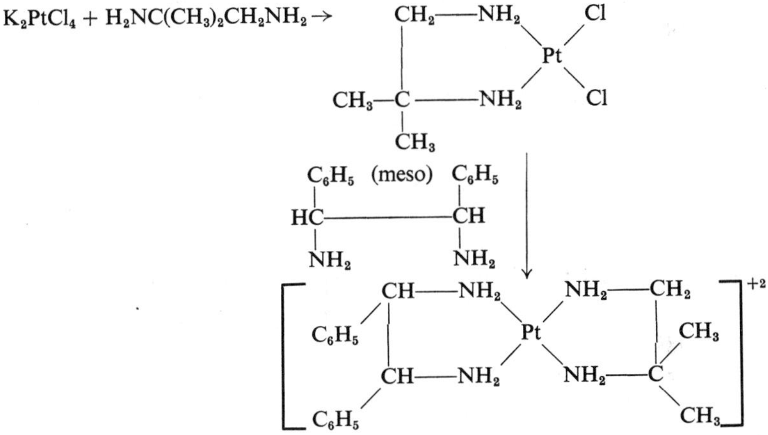

The resulting ion will possess a plane of symmetry if the bonds about the platinum have a tetrahedral arrangement as the plane of symmetry of the ring containing the *meso* diphenylethylenediamine (stilbenediamine) will then coincide with the plane of the ring of the isobutylenediamine ligand. A *meso* compound is one which contains an even number of asymmetric atoms so disposed that its mirror image is superposable on the original compound. These are often spoken of as *internally compensated* asymmetric forms. If, however, the disposition of bonds is planar and extends toward the corners of a square, the cation will be asymmetric. Mills and Quibell succeeded in resolving this cation through its salt with *d*-diacetyltartaric acid. This is consistent with the square planar

[13] A. Werner, *Zeit. anorg. Chem.* 3, 267, 351 (1893).
[14] W. H. Mills and T. H. H. Quibell, *J. Chem. Soc.* 839 (1935).

arrangement of the bonds, but not the tetrahedral arrangement. The resulting complexes are quite stable and lose their optical activity only slowly when heated with dilute hydrochloric acid at 100°. The symmetry which arises when a tetrahedral configuration is assigned the Pt(II) can be seen in Figure 6. Here

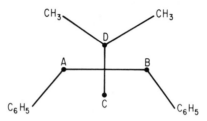

Fig. 6 Symmetry of tetrahedral structure for the complex studied by Mills and Quibell. Since the complex was resolved, this structure is ruled out.

the corners of the tetrahedron are designated *A*, *B*, *C*, and *D*. It is apparent that a plane of symmetry passes through the edge *DC*. The resolution of this compound settled the confused picture which resulted from the claims of Reihlen and his co-workers[15] that the complexes of Pt(II) had tetrahedrally arranged ligands.

   In many respects the reactions of the square planar complexes of platinum(II) are analogous to the reactions of carbon compounds. This is especially evident when some of the substitution reactions which these complexes undergo are examined. Here the structural integrity of the complexes is great enough to preserve the general features of a compound throughout a series of reactions.[16] This is in marked contrast to the general picture of inorganic reactions gained by an examination of the reactions of the more labile complexes of copper(II) or zinc(II). In the platinum(II) complexes it is found that isomerization rarely accompanies substitution. Some typical substitution reactions are given below:

$$
\begin{array}{c}
\text{NH}_3\diagdown\quad\diagup\text{Cl} \\
\text{Pt} \qquad + \text{ 2KBr} \rightarrow \\
\text{Cl}\diagup\quad\diagdown\text{NH}_3 \\
\textit{trans}
\end{array}
\qquad
\begin{array}{c}
\text{NH}_3\diagdown\quad\diagup\text{Br} \\
\text{Pt} \qquad + \text{ 2KCl} \\
\text{Br}\diagup\quad\diagdown\text{NH}_3 \\
\textit{trans}
\end{array}
$$

$$
\begin{array}{c}
\text{NH}_3\diagdown\quad\diagup\text{Cl} \\
\text{Pt} \qquad + \text{ 2KBr} \rightarrow \\
\text{NH}_3\diagup\quad\diagdown\text{Cl} \\
\textit{cis}
\end{array}
\qquad
\begin{array}{c}
\text{NH}_3\diagdown\quad\diagup\text{Br} \\
\text{Pt} \qquad + \text{ 2KCl} \\
\text{NH}_3\diagup\quad\diagdown\text{Br} \\
\textit{cis}
\end{array}
$$

[15] H. Reihlen and W. Huhn, *Ann.* **489**, 42 (1931); *ibid.*, **519**, 80 (1935); H. Reihlen, G. Seipel, and E. Weinbrenner, *ibid.*, **520**, 256 (1935).

[16] For some exceptions see, J. Chatt and F. A. Hart, *J. Chem. Soc.* 2807 (1960).

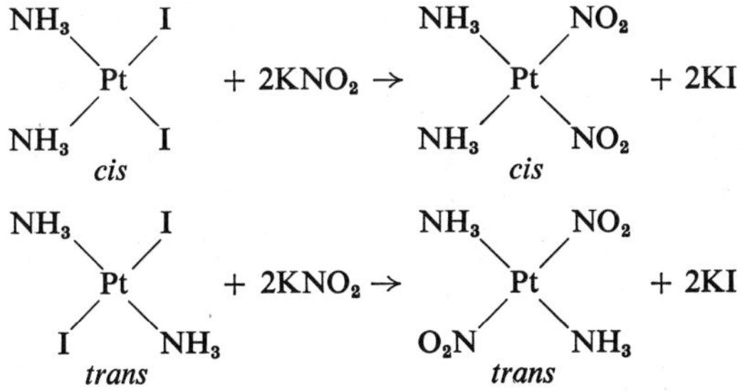

$$\underset{cis}{\begin{array}{c} NH_3 \quad\quad I \\ \diagdown \quad\diagup \\ Pt \\ \diagup \quad\diagdown \\ NH_3 \quad\quad I \end{array}} + 2KNO_2 \rightarrow \underset{cis}{\begin{array}{c} NH_3 \quad\quad NO_2 \\ \diagdown \quad\diagup \\ Pt \\ \diagup \quad\diagdown \\ NH_3 \quad\quad NO_2 \end{array}} + 2KI$$

$$\underset{trans}{\begin{array}{c} NH_3 \quad\quad I \\ \diagdown \quad\diagup \\ Pt \\ \diagup \quad\diagdown \\ I \quad\quad NH_3 \end{array}} + 2KNO_2 \rightarrow \underset{trans}{\begin{array}{c} NH_3 \quad\quad NO_2 \\ \diagdown \quad\diagup \\ Pt \\ \diagup \quad\diagdown \\ O_2N \quad\quad NH_3 \end{array}} + 2KI$$

OCTAHEDRAL PLATINUM(IV) COMPLEXES

Octahedral complexes of platinum(IV) show the same kind of stability that is encountered in the complexes of cobalt(III) and show this to a higher degree than the cobalt(III) complexes. Accordingly, their stereochemistry has been studied in considerable detail. These complexes may be prepared from either chloroplatinic acid or from Pt(II) compounds. The reactions starting from planar Pt(II) compounds proceed with the retention of configuration of the four groups originally present in the plane.

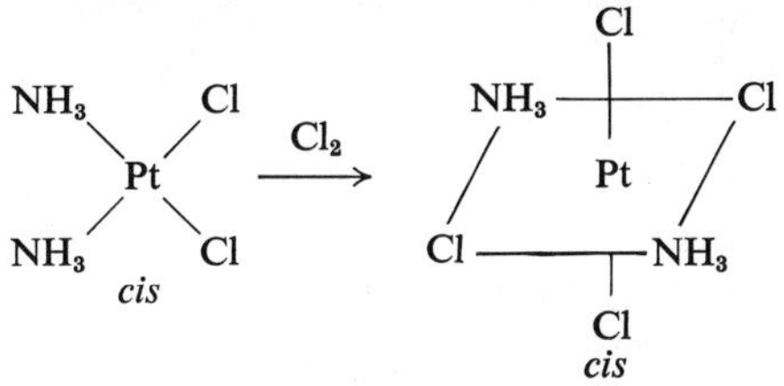

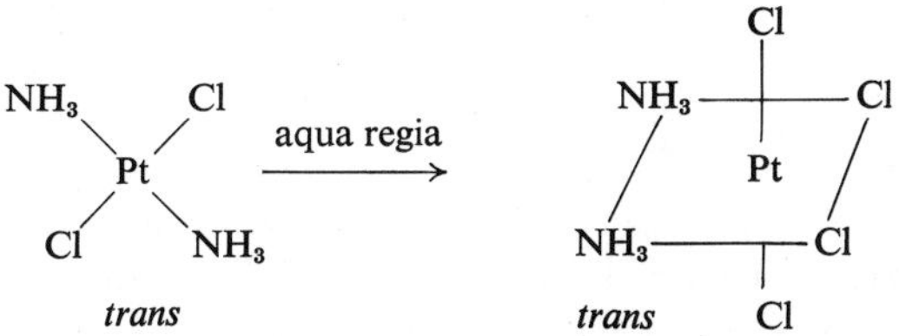

Under more drastic conditions, all of a given type of ligand may be displaced from the coordination sphere. Thus ammonia or amines can displace all of the chloro groups from hexachloroplatinate(IV) when present in excess:

$$(NH_4)_2PtCl_6 + 6NH_3 \xrightarrow{\text{liquid } NH_3} [Pt(NH_3)_6]Cl_4 + 2NH_4Cl$$

$$(NH_4)_2PtCl_6 + 3NH_2CH_2CH_2NH_2 \xrightarrow[\text{diamine}]{\text{ethylene-}} [Pt(en)_3]Cl_4 + 2NH_4Cl$$

The stability of these compounds may be judged from the fact that the racemization of the optically active forms of $[Pt(en)_3]^{+4}$ does not occur in boiling water (in the absence of catalysts). The firmness with which ligands are held to the platinum atom allows the preparation of complexes with several different types of groups coordinated to the central atom. Furthermore, in most cases compounds can be obtained in the form of geometrical isomers whose number corresponds to that predicted theoretically. A very impressive example of this may be seen in the synthesis of $[Pt(I)(Br)(NH_3)(NO_2)Cl(Pyridine)]$ which is a stable compound.[17] This is the only known example of such a compound. Attempts to make similar complex ions with most other central metal ions lead to mixtures of complex ions in which there is a more symmetrical disposition of ligands. This is to be contrasted with the behavior of the corresponding complexes of cobalt(III) which do not contain chelate rings. In such instances, only a small fraction of the total possible number of geometrical isomers has been found.

SOME TYPICAL SYNTHETIC PROCEDURES FOR SPECIFIC COMPLEXES

Of the elements in the first transition series, cobalt and chromium are outstanding because of their ability to form very stable complexes when they are in the $+3$ oxidation state. Chromium differs from cobalt in showing oxidation states of $+6$ and $+2$ and in the fact that the $+3$ salts are far more stable than those of cobalt. This leads to a somewhat wider choice of preparative methods for the complexes of Cr(III). In many cases, it is found more convenient to start with a compound in which the chromium is in the $+2$ or $+6$ oxidation state. This is especially true when the preparation is to be carried out in aqueous solution. Cr(III) has a very great tendency to coordinate with the oxygen of water and this introduces complications which can frequently be eliminated by forming the Cr(III) species *in situ* from the higher or the lower oxidation state.

An example of the use of dichromate as a starting material may be seen in the preparation of $K_3[Cr(C_2O_4)_3] \cdot 3H_2O$. Potassium dichromate is added to a solution containing potassium oxalate and oxalic acid[18] and the resulting reduction of the Cr(VI) to Cr(III) in the presence of the oxalate ion results in the formation of the ion $Cr(C_2O_4)_3^{-3}$ which can be obtained from this solution in the crystalline compound $K_3[Cr(C_2O_4)_3] \cdot 3H_2O$. The corresponding reaction using a solution of Cr(III) salt is not of preparative utility since these solutions contain the complex ions $[Cr(H_2O)_6]^{+3}$ or ions derived from it such as $[Cr(H_2O)_5Cl]^{+2}$ or $[Cr(H_2O)_4Cl_2]^+$ which do not readily undergo complete substitution.

Some further aspects are illustrated in the preparations of *cis*-$[Cr(en)_2Cl_2]Cl$

[17] A. D. Gelman and L. N. Essen, *Doklady Akad. Nauk, S.S.S.R.* **75**, 693 (1950); *C.A.* 45:3279.

[18] J. C. Bailar, Jr. and E. M. Jones, *Inorganic Syntheses*, McGraw-Hill, Inc., New York (1939), Vol. I, p. 35.

and *trans*-[Cr(en)$_2$(SCN)$_2$](SCN). The first is that the relative stabilities of *cis*- and *trans*-isomers vary considerably as the ligands are varied. In some cases the greater stability of one of the geometrical isomers results in only one of them being known. The second aspect is that anhydrous salts are often auto-complexes involving coordinated anions. (An autocomplex is simply a salt of normal composition in which appreciable coordination of anion to cation occurs, e.g., CdI$_2$ and PtCl$_2$). Such anhydrous salts are often readily prepared and are very convenient starting materials for preparations. In many instances, it is possible to dehydrate a tervalent sulfate where dehydration of the corresponding halide leads to the loss of hydrogen halide; chromium(III) is one such instance. This is due to the relative nonvolatility of sulfuric acid and to the coordinating properties of the sulfate anion. That the sulfate is autocomplex when anhydrous is shown by its very slow reaction with water, in which its solubility is very considerable. The steps involved in the synthesis of the compounds given above are the following:[19]

$$1. \quad Cr_2(SO_4)_3 \cdot 12H_2O \xrightarrow[110°]{} Cr_2(SO_4)_3 + 12H_2O \uparrow$$

$$2. \quad Cr_2(SO_4)_3 + 6\,en \xrightarrow{\Delta} [Cr(en)_3]_2(SO_4)_3$$

The subsequent steps in the syntheses of these compounds are based on the general change which occurs on heating compounds of the type [Cr(en)$_3$]X$_3$:

$$[Cr(en)_3]X_3 \xrightarrow{heat} [Cr(en)_2X_2]X + en \uparrow$$

From the chloride the product is the *cis*-dichloro compound but with the thiocyanate the *trans*-dithiocyanato salt results. The other steps required are:

$$[Cr(en)_3]_2(SO_4)_3 \xrightarrow[alcohol]{conc.\ HCl} [Cr(en)_3]Cl_3 \cdot 3\tfrac{1}{2}H_2O + 3H_2SO_4$$

$$[Cr(en)_3]Cl_3 \cdot 3\tfrac{1}{2}H_2O \xrightarrow[with\ NH_4Cl\ catalyst]{heat\ at\ 210°} cis\text{-}[Cr(en)_2Cl_2]Cl + en \uparrow + 3\tfrac{1}{2}H_2O \uparrow$$

$$[Cr(en)_3]_2(SO_4)_3 \xrightarrow[aqueous\ soln.]{excess\ NaSCN\ in} [Cr(en)_3](SCN)_3 \cdot H_2O + Na_2SO_4$$

$$[Cr(en)_3](SCN)_3 \cdot H_2O \xrightarrow[with\ NH_4SCN]{heat\ at\ 130°} trans\text{-}[Cr(en)_2(SCN)_2]SCN + H_2O + en$$

The use of anhydrous chromium(III) halides is also very convenient in many syntheses of chromium(III) complexes. These are usually rather inert, unreactive solids and it is usually convenient to add a catalyst to hasten the reaction. In many cases the use of an anhydrous reducing agent such as granulated zinc will be found to speed up the reaction considerably. This is because

[19] C. L. Rollinson and J. C. Bailar, Jr., *Inorganic Syntheses*, McGraw-Hill Book Company, New York (1946), Vol. II, pp. 200–202.

the chromium(III) is reduced to chromium(II) by such a material and the chromium(II) accelerates the breakdown of the autocomplex solid chromium-(III) halide. In the preparation of chromium(III) complexes the heating of a mixture of the anhydrous chromium(III) halide, granulated or powdered zinc and the ligand will generally result in the formation of a complex. In the preparation of hexamminechromium(III) chloride such a catalyst is not necessary but the conversion of the initially formed chloropentamminechromium(III) to the hexamminechromium(III) is a problem here just as in the corresponding preparation of hexamminecobalt(III). For the chromium compound, the reaction between anhydrous chromium(III) chloride and excess liquid ammonia can be used if $NaNH_2$ is employed as a catalyst.[20] The reaction used is:

$$CrCl_3 + 6NH_3 \rightarrow [Cr(NH_3)_6]Cl_3$$

The oxidation of chromium(II) solutions can also be used to prepare various chromium(III) complexes though it has not been a popular method. Chromium(II) solutions containing an excess of ammonia and ammonium chloride can be oxidized to polynuclear chromium(III) complexes which can be converted to the chloropentamminechromium(III) chloride by heating with concentrated hydrochloric acid.[21]

The complexity which may be found even with simple chromium(III) compounds is very strikingly shown in the green chromic chloride of commerce. This material, which is usually assigned the formula $[Cr(H_2O)_4Cl_2]Cl$·$2H_2O$, is usually deficient in chloride and contains appreciable amounts of polymeric complexes. In order to obtain a product of the required composition it is necessary that the carefully dried crude material be thoroughly ground with dry acetone in a mortar. The polymeric complexes are soluble in the acetone and can be removed by this process.[22]

This same compound has been used to illustrate the separation of *cis-* and *trans-*isomers on a cation exchange column.[23] The more symmetrical distribution of charges in the *trans-*isomer should lead to a weaker electrostatic interaction with the resin and hence the *trans-*isomer should be more readily eluted from the column. This method was used by King and his co-workers to obtain solutions of the *trans-*isomer of $[Cr(H_2O)_4Cl_2]^+$, starting with a mixture of the *cis-* and *trans-*forms. In the cases studied so far the *trans-*isomer is always eluted more readily from the ion exchange column than the *cis-*isomer.

The stabilization of an unusual oxidation state by coordination is a common feature of the coordination compounds of the transition elements. This is dis-

[20] A. L. Oppegard and J. C. Bailar, Jr., *Inorganic Syntheses*, McGraw-Hill Book Company, New York (1950), Vol. III, p. 153.

[21] S. M. Jorgensen, *J. prakt. Chem.* (2), **20**, 105 (1879); (2) **30**, 2 (1884); O. Christensen, *J. prakt. Chem.* (2) **23**, 54 (1881).

[22] W. B. Guenther and J. J. Stuart, *J. Tennessee Acad. Science* **35**, 244 (1960).

[23] E. L. King, Sister M. J. M. Woods, and H. S. Gates, *J. Amer. Chem. Soc.* **80**, 5015 (1959).

cussed in more detail in Chapter 9. An example of this may be seen in the preparation of $K_3[Mn(CN)_6]$. Manganese(III) is not a common oxidation state for manganese to exhibit when in aqueous solution but may be stabilized by coordination to cyanide or through the formation of a very insoluble compound. The preparation of $K_3[Mn(CN)_6]$ involves both of these processes.[24] The initial step is the oxidation of manganous ion to Mn(III) in the presence of phosphoric acid. This yields the relatively insoluble manganese(III) orthophosphate 1-hydrate:

$$3MnCl_2 + HNO_3 + 3H_3PO_4 + H_2O \rightarrow 3MnPO_4 \cdot H_2O + NO + 6HCl$$

Then, this compound is treated with potassium cyanide to obtain the desired complex:

$$6KCN + MnPO_4 \cdot H_2O \rightarrow K_3[Mn(CN)_6] + K_3PO_4 + H_2O$$

This is only one of the many instances where an unusual oxidation state is stabilized by coordination.

The variation in the relative stabilities of *cis*- and *trans*-isomers with the presence of other species in solution may be quite considerable and can sometimes be put to use in preparative work. In the presence of hydrochloric acid, the *trans*-form of $[Co(en)_2Cl_2]^+$ can be crystallized from solution as the acid salt *trans*-$[Co(en)_2Cl_2]Cl \cdot HCl$. The *cis*-complex does not form a corresponding compound. The *cis*-isomer can be obtained from the *trans* by heating in a neutral aqueous solution. The preparation of the *trans*-isomer is carried out by first oxidizing a solution of cobaltous chloride and ethylenediamine with a stream of oxygen. This solution is then treated with concentrated hydrochloric acid and evaporated to crystallization whereupon the hydrochloride of the *trans*-isomer separates. When this is heated at 110°, hydrochloric acid is evolved and the neutral complex remains. Subsequent heating of an aqueous solution of the *trans*-complex results in its conversion to the *cis*-isomer. The *cis*-isomer can then be resolved through its salt with D-(+)α-bromcamphor-π-sulfonic acid. The reaction sequence for these preparations is:

$$CoCl_2 + 2NH_2CH_2CH_2NH_2 \xrightarrow[\text{3. Crystallize}]{\substack{\text{1. oxidize with } O_2 \\ \text{2. add HCl}}} \textit{trans-}[Co(en)_2Cl_2]Cl \cdot HCl + H_2O$$

$$\textit{trans-}[Co(en)_2Cl_2]Cl \cdot HCl \xrightarrow{\text{heat at } 110°} \textit{trans-}[Co(en)_2Cl_2]Cl + HCl$$

$$\textit{trans-}[Co(en)_2Cl_2]Cl \xrightarrow[\text{to dryness}]{\text{evap. aq. sol.}} \textit{cis-}[Co(en)_2Cl_2]Cl \quad {}^{25}$$

[24] J. A. Lower and W. C. Fernelius, *Inorganic Syntheses*, McGraw-Hill Book Company, New York (1946), Vol. II, p. 213.

[25] J. C. Bailar, Jr., *Inorganic Syntheses*, McGraw-Hill Book Company, New York (1946), Vol. II, p. 222.

In the case of the geometrical isomers of platinum and palladium complexes one may take advantage of the fact that in many cases a given isomer will be produced by a given reagent to the total exclusion of alternative isomeric compounds. Furthermore, many of these compounds are of considerably greater stability than the analogous compounds of cobalt(III) or chromium-(III). Such a sequence of reactions is seen in the preparation of *trans*-dinitrodiamminepalladium(II) of Cull and Jonassen.[26] Here the *trans*-isomer is the only one obtained when $[Pd(NH_3)_4] X_2$ is treated with sodium nitrite in the pressence of a small amount of formic acid at $10-15°$. The reactions used, starting from palladous chloride are:

$$PdCl_2 + 4NH_3 \rightarrow [Pd(NH_3)_4]Cl_2$$

$$[Pd(NH_3)_4]Cl_2 \xrightarrow[\text{at } 10-15°]{\substack{1.\ H_2O \\ 2.\ NaNO_2 \text{ and } HCOOH}} \textit{trans-}[Pd(NH_3)_2(NO_2)_2]$$

PREPARATIONS USING NON-AQUEOUS SOLVENTS

The use of non-aqueous solvents has many advantages in the preparation of compounds in which elements exhibit abnormally low oxidation states. For this purpose liquid ammonia has shown itself to be admirably suited and organic amines have also been used. The essential requirement is that the solvent be very resistant to the action of reducing agents. Since solutions of the alkali metals in liquid ammonia can be prepared with great ease and since these solutions are very powerful reducing agents they are the reagent of choice in many such preparations. An example of a compound which can be prepared by such a process and which is inaccessible in a water system is $K_3[Co(CN)_4]$.[27] This compound can be prepared by the reduction of liquid ammonia systems containing $K_3[Co(CN)_6]$ with liquid ammonia solutions of potassium:

$$K_3[Co(CN)_6] + 2K \xrightarrow[\text{ammonia}]{\text{liquid}} K_3[Co(CN)_4] + 2KCN$$

NON-METALLIC COORDINATION CENTERS

Although we customarily think of coordination compounds as consisting of a central metallic species surrounded by several non-metallic species, some compounds are known in which the reverse situation is found. The possibility of such complexes was apparently first discussed by Kistiakowsky[28] on the basis of evidence furnished by transference number measurements. The first

[26] N. L. Cull and H. B. Jonassen, *Inorganic Syntheses*, McGraw-Hill Book Company, New York (1955), Vol. IV, p. 179.

[27] G. W. Watt and R. J. Thompson, *J. Inorg. Nuclear Chem.* **9**, 311 (1959).

[28] W. A. Kistiakowsky, *Zeit. phys. Chem.* **6**, 97 (1890).

solid compounds characterized as such were prepared by Hellwig[29] and contained ions of the type $[Ag_3I]^{+2}$. Silver iodide is *extremely* soluble in concentrated silver salt solutions and from such solutions several compounds of this sort have been obtained. Hellwig's results were confirmed and extended by Kistiakowsky[30] who used e. m. f. measurements on cells of the type $Ag\,|\,AgNO_3$, $AgI\,|\,AgNO_3(conc.)\,|\,AgNO_3\,|\,Ag$ to determine the composition of the complexes formed. In general, such complexes are found with large easily polarized anions such as iodide, sulfide, selenide, telluride, etc. Examples of this kind of compound are the solids $[Ag_3S]NO_3$ and $[Ag_3I](NO_3)_2$. The first compound is prepared by the hydrolysis of carbon disulfide in a concentrated solution of silver nitrate.[31]

$$6AgNO_3 + CS_2 + 2H_2O \rightarrow CO_2 + 2[Ag_3S](NO_3) + 4HNO_3$$

The $[Ag_3S](NO_3)$ is obtained as a yellow powder. The crystal structure has been determined (Bergerhoff, loc. cit.) and found to contain an infinite polymeric cation in which each sulfur is surrounded by six silver ions at the apices of a distorted trigonal prism (Figure 7).

[Ag_3I](NO_3)_2 is prepared by saturating a concentrated solution of silver nitrate with silver iodide, diluting this with water and then setting it aside to crystallize. The crystals which separate have the composition $[Ag_3I](NO_3)_2$ (Hellwig, loc. cit.). The crystal structure of this compound has not yet been

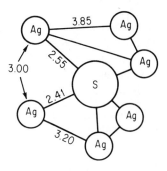

Fig. 7   Basic structure found in complexes containing the $[Ag_3S]^+$ group.

determined, but it has been assumed to contain $[Ag_3I]^{+2}$ ions. These and similar complexes such as $[Ag_2I]F$, $[Ag_2Br]F$, $[Ag_8Te](NO_3)_6$, and the like have been characterized to date.[32] The behavior of concentrated silver nitrate solutions which contain dissolved silver iodide is in accord with this interpretation as silver and silver iodide migrate toward the *cathode* when such solutions are electrolyzed (Hellwig, loc. cit.). These complexes are related to, but not identical with, the polynuclear complexes formed when silver iodide dissolves in concentrated solutions of iodides.[33] Under such circumstances the silver ion is generally considered to be the coordination center.

[29] K. A. Hellwig, *Zeit. anorg. Chem.* **25**, 157 (1900).

[30] W. A. Kistiakowsky, *J. Russ. Phys. Soc.* **33**, 480, 592 (1901), *Chem. Soc. Abstracts* ii, 121 (1902).

[31] G. Bergerhoff, *Zeit. anorg. Chem.* **299**, 328 (1959).

[32] K. H. Leiser, *Zeit. anorg. Chem.* **292**, 114 (1957); **305**, 133, 255 (1960) and the literature cited therein.

[33] R. O. Nilsson, *Arkiv för Kemi* **12**, 513 (1958).

TYPICAL COMPLEXES OF THE ELEMENTS IN THE GROUPS OF THE PERIODIC TABLE

The factors governing the stability and stereochemistry of complexes are very numerous. The relation of the size of the central atom to the number of atoms which can be coordinated to it has been known for some time. Thus the maximum coordination number of elements in the second row of the periodic table is four, for elements in the third and fourth rows the maximum coordination number is six, and for elements in the fifth and sixth rows, ten is the number (although six or eight are more commonly seen). For the seventh row there seems to some possibility of a coordination number of twelve. This variation in coordination number is superimposed on those reactions which are typical of a given group of the periodic table in determining the number, kind, and stereochemistry of the coordination compounds which can be formed. The typical coordination numbers for many coordination centers are given in Table 3.1. The chemical factors governing the types and stabilities of the complexes formed by various elements were first systematized by Sidgwick.[34] These factors can be summarized in the following statements which deal primarily with the descriptive chemistry of coordination compounds.

1. Stable ammines will form in aqueous solution with chromium, cobalt, nickel, rhodium, palladium, iridium, platinum, copper, ruthenium, silver, zinc, and cadmium. Less stable ammine complexes are formed by many other species but frequently the preferred process in such a solution is precipitation of the hydroxide or hydrated oxide. Chelate nitrogen compounds are formed by the elements mentioned above and also by iron and osmium.

2. Small inert gas type ions tend to form stable fluoride complexes but rather unstable complexes with the other halide ions. Examples of such stable complexes are BeF_4^{-2}, BF_4^{-}, AlF_6^{-3}, and SiF_6^{-2}.

3. Small ions having an external shell with 18 electrons or with 18 plus 2 electrons usually form stable complexes with halide ions. For those with 18 electrons the complexes with the heavier halides are more stable; for those with 18 plus 2 electrons the reverse trend is often observed.

4. As a general rule, ions with an inert gas structure have a greater tendency to coordinate to oxygen than to nitrogen or sulfur.

5. Ions with an external electronic shell of 18 or 18 plus 2 electrons generally form stable complexes with ligands containing divalent sulfur or derivatives of sulfide.

---

[34] N. V. Sidgwick, *J. Chem. Soc.* 440 (1941), collects much of this. A great deal of the detailed discussion may be found in the relevant portions of this same author's *The Chemical Elements and Their Compounds*, Oxford University Press, (1949).

TABLE 3.1

SOME COORDINATION NUMBERS OBSERVED FOR TYPICAL COORDINATION CENTERS
(for neutral or univalent ligands)

Species	C.N.	Species	C.N.
Al(III)	4, 6	Mo(IV)	6, 8
Sb(III)	4	Mo(V)	8
Sb(V)	6	Nd(III)	6, 9
As(III)	4	Ni(O)	4
As(V)	6	Ni(I)	4
Ba(II)	6, 8	Ni(II)	4, 6
Be(II)	4	Nb(V)	6, 7, 8
Bi(III)	4, 5, 6	Os(III)	6
Bi(V)	6	Pd(II)	4, 6
Cd(II)	4, 6	Pd(IV)	6
Ca(II)	6, (8?)	P(V)	6
Ce(III)	6	Pt(II)	4, 6
Ce(IV)	6, 8	Pt(IV)	6
Cs(I)	8	K(I)	6, 8
Cr(II)	6	Re(III)	4, 6
Cr(III)	6	Re(IV)	6
Co(II)	4, 6	Rh(III)	6
Co(III)	6	Rb(I)	8
Cu(I)	2, 3	Ru(II)	6
Cu(II)	4, 6	Ru(III)	6
Ga(III)	4, 6	Sc(III)	6
Ge(IV)	6	Si(IV)	6
Au(I)	2, 3	Ag(I)	2, 3
Au(III)	4	Ag(II)	4
Hf(IV)	6, 8	Na(I)	6
In(III)	4, 6	Sr(II)	6, (8?)
I(VII)	6, 7	Ta(V)	6, 7, 8
Ir(III)	6	Tl(I)	2, 4
Fe(II)	4, 6	Th(IV)	8, (10?), 12
Fe(III)	4, 6	Sn(II)	4
Pb(II)	4	Sn(IV)	6
Pb(IV)	6	Ti(IV)	6
Li(I)	4	W(V)	6, 8
Mg(II)	4, 6	V(III)	6
Mn(I)	6	V(IV)	5, 6
Mn(II)	4, 6	Y(III)	6
Mn(III)	6	Zn(II)	4, 5, 6
Hg(II)	4, 6	Zr(IV)	6, 8
Mo(III)	6		

6. Usually, the heavier members in a transition element family will form more stable complexes with sulfide containing ligands than the lightest member of such a family.

7. Elements which form stable ammine complexes will form complexes with the corresponding phosphine, arsine, and stibine derivatives in many cases. There is little quantitative information available on the stability of such complexes but it seems that in some cases they can be considerably more stable than the ammine complexes.

8. Double bond formation between the ligand and the central metal ion will result in complexes more stable than would be expected on elementary considerations. If a series of ligands is compared, the occurrence of such double bonding is found to be dependent upon the properties of both the ligand and the central ion. The present interpretation considers this to arise most frequently when the metal ion can *back donate* a pair of electrons in a *d* orbital to an empty orbital of the ligand molecule.[35] Thus carbon, phosphorus, arsenic, and nitrogen ligands can use this process to increase the stability of their bonds with a central atom when present in ligands such as CO or pyridine.

9. In general, elements of the regular groups of the periodic table have less tendency to form complexes than the elements of transition element families.

10. The tendency to coordinate to oxygen is greater than the tendency to coordinate with nitrogen for the alkali metals, the alkaline earths, Ga, In, Tl, Ti, Zr, Hf, Th, Si, Ge, Sn, V(V), V(IV), Nb(V), Ta(V), Mo(VI), U(VI), U(V), U(IV), Fe(III), and Co(II).

11. The tendency to coordinate to nitrogen is greater than the tendency to coordinate to oxygen for Cu(I), Ag(I), Au(I), Cu(II), Cd, Hg(II), V(III), Co(III), and Ni(II).

12. The species which have the greatest tendency to form ammines are Cu(II), Be, V(III), Cr(III), Fe(II), Co(III), Ni(II), Ru(II), Ru(III), Rh(III), Ir(III), Pd(II), Pd(IV), Pt(II), and Pt(IV). It will be noted that with the exception of Be and V(III), these are confined to Group VIII and the cupric and the chromic compounds.

13. Elements which coordinate more strongly with sulfur(-II) than they do with oxygen include Cu(I), Ag(I), Au(I), and Hg(II), and the platinum metals.

Before passing on to more recent attempts to arrange the elements in respect to their coordinating ability for various ligand species it will be necessary to look more closely at the term "stability". The vague usage of the term "stability" in the paragraphs above should be noted. In no case is it possible to draw

---

[35] L. Pauling, *The Nature of the Chemical Bond*, Cornell University Press, Ithaca, New York, 3rd ed. (1960), Ch. 9.

a sharp line between unstable and stable complexes that is completely free from dispute. This has the result that any such set of rules may require some caution in their general application. Stability is of two kinds: stability in the kinetic sense of undergoing reaction slowly in a given environment and stability in the thermodynamic sense of being the favored equilibrium constituent in a given environment. These are completely different types of criteria as we shall see later. Furthermore, there are two ways of measuring the thermodynamic stability—on a solid phase or in aqueous solution. Since there is such a small amount of data on the thermodynamic properties of solid complexes compared to the amount available on aqueous solutions, it is almost invariably this second type of thermodynamic stability which is meant when thermodynamic stability is discussed without further qualification. These two sorts are by no means equivalent. Thus when silver chloride is dissolved in aqueous ammonia, the ion $[Ag(NH_3)_2]^+$ is the form in which practically all of the silver is present; yet the stable solid phases in the $AgCl$-NH_3 system are the three solids $AgCl \cdot 3NH_3$, $2AgCl \cdot 3NH_3$, and $AgCl \cdot NH_3$, with no evidence of the existence of $AgCl \cdot 2NH_3$ being found at all.[36] Many complexes which possess considerable thermodynamic stability are completely broken down in the presence of water. Thus $BeCl_2$ takes up NH_3 to form the ammine $[Be(NH_3)_4]Cl_2$, whose vapor pressure of ammonia is 175 mm at 170° while the vapor pressure of ammonia over $[Ni(NH_3)_6]Cl_2$ is 175 mm at 140°.[37] In water the relative stabilities of these complexes are reversed. For the reaction:

$$Ni(H_2O)_6^{+2} + NH_3 \rightleftharpoons [Ni(NH_3)(H_2O)_5]^{+2} + H_2O$$

the equilibrium constant in water solution is

$$K = \frac{[Ni(NH_3)(H_2O)_5^{+2}]}{[Ni(H_2O)_6^{+2}][NH_3]} \approx 500$$ [38]

The reaction of beryllium(II) with an aqueous solution of ammonia produces not ammines, but hydroxo complexes whose stability is much greater than the ammines which might be formed.[39] The corresponding beryllium ammines may be considered to be so completely broken down in aqueous solution that measurements on such a system are not capable of detecting them.

Another illustration of the limitations of merely qualitative statements can be seen in the data in Table 3.2. In making up any list of ions which form stable complexes with a given donor atom we are forced to make a choice between (a) listing all ions for which there is any evidence of some complex formation, however slight, or (b) listing only those ions which form a complex with a

[36] W. Biltz and W. Stollenwerk, *Zeit. anorg. Chem.* **114**, 174 (1920).

[37] F. Ephraim, *Ber.* **45**, 1324 (1912).

[38] J. Bjerrum, G. Schwarzenbach, and L. G. Sillen, *Stability Constants*, The Chemical Society, London (1957), Part II, p. 47.

[39] J. Bjerrum, Thesis (*Metal Ammine Formation in Aqueous Solution*), Copenhagen (1941), pp. 169–173.

TABLE 3.2

ILLUSTRATIVE VARIATIONS IN STABILITY CONSTANTS*

Complex Ion	$\log_{10} K_6$	$\log_{10} \beta_6$
$Mg(NH_3)_6^{+2}$	-1.3	$\cdots$
$Ca(NH_3)_6^{+2}$	-1.7	$\cdots$
$Co(NH_3)_6^{+2}$	-0.7	4.39
$Mn(NH_3)_6^{+2}$	$\cdots$	9
$Co(NH_3)_6^{+3}$	$\cdots$	33.66
$Ni(NH_3)_6^{+2}$	-0.09	8.01
$Cd(NH_3)_6^{+2}$	$\cdots$	8.77
$Fe(CN)_6^{-4}$	9	24
$Fe(CN)_6^{-3}$	$\cdots$	31
$Co(CN)_6^{-4}$	$\cdots$	19
$Co(CN)_6^{-3}$	$\cdots$	64(?)

* Values from ref. 38.

$$K_6 = \frac{[M(X)_6]}{[M(X)_5(H_2O)]\,[X]}$$, i.e., the constant for the formation of the sixth complex from the fifth.

$$\beta_6 = \frac{[M(X)_6]}{[M]\,[X]^6}$$, i.e., this is the cumulative stability constant for the sixth complex.

stability constant equal to or greater than a certain arbitrary value. If we choose alternative (a) we soon find that evidence for some feeble interaction can be found for almost any given ion-ligand combination. From Table 3.2 it can be appreciated that the complex ions $Mg(NH_3)_6^{+2}$ or $Ca(NH_3)_6^{+2}$ are so unstable that they are not customarily classed with the stable ammines nor are calcium and magnesium generally considered to form ammines at all. Yet here we have definite physical evidence that such ammine formation does occur. It is only when dealing with very stable complexes such as the cyano complexes at the bottom of the table or a complex such as the hexamminecobalt(III) ion that the sweeping generalizations seem not only sweeping but rigorously valid. A further difficulty arises when one considers the relation between ion-pair formation (which is a general phenomenon in concentrated solutions of electrolytes) and complex formation (which is usually assumed to be a more specific type of interaction). The enormous number of complexes which arise when ion-pair formation is included in our classification scheme may be emotionally satisfying to the inorganic chemist, but is found to be such a heterogeneous collection that its organization is very difficult. Such a collection would also tend to underestimate the importance of the very stable complexes in the formulation of a suitable structural theory.

Accordingly, alternative (b) will be chosen with the understanding that it is impossible to give an exact definition to that lower limit of stability that will be deemed sufficient in the discussion of the various aspects of coordination chemistry. This attitude passively accepts the dictum that it is not possible to give an exact, all-inclusive definition of a coordination compound.[40]

One of the most extensive of the recent attempts to systematize donor atom coordination tendencies to various metal ions is that of Ahrland, Chatt, and Davies.[41] Their generalizations are based to a considerable extent on the very numerous studies of stability constants which have been published since Sidgwick's work. It is necessary to note that this study has provided further detailed information on trends involving specific cases but has not provided a general basis for *predicting* relative stabilities with any certainty. The great variability in behavior obviously precludes any *simple* theory of the Lewis acid-base type from serious consideration. The chief difficulty which arises is the lack of a general scale of basicities for such behavior. The order of basicities depends on the species interacting in a manner dependent on factors in addition to those involved in mere single (or sigma) bond formation. As evidence, these authors cite the relative donor properties of the alkyl derivatives of the elements of Groups V and VI toward three typical acceptor centers: $Ga(CH_3)_3$, Pt(II), and Ag(I). These are:

$$Ga(CH_3)_3: \quad N > P > As > Sb \quad \text{and} \quad O > S < Se > Te$$
$$Pt(II): \quad N \ll P > As > Sb \quad \text{and} \quad O \ll S \gg Se < Te$$
$$Ag(I): \quad N \ll P > As \quad \text{and} \quad O \ll S < Se < Te$$

They propose that there are two classes of acceptor species: class (a) which forms the most stable complex with the first ligand atom of Groups V, VI, and VII (i.e., N, O, and F) and class (b) which forms the most stable complex with the second ligand atom or even one further down the periodic table. The classification requires recognition of the generally ignored fact that different oxidation states of the same element may differ considerably in coordination properties and must be considered as different acceptor species. Furthermore, there is a large class of borderline acceptors where such a simple picture is subject to variations in specific interactions. The acceptors in class (a) are the ions of the alkali metals, the alkaline earths, Sc through Ac, Ti through Th, V through Pa, Cr, U, Al, Ga, In, Zn, Si, Ge, Sn, P, As, Sb, S, Se, Cl, Br, and I. The elements in class (b) are Rh, Ir, Pd, Pt, Ag, Au, and Hg. The large group of borderline elements includes Mn, Fe, Co, Ni, Cu, Mo, Tc, Ru, W, Re, Os, Cd, Tl, Pb, Bi, and Po. In the borderline elements one finds numerous examples of different oxidation states of the same element falling into different classes.

A somewhat different approach to the problem of selectivity in coordina-

---

[40] A. A. Grinberg, *Einführung in die Chemie der Komplexverbindungen*, VEB Verlag Technik, Berlin (1955), Ch. 1.

[41] S. Ahrland, J. Chatt, and N. R. Davies, *Quarterly Reviews* **12**, 265 (1958).

tion may be seen in the studies of several Russian workers which have been extended and concisely summarized by Jazimirsky (Yatsimirsky).[42] He considers central ions *and* ligands to be both divided into four types or classes which are the same for both central ions and ligands. The first class is "electrostatic complex formers and ligands." Both the central ions and the ligands in this class have those features tending to favor the formation of compounds by electrostatic interaction, i.e., a high charge for the cation, a small radius for the anion or a high dipole moment for an uncharged ligand, a high electron affinity for the ligand and a relatively small ionization potential for the cation. Cations in this group include Be^{+2}, Al^{+3}, Th^{+4}, Sc^{+3}, and Ti^{+4}; ligands here include F^-, H_2O, ROH, CO_3^{-2}, and SO_4^{-2}. The second class is designated "covalent complex formers and ligands." It includes cations with a high ionization potential and ligands with a low electron affinity. Species falling in this class include the cations Au^+, Hg^{+2}, Pb^{+2}, Bi^{+3}, and Tl^+ and the ligands $S_2O_3^{-2}$, I^-, Br^-, CNS^-, and $(NH_2)_2C{=}S$ (thiourea). The third class is designated "universal complex formers." It contains cations with a high ionization potential, anions with a small electron affinity, species with a high charge, and cations with a small radius. In this group are placed the cations Co^{+3}, Pt^{+4}, Rh^{+3}, Ir^{+3}, and Cu^{+2} and the anions $C_2O_4^{-2}$, CN^-, and $C_4H_4O_6^{-2}$. In the fourth class are placed the "transitional (intermediate) complex formers and ligands." These are cations with intermediate values for the ionization potential, anions with intermediate electron affinities, etc. Here one finds Ni^{+2}, Zn^{+2}, Co^{+2}, Fe^{+2}, Ag^+, Cu^+, Cd^{+2} as well as NH_3, $C_2H_4(NH_2)_2$, NO_2^-, and HCO_2^-. Yatsimirsky's classification is based upon an electrostatic view of complex formation and considers primarily the factors which effect the electrostatic interaction. It has the advantage that it clearly represents the complementary aspects of the metal-ligand interaction. It does not include any allowance for some of the less frequently encountered factors governing coordinate bonding such as double bonding. Thus ligands for which double bonding may be important are not systematically sorted out. It must be emphasized that Yatsimirsky's scheme is primarily based on thermochemical data on the pure compounds and thus differs from other schemes based upon observations in aqueous systems of various concentration. The book of Yatsimirsky's cited above is the only comprehensive collection of thermodynamic data on pure complexes available.

An extensive discussion of the numerous factors affecting bonding in complexes may be found in an impressive review by Magnusson.[43] Magnusson's critical comments provide a very useful and sobering orientation in the enormous problems still remaining unsolved in this field. When the theoretical analysis of bonding in complexes is considered in greater detail in Chapter 6 it

[42] K. B. Jazimirsky, *Thermochemie von Komplexverbindungen*, Akademie-Verlag, Berlin (1956), pp. 86–91.
[43] E. A. Magnusson, *Reviews Pure Applied Chem.* **7**, 195–260 (1957).

will be seen that none of the really compact classification schemes (which are all based on a specific theory of bonding) are an infallible guide.

THE ORGANIZATION OF THE FIELD BY WERNER

The enormous influence which Werner exerted on the development of coordination chemistry was based upon two major contributions: the laying of the stereochemical foundations of this field and the great systematization of valency which he effected by presenting a master plan by which both simple compounds and adducts of all sorts were incorporated into a single scheme. The second of these accomplishments is rarely noted today, but must certainly be ranked with the first in importance. It should be remembered that Werner's interests were wide ranging; to him we owe the tetrahedral stereochemistry of ammonium derivatives, the hydrogen bond (proposed by him to explain the FHF^- ion as early as 1908), and numerous other ideas which have since been reformulated in more elegant and modern theoretical terms. Werner divided all chemical compounds into two classes: compounds of the first order (such as NaCl or $AlCl_3$) and compounds of higher order (such as $BF_3 \cdot O(Et)_2$ or $Co(NH_3)_6Cl_3$). It is in dealing with the compounds of higher order that Werner's ideas were most strikingly effective. This grand scheme of organization, which he proposed for all chemical compounds, forms the basis for his book, in which it is ably presented.

Werner's book[44] tried to show the interrelationships of practically all classes of inorganic compounds. Regular salts such as NaCl (compounds of the first order) can be explained upon simple valency rules and are what might be designated the "expected compounds" formed by any two elements. All other compounds containing two or more species, each of which is capable of an independent existence, are called "compounds of higher order." Two main classes of these compounds of higher order were the addition compounds (Anlagerungsverbindungen) and the intercalation compounds (Einlagerungsverbindungen). Addition compounds included H_2SO_4 (H_2O plus SO_3), $KAuCl_4$, etc. Intercalation compounds were defined by Werner as being compounds of the type $M(R)_mX_n$ where the addition of the group or compound, R, to MX_n leads to a change in which the originally covalently bonded X changes to an ionizable X. This division was influenced to a large extent by Werner's studies of the molar electrical conductances of solutions of complexes. This property allows such changes to be detected in a direct and obvious manner. Following this initial division of the field, Werner classified all complexes into one or the other of these two great classes, insofar as the available data allowed. He recognized that some compounds could not satisfactorily be accommodated

[44] A. Werner, *Neure Anschauungen auf dem Gebiete der Anorganischen Chemie*, F. Vieweg & Sohn, Braunschweig, Germany, appeared in five editions, two of which were posthumous; 1905, 1908, 1913, 1920 (P. Karrer, editor), and 1923 (P. Pfeiffer, editor).

in either of these groups, but rather exhibited behavior of an intermediate character. He also considered inner complexes such as bis(glycinato)copper-(II) to be of enough importance to demand special treatment without actually forming a third class of compounds.

While these major classes have been subjected to extensive revision and are rarely seen in their original form today, many of the subsidiary divisions are frequently encountered since they allow considerable systematization to be introduced into the descriptive chemistry of these complexes. Three of these terms which may still be encountered are:

acidopentammine for compounds of the type $[M(NH_3)_5X]$
diacidotetrammine for compounds of the type $[M(NH_3)_4X_2]$
triacidotriammine for compounds of the type $[M(NH_3)_3X_3]$

where X is a singly charged anion. These terms may be found in many works, such as Gmelin, where the descriptive chemistry of complexes is treated in great detail.

Much thought has been expended in attempts to provide reasonable definitions for the two commonly encountered types of complex. The one class consists of complexes which dissociate rapidly in aqueous solution and are in rapid dynamic equilibrium with their constituents in such a solution. The second class dissociates slowly under such circumstances and is not in rapidly attained equilibrium with its constituents in aqueous solution. The names which have been suggested for these two broad classes depend upon the particular definition accepted and whether an empirical or theoretical basis of classification is used. The following lists contain the ways in which various authors have designated these two classes. The words in each list *are not* strictly synonymous.

I	II
addition compound	intercalation compound
normal complex	penetration complex
labile complex	inert complex, stable complex, robust complex
outer orbital complex	inner orbital complex
ionic complex	covalent complex
spin free complex	spin paired complex

This aspect of the field is definitely still in an unsettled condition as there is no general agreement on either terms or definitions. The empirical definition of Taube, which leads to the classes of labile and inert complexes, is perhaps the safest to use. A *labile complex*, by Taube's definition, is simply one which attains equilibrium with a solution environment in a time not very different from the time of mixing (say, one minute).

ISOMERISM IN COORDINATION COMPOUNDS

One of the characteristic features of covalent structures of reasonable stability is the occurrence of isomeric forms. The structural theory of Werner accommodated the few isomeric complexes known at the time of its origin and successfully predicted many other types of isomers which at that time were completely unknown in this field. Because of Werner's influence several types of isomers have been given special names. Since these terms are met in the literature, it is necessary to have some familiarity with them. The more important of these types will recur frequently in the remainder of this book. The following listing is adapted from the one given by Werner.[45]

1. Coordination Polymerization Isomers. These are isomeric coordination compounds which differ in their formula weights (or less exactly, their molecular weights).

Examples:

$$[Co(NH_3)_3(NO_2)_3] \quad \text{and} \quad [Co(NH_3)_6][Co(NO_2)_6]$$
$$[Pt(NH_3)_2Cl_2] \quad \text{and} \quad [Pt(NH_3)_4][PtCl_4]$$

2. Nuclear Coordination Polymerization Isomers. When two complex cations have the same composition but different ionic weights they can give rise to isomeric compounds.

Examples:

$$\left[(H_3N)_3Co\overset{OH}{\underset{OH}{\diagup\diagdown}}Co(NH_3)_3 \right] X_3 \quad \text{and} \quad \left[Co\left(\overset{HO}{\underset{HO}{\diagdown\diagup}}Co(NH_3)_4 \right)_3 \right] X_6$$

$$\left[(H_3N)_4Co\overset{OH}{\underset{OH}{\diagup\diagdown}}Co(NH_3)_4 \right] Br_4 \cdot 2H_2O \quad \text{and} \quad \left[(H_3N)_4Co\overset{OH}{\underset{OH_2}{\diagup\diagdown}} \right] Br_2$$

3. Coordination Isomerism. Two metal atoms with similar coordination properties give rise to what are called coordination isomers if either of them can be the central atom in a given cation-anion pair such as $[M(NH_3)_6]$ $[M'(CN)_6]$.

Examples:

$$[Co(NH_3)_6][Cr(CN)_6] \quad \text{and} \quad [Cr(NH_3)_6][Co(CN)_6]$$
$$[Cr(en)_3][Co(C_2O_4)_3] \quad \text{and} \quad [Co(en)_3][Cr(C_2O_4)_3]$$

4. Hydrate Isomerism. In a crystalline complex salt one may have water present as coordinated water or as more loosely bound crystal water. When two solids of the same composition differ in the manner in which the water is held they are designated hydrate isomers.

Examples:

$$\underset{\text{gray-blue}}{[Cr(H_2O)_6]Cl_3} \quad \underset{\text{light green}}{[Cr(H_2O)_5Cl]Cl_2 \cdot H_2O}$$
$$\underset{\text{dark green}}{[Cr(H_2O)_4Cl_2]Cl \cdot 2H_2O}$$

[45] ref. 44, 4th ed., p. 327 ff.

5. Ionization Isomerism. When a complex salt is prepared which contains a free potential donor anion and coordinated donor anions, isomerism may arise by the interchange of the positions of the anions. The ionization of such isomers in water will obviously produce different species.

Examples:

$$[Co(NH_3)_5NO_3]SO_4 \quad \text{and} \quad [Co(NH_3)_5SO_4]NO_3$$
$$[Co(en)_2Cl(NO_2)]NO_2 \quad \text{and} \quad [Co(en)_2(NO_2)_2]Cl$$

6. Salt Isomerism (Linkage Isomerism). When a given polynuclear anion can coordinate through either of two different atoms to a given central metal ion, salt isomerism may arise. In spite of some controversy over the actual existence of this type of isomerism, it is now established beyond all reasonable doubt. The known instances involve the nitrite anion which can coordinate through the oxygen atoms to give nitrite complexes or through the nitrogen atom to give the nitro complexes.

Examples:

$$[Co(en)_2(ONO)_2]X \quad \text{and} \quad [Co(en)_2(NO_2)_2]X$$
$$[Ir(NH_3)_5(ONO)]Cl_2 \quad \text{and} \quad [Ir(NH_3)_5(NO_2)]Cl_2 \qquad [46]$$

In writing the ligand, ONO is used to designate coordination through oxygen, and NO_2 coordination through nitrogen. Although some other simple anions, such as SCN^-, can coordinate at either end, there is no certain evidence that it ever does so to the *same* central atom. Thus, $Cr(NCS)_6^{-3}$, in which the chromium is coordinated to the nitrogen, can *also* coordinate to Ag(I) or Hg(II) through the sulfur at the periphery of the complex.[47]

7. Structural Isomerism. The isomerism of thiourea and ammonium thiocyanate forms the basis for some of the isomeric complexes of this type. Both thiourea and thiocyanate are effective donors for many of the heavy metals.

Examples:

$$[(H_2N)_2CS]_2 Hg(SCN)_2 \quad \text{and} \quad (NH_4)_2[Hg(SCN)_4]$$
$$[(H_2N)_2CS]_2 Zn(SCN)_2 \quad \text{and} \quad (NH_4)_2[Zn(SCN)_4]$$

8. Coordinative Positional Isomerism. In polynuclear complexes, isomers may arise by the interchange of two different species coordinated to two different central atoms.

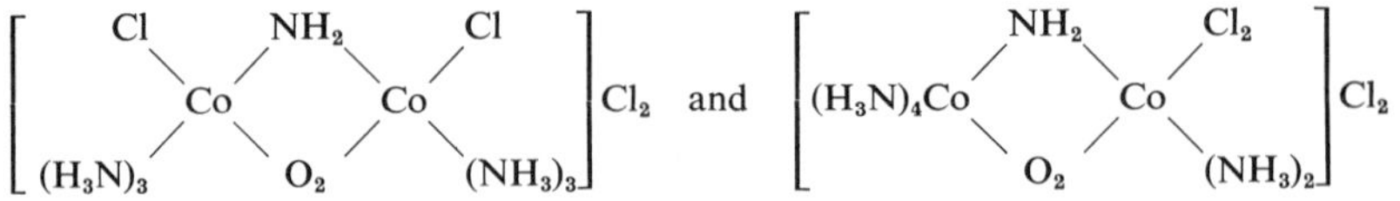

[46] F. Basolo and G. Hammaker, *J. Amer. Chem. Soc.* **82**, 1001 (1960); *Inorg. Chem.* **1**, 1 (1962).

[47] W. C. Waggener, J. A. Mattern, and G. H. Cartledge, *J. Amer. Chem. Soc.* **81**, 2958 (1959).

9. Valence Isomerism. Werner restricted the members of this class to those complexes containing the same molecular components, but showing differences in the ways in which these were bonded together. Most of the examples which Werner cited had the particular type of difference in bonding shown in the pair of complexes below. The examples of this class which were originally cited have all been disproven with the possible exception of:

$$\left[(en)_2Co \overset{O_2}{\underset{NH_2}{\diagup\diagdown}} Co(en)_2 \right] X_4 \quad and \quad \left[(en)_2Co \overset{O_2}{\underset{\underset{HX}{\overset{|}{NH}}}{\diagup\diagdown}} Co(en)_2 \right] X_3$$

10. Geometrical Isomerism. This kind of positional isomerism is very well established for both square planar and octahedral complexes and several examples have been given earlier. Other examples which include more than two geometrical isomers arise in square planar complexes of Pt(II) with four different ligands; see Figure 8 for examples.

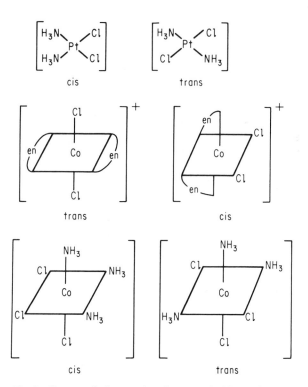

Fig. 8 Some typical examples of geometrical isomerism.

11. Mirror Image Isomers (Enantiomorphs, optical isomers, antipodes). If a molecule or ion possesses only axes of symmetry or no symmetry elements at all, its mirror image will not be superposable on itself. In such cases the resulting isomers possess chemical and physical properties which are alike *except* for their interaction with polarized light or other mirror image isomers. In common parlance such species are called *asymmetric* or *dissymmetric molecules*, though the implication that no elements of symmetry are present need not be taken strictly. Two typical examples are presented in Figure 9.

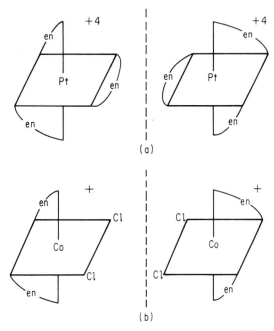

Fig. 9   The enantiomeric forms of $[Pt(en)_3]^{+4}$ and $[Co(en)_2Cl_2]^+$.

Of the types of isomerism listed above, geometrical and mirror-image isomers are by far the most important. Their occurrence has innumerable ramifications, many of which will arise in the remaining chapters of this book.

CHEMICAL METHODS FOR ESTABLISHING THE STRUCTURES OF COMPLEXES

ISOMERISM AND THE STEREOCHEMISTRY OF SIX-COORDINATED COMPLEXES. The number and types of isomerism which have been found for six-coordinated complexes can be used to establish the structure of these complexes in much the same way that Körner's work established a regular hexagonal structure for benzene. Such data represent what is perhaps the limit of strictly chemical

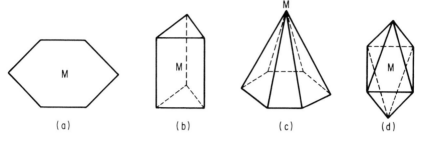

Fig. 10 Alternative methods of arranging six groups about a single central atom as given by Pfeiffer: (a) hexagon, (b) trigonal prism, (c) hexagonal pyramid, and (d) octahedron.

methods for the establishment of structures. There are four configurations for compounds of the type Ma_6 which possess high symmetry. These are shown in Figure 10 and are the regular hexagon(a), the trigonal prism(b), the hexagonal pyramid(c), and the octahedron(d). It must be remembered that in the octahedron all positions are equivalent. For various compounds it is possible to list the predicted types of isomerism for each structure and finally the types of isomers found experimentally. The structure which predicts both the number and types of isomers found is then assumed (and safely so) to be the correct one. This information is collected in Table 3.3. As can be seen, the octahedral

TABLE 3.3

PREDICTED NUMBERS OF GEOMETRICAL AND OPTICAL ISOMERS

Compound type	a	b	c	d	Exptl. no.
Ma_4b_2	3 geo	3 geo	3 geo	2 geo	2 geo
$M(en)a_4$	1 geo	2 geo	1 geo	1 geo	1 geo
$M(en)_2a_2$	2 geo	5 geo, plus optical	2 geo	2 geo, one of which is asymmetric	2 geo, one of which is asymmetric
$M(en)_3$	1	2 geo, no optical	1	one pair of antipodes	one pair of antipodes

configuration is thus the only one which predicts the correct number of each type of isomer actually found. The evidence from optical isomerism is perhaps the most striking and was historically the most important.

The work of Werner provided numerous examples where his stereochemical predictions, based upon this octahedral model, were confirmed in every respect. A more complicated example of this is the isomerism which arises when one of the ligands is both unsymmetrically coordinated and is also asymmetric. This may be seen in some complexes in which the chelating properties of propylenediamine are in evidence. Further possible isomers arise from two causes

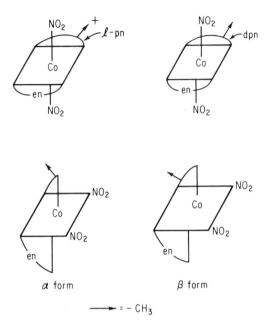

Fig. 11   Some isomeric forms of $[Co(pn)(en)(NO_2)_2]^+$: (a) the *trans*-form,
(b) the alpha and beta forms of the *cis*-isomers. These latter differ
in the relative positions of the methyl group *vis-a-vis* the rest of
the complex.

(a) the complex may contain either the *d* or the *l* form of the chelating agent and
(b) the unsymmetrical coordination of the chelating agent may lead to a structural isomerism which is superimposed upon any geometrical isomerism due
to the coordination arrangement of the donor atoms. Werner prepared the
complex ion $[Co(pn)(en)(NO_2)_2]^+$ and found that all ten of the predicted
isomers could be obtained, though he was unable to assign unambiguous
structures to all of these. First, there are two *trans*-isomers and two *cis*-isomers
shown in Figure 11. Then, each of the *cis*-forms may have either *d* or *l* propylenediamine, and finally, each of the *cis*-forms may exist in enantiomorphic
forms because of the asymmetric cobalt atom. The list of isomeric forms for
this ion then includes the following:

trans-isomer with *d* pn	
trans-isomer with *l* pn	
cis-α *d* pn *d* Co	*cis*-β *d* pn *d* Co
cis-α *d* pn *l* Co	*cis*-β *d* pn *l* Co
cis-α *l* pn *d* Co	*cis*-β *l* pn *d* Co
cis-α *l* pn *l* Co	*cis*-β *l* pn *l* Co

All ten isomers were prepared by Werner and his students.[48]

[48] A. Werner, *Helv. Chim. Acta* **1**, 5 (1918).

A point of interest which should be noted about complexes that contain asymmetric carbon atoms and asymmetric cobalt (or other transition metal atoms) is the behavior of their rotatory dispersion curves. These are simply plots of the optical rotation at various wavelengths. If d pn is used to make $[Co(d-pn)_3]^{+3}$, the rotatory dispersion curves of the resultant salt solutions will be normal, i.e., the optical rotation can be expressed as $\alpha = k/\lambda^2$ and the rotatory power, α, will decrease with increasing wave length, λ. If this complex is resolved into its enantiomorphs, they will have anomalous rotatory dispersion curves because of the absorption of light by the cobalt atom. While the cobalt absorbs light when present in the racemic mixture, such a mixture shows no rotation due to cobalt and this effect cannot be noted. This distinction between the two types of behavior may be seen more clearly in Figure 12. The

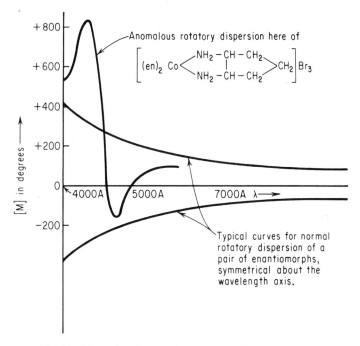

Fig. 12 Normal and anomalous rotatory dispersion curves.

anomalous curve usually shows a change in the sign of the rotation in the neighborhood of a maximum in the absorption spectra. The rotation of light in anomalous rotatory dispersion is a more complicated function of the wave length and can usually be represented by an equation proposed by Drude:

$$\alpha = \sum_m \frac{K_m}{(\lambda^2 - \lambda_m^2)}$$

The occurrence of an anomalous rotatory dispersion curve usually indicates that the asymmetric atoms are coincident with or coupled to those parts of the complex which are responsible for the absorption of light in the region of the anomaly.

Other studies of the type carried out by Werner and cited above have confirmed the possibility of this kind of isomerism.[49]

THE METHOD OF WERNER FOR DETERMINING THE STRUCTURE OF PLATINUM(II) COMPLEXES. Werner[50] proposed a chemical method for determining the structures of platinum(II) complexes based upon the following assumptions:

1. These complexes have a square planar configuration.

2. The substitution reactions of these complexes proceed in such a manner that the entering group takes the place of the group which is replaced. Thus there is no process here analogous to the Walden Inversion which occurs in the reactions of the tetrahedral carbon atom.

3. Thermal decomposition of a compound of the type $[Pt(Am)_4]X_2$ gives compounds of the type $[Pt(Am)_2X_2]$ by a reaction involving *trans*-elimination.

The use of these three assumptions with the two forms of $[Pt(NH_3)_2Cl_2]$ and $[Pt(py)_2Cl_2]$ allows their configurations to be established from the number of compounds which result from a reaction. There are two forms of these compounds, an alpha compound which is the more deeply colored and a beta form which is lighter in color. Werner examined the following series of reactions for these compounds:

$$\begin{array}{ll} [Pt(NH_3)_2Cl_2] + 2py & \\ \quad \text{alpha form} & \searrow \\ & \quad \text{alpha}\,[Pt(NH_3)_2(py)_2]Cl_2 \\ [Pt(py)_2Cl_2] + 2NH_3 & \nearrow \\ \quad \text{alpha form} & \end{array}$$

$$\begin{array}{ll} \text{beta}\,[Pt(NH_3)_2Cl_2] + 2py & \searrow \\ & \quad \text{beta}\,[Pt(NH_3)_2(py)_2]Cl_2 \\ \text{beta}\,[Pt(py)_2Cl_2] + 2NH_3 & \nearrow \end{array}$$

$$\text{alpha}\,[Pt(NH_3)_2(py)_2]Cl_2 \xrightarrow{\text{heat}} \text{beta}\,[Pt(NH_3)(py)Cl_2]$$

$$\text{beta}\,[Pt(NH_3)_2(py)_2]Cl_2 \xrightarrow{\text{heat}} \left\{ \begin{array}{l} \text{beta}\,[Pt(NH_3)_2Cl_2] \\ \quad + \\ \text{beta}\,[Pt(py)_2Cl_2] \end{array} \right.$$

These reactions are all consistent with the assignment of a *cis*-configuration to the alpha form and a *trans*-configuration to the beta form of each of these complexes. The thermal decomposition reactions may then be written as indicated

---

[49] W. E. Cooley, C. F. Liu, and J. C. Bailar, Jr., *J. Amer. Chem. Soc.* **81**, 4189 (1959) present a study of the isomers of *cis*-dinitroethylenediamine(2,3-butylenediamine)cobalt-(III) compounds.

[50] A. Werner, *Zeit. anorg. Chem.* **3**, 267 (1893).

below. The first chloro group which enters labilizes the group *trans* to it which is then lost in the next step.

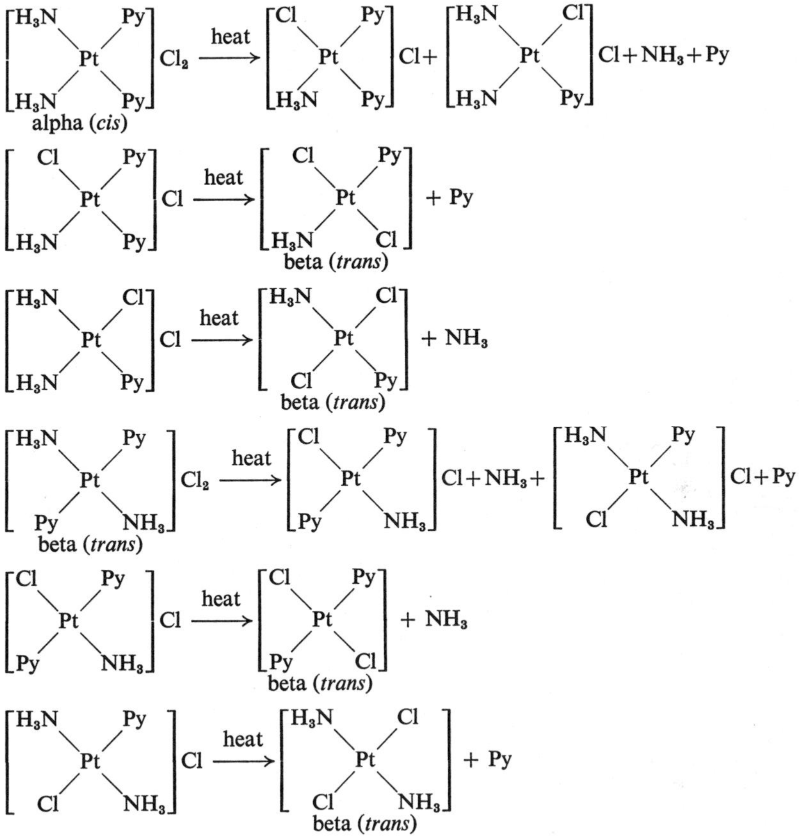

$$\begin{bmatrix} H_3N & & Py \\ & Pt & \\ H_3N & & Py \end{bmatrix} Cl_2 \xrightarrow{heat} \begin{bmatrix} Cl & & Py \\ & Pt & \\ H_3N & & Py \end{bmatrix} Cl + \begin{bmatrix} H_3N & & Cl \\ & Pt & \\ H_3N & & Py \end{bmatrix} Cl + NH_3 + Py$$

alpha (*cis*)

$$\begin{bmatrix} Cl & & Py \\ & Pt & \\ H_3N & & Py \end{bmatrix} Cl \xrightarrow{heat} \begin{bmatrix} Cl & & Py \\ & Pt & \\ H_3N & & Cl \end{bmatrix} + Py$$

beta (*trans*)

$$\begin{bmatrix} H_3N & & Cl \\ & Pt & \\ H_3N & & Py \end{bmatrix} Cl \xrightarrow{heat} \begin{bmatrix} H_3N & & Cl \\ & Pt & \\ Cl & & Py \end{bmatrix} + NH_3$$

beta (*trans*)

$$\begin{bmatrix} H_3N & & Py \\ & Pt & \\ Py & & NH_3 \end{bmatrix} Cl_2 \xrightarrow{heat} \begin{bmatrix} Cl & & Py \\ & Pt & \\ Py & & NH_3 \end{bmatrix} Cl + NH_3 + \begin{bmatrix} H_3N & & Py \\ & Pt & \\ Cl & & NH_3 \end{bmatrix} Cl + Py$$

beta (*trans*)

$$\begin{bmatrix} Cl & & Py \\ & Pt & \\ Py & & NH_3 \end{bmatrix} Cl \xrightarrow{heat} \begin{bmatrix} Cl & & Py \\ & Pt & \\ Py & & Cl \end{bmatrix} + NH_3$$

beta (*trans*)

$$\begin{bmatrix} H_3N & & Py \\ & Pt & \\ Cl & & NH_3 \end{bmatrix} Cl \xrightarrow{heat} \begin{bmatrix} H_3N & & Cl \\ & Pt & \\ Cl & & NH_3 \end{bmatrix} + Py$$

beta (*trans*)

The assumptions made by Werner have been used extensively by subsequent workers and have shown themselves to be quite useful without possessing the universal validity originally attributed to them. They form the basis for the discussion of the *trans*-effect and will be examined later.

GRINBERG'S METHOD FOR DETERMINING THE STRUCTURES OF PLATINUM(II) COMPLEXES

Grinberg's method uses the assumptions of Werner with the additional assumption that when a chelating agent with two donor atoms separated by two to four other atoms coordinates to *two* positions of a given central atom, then these two positions must be *cis*-positions.[51] The chelating agents used

[51] A. A. Grinberg, *Helv. Chim. Acta* **14**, 455 (1931); idem, *Einfuhrung in die Chemie der Komplexverbindungen* VEB Verlag Technik, Berlin (1955), Ch. 5, pp. 170–173.

must then be of such a size that any possibility of other than *cis*-ring formation will lead to complexes of different composition. Typical chelating agents used for this purpose are oxalic acid, glycine, and less commonly, ethylenediamine. The behavior of *cis*- and *trans*-isomers toward such reagents is quite different. A typical example of such behavior is the reaction of oxalic acid with the *cis*- and *trans*-isomers of $[Pt(NH_3)_2Cl_2]$:

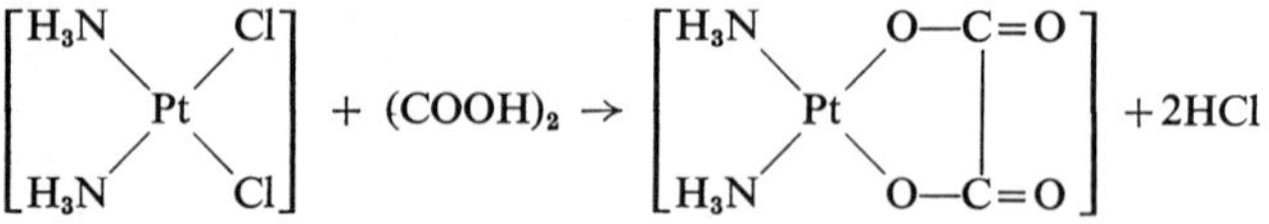

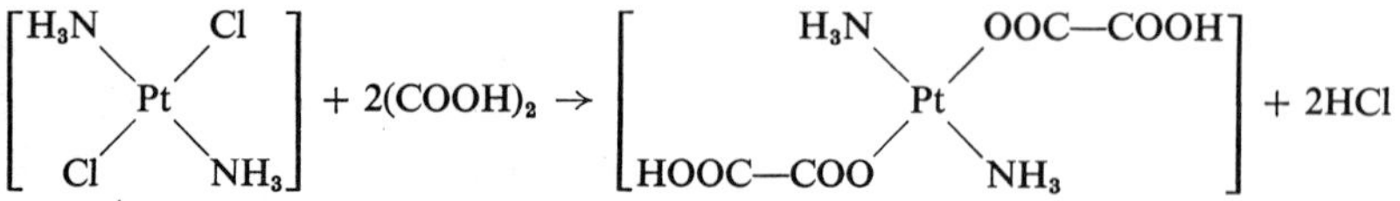

The *trans*-isomer cannot react with such a chelating agent to produce a chelate complex. The experiments of Grinberg support the assignments of structures made by Werner.

Analogous results are obtained when glycine is used as the chelating agent:

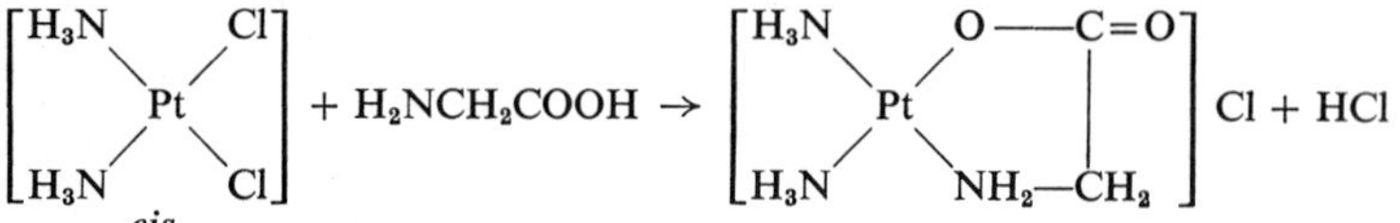

KURNAKOV'S REACTION

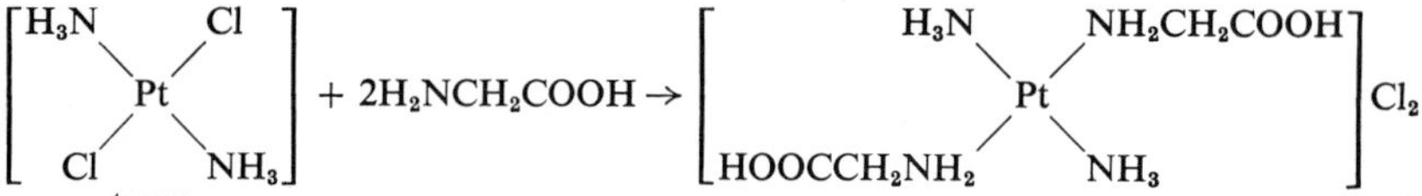

Kurnakov[52] found that the reaction of *cis*-$[Pt(NH_3)_2Cl_2]$ and thiourea (tu) results in $[Pt(tu)_4]^{+2}$ while *trans*-$[Pt(NH_3)_2Cl_2]$ gives $[Pt(NH_3)_2(tu)_2]^{+2}$. Grinberg used this reaction to examine pairs of *cis-trans*-isomers and found that it could be used to distinguish *cis*-forms from *trans*-forms (of Pt(II) complexes). A number of compounds of the general type $[Pta_2X_2]$ were studied and the results were in agreement with those obtained by other chemical methods. The substituents used were:

$$a = NH_3, C_2H_5NH_2, Py, en/2$$

$$X = Cl^-, Br^-, I^-, SCN^-, NO_3^-, C_2O_4H^-, \text{ and } C_2O_4^{-2}$$

[52] N. Kurnakov, *J. prakt. Chem.* (2) **50**, 483, 501 (1894); A. A. Grinberg, loc. cit., Kurnakov reported studies on other platinum complexes also.

CHERNYAEV'S SYNTHESIS OF THE THREE ISOMERIC FORMS OF $[Pt(NH_3)(NH_2OH)(py)(NO_2)]^+$

If platinum(II) complexes which are four-coordinated actually have a square planar configuration, there should be three geometrical isomers of the complexes of the type [Ptabcd]. Thus an additional proof of the correctness of the square planar configuration of the platinum(II) complexes was furnished by Chernyaev's synthesis and characterization of all three geometrically isomeric forms of the ion $[Pt(NH_3)(NH_2OH)(py)(NO_2)]^+$. These three forms are:

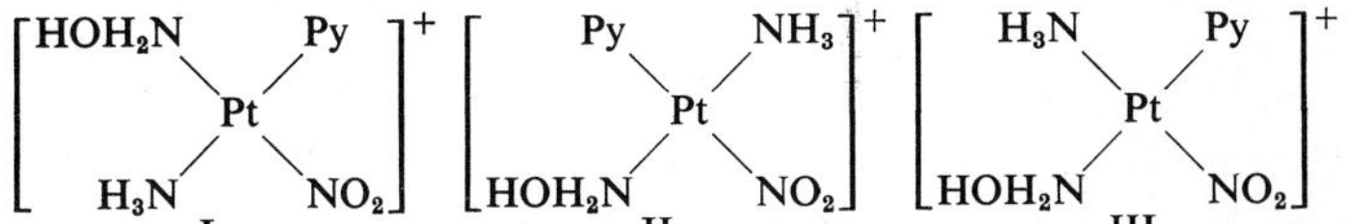

The syntheses of these forms was based upon the assumptions of Werner plus some additional ideas of Chernyaev's which will be examined in some detail in Chapter 7. Portions of the reaction schemes for two of these isomers are summarized below.[53]

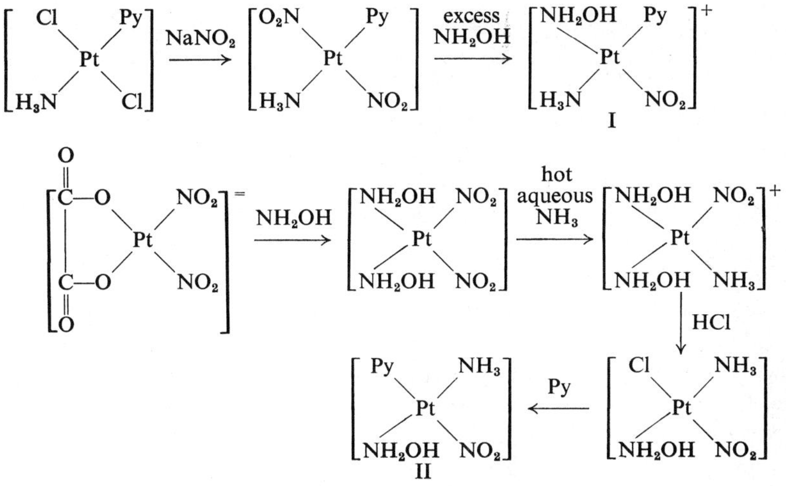

LIMITATIONS OF PURELY CHEMICAL METHODS FOR DETERMINING STRUCTURES

There are a number of inherent properties of coordination compounds as a class which restrict the construction of a general structural theory on purely chemical grounds such as was accomplished in the field of organic chemistry.

[53] I. I. Chernyaev, *Annales de l'Institute de platine* **4**, 243 (1925); *Chem. Zentrallblatt* II, 1628 (1926).

The most obvious of these properties is the ease with which many metal-ligand bonds can be ruptured. The considerable stability of the carbon-carbon bond finds no *strict* analog in the field of coordination compounds. This means that many chemical methods, used with, say, chromium(III) or cobalt(III) complexes, are quite unsuitable for determining the structures of mixed complexes of copper(II) or zinc(II).

It is exactly in this respect that the classical chemical methods for determining structures fail most seriously. They are simply not reliable with complexes which are either labile or possess labile groupings. Even with elements which presumably form inert complexes, there appears to be a wide gradation in the inertness as the ligand species is varied. Thus chromium(III) complexes are rightly regarded as being inert in most cases and where nitrogen or oxygen is the donor this inertness usually satisfies all the experimental criteria. Where chloride is the donor species, however, the inertness is not particularly apparent in some cases. Thus it has been established that *trans*-$[Cr(en)_2Cl_2]Cl$, unlike *trans*-$[Co(en)_2Cl_2]Cl$, release ligand chloride at a measurable rate in methanol.[54] Furthermore, $[Cr(pyridine)_3Cl_3]$ reacts almost immediately in glacial acetic acid to give conducting species.[55] A more unsettling example is provided by PtI_6^{-2} which undergoes very rapid exchange with radioactive iodide in aqueous solution. This exchange is complete in 30 seconds at 25° in the light and in the same time at 0° in the dark.[56] The rearrangement or lability of coordinated groups has also been encountered in some studies of the *trans*-effect, i.e., the determination of which ligand is most readily lost in substitution reactions of Pt(II) where such complications add to the difficulty of assigning structures to the products of the reactions.[57]

This kind of difficulty is found with continually increasing frequency as the stability of the complexes decreases. The result of this is that for a large number of complexes the only *certain* knowledge of their intimate structure which we can have at present is that derived from X-ray analyses of the crystalline solids. Most other physical methods of determining structures as well as *all* of the chemical methods require a known point of departure in a sequence of steps or reference compounds of *known* structure. Until information is available from X-ray studies to furnish these reference points, these methods, especially the physical ones, will only furnish a small portion of the total information which is capable of being derived from them. The slow development of infrared absorption spectroscopy in structure determinations of coordination compounds is due, in part, to this defect of the method.

[54] L. C. Slaten and C. S. Garner, *J. Phys. Chem.* **63**, 1214 (1959).

[55] J. C. Taft and M. M. Jones, *J. Amer. Chem. Soc.* **82**, 4196 (1960).

[56] A. J. Poë and M. S. Vaidya, *J. Chem. Soc.* 187 (1960).

[57] I. I. Chernyaev and A. D. Gelman, *Compt. rend., U.R.S.S.* (*N.S.*) **4**, 181 (1936); *Ann. secteur platine Inst. chim. gen.* USSR No. 15, 5 (1938), *C.A.*: 31:2541, *C.A.*: 33:2060; A. A. Grinberg, A. I. Dobroborskaya, and G. A. Shagisultanova, *Isvest. Akad. Nauk S.S.S.R., Otdel Khim. Nauk* 1953, 968 (1953), *C.A.*: 48:9250.

In conclusion, it seems reasonable to say that few, if any, structures of labile complexes can be determined by purely chemical methods except in those trivial cases where only one structure is possible. For inert complexes the classical chemical methods *are* capable of furnishing a good deal of structural information, but this is always subject to verification or correction by the more fundamental physical methods.

EXERCISES

1. Suggest preparative methods for the following complexes. Use readily available materials in the first step of each synthesis.

$[Cr(NH_2CH_2CH(NH_2)CH_3)_3]_2(SO_4)_3$ $[Co(NH_3)_6]Br_3$
$[PtCl_2(C_2H_5CN)_2]$ $[Pt(en)_2]Cl_2$
K_2PtBr_4 $[Pt(en)Cl_2]$
K_2PtCl_6 $[Pt(en)_3]Cl_4$

2. Predict the product which would be expected to result from the reaction between alanine and *trans*-dichlorodiammineplatinum(II).

3. Predict which one of each of the following pairs of ligands would be expected to form the more stable complex with the ion given:

$\left.\begin{array}{l}Cl^-\\F^-\end{array}\right\}Al^{+3}$ $\left.\begin{array}{l}RSH\\ROH\end{array}\right\}Pd^{+2}$ $\left.\begin{array}{l}NH_3\\CH_3NH_2\end{array}\right\}Ag^+$ $\left.\begin{array}{l}Cl^-\\Br^-\end{array}\right\}Hg^{+2}$ $\left.\begin{array}{l}Br^-\\I^-\end{array}\right\}Cd^{+2}$

$\left.\begin{array}{l}Br^-\\Cl^-\end{array}\right\}Au^{+3}$ $\left.\begin{array}{l}HO^-\\HS^-\end{array}\right\}Al^{+3}$ $\left.\begin{array}{l}C_2H_2(NH_2)_2\\CH_3NH_2\end{array}\right\}Cu^{+2}$ $\left.\begin{array}{l}H_2NCH_2COOH\\H_2NCH_2CH_2NH_2\end{array}\right\}Cu^{+2}$

You may check your predictions by referring to *Stability Constants* by J. Bjerrum, G. Schwarzenbach, and L. G. Sillen, The Chemical Society, London (1958), 2 vols.

4. M. Linhard and M. Weigel [*Zeit. anorg. Chem.* **299**, 15 (1959)] carried out a very thorough examination of the preparation of rhodo-, erythro-, and acido-erythro- complexes of chromium(III). One of their goals was to decide which of the alternative reaction schemes given below actually represented the processes and compounds under study.

Scheme 1 [A. Werner, *Neuere Anschauungen auf dem Gebeite der Anorganischen Chemie*, F. Vieweg & Sohn, Braunschweig, Germany, 5th ed. (1923), p. 273]:

Rhodo salts

$$[(NH_3)_5Cr-OH\cdots Cr(NH_3)_5]X_5 \underset{H^+}{\overset{OH^-}{\rightleftharpoons}} [(NH_3)_5Cr-OH\cdots Cr(NH_3)_5]^{X_4}_{OH}$$

normal rhodo salt   basic rhodo salt

↑ dry at 100°   ↓ spontaneously in solution

$$[(NH_3)_5Cr-O-Cr(NH_3)_5]X_4 \underset{H^+}{\overset{OH^-}{\rightleftharpoons}} [(NH_3)_5Cr-O-Cr(NH_3)_5]^{X_4}_{H_2O}$$

HX

Erythro salts

Scheme 2 [K. A. Jensen, *Zeit. anorg. Chem.* **232**, 257 (1937).]

Rhodo salts

$$[(NH_3)_5Cr\!-\!OH\cdots Cr(NH_3)_5]X_5 \underset{H^+}{\overset{OH^-}{\rightleftharpoons}} [(NH_3)_5Cr\!-\!O\!-\!Cr(NH_3)_5]X_4\cdot H_2O$$

normal rhodo salt   basic rhodo salt

↑ dry at   ↓ spontaneously
100°   in solution

$$[(NH_3)_5Cr\!-\!NH_2\cdots Cr(NH_3)_4(H_2O)]X_5 \underset{H^+}{\overset{OH^-}{\rightleftharpoons}} [(NH_3)_5Cr\!-\!NH_2\cdots Cr(NH_3)_4(OH)]X_4$$

Erythro salts

Scheme 3 [W. L. Wilmarth, H. Graff, and S. T, Gustin, *J. Amer. Chem. Soc.* **78**, 2683 (1956).]

Rhodo salts

$$[(NH_3)_5Cr\cdot OH\cdot Cr(NH_3)_5]X_5 \underset{H^+}{\overset{OH^-}{\rightleftharpoons}} [(NH_3)_5Cr\!-\!O\!-\!Cr(NH_3)_5]X_4$$

normal rhodo salt   basic rhodo salt

↓ spontaneously in
solution + H₂O—NH₃

$$[(NH_3)_5Cr\!-\!OH\!-\!Cr(NH_3)_4(H_2O)]X_5 \underset{H^+}{\overset{OH^-}{\rightleftharpoons}} [(NH_3)_5Cr\!-\!OH\!-\!Cr(NH_3)_4(OH)]X_4$$

Erythro salts

Which of these schemes is consistent with the following data?
Normal rhodo chloride mono-hydrate:

    3.76% H_2O; 21.16% Cr; 34.83% NH_3; 36.33% Cl

basic erythro chloride 2-hydrate:

    7.73% H_2O; 22.13% Cr; 35.38% NH_3; 32.46% Cl

erythro chloride mono hydrate (from acidic solution):

    7.42% H_2O; 21.26% Cr; 31.45% NH_3; 36.22% Cl

5. It has occasionally been remarked that many of the types of isomerism in coordination compounds may be different from each other in only a trivial way. Show in the case of *one* pair, from types 1 through 9, that examples can be cited where the classification is definitely ambiguous. (Suggested pairs are 1 and 3, 1 and 2, 4 and 6, 2 and 8, and 7 and 9.)

6. Assume that you wish to explain some of the jargon of coordination chemistry to a friend who is a competent chemist but rather unfamiliar with this field. Provide clear definitions (in operational terms if you prefer) for the following terms: ligand, stability constant, *cis*- and *trans*-isomers of an octahedral complex, binuclear complex, complexes with anionic centers, and linkage isomerism.

7. How would you go about convincing someone that the ion $Co(en)_3^{+3}$ can exist in enantiomorphic forms if their retort to the bald claim is "Don't be ridiculous, there isn't an asymmetric atom present!"?

8. An acquaintance claims that the whole field of descriptive coordination chemistry will all fall into a nice pattern once someone has worked out a general scale of acidity for Lewis acid-base behavior into which these reactions can then be fit. Citing such experimental evidence as you can gather, produce arguments supporting or refuting this claim.

9. Explain how you would proceed experimentally to prove the occurrence of the following types of isomerism in the pairs of compounds listed.
   Ionization isomerism in
   $[Co(en)_2Cl(NO_2)]SCN$ and $[Co(en)_2Cl(SCN)]NO_2$
   Hydrate isomerism in
   $[Co(NH_3)_4Cl(H_2O)]Cl_2$ and $[Co(NH_3)_4Cl_2]Cl \cdot H_2O$
   Coordination isomerism in
   $[Zn(NH_3)_4][PtCl_4]$ and $[Pt(NH_3)_4][ZnCl_4]$
   Polymerization isomerism in
   $[Pt(Pyridine)_2Cl_4]$ and $[Pt(Pyridine)_4Cl_2][PtCl_6]$

10. Using such ligands as are known to coordinate to the central ions cited [this is most easily checked by reference to N. V. Sidgwick's, *The Chemical Elements and Their Compounds*, Oxford University Press, (1950)] propose how you would proceed to prepare new isomers of the types listed below.
    Coordination isomerism involving Co(III) and Rh(III)
    Ionization isomerism involving Pt(IV)
    Structural isomerism involving Cd(II)
    Mirror-image isomerism involving Rh(III)

11. L. M. Volshtein and I. O. Volodina [*Doklady Akad. Nauk, S.S.S.R.* **131**, 309 (1959), *C.A.* 54:15061f] prepared an inner complex salt of platinum(II) and alanine, $CH_3CH(NH_2)COOH$, and found it to be isomeric with a previously characterized inner complex involving the same two species. As part of their examination of the reactions of these compounds, they studied the reaction of each with thiourea(tu). The results were

$$[Pt(CH_3CH(NH_2)COO)_2] + 4tu \xrightarrow{\ Cl^- \ } [Pt(tu)_4]Cl_2$$
   isomer I

$$[Pt(CH_3CH(NH_2)COO)_2] + 2tu \xrightarrow{\ Cl^- \ } [Pt(CH_3CH(NH_2)COOH)_2(tu)_2]Cl_2$$
   isomer II

To which isomer would you assign the *trans*-configuration and why would you make this assignment?

4

Typical Complexes of the Various Elements

A SYSTEMATIC SURVEY OF DESCRIPTIVE COORDINATION CHEMISTRY BY GROUPS

To a considerable extent the periodic table can be used as a satisfactory basis for organizing the gross coordination behavior of the elements. Unfortunately, the transition elements, which are of the greatest interest for their coordination compounds, show significant differences as one passes down a group. This is due to a number of factors, including great differences in the relative stabilities of the accessible oxidation states, the larger tendency favoring spin-pairing in the heavier transition elements, and differences in atomic radii. For the elements of the regular groups the periodic table furnishes a much more satisfactory guide in both organizing and predicting coordination behavior.

GROUP I: THE ALKALI METALS. Although the coordination compounds of the alkali metal ions are not numerous, several of them have been very thoroughly characterized. The maximum coordination numbers typical for these elements are Li, 4; Na, 6; K, 6; Rb, 8; Cs, 8; and presumably Fr, 8. In actual complexes of these ions the coordination numbers of four and six are observed. Thus, while none of the ions seems to exceed its maximum coordination number, the heaviest elements do not seem to have attained it in any solid coordination compounds of the usual sort isolated to date (though they do in solid halides with the cesium chloride structure). Those complexes which have been characterized to date involve oxygen or oxygen and nitrogen donor atoms, although historically one of the first claims for coordination compounds of the alkali metals involved thiourea in the compounds $[K(SC(NH_2)_2)_4]I$ and $[Cs(SC(NH_2)_2)_6]Cl$.[1]

Lithium shows by far the most pronounced tendency to form complexes of any of the alkali metals and shows many similarities to magnesium in this respect. Lithium halides absorb ammonia and amines to form rather unstable complexes which presumably undergo decomposition in aqueous solution when the lithium ion becomes hydrated. $[Li(NH_3)_4]Cl$, stable below 13°, and the corresponding bromide, stable below −18°, have been prepared and characterized.[2] These complexes undergo stepwise dissociation forming the tri-, di-, and mono- ammines at successively higher temperatures. Tetramminelithium salts such as the nitrate, perchlorate, and chlorate have also been made.[3] An unstable pentamminesodium chloride, $[Na(NH_3)_5]Cl$, has been reported to form when a solution of sodium chloride in liquid ammonia is evaporated at −24°. The ammines of alkali metal salts have been studied in some detail by Biltz and Hansen.[4]

Coordinated water of hydration is found for lithium and sodium salts but rather rarely for potassium salts. Lembert[5] has called attention to the fact that when a potassium salt of an anion is hydrated, the corresponding ammonium salt is hydrated also. Since the ammonium ion is roughly the same size as the potassium ion but completely incapable of further coordination, such water must be present in association with the anion or lattice holes.

A series of alkali metal chelate compounds are also well characterized. The first of these was obtained by the action of strong base on ψ indoxylspirocyclopentane[6]:

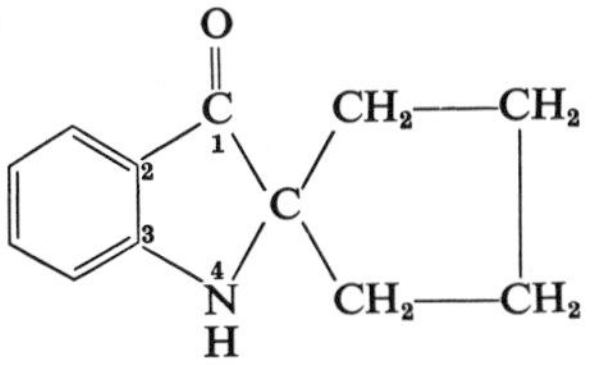

These compounds were of the type MB·HB where HB is ψ indoxylspirocyclopentane and M is Na⁺, K⁺, or Li⁺. These were formulated as chelates involving the ring systems:

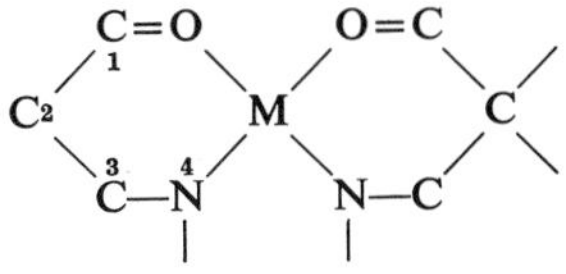

[1] A. Rosenheim and W. Lowenstamm, *Zeit. anorg. Chem.* **34**, 75 (1903).
[2] J. Bonnefoi, *Compt. rend.* **127**, 367 (1898); **130**, 1394 (1900).
[3] F. Ephraim, *Ber.* **52**, 236 (1919).
[4] W. Biltz and W. Hansen, *Zeit. anorg. Chem.*, **127**, 1 (1923).
[5] M. E. Lembert, *Zeit. phys. Chem.* **104**, 101 (1923).
[6] N. V. Sidgwick and S. G. P. Plant, *J. Chem. Soc.* **127**, 209 (1925).

and so contain four-coordinate alkali metal ions. Subsequently, Sidgwick and Brewer[7] prepared alkali metal complexes of a number of other organic chelating agents. As a criterion for the formation of a non-polar chelate, the solubilities in organic solvents were used. Among the compounds found to possess an appreciable solubility in toluene is the sodium compound of ethyl acetoacetate, the dihydrate of lithium methylsalicylate, and the dihydrate of potassium o-nitrophenoxide. This behavior is very good evidence for the formation of an inner complex salt but compounds of this type which are appreciably polar need not exhibit such ready solubility in toluene. Brewer also studied the salicylaldehyde and beta-diketone complexes and found that several four-coordinate complexes could be prepared for each of the alkali metals. He found, for example, that rubidium benzoylacetonate (salt-like) was soluble in toluene if the toluene contained benzoylacetone. Obviously the solution process allowed the coordination act to proceed to completion. For the heavier alkali ions six-coordinate derivatives were also found.

In more recent years a number of studies have been carried out on sodium complexes in solution. Among these are studies on phenols[8], dibenzoylmethane,[9] and uramil-diacetic acid.[10] The structure of this last compound is:

$$
\begin{array}{ccc}
\text{H--N---C--O}^- & & \\
\;\;|\qquad\;\; \| & & \text{CH}_2\text{COOH} \\
& & {}^+ \diagup \\
\text{O}=\text{C}\quad\text{C--N--H} & & \\
\;\;|\qquad\;\; | & & \diagdown \\
\text{H--N---C}=\text{O} & & \text{CH}_2\text{COOH}
\end{array}
$$

It gives complexes with lithium, sodium, and potassium whose stabilities decrease in the order given. The formation constants for the lithium and sodium complexes are 2.5×10^5 and 2.1×10^3, respectively. In non-aqueous solvents of low dielectric constant as well as solvent mixtures containing water whose net dielectric constant is low, one finds that the stability constants of the alkali metal complexes are much higher than in water. An example of this may be seen in the work of Fernelius and van Uitert (loc. cit.) where the stability constants of dibenzoylmethane complexes of the alkali metals were determined in 75% dioxane–25% water as a solvent. The logs of these stability constants were found to be Li: 5.95; Na:4.18; K:3.67; Rb: 3.52; Cs:3.42 (all at 30°).

It is very likely that numerous other examples of weak complexes will be found for the ions of the alkali metals as newer and more powerful methods are used to study their interactions in solution. A study using nuclear magnetic

[7] N. V. Sidgwick and F. M. Brewer, *ibid.*, **127**, 2379 (1925); F. M. Brewer, *ibid.*, 361 (1931).

[8] J. F. Ehlers, *Kolloid Zeit.*, **130**, 161 (1953), C.A. 47:7361; J. F. Ehlers and F. Heske, *ibid.*, **130**, 165 (1953), C.A. 47:7361.

[9] W. C. Fernelius and L. G. van Uitert, *Acta Chem. Scand.* **8**, 1726 (1954).

[10] G. Schwarzenbach, E. Kampitsch, and R. Steiner, *Helv. Chim. Acta* **29**, 364 (1946); W. Buser, *ibid.*, **34**, 1635 (1951).

resonance has shown that this method is capable of detecting weak complexes of the sodium ion if a suitable isotope is used.[11] Thus the nuclear spin resonance absorption of Na^{23} in aqueous solutions suggests that weak complexes are formed between sodium ions and phosphate anions, anions of hydroxy- and keto-acids, and some alcohols in rather concentrated solutions (2–3N). Specific interactions attributable to complex formation were found with the sodium salts of EDTA and citric acid, among others.

In addition to the more or less conventional types of complexes mentioned above, the alkali metals form rather stable "ion-pair" complexes with ketyls[12] and some hydrocarbon anions. Very weak complexes are also formed between alkali metal salts and simple ketones, as is evidenced by changes in both the infrared and ultraviolet absorption spectra of the ketone when the alkali metal salts are added.[13]

GROUP II. Of the ions of this group, beryllium shows the greatest tendency to form complexes. The ions of the other elements, however, all form complexes with appreciably greater stabilities than those of the alkali metal ions of the same period. When considered as a group, the stable complexes of these elements are found to be with oxygen or nitrogen donors, the oxygen donor complexes being the form usually found in aqueous solution. In the case of beryllium the fluoro complexes are also stable in aqueous solution. The great difference in the stability of the beryllium complexes as compared to those of the other elements are quite striking. As a whole, these differences can be attributed to the small size of the Be^{+2} ion. The radii of the ions of this group are: Be^{+2}, 0.31 A; Mg^{+2}, 0.65 A; Ca^{+2}, 0.99 A; Sr^{+2}, 1.13 A; Ba^{+2}, 1.35 A.[14]

Beryllium typically forms tetrahedral complexes, some of which have been resolved in part.[15] The ease with which beryllium coordinates to oxygen is responsible for the extensive hydrolysis of beryllium salts in aqueous solution,[16] as well as its numerous complexes with both oxyanions and organic compounds such as acetone[17] and ether.[18] Depending upon the environment, various complexes of beryllium have been obtained with sulfate,[19a] oxalate,[19b] acetate,[19c] carbonate,[19d] and a wide variety of organic acids, ketones, ethers, and amines.[19e]

[11] O. Jardetzky and J. E. Wertz, *J. Amer. Chem. Soc.* **82**, 318 (1960).

[12] H. V. Carter, B. J. McClelland, and E. Warhurst, *Trans. Farad. Soc.* **56**, 455 (1960) and the references cited therein.

[13] H. Yamada, *Bull. Chem. Soc. Japan* **33**, 780 (1960).

[14] L. Pauling, *The Nature of the Chemical Bond*, 3rd ed. Cornell University Press, Ithaca, N.Y., (1960), p. 514.

[15] W. H. Mills and R. A. Gotts, *J. Chem. Soc.* 3121 (1926); D. H. Busch and J. C. Bailar, Jr., *J. Amer. Chem. Soc.* **76**, 5352 (1954); H. Burgess and T. M. Lowry, *J. Chem, Soc.*, 2081 (1924).

[16] H. Kakihana and L. G. Sillen, *Acta Chem. Scand.* **10**, 985 (1956).

[17] R. Fricke and F. Ruschhaupt, *Zeit. anorg. Chem.* **146**, 103 (1925).

[18] R. Fricke and L. Havestadt, *ibid.*, **146**, 121 (1925).

[19] P. Silber, "Glucinium" in P. Pascal, *Nouveau Traite de Chimie Minerale*, Vol. IV, (a) 83, (b) 119, (c) 108 ff., (d) 107, (e) 121–131.

Of these the basic acetate is perhaps the most unusual. Its composition is $Be_4O(CH_3COO)_6$ and it consists of a central oxygen atom surrounded tetrahedrally by four Be^{+2} ions. Across each edge of the resulting tetrahedron of beryllium ions is coordinated an acetate group with an oxygen atom bonded to each of the beryllium ions at the apices of that edge. This is done in such a manner that each beryllium atom is surrounded by a tetrahedron of oxygens.[20] This compound sublimes at 230° at one atmosphere pressure; its melting point is 283–285°.[19] Other basic salts have been reported which contain different carboxylic acids as well as the carbonate ion.[21] Complexes of the anhydrous chloride, bromide, and iodide with *simple* aliphatic amines are known but are not stable in the presence of water. Ethylenediamine and dipyridyl and presumably other chelating amines as well are capable of forming complexes stable in the presence of water.

The beryllium complexes with fluoride ion have been studied in detail and solid tetrafluoroberyllates containing the BeF_4^{-2} ion are well known. The species BeF^+, BeF_2, BeF_3^- and BeF_4^{-2} are formed in aqueous solutions of beryllium in the presence of fluoride, the coordination sphere of the beryllium is completed by water molecules in these ions. The complexes with oxide and hydroxide are also very easily prepared. BeO is appreciably soluble in most aqueous solutions of beryllium salts (e.g., solutions of $BeSO_4$) and polynuclear complexes containing bridging —OH (called "ol" groups) or —O— (called "oxo" groups) are presumably present in these solutions.[16, 22] BeO is also amphoteric and gives rise to beryllates such as $Na_2Be(OH)_4$ (or $NaBeO_2$) in the presence of strong bases.

The appreciable toxicity of beryllium may be due in part to the great stability of the complexes which it forms with biologically important oxygen donor groups such as phosphate derivatives.[23] Magnesium ion is the ion normally used for *in vivo* activation of several such enzyme systems. This is a process which involves the formation of a relatively unstable chelate as an intermediate which then undergoes further reaction in which the chelate is disrupted. In the presence of beryllium ion, the magnesium ion loses out in the competition for coordination sites and the more stable and biologically inactive beryllium complex is formed. Thus the presence of beryllium represses the activity of plasma alkaline phosphatase in vitro.[24] As will be seen later, a relatively unstable complex is often involved in metal activated enzyme systems and

[20] A. F. Wells, *Structural Inorganic Chemistry*, Oxford University Press, England (1945), pp. 307–308.

[21] A. K. Sen Gupta, *Science and Culture* **25**, 426 (1960); C. A. 54:16249 reports $K_6[Be_4O(CO_3)_6]$.

[22] N. V. Sidgwick, *The Chemical Elements and Their Compounds*, Oxford University Press, England (1950), Vol. I, pp. 210–212.

[23] J. Schubert and M. W. Rosenthal, *A. M. A. Archives of Industrial Health* **19**, 169 (1959) and the literature cited therein.

[24] J. Schubert and A. Lindenbaum, *J. Biol. Chem.* **208**, 359 (1954).

this instability is absolutely essential to the proper functioning of the system.[25]

The complexes of the remaining alkaline earth ions involve oxygen donor atoms for the most part. There are some unstable ammines such as [Mg(NH$_3$)$_6$]Cl$_2$, [Mg(en)$_3$]Cl$_2$, [Ca(NH$_3$)$_6$]Br$_2$, and the like which can be formed from the anhydrous salts and ammonia or the amine. In aqueous solution the first four ammonia complexes of magnesium and calcium have been detected,[26] though the corresponding complexes of beryllium do not form because of the extensive hydrolysis of Be^{+2}. Of the remaining complexes of these elements, the majority are with organic or inorganic ligands which contain oxygen atoms available for coordination. These include tartaric acid [CH(OH)(COOH)]$_2$, succinic acid (CH$_2$COOH)$_2$, maleic acid (*cis*-HOOCCH=CHCOOH), lactic acid [CH$_3$CH(OH)COOH], oxalic acid [(COOH)$_2$], iminodiacetic acid [HN(CH$_2$COOH)$_2$], ethylenediaminetetraacetic acid [(HOOCCH$_2$)$_2$NCH$_2$CH$_2$N(CH$_2$COOH)$_2$], and salicylic acid (orthohydroxybenzoic acid). Usually nitrogen donors are effective only in combination with oxygen donors.

The problem of treating hard water which contains calcium or magnesium salts is one of great industrial importance and in many cases a solution can be achieved by the use of the appropriate chelating agent. In such cases the compound added is often referred to as a *sequestering agent*, i.e., an agent which sequesters or ties up the metal ion in such a form that any deleterious effects due to its presence are suppressed.[27]

Two aspects of the coordination chemistry of magnesium which can only be given brief mention are the Grignard reagent and chlorophyll. The Grignard reagent is prepared by the reaction of magnesium metal and organic halides in a suitable solvent (generally diethyl ether). The constitution of the Grignard reagent has been the subject of numerous, often conflicting, reports. One requirement for the formation of the Grignard reagent does seem to be the presence of a suitable donor solvent which is resistant to reduction, such as ether. The evidence on the constitution of the Grignard reagent is generally in favor of an equilibrium mixture for which the following equations are given:

$$R_2Mg + MgX_2 \rightleftharpoons R_2Mg \cdot MgX_2 \quad ^{28-31}$$

[25] J. Schubert, *Chimia* **11**, 113 (1957).

[26] J. Bjerrum, Thesis, P. Haase and Sons, Copenhagen (1941 and 1957).

[27] There is an enormous literature on both the practical and the theoretical aspects of sequestering agents. Two recent references which summarize much of this are: S. Chaberek and A. E. Martell, *Organic Sequestering Agents*, John Wiley & Sons, Inc., New York (1959); R. L. Smith, *The Sequestration of Metals*, Chapman & Hall, Ltd., London (1959). The analytical applications of these compounds are treated in many books. Some of these are: G. Schwarzenbach, *Complexometric Titrations*, Methuen & Co., Ltd., London (1957); H. Flaschka, *EDTA Titrations*, Pergamon Press, New York (1959); F. B. Martinez and A. P. Bouza, *Applicaciones Analiticas de AEDT y Similares*, Santiago de Compostela (1960).

[28] J. H. Wotiz, C. A. Hollingsworth, and R. E. Dessy, *J. Org. Chem.* **21**, 1063 (1956).

[29] R. E. Dessy and G. S. Handler, *J. Amer. Chem. Soc.* **80**, 5824 (1958).

[30] R. E. Dessy and R. M. Jones, *J. Org. Chem.* **24**, 1685 (1959).

[31] R. E. Dessy, *J. Org. Chem.* **25**, 2260 (1960).

Previously, an additional step had been written:

$$2RMgX \rightleftharpoons R_2Mg + MgX_2$$

This was shown to be untenable by the lack of exchange of radioactive magnesium between MgX_2 and R_2Mg.[29] The infrared spectra of ethereal solutions of Grignard reagents indicate that the ether is coordinated and that a more complete formulation of the equilibrium between R_2Mg and MgX_2 should include solvent molecules.[32–35] The older literature on this subject has been exhaustively reviewed.[36]

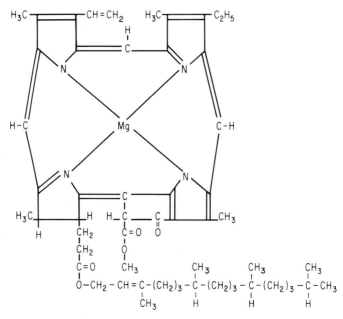

Fig. 13 The "chlorophyll a" molecule.

Chlorophyll is one of the most unusual as well as one of the most important of the magnesium complexes. This compound is a magnesium porphyrin. In higher plants there are actually two chlorophylls: chlorophyll (a) and chlorophyll (b). The structure of chlorophyll (a) has been proven by a total synthesis[37] and is given in Figure 13. Here the magnesium is constrained to a planar

[32] A. Kirrmann and R. Hamelin, *Compt. rend.* **251**, 2990 (1960).

[33] R. Hamelin, *Compt. rend.* **252**, 161 (1961).

[34] R. Hamelin, *Bull. Soc. Chim. France*, 684, 698, 915, 926 (1961).

[35] R. Hamelin and S. Hayes, *ibid.*, 692 (1961).

[36] M. Kharasch and O. Reinmuth, *Grignard Reactions of Nonmetallic Substances*, Prentice-Hall, Inc., Englewood Cliffs, N.J. (1954).

[37] R. B. Woodward *et al.*, *J. Amer. Chem. Soc.* **82**, 3800 (1960).

stereochemistry by the rigid porphyrin framework in which it is contained. The role of the chlorophyll appears to be intimately related to the absorption of energy from sunlight and the subsequent transfer of this energy in a chemically useful form. Energy can be readily exchanged between chlorophyll molecules as much as 50 A apart.[38] Because of the great importance of this particular complex an enormous amount of work has been carried out on it and its reactions.[39]

GROUP III: B, AL, GA, IN, TL. In this group the pattern met in group II is met again—anhydrous halides which form ammines unstable in the presence of water, insoluble or easily complexed fluorides, numerous complexes with oxygen-containing organic compounds, cations which are extensively hydrolyzed in aqueous solution, and an increasing reluctance to form complexes with increasing atomic number. In this family there is also the factor of the greater stability of the $+1$ oxidation state with the heavier members. Although many of the precipitation reactions of Tl(I) are analogous to those of Ag(I) the coordination chemistry of these two species is definitely quite different; in general, Tl(I) shows little tendency to form ammines and its complexes are invariably less stable than those of Ag(I) with the same ligand.

The extreme practical importance of the organic complexes of BF_3 and $AlCl_3$ must be emphasized but space does not allow the detailed treatment such importance might demand.[40] These compounds form complexes with amines:

$$BF_3 + C_5H_5N(\text{pyridine}) \rightarrow C_5H_5N:BF_3$$

ethers:

$$BF_3 + O(C_2H_5)_2 \rightarrow (C_2H_5)_2O:BF_3$$

ketones:

$$AlCl_3 + (C_6H_5)_2C{=}O \rightarrow (C_6H_5)_2C{=}O:AlCl_3$$

These two compounds also form a large number of "complexes" with unsaturated hydrocarbons. Among the compounds of the heavier elements at

[38] W. F. Watson and R. Livingston, *J. Chem. Phys.* **18**, 802 (1950); L. Duysens, *Nature* **168**, 548 (1951).

[39] Reviews include: E. Rabinowitch, *Photosynthesis*, Interscience Publishers, Inc., New York (1945–1957), 2 Vols. in 3 parts; H. Gaffron *et al.*, editors, *Research in Photosynthesis*, Interscience Publishers, Inc., New York (1957); J. D. Spikes, *Ann. Reviews Phys. Chem.* **11**, 501–530 (1960); W. Bladergroen, *Problems in Photosynthesis*, Charles C. Thomas, Publisher, Springfield, Ill. (1960); H. Gaffron, *Plant Physiol.* **1B**, 3–277 (1960); M. Gibbs and J. A. Schiff, *Plant Physiol.* **1B**, 279–319 (1960).

[40] These have been treated in great detail in several excellent books: H. S. Booth and D. R. Martin, *Boron Trifluoride and its Derivatives*, John Wiley & Sons, Inc., New York (1949); A. V. Topchiev, S. V. Zavgorodnii, and Ya. M. Paushkin, *Boron Trifluoride and Its Compounds as Catalysts in Organic Chemistry*, translated by J. T. Greaves, Pergamon Press, New York (1959); G. Kranzlein, *Aluminiumchlorid in der organischem Chemie*, Verlag Chemie, Berlin (1932); C. A. Thomas, M. B. Moshier, H. E. Morris, and R. W. Moshier, *Anhydrous Aluminium Chloride in Organic Chemistry*, Reinhold Publishing Corp., New York (1941).

least one, $(GaCl_3)_2$, appears to behave similarly.[41] It should be remembered that aluminum chloride and bromide may exist as the dimer, $(AlX_3)_2$, under many conditions, e.g., in the vapor[42] or in benzene solution,[43] and its complexes with aromatic compounds may do the same.[43] Of the numerous practical applications, the Friedel-Crafts reaction is the most widely known. This reaction involves the alkylation or acylation of an aromatic ring in the presence of a suitable Lewis acid catalyst.[44] The importance of the Lewis acid seems to be in the assistance that it furnishes to the generation of a carbonium ion which then attacks the aromatic ring.

In aqueous solutions the coordination chemistry of these elements is almost exclusively that of the complexes of fluoride and oxygen donor ligands. The hydrolysis of compounds such as BCl_3 or $AlCl_3$ in water is immediate and effectively complete, though tetrachloroborate[45] and tetrachloroaluminate[46] complexes can be made in the absence of water, e.g., from melts. The fluorides show notable differences in their behavior in water:

$$4BF_3 + 3H_2O \rightarrow 3BF_4^- + H_3BO_3 + \text{(mixed complexes)} + 3H^+$$

It should also be recalled that Na_3AlF_6 occurs naturally as the mineral cryolite. The fluoro complexes of boron, aluminum, gallium, indium, and thallium have been studied in aqueous solution.[47] The logarithms of the stability constants for the first complex (MF^{+2}) fall off from aluminum to indium: Al($\sim$6.2) — Ga($\sim$5.0) — In($\sim$3.8) as expected for a series in which electrostatic interaction is of predominant importance. The complexes of the plus three ions of aluminum, gallium, and indium with organic compounds such as acetylacetone, EDTA, oxalic acid, catechol, and salicylic acid have been studied in some detail. The order of the stabilities of these complexes is sometimes the reverse of the order found with the fluoro complexes, thus with EDTA the order of the stability constants is $In^{+3} > Ga^{+3} > Al^{+3}$![48] These elements usually form labile complexes, i.e., complexes which are in dynamic equilibrium with their constituent ions in aqueous solution. In some cases it has

[41] H. Ulich and G. Heyne, *Zeit. Elektrochem.* **41**, 509 (1935); Ya. A. Fialkov and Z. A. Fokina, *Zhur. Neor. Khim.* **4**, 2611 (1959), C.A. 54:16152.

[42] K. J. Palmer and N. Elliott, *J. Amer. Chem. Soc.* **60**, 1852 (1938).

[43] H. Ulich, *Zeit. phys. Chem. Bodenstein-Festband*, 423 (1931); F. Nagy, O. Dobis, G. Litvan, and I. Telcs, *Acta Chim. Acad. Sci. Hung.* **21**, 397 (1959), C.A. 54:17001.

[44] G. Baddeley, Quarterly Reviews **8**, 355 (1954); C. C. Price, *Organic Reactions* III, 1 (1946); K. L. Nelson, *Ind. Eng. Chem.* **48**, 1670 (1956); V. Franzen, *Chemiker-Ztg.* **81**, 68 (1957); G. Olah, ed. "Friedel-Crafts and Related Reactions," Interscience Publishers, New York, 1963–1964, four Vols.

[45] W. Knyaston, B. E. Lascombe, and H. S. Turner, *J. Chem. Soc.*, 1772 (1960); E. L. Muetterties, *J. Inorg. Nuclear Chem.* **12**, 355 (1960).

[46] J. Kendall, E. D. Crittenden, and H. K. Miller, *J. Amer. Chem. Soc.* **45**, 969 (1923).

[47] J. Bjerrum, G. Schwarzenbach, and L. G. Sillen, *Stability Constants*, The Chemical Society, London (1958), Part II.

[48] Ref. 47, pp. 76–77.

apparently been possible to resolve asymmetric complexes, though the literature on this subject indicates that the claims are of varying value. The tetrahedral complexes of boron with γ-chlorocatechol, 3-nitrocatechol, and α hydroxybutyric acid have been at least partially resolved (i.e., their diastereoisomers have been separated).[49] The resolutions reported for $Al(C_2O_4)_3^{-3}$ and $Al(C_6H_4O_2)_3^{-3}$ have subsequently been found to be in error.[50] The only resolution of an aluminum complex which has not yet been challenged is that with the Schiff base of salicylaldehyde and triethylenetetramine.[51] The half-time for the exchange of $Al(H_2O)_6^{+3}$ with water is greater than 0.02 sec but still much smaller than that found for inert aquo complexes.[52] Recent attempts to resolve $Ga(C_2O_4)_3^{-3,}$ [53] and gallium acetylacetonate[54] have been unsuccessful.

The complexes of the plus three ions of this group are generally six-coordinate, though four-coordinate complexes are found when the ratio (anion size)/(cation size) is sufficiently large, e.g., $AlCl_4^-$. Some typical solid complexes which have been characterized are:

Al(III)	Ga(III)	In(III)	Tl(III)
$K_3[Al(C_2O_4)_3]$	$K_3[Ga(C_2O_4)_3]$	$K_3[In(C_2O_4)_3]$	$(NH_4)_3[Tl(C_2O_4)_3]$
$NaAlF_6$	Li_3GaF_6	K_3InCl_6	Li_3TlCl_6
$LiAlBr_4$	. . .	. . .	$KTlBr_4$

The considerable oxidizing power of Tl(III) is a factor which limits the types of ligands with which it can form stable complexes.

The coordination behavior of Tl(I) is unusual in several respects, the most striking is the general reluctance of the Tl(I) species to form complexes of any appreciable stability with many common donors. The most stable usually involve coordination to oxygen or sulfur. It is typical for silver halides to be more soluble in solutions containing high concentrations of halide ion than they are in water. This is due to the formation of halo complexes of Ag(I). The behavior of the insoluble thallous halides is quite different. Thallous chloride, bromide, and iodide are all rather insoluble in water, but their solubility in solutions of halides does not increase until the concentration of halides reaches very high values. The amounts of halide required to produce this effect make it more reasonable to describe the behavior as arising from the enormous changes in ionic strength.[55] Thallous sulfate is more soluble in sulfuric acid than in water,[56] but the effect here is probably caused by the removal of sulfate

[49] J. Boeseken and J. A. Mijs, *Rec. trav. chim.* **44**, 758 (1925); J. Boeseken, H. D. Miller, and R. T. Japhongjouw, *ibid.*, **45**, 919 (1926).

[50] F. Basolo and R. G. Pearson, *Mechanisms of Inorganic Reactions*, John Wiley & Sons, Inc., New York (1958), Ch. 6; K. D. Maguire and M. M. Jones, *J. Inorg. Nuclear Chem.* **17**, 240 (1961).

[51] B. Das Sarma and J. C. Bailar, Jr., *J. Amer. Chem. Soc.* **77**, 5476 (1955).

[52] H. W. Baldwin and H. Taube, *J. Chem. Phys.* **33**, 206 (1960).

[53] T. Moeller and E. H. Grahn, *J. Inorg. Nuclear Chem.* **5**, 53 (1957).

[54] T. Moeller and E. Gulyas, *ibid.*, **5**, 245 (1957).

[55] A. Benrath and G. Ammer, *Zeit. anorg. Chem.* **177**, 129 (1929).

[56] W. Stortenbecker, *Rec. trav. chim.* **21**, 87 (1902).

as HSO_4^- as the acid is added. Thallous oxalate is more soluble in potassium oxalate solution than in water and here the formation of some sort of chelate is probable. Thallium(I) is even poorly complexed by EDTA.[57] One well-established complex with sulfur as donor is that with thiourea, [Tl(SC-$(NH_2)_2)_4$]X, in which the stereochemistry of Tl(I) is square planar.[58] Thallium salts of alcohols and compounds such as acetylacetone are often polymeric. Sidgwick suggested that the structures of these materials were based upon a cube in which alternate corners are occupied by oxygen and thallium atoms respectively.[59] These compounds are perhaps the ones in which the coordinating power of Tl(I) reaches its most impressive state.

GROUP IV, C, SI, GE, SN, PB. Carbon shows none of the behavior found with typical coordination centers; its almost invariable covalence of four also represents the maximum number of groups which it can accommodate as carbon cannot expand its valence shell of electrons beyond an octet. The remaining elements in this family all have accessible coordination numbers greater than four (their maximum covalence) and can act as typical coordination centers. For Si(IV), Ge(IV), Sn(IV), and Pb(IV) the octahedral six-coordinate complexes are all well characterized. In this family regularities in the behavior toward various donor atoms are less than obvious. Silicon(IV) forms its most stable complexes with fluoride or oxygen donors; its other complexes are usually readily hydrolyzed by water and it shows no evidence of ever preferring sulfur to oxygen. This pattern changes as the heavier elements are considered in succession. With Ge(IV), the formation of thiogermanates, GeS_3^{-2}, occurs when aqueous solutions of germanic acid or germanates are treated with an alkali sulfide. Sn(IV) undergoes a similar reaction; Pb(IV) is reduced to Pb(II) by sulfides. The tetrachlorides of the heavier elements are, unlike $SiCl_4$, *reversibly* hydrolyzed in water. The trend in coordinating tendencies from light elements which favor fluoride or oxygen to heavier elements which favor larger, more polarizable ions is also found in Group V. With the $+2$ oxidation states of germanium, tin, and lead, stable complexes are formed with both oxygen donors (especially chelates) and sulfur donors such as thiourea. A well-known reaction of this sort which is used in qualitative analysis is the solubility of many slightly soluble lead(II) salts in acetate solutions:

$$PbCl_2 + x\ CH_3COO^- \rightleftharpoons Pb(CH_3COO)_x^{+2-x} + 2Cl^-\ (x \text{ runs from 1 to 4})$$

Some typical complexes of these elements in their various oxidation states are listed at the top of p. 75.

[57] J. Bouten, F. Verbeek, and J. Eeckhart, *Anal. Chim. Acta,* 17, 339 (1957). The instability constant is $10^{-5.81}$.

[58] E. G. Cox, A. J. Shorter, and W. Wardlaw, *J. Chem. Soc.,* 1886 (1938).

[59] Ref. 22, p. 485.

SPECIES	COMPLEX	STEREOCHEMISTRY
Si(IV)	K_2SiF_6	octahedral
Ge(IV)	Cs_2GeF_6	octahedral
Sn(IV)	$SnCl_4 \cdot 2Pyridine$	presumably octahedral
Pb(IV)	K_2PbCl_6	octahedral
Ge(II)	$GeCl_3^-$	?
Sn(II)	$K_2SnCl_4 \cdot H_2O$ [60]	square planar/distorted octahedral
Pb(II)	$Pb(C_5H_7O_2)_2$ [61]	square planar

The fluorides of these elements in the $+4$ state form a large number of complexes with both organic and inorganic ligands.[62] These elements may also form complexes in which the coordination number is neither four nor six. Stannic chloride gives a five-coordinate complex with o-acetylphenol:[63]

Similarly, three-coordinate complexes are found with Ge(II) and Pb(II), though these have not been extensively studied.

Silicon(IV) and germanium(IV) also are among the very few nontransition elements whose coordination compounds have been resolved. The cationic complex, $Si(C_5H_7O_2)_3^+$, whose chloride is obtained by the reaction of silicon tetrachloride and acetylacetone, has been resolved[64] and a kinetic study of its hydrolytic "racemization" has been carried out.[65] The tris(oxalato)germanate-(IV) ion has been resolved in part via its quinine diastereoisomer.[66]

Germanic acid, like boric acid, forms complexes with polyhydric alcohols and ortho phenols.[67] These compounds have not been as thoroughly studied as the boric acid complexes and there is reason to believe that some asymmetric complexes of this type will be sufficiently stable to be resolved.

GROUP V: N, P, As, Sb, Bi. In this family we again meet a group where the first member is unable to expand its octet and hence, cannot act as an electron pair acceptor in the usual sense of the term. The other elements all form com-

---

[60] H. Brasseur and A. De Rassenfosse, *Nature* **143**, 332 (1939).

[61] E. G. Cox, A. J. Shorter, and W. Wardlaw, *Nature* **139**, 71 (1937).

[62] For example, $SiF_4 \cdot (CH_3)_2SO_2$ has been prepared by V. Gutmann and K. Utvary, *Monatsh.* **90**, 706 (1959). More similar examples may be found in E. L. Muetterties, *J. Amer. Chem. Soc.* **82**, 1082 (1960); A. L. Oppegard, W. C. Smith, E. L. Muetterties, and V. A. Engelhardt, *ibid.*, **82**, 3835, 3838 (1960).

[63] P. Pfeiffer, *Ann.* **398**, 137 (1913).

[64] S. K. Dhar, V. Doron, and S. Kirshner, *J. Amer. Chem. Soc.* **80**, 753 (1958).

[65] idem, *ibid.*, **81**, 6372 (1959).

[66] T. Moeller and N. C. Neilsen, *J. Amer. Chem. Soc.* **75**, 5106 (1953).

[67] D. A. Everest and J. C. Harrison, *J. Chem. Soc.*, 1745 (1960) and the references cited therein.

plexes, especially with oxygen donors or fluoride. Aside from the phosphates and hexafluorophosphates, phosphorus does not commonly act as a coordination center in the presence of water. In the absence of water the possibilities for coordination are greater and many solid pentavalent phosphorus compounds are actually coordination compounds. The lower oxidation states of phosphorus customarily are donor species. Following Werner we may consider the phosphates and their numerous derivatives[68] as complexes between P^{+5} and O^{--} ions. Phosphorus acts as a typical coordination center in the hexahalophosphates, PF_6^- and PCl_6^-.[69] The hexafluophosphates are remarkably stable toward hydrolysis.[70] They are only slightly affected after several days in hot aqueous alkali. The hexachlorophosphates are very easily hydrolyzed.

The complexes of arsenic, antimony, and bismuth are more numerous but many of them are rather poorly characterized. Among the simpler complexes of arsenic which are well established are AsF_4^-, AsF_6^-, AsF_2^+, $AsCl_4^+$, $AsCl_3 \cdot Pyr$, $AsCl_3 \cdot 2Pyr$, and the thio complexes AsS_3^{-3} and AsS_4^{-3}. The reaction of the arsenic halides with ammonia generally leads not to ammines but to amides,[71] except possibly with AsF_3. As(V) forms complexes with orthodiphenols such as catechol and the catechol complex has been resolved. The structure of this material is either $[As(C_6H_4O_2)_3]^-$ or

$$cis\text{-}[As(C_6H_4O_2)_2(C_6H_4O(OH))(H_2O)]^- \text{[72]}$$

and it has an octahedral configuration. Complexes of arsenious acid with polyhydroxy compounds are also well known.[73]

The complexes of antimony are similar in many respects to those of arsenic. In addition to the halo and thio complexes of the types cited above, complexes with organic oxygen donors are quite well known. Both $SbCl_3$ and $SbCl_5$ form coordinate bonds with ethers, ketones, aldehydes, and other oxygen functional

[68] An especially valuable recent treatment may be found in J. R. Van Wazer, *Phosphorus and its Compounds*, Interscience Publishers, Inc., New York (1958), 2 Vols. Another briefer listing may be found in P. Pascal, *Traite de Chimie Minerale*, Vol. X; R. Dubrisay, *Phosphore*, Masson et Cie, Paris (1956), pp. 812–838.

[69] D. Clark, H. M. Powell, and A. F. Wells, *J. Chem. Soc.* 642 (1942) showed that solid PCl_5 consists of PCl_4^+ and PCl_6^- ions from an X-ray determination of the structure. The PF_6^- ion is also found in solid "PF_3Cl_2" which is composed of PCl_4^+ and PF_6^- ions: L. Kolditz, *Zeit. anorg. Chem.* **284**, 144 (1956).

[70] W. Lange, *Ber.* **61**, 799 (1928).

[71] M. M. J. Sutherland, *The Metal Ammines*, Vol. X of J. N. Friend, editor, *A Textbook of Inorganic Chemistry*, C. Griffin and Co., London (1928), Ch. VII; H. Remy and G. Tiedemann, *Naturwissenschaften* **47**, 178 (1960) present the results of work on the reaction of ammonia with SbI_3 and AsI_3. A number of other examples may be found in P. Pascal, *Traite de Chimie Minerale*, Vol. XI, pp. 132–155.

[72] R. F. Weinland and J. Heinzler, *Ber.* **52**, 1316 (1919) (preparation); A. Rosenheim and W. Plato, *ibid.*, **58**, 2000 (1925) (resolution); J. H. Craddock and M. M. Jones, *J. Amer. Chem. Soc.* **83**, 2839 (1961) (study of hydrolytic "racemization").

[73] P. Antikainen and K. Tevanen, *Suomen Kemistilehti* **33B**, 7 (1960) is a study of such complexes with sugars.

groups. $SbCl_3$ (like $AlCl_3$) also forms complexes with purely aromatic compounds. The more nearly "metallic" nature of antimony is illustrated in the complexes of Sb^{+3} with sulfate[74] and oxalate.[75] Far better known is tartar emetic, potassium antimonyl tartrate, $K[SbO(C_4H_4O_6)]$ H_2O, a reasonably stable complex which finds use in pharmacy and as a resolving agent.[76] Other complexes with oxygen containing organic compounds include those with catechol,[77] citric acid,[78] gluconic acid,[79] lactic acid,[80] and a large number of similar ligands. Complexes of Sb(V) other than the adducts of $SbCl_5$ and SbF_5 are less common because of the considerable oxidizing power of Sb(V) in aqueous solution. It is worth noting that $SbCl_5 \cdot 6NH_3$ has been prepared,[81] and this may be the ammine. SbF_6^- unlike PF_6^- is rather sensitive to the presence of alkali but is nevertheless more stable than $SbCl_6^-$ in this respect. The hydrolysis of the halo complexes of antimony(V) is more rapid and also more readily reversible than that of the corresponding complexes of phosphorus(V) or arsenic(V).

Bi(V) is an even more potent oxidizing agent than Sb(V) and as a result little is known about the coordination chemistry of this oxidation state. Insofar as Bi(III) is concerned the situation is quite otherwise and a large variety of complexes have been prepared and characterized. Although Bi(III) undergoes hydrolysis rather easily,[82] it is still less readily hydrolyzed than Sb(III). From aqueous solutions of Bi(III) one may obtain hexanitrobismuthate(III) complexes,[83] $[Bi(NO_2)_6]^{-3}$, complexes with organic hydroxy or hydroxyacid compounds, as well as with phosphate,[84] thiocyanate,[85] thiourea,[86] orthoaminobenzenethiol[87] and a wide variety of other ligands. The crystals of $[Co(NH_3)_6][BiCl_6]$ are completely isomorphous with those of $[Co(NH_3)_6]$ $[TlCl_6]$ and presumably[88] contain regular $BiCl_6^{-3}$ octahedra. The maximum coordination number for bismuth in any of its complexes is apparently six,[89]

[74] S. Metzl, *Zeit. anorg. Chem.* **48**, 140 (1905).

[75] A. Rosenheim and K. Bierbrauer, *ibid.*, **20**, 290 (1899).

[76] E. Chinoporos and N. Papathanasopoulous, *J. Phys. Chem.* **65**, 1643 (1961) discuss the structure of this compound and the previous literature.

[77] R. Weinland and R. Scholder, *Zeit. anorg. Chem.* **127**, 343 (1923).

[78] R. Das and S. Pani, *J. Indian Chem. Soc.* **32**, 537 (1955).

[79] S. J. DasGupta, *Indian J. Pharmacy* **15**, 84 (1953), C.A. **54**: 12764.

[80] G. Patra and S. Pani, *J. Indian Chem. Soc.* **32**, 161 (1955).

[81] A. Meuwsen and H. Mogling, *Zeit. anorg. Chem.* **285**, 268 (1956).

[82] F. Graner, A. Olin, and L. G. Sillen, *Acta Chem. Scand.* **10**, 476 (1956); A. Olin, *ibid.*, **11**, 1445 (1957).

[83] A. Ferrari and Z. Ciccioli, *Gazz. chim. ital.* **66**, 581 (1936).

[84] A. Holroyd and J. E. Salmon, *J. Chem. Soc.*, 269 (1956).

[85] W. D. Kingery and D. N. Hume, *J. Amer. Chem. Soc.* **71**, 2393 (1949).

[86] O. S. Fedorova, *J. Gen. Chem. U. S. S. R.* **24**, 62 (1954), C.A. **54**: 8002.

[87] R. G. Charles and H. Frieser, *J. Amer. Chem. Soc.* **74**. 1385 (1952).

[88] M. Atoji and T. Watanabe, *J. Chem. Phys.* **20**, 1045 (1952).

[89] W. J. Lile and R. C. Menzies, *J. Chem. Soc.*, 617 (1950).

though a theoretical maximum of eight is generally considered possible. Oddly enough, the most common fluoro complex ion has a coordination number of only *four* and is seen in salts of the type NH_4BiF_4.[90] It should be remembered that BiF_3 is rather insoluble in water. At present the stereochemistry of the coordination compounds of bismuth is not known in great detail.

GROUP VI: O, S, SE, TE, PO. These elements are known most commonly as donors rather than as acceptors, though the occurrence of typical coordination compounds is well established with the heavier members. In Werner's work ions such as SO_4^{--} and SeO_4^{--} are treated as complexes of S^{+6} or Se^{+6} and O^{--} ions; such a view is no longer commonly taught. In spite of this, the numerous related complexes of SO_3 are coordination compounds in the literal sense of the term. This compound reacts with a large number of typical donor molecules, e.g.:

$$SO_3 + C_5H_5N(\text{pyridine}) \rightarrow O_3S:NC_5H_5$$

$$SO_3 + (CH_3)_3N \rightarrow O_3S:N(CH_3)_3$$

With the heavier elements in this family coordination behavior similar to that found for most metals may be seen. The complex halides of selenium and tellurium are similar in composition to those of the transition metals; K_2SeCl_6, $(NH_4)_2SeBr_6$, $H[TeCl_5 \cdot H_2O]$, and salts of the ions $TeCl_6^{-2}$, $TeBr_6^{-2}$, and TeI_6^{-2} have been characterized.[91] The lower halides of selenium and tellurium as well as SO_2 form numerous adducts with typical Lewis bases which are coordination compounds of the usual sort except that these elements can expand their octet. Thus, $TeBr_4$ forms adducts with pyridine which contain two and one molecules of pyridine, respectively.[92] In adducts such as $TeBr_4 \cdot 2C_5H_5N$ the tellurium must accommodate 10 electrons in its outermost shell if it accepts a share in a pair of each of the nitrogens of the pyridines.

Even though the difficulties involved in the investigation of the chemistry of polonium are great, enough is known to show very definitely that coordination compounds play an important role in this chemistry.[93] In many respects the analogies expected with tellurium are borne out in some detail and it is certainly with this element that polonium shows the greatest similarities. In addition to well-characterized hexahalides, $(NH_4)_2PoCl_6$, $(NH_4)_2PoBr_6$, and Cs_2PoI_6, polonium forms complexes with many of the common organic chelating agents such as tributylphosphate, diethyldithiocarbamate, and dithizone. The acetylacetonates—$Po(C_5H_7O_2)_3$ and $Po(C_5H_7O_2)_4$—have also been characterized.[93]

[90] H. von Helmont, *Zeit. anorg. Chem.* **3**, 143 (1893).

[91] Ref. 22, pp. 989, 990, 993, 994.

[92] E. Montignie, *Zeit. anorg. Chem.* **306**, 234 (1960).

[93] K. W. Bagnall, *Chemistry of the Rare Radioelements*, Butterworth's Scientific Publications, London (1957), especially Chs. 1, 2, 5, 6, 7, 8; Idem, *Advances Inorg. Chem. Radiochem.* **4**, 198 (1962).

GROUP VII: F, CL, BR, I, AT. Even in this family in which the tendency to exhibit coordination behavior (as acceptors) is a minimum, there are still examples of what must be considered *typical, if rather bizarre,* coordination compounds. These are found among the compounds in which the halogens have positive oxidation numbers; none are known for fluorine. Aside from the oxyanions such as ClO_4^-, IO_4^-, IO_6^{-5}, BrO_3^-, and the like, there are complex halides such as those derived from the interhalogens or interhalides: BrF_2^-, BrF_4^-,[94] ICl_4^-,[95]. Both bromine and iodine also form ammine complexes with nitrogen bases which are sufficiently stable against chemical attack, such as pyridine and dipyridyl. These complexes are prepared by reactions which generate a positive halogen species in the presence of the base. A typical reaction is:

$$AgNO_3 + 2C_5H_5N + I_2 \rightarrow [I(py)_2]NO_3 + AgI \quad [96]$$

Similar complexes of the type $[I(py)]^+$ can also be prepared. The stabilization of I^+ in the presence of F^- via coordination to pyridine leads to the compound $[I(py)]F$ even though the compound IF is not stable.[97] In a similar manner the compounds $[I(py)_2]F_3$ and $[I(py)_2]F$ illustrate the stabilization of positive iodine.[98] The corresponding bromine complexes have been made in some cases but are generally less stable.[99]

With astatine one has an element which has so little nuclear stability (the isotope of longest half-life is $^{210}At_{85}$ with $t\frac{1}{2}$ of 8.3 hr)[100] that all studies to date have been carried out by tracer techniques and these have yielded only meagre information on the nature of the species present.[93] Although only tracer studies have been carried out it is extremely probable that astatine follows iodine in the formation of complexes such as $[At(py)_2]^+$.[101]

THE TRANSITION ELEMENTS

Practically all aspects of the solution chemistry of the transition elements involve coordination phenomena, and explanations of the behavior of transition metal salts in any polar solvent usually involve complexes with the solvent. In some cases these are quite stable (e.g., $Cr(H_2O)_6^{+3}$) and in other cases rather

[94] A. G. Sharpe, *Quarterly Reviews* **4**, 115 (1950).

[95] G. B. Hargreaves and R. D. Peacock, *J. Chem. Soc.*, 2373 (1960).

[96] J. Kleinberg, *Unfamiliar Oxidation States and Their Stabilization*, University of Kansas Press, Lawrence, Kansas (1950), pp. 37–49.

[97] R. A. Zingaro and W. E. Tolberg, *J. Amer. Chem. Soc.* **81**, 1353 (1959).

[98] M. Schmeisser and E. Scharf, *Angew. Chem.* **72**, 324 (1960); ICl and ICl_3 complexes with heterocyclic amines are also known: R. D. Whitaker, J. R. Ambrose, and C. W. Hickam, *J. Inorg. Nuclear Chem.* **17**, 254 (1961).

[99] W. B. Witmer and R. A. Zingaro, *J. Inorg. Nuclear Chem.* **15**, 82 (1960).

[100] Ref. 93, p. 99.

[101] J. J. C. Schats and A. H. W. Aten, Jr., *J. Inorg. Nuclear Chem.* **15**, 197 (1960).

unstable (e.g., $Fe(H_2O)_x^{+3}$ or $Ni(H_2O)_x^{+2,\,60}$). It is with the transition elements that one sees the greatest changes in chemical behavior of the central ion made possible through coordination.

SCANDIUM, YTTRIUM, AND LANTHANUM. These three elements are the initial transition elements in their respective periods but their chemistry does not involve any d electrons in the simple ion as these are all lost in the formation of the simple trivalent ions. Subsequently the inner d orbitals may be used to accommodate electrons from various donor species though evidence on this point is presently indecisive as such an accommodation would not be required for purely ionic complexes.

The chemistry of scandium furnishes more examples of stable complexes than may be found with either yttrium or lanthanum. This is easily reconciled with the trend in the ionic radii as Sc^{+3} is the smallest of these trivalent ions and is thus capable of the strongest electrostatic interaction with anions or polar molecules. In general the complexes of scandium are similar to those of aluminum. Thus ScF_3 is not very soluble in water, but is readily soluble in aqueous fluoride solutions and derivatives of ScF_6^{-3} are well known,[102] and coordinated water of hydration in the $Sc(H_2O)_6^{+3}$ ion is present in many simple salts. Scandium hydroxide apparently shows little tendency to dissolve in solutions of the alkali hydroxides[103] though scandium carbonate dissolves in sodium carbonate solutions to give solutions of a complex carbonate, probably, $[Sc(CO_3)_3]^{-3}$. Scandium oxalate also dissolves in oxalate solutions to form the ion $[Sc(C_2O_4)_3]^{-3}$. The acetylacetonate, $Sc(C_5H_7O_2)_3$, like many other acetylacetonates which are inner complex salts, melts at a low temperature (188°) and can be sublimed at or below 250° without suffering extensive decomposition.[104] In addition to the similarities to aluminum, scandium shows some resemblance to zirconium(IV) (diagonal relationship in the periodic table) as is seen in the carbonato, oxalato, and related complexes. One reason for our sparse knowledge of the complexes is the relatively high cost of the compounds of scandium—one of the rarest of the transition elements.

The complexes of yttrium are less stable than those of scandium but are otherwise qualitatively similar in composition. Thus complex fluorides, YF_6^{-3}, carbonates, oxalates, and sulfates are known, in most of which yttrium is six-coordinate, though fluorides of the type YF_4^- are also known.[105] For

[102] H. F. V. Little, "Aluminium and its Congeners including the Rare Earth Metals" in J. N. Friend, *A Textbook of Inorganic Chemistry*, Charles Griffin and Co., London (1921), Vol. IV, 204–215; J. W. Mellor, *A Comprehensive Treatise on Inorganic and Theoretical Chemistry*, Longmans, Green & Co., London (1924), Vol. V, p. 489; R. C. Vickery, *The Chemistry of Yttrium and Scandium*, Pergamon Press, Inc., New York (1960).

[103] The alkali scandates can be prepared by reactions of the type: $Li_2CO_3 + Sc_2O_3 \rightarrow 2LiScO_2 + CO_2$ at elevated temperatures (~650°). V. I. Spitsyn, L. N. Komissarova, V. M. Shatskii, and N. P. Anoshina, *Zeit. Chem.* **1**, 328 (1961), C.A. 56: 9683.

[104] G. T. Morgan and H. W. Moss, *J. Chem. Soc.* **105**, 196 (1914).

[105] F. Hund, *Zeit. anorg. Chem.* **261**, 106 (1950).

lanthanum the trends observed in the first two members of this group are continued. For lanthanum, as for the rare earths, the characteristic reaction in the presence of fluoride ion is the precipitation of the insoluble fluoride and there is very little tendency for the higher fluorocomplexes to form. For the family as a whole one may cite several examples of stable complexes with organic chelating agents, among which are: those with citric acid, EDTA, and compounds related to EDTA such as ammoniatriacetic acid, $N(CH_2COOH)_3$. These complexes possess rather large stability constants (LaEDTA has a stability constant of about 10^{15}) and have been widely used in separating these elements from each other and from the rare earths in whose company they are found in nature.[106]

TITANIUM, ZIRCONIUM, AND HAFNIUM. With the elements in this family one finds a much greater variety of coordination phenomena and also some striking examples of the stabilization of unusual oxidation states by coordination. While titanium appears to exhibit a coordination number of six in all of the complexes which have been thoroughly characterized; zirconium and hafnium may show coordination numbers of six, seven, or eight, depending on the ligand and the preparative conditions. All of the salts of these elements in the $+4$ oxidation state are extensively hydrolyzed in water and in this oxidation state there is a pronounced tendency to coordinate to oxygen rather than to nitrogen. There is practically no tendency to coordinate to sulfur. The following list gives some of the typical complexes of these elements in this oxidation state.

SPECIES	COORDINATION NO.	COMPLEX
Ti(IV)	6	TiF_6^{-2}
Ti(IV)	6	$[Ti(C_6H_4O_2)_3]^{-3}$ [107]
Zr(IV)	6	ZrF_6^{-2}
Zr(IV)	6	$Zr(C_5H_7O_2)_2Cl_2$
Zr(IV)	7	ZrF_7^{-3}
Zr(IV)	8	$Zr(C_5H_7O_2)_4$
Zr(IV)	8	$Zr(C_2O_4)_4^{-4}$
Zr(IV)	8	ZrF_8^{-4}
Hf(IV)	6	HfF_6^{-2}
Hf(IV)	7	HfF_7^{-3}
Hf(IV)	8	$Hf(C_5H_7O_2)_4$

The stereochemistries observed for these coordination numbers are octahedral for six and presumably an Archimedean antiprism for eight-coordinate systems such as the acetylacetonates. This is expected on the basis of analogy

---

[106] Some of these methods may be found in R. C. Vickery, *Chemistry of the Lanthanons*, Butterworth's Scientific Publications, London (1953).

[107] Resolved by A. Rosenheim, B. Raibmann, and G. Schendel, *Zeit. anorg. Chem.* **196**, 168 (1931).

with the corresponding Th(VI) complex.[108] For a coordination number of seven the most probable arrangement is a pentagonal biprism,[109] though a distorted octahedron with one face expanded to accommodate the extra ligand has also been reported.[110]

The hydrolysis of the tetravalent salts of titanium, zirconium and hafnium in water is very extensive and has rendered studies of complex equilibria involving these species difficult to carry out and ambiguous in interpretation.[111] One study of the interaction of Zr(IV) and chelating agents in water showed that polymerization occurred with many common chelating agents as the pH of the zirconium solutions was increased.[112] The order of the coordinating tendency of the groups studied varied as $O^{-2} \gg OH^- > RO^- > RCOO^- \gg ROR > NR_3$.

The coordination chemistry of the lower oxidation states of titanium has been studied in some detail in very recent years. In these lower oxidation states titanium shows a greater tendency to coordinate to nitrogen than is found with Ti(IV), but Ti(III) does not form the expected ammines such as $[Ti(NH_3)_6]$ Cl_3 and $[Ti(dipyr)_3]Cl_3$. The existence of fluo complexes of the type TiF is well established,[113] but it must be remembered that the complexes of this oxidation state dissociate very rapidly in aqueous solution. If a mixture of $TiCl_4$ and excess dipyridyl in tetrahydrofuran is reduced with lithium metal (or the lithium adduct with dipyridyl) one obtains $[Ti(dipyr)_3]$ or $Li[Ti(dipyr)_3] \cdot 3.5THF$ (THF is tetrahydrofuran) depending on the number of equivalents of lithium used.[114] $[Ti(dipyr)_3]$ is diamagnetic and $Li[Ti(dipyr)_3] \cdot 3.5THF$ is paramagnetic with a susceptibility corresponding to one unpaired electron. These compounds are very rapidly oxidized in air; their existence indicates what unusual behavior may be seen when complexes are reduced in an inert solvent in the absence of air. The analogous Zr(O) complex with dipyridyl, $[Zr(dipyr)_3]$, has been prepared in a similar manner.[115]

VANADIUM, NIOBIUM, AND TANTALUM. In this family the large number of accessible oxidation states leads to a great variety of coordination behavior. Because these are more readily obtained with vanadium than with niobium or tantalum, the complexes of vanadium have been much more thoroughly studied. In this family the $+5$ oxidation state shows the coordination behavior typical of inert gas electronic structures: the predominant forms involve coor-

---

[108] D. Grdenic and B. Matkovic, *Nature* **182**, 465 (1958).

[109] W. H. Zachariasen, *Acta Cryst* **7**, 783, 792 (1954).

[110] G. C. Hampson and L. Pauling, *J. Amer. Chem. Soc.* **60**, 2702 (1938).

[111] W. B. Blumenthal, *The Chemical Behavior of Zirconium*, D. Van Nostrand Co., Inc., Princeton, N. J. (1958), especially Chs. 4, 6, 7, 8.

[112] B. I. Intorre and A. E. Martell, *J. Amer. Chem. Soc.* **82**, 358 (1960).

[113] N. F. H. Bright and J. G. Wurm, *Canadian J. Chem.* **36**, 615 (1958).

[114] S. Herzog and R. Taube, *Angew. Chem.* **70**, 469 (1958); idem, *Zeit. anorg. Chem.* **306**, 159, (1960).

[115] S. Herzog and H. Zahlke, *Zeit. Naturforschung* **15b**, 466 (1960).

dination to oxygen donors or fluoride or both. Typical of such complexes are VF_6^-,[116] $NbOF_5^{-2}$, NbF_7^{-2}, NbF_8^{-3}, TaF_7^{-2}, TaF_8^{-3}, $TaOF_6^{-3}$, and $TaOF_5^{-2}$. The six-coordinate structures are probably octahedral while TaF_8^{-3} has a square antiprism structure (Archimedean).[117] The structures of NbF_7^{-2} and TaF_7^{-2} are trigonal prisms with the metal atoms at the centers, a fluoride at each apex, and a seventh fluoride placed at the center and above one of the square faces.

Vanadium pentoxide dissolves in concentrated sulfuric acid to give the oxycation VO_2^+ or $V(OH)_4^+$. The anions derived from V_2O_5, VO_3^-, or VO_4^{-3} (metavanadate or orthovanadate) are very extensively hydrolyzed in water and yield the isopolyvanadates which are polymeric anions that arise as hydrogen ions in such solutions are neutralized.[118] A vanadium(V) complex with salicylaldoxime has been reported in which the central ion is presumably VO_2^+,[119] though very few such instances are known. A more common result is the reduction of V(V) by the ligand and the production of complexes of lower oxidation states of vanadium.

The lower oxidation states of vanadium whose coordination compounds have been studied include V(IV), V(III), V(II), V(I), V(O), and V($-$I). Most of the V(IV) complexes which have been examined are derivatives of the oxovanadium(IV) ion, VO^{+2}, also referred to as the vanadyl ion. This ion usually precipitates as the hydroxide in the presence of aqueous solutions of strong nitrogen bases. It forms chelates with a great variety of organic compounds with oxygen donor atoms, such as acetylacetone:

$$VO^{+2} + 2CH_3\underset{\substack{\|\\O}}{C}CH_2\underset{\substack{\|\\O}}{C}CH_3 \xrightarrow{NH_3} VO(C_5H_7O_2)_2 \downarrow$$

This illustrates a widely useful method for the preparation of chelates which are not very soluble in water: their formation from an aqueous solution of their constituents on the slow addition of a weak base. The acetylacetonate of vanadium contains five-coordinate vanadium and has a tetragonal pyramidal structure[120] which changes rather readily to an octahedral one by the addition of a suitable Lewis base. Such behavior, which seems so strange when the first example is encountered, is actually of rather widespread occurrence in the

[116] H. J. Emeleus and V. Gutmann, *J. Chem. Soc.*, 2979 (1949).

[117] J. L. Hoard, W. J. Martin, M. E. Smith, and J. F. Whitney, *J. Amer. Chem. Soc.* **76**, 3820 (1954).

[118] F. J. C. Rossotti and H. Rossotti, *Acta Chem. Scand.* **10**, 957 (1956).

[119] H. J. Bielig and H. Mollinger, *Ann.* **605**, 119 (1957).

[120] M. M. Jones, *J. Amer. Chem. Soc.* **76**, 5995 (1954); idem, *Zeit. Naturforschung* **12b**, 595 (1957); R. P. Dodge, "UCRL report 8225"; V. V. Zelentsov, I. A. Savich, and V. I. Spitsyn, *Doklady Akad. Nauk S.S.S.R.* **122**, 80 (1958), C.A. 54: 23509. See, however, D. P. Graddon, *Nature* **195**, 891 (1962). A theoretical treatment of this ion may be found in C. J. Ballhausen and H. Gray, *Inorg. Chem.* **1**, 111 (1962).

coordination chemistry of both the regular and the transition elements, though the number of such cases which have been studied in detail is not large.[121] The constancy of coordination number is a guide in the elucidation of the structures of complexes but not an infallible one. Vanadium(IV) complexes with porphyrins are present in many petroleum stocks[122] and rather similar compounds are found in the bodies of certain ascidians and holothurians.[123]

The complexes of V(III) show many resemblances to those of Fe(III). Thus they both form anhydrous complex sulfates, $M_2(SO_4)_3$, easily hydrolyzed ammines, $[M(NH_3)_6]^{+3}$, an aquo ion, $[M(H_2O)_6]^{+3}$, thiocyanate complexes such as $M(SCN)^{+2}$, and several related species. There are some differences which arise from the ease with which V(III) can be oxidized or from other reasons. Thus vanadium(III) forms hexachlorovanadate(III), as in K_3VCl_6[124] while iron usually forms tetrachloroferrate(III) or aquopentachloroferrate(III).

The coordination compounds of V(II) are more stable *toward dissociation* than those of V(III) but are more readily oxidized. Insofar as stability toward dissociation is concerned, the complexes of V(II) are expected to be comparable to those of Cr(III). Typical V(II) complexes are six-coordinate and presumably octahedral. Examples include: $V(CN)_6^{-4}$, $V(NH_3)_6^{+2}$, $V(dipyr)_3^{+2}$, and $V(H_2O)_6^{+2}$. The ligand exchange reactions of this oxidation state are not all slow.[125]

In addition to the carbonyl, $V(CO)_6$ (Ch. 10), vanadium forms a number of interesting complexes in which it exists in an abnormally low oxidation state stabilized by coordination. The compound $K_5[V(CN)_5(NO)]$ has already been mentioned.[126] Combinations are also found with aromatic compounds such as $[V(C_5H_5)_2]^+$, $[V(C_6H_6)_2]^+$, and $[V(C_6H_6)_2]$ which are discussed more fully in Chapter 10. There are also compounds which are more obviously related to the typical complexes, though they contain vanadium in unusually low oxidation states. These compounds are prepared by the reduction of $V(dipyr)_3^{+2}$ by magnesium or zinc in the absence of air:[127]

[121] H. D. K. Drew and J. K. Landquist, *J. Chem. Soc.*, 292 (1938); J. N. Phillips, *Reviews of Pure and Applied Chemistry* **10**, 35 (1960); R. T. Claunch, T. W. Martin, and M. M. Jones, *J. Amer. Chem. Soc.* **83**, 1073 (1961).

[122] A. Triebs, *Ann.* **509**, 103 (1934); idem, *Angew. Chem.* **49**, 682 (1936); D. A. Skinner, *Ind. Eng. Chem.* **44**, 1159 (1952).

[123] M. Henze, *Zeit. physiol. Chem.* **72**, 494 (1911); idem, *ibid.*, **79**, 215 (1912); H. J. Bielig and E. Bayer, *Experientia* **10**, 300 (1954); idem, *Ann.* **580**, 135 (1953); idem, *ibid.*, **584**, 96 (1953); E. P. Levine, *Science* **133**, 1352 (1961).

[124] C. Grena, *Bull. soc. Chim. France*, No. 4, 655 (1960).

[125] K. V. Krishnamurty and A. C. Wahl, *J. Amer. Chem. Soc.* **80**, 5921 (1958), found O^{18} exchange between H_2O and hydrated V^{+2} to be complete in 10 min. or less.

[126] W. P. Griffith, J. Lewis, and G. Wilkinson, *J. Chem. Soc.*, 1632 (1959).

[127] S. Herzog, *Zeit. anorg. Chem.* **294**, 155 (1958); idem, *J. Inorg. Nuclear Chem.* **8**, 557 (1958); *Chem. Tech.* (Berlin) **8**, 544 (1956); *Naturwissenschaften* **43**, 35 (1956); S. Herzog and R. Taube, *ibid.*, **43**, 349 (1956).

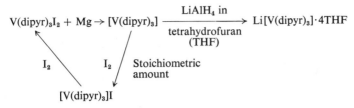

$$V(dipyr)_3I_2 + Mg \rightarrow [V(dipyr)_3] \xrightarrow[\text{tetrahydrofuran (THF)}]{\text{LiAlH}_4 \text{ in}} Li[V(dipyr)_3] \cdot 4THF$$

with branches labeled I₂ and I₂ (Stoichiometric amount) leading to [V(dipyr)₃]I

The ion V(dipyr)$_3^-$ represents a logical end to the reduction process as this ion contains a central ion with filled 3d, 4s, and 4p orbitals. This work of Herzog's on the lower oxidation states of the transition elements is of importance because it provides experimental evidence bridging the gap between the carbonyls and the classical ammine complexes.

The complexes which are formed by the lower oxidation states of niobium and tantalum include the rather unusual Nb_6Cl_{14} and Ta_6Cl_{14}. These are exceptionally stable after they have been prepared and contain only *two* readily ionized chlorides. The structure of the $M_6Cl_{12}^{+2}$ ions has been determined by X-ray methods[128] and is shown in Figure 14.

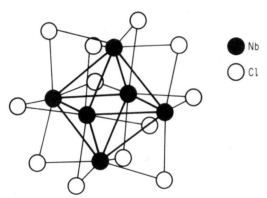

Fig. 14 The $[Nb_6Cl_{12}]^{+4}$ ion.

Niobium(V) can be reduced in aqueous solution by the use of a fairly active reducing agent such as zinc. The nature of the niobium species in these solutions is rather uncertain. A divalent niobium species also has been reported to result from the polarographic reduction of niobium(V) in a solution in concentrated hydrochloric acid containing 10–20% ethylene glycol[129] but again, little is known of its composition. The complexes of niobium(V) and tantalum(V) which are known in aqueous solution are either fluo complexes or

[128] P. A. Vaughan, J. H. Sturdivant, and L. Pauling, *J. Amer. Chem. Soc.* **72**, 5477 (1950); prepn. of $Nb_6Cl_{14} \cdot 7H_2O$; H. S. Harned, L. Pauling, and R. B. Corey, *ibid.*, **82**, 4815 (1960).
[129] D. Gozzi and S. Vivarelli, *Zeit. anorg. Chem.* **279**, 165 (1955).

complexes with polyhydroxy organic chelating agents such as gluconic acid.

CHROMIUM, MOLYBDENUM, AND TUNGSTEN. These three elements show greater differences in their coordination chemistry than would be expected on the basis of any predictions stemming from their position in the same family of transition elements. The chief factors responsible for this are: (a) the $+6$ oxidation state in chromium is strongly oxidizing but shows no such great tendency in either molybdenum or tungsten, (b) the lower oxidation states of molybdenum and tungsten ($+3$, $+4$, and $+5$) are rather easily oxidized to the $+6$ state while the $+3$ state of chromium is fairly stable in this respect, (c) chromium has a maximum coordination number of six while both molybdenum and tungsten may coordinate to eight ligands, finally (d) both molybdenum and tungsten form complexes in their lower oxidation states which contain metal to metal bonds while chromium shows little, if any, tendency to do this in the chromium(II) complexes that have been studied so far (other than the acetate hydrate).

The complexes of chromium(III) are among the most extensively studied coordination compounds. They are invariably six-coordinate.[130] Chromium is unusual in that it forms very stable complexes with ligands having a very wide variety of donor groups: oxygen, nitrogen, halide, carbon, and sulfur are among them. The stability of the complexes varies as the ligand species change and the traditionally sluggish reactions of chromium(III) complexes are most typical for ligands with oxygen donors or chelated nitrogen. Under some circumstances halide may be replaced in very rapid reactions. When present in aqueous solutions, chromium(III) salts of noncomplexing anions give rise to the $[Cr(H_2O)_6]^{+3}$ ion which is quite stable. In the presence of complexing anions it is common for some of the water to be replaced by the anion. Thus chromic chloride in water solution contains both $[Cr(H_2O)_5Cl]^{+2}$ and $[Cr(H_2O)_4Cl_2]^+$, and the commercial chromic chloride is usually $[Cr(H_2O)_4Cl_2]Cl \cdot 2H_2O$ admixed with varying amounts of polymeric complexes. This type of replacement is the reason for the three isomeric forms of "CrCl$_3 \cdot$6H$_2$O". These isomers are the gray-blue $[Cr(H_2O)_6]Cl_3$, the light green $[Cr(H_2O)_5Cl]Cl_2 \cdot H_2O$, and the dark green $[Cr(H_2O)_4Cl_2]Cl \cdot 2H_2O$. The tenacity with which coordinated water is retained by chromium(III) often makes syntheses from commercial salts difficult when the replacement of this water is required.[131] In many cases reduction from CrO_4^{-2} to Cr(III) in the presence of an excess of ligand is a more practical route [or alternatively oxidation of Cr(II)]. The direct reaction of anhydrous chromic chloride with most ligands is usually a very slow reaction, although successful synthetic procedures based upon the catalyzed reactions

[130] R. Duval and C. Duval, "Complexes du Chrome" in P. Pascal's, *Nouveau Traité de Chimie Mineral* Masson et Cie, Paris (1959), Vol. XIV, pp. 415–551.

[131] See, however, C. L. Rollinson and R. C. White, *Inorg. Chem.* **1**, 281 (1962), for syntheses starting from $[Cr(H_2O)_4Cl_2]Cl \cdot 2H_2O$.

in the presence of small amounts of zinc have been developed[132] and the reaction with liquid ammonia requires no such catalysis. Chromium(III) complexes are sufficiently stable that they exhibit a number of kinds of isomerism, some of which have already been cited. Numerous asymmetric chromium(III) complexes have been resolved.

The complexes of the other oxidation states of chromium are less numerous. Chromium(II) is formed when chromate is reduced in an acidic solution by a strong reducing agent such as zinc. Its complexes are readily oxidized by atmospheric oxygen. There are a hexammine, $[Cr(NH_3)_6]^{+2}$, complexes with related nitrogen bases, a cyanide, $[Cr(CN)_6]^{-4}$, and similar complexes.[130] Chromium(II) ammines are also *oxidized* by water.[133] Hein and Herzog[134] and Herzog and his colleagues prepared complexes of Cr(I) and Cr(O) with dipyridyl. In the initial study, $[Cr(dipyr)_3]I_2 \cdot 4H_2O$ was found to undergo a striking color change in an aqueous solution which was rendered alkaline. Subsequent work with air-free solutions of the more stable $[Cr(dipyr)_3](ClO_4)_2$ showed that reduction with powdered magnesium in the presence of NH_4ClO_4 resulted in the formation of a blue compound which was almost completely separated as the precipitate $[Cr(dipyr)_3]ClO_4$. The reaction which occurred on alkalization of the $Cr(dipyr)_3^{+2}$ solution was a disproportionation:

$$2[Cr(dipyr)_3]^{+2} \xrightarrow{OH^-} [Cr(dipyr)_3]^+ + [Cr(dipyr)_3]^{+3}$$

Studies of the further reduction of $[Cr(dipyr)_3]^+$ led[135] to the preparation of $[Cr(dipyr)_3]$. This is a dark powder; it bursts into flame in the presence of air, is insoluble in water but dissolves in pyridine, dimethylformamide, and benzene. A similar situation was discovered by Malatesta and his co-workers[136] who found that chromous acetate undergoes a disproportionation in the presence of an arylisonitrile to give an arylisonitrile complex of Cr(O) (and one of Cr(III)):

$$3Cr(C_2H_3O_2)_2 + 18RNC \rightarrow [Cr(CNR)_6] + 2[Cr(CNR)_6](C_2H_3O_2)_3$$

Since the Cr(O) six-coordinate complexes have filled $3d$, $4s$, and $4p$ orbitals, one would not expect further reduction to be possible. Zerovalent complexes involving a ditertiary phosphine as ligand have been reported by Chatt and Watson.[137]

[132] K. Taylor and C. E. Milstead, "Abstracts of Papers," American Chemical Society meeting, New York (Sept. 11-16, 1960), 18N.

[133] K. D. Kopple, G. F. Svatos, and H. Taube, *Nature* **189**, 393 (1961).

[134] F. Hein and S. Herzog, *Zeit. anorg. Chem.* **267**, 337 (1952).

[135] S. Herzog, K. C. Renner, and W. Schon, *Zeit. Naturforschung* **12b**, 809 (1957); S. Herzog and W. Schon, *Zeit. anorg. Chem.* **297**, 323 (1958). Polarographic reduction of $Cr(dipyr)_3^{+3}$ apparently leads to the same products: A. Vlcek, *Nature* **189**, 393 (1961).

[136] L. Malatesta, A. Sacco, and S. Ghielmi, *Gazz. chim. ital.* **82**, 516 (1952); L. Malatesta, *Progress in Inorganic Chemistry* **1**, 283 (1959) contains a complete review of the literature on the isonitrile complexes.

[137] J. Chatt and H. R. Watson, *Nature* **189**, 1003 (1961) also reports similar complexes of V, Mo, and W.

Although the complexes of the higher oxidation states of chromium(V and VI) have been known for many years they have been studied sporadically.[130] Complex anions of the types $CrOCl_4^-$,[138] and $CrOCl_5^{-2}$,[139, 140] have been obtained by the careful reduction of CrO_3 in hydrochloric acid at $0°$. A cation, in $[CrCl_3(OH)(H_2O)(py)]Cl$ has also been reported.[140] The complexes of CrO_3 may be thought of as analogous to those of SO_3; for the most part they conform to the pattern:

$$CrO_3 + B^z \rightarrow [CrO_3B]^z$$

where B is some species which can share a pair of electrons and z is the charge (if any) on B. Typical complex anions include CrO_3F^-, CrO_3Cl^-, and CrO_3 $(CH_3COO)^-$. The crystal structures of some alkali metal monofluochromates have been examined[141] and the CrO_3F^- group is an almost regular tetrahedron. The report that fluorine is produced by the thermal decomposition of $KCrO_3F$ has been disproved.[142] With heterocyclic bases, CrO_3 forms adducts with two molecules of the base[143] and with one molecule of base.[144] The reaction with liquid ammonia[145] leads to partial reduction of the chromium and the formation of chromium(III) complexes.

The complexes of molybdenum and tungsten are different from those of chromium in the ways listed above. In the $+6$ oxidation state one finds oxyfluoanions such as $MoO_3F_3^{-3}$, $MoO_2F_4^{-2}$, $WO_3F_3^{-3}$, and $WO_2F_4^{-2}$ as well as a great number of polymeric anions derived from the molybdates and tungstates[146] including the heteropolyacids. In this oxidation state, sulfur can replace oxygen stepwise in the molybdates[147] and tungstates[148] to give rise to ions $MoO_xS_{4-x}^{-2}$ and $WO_xS_{4-x}^{-2}$ where x runs from one to four. Although there are reports that solutions of molybdic acid in mineral acids contain large amounts of the ion MoO_2^{+2}, it is probable that this species is polymeric in non-complexing acids.[149] Complexes of this ion are well characterized.[150] The completely fluorinated complexes of molybdenum(VI) have been prepared by

[138] R. J. Meyer and H. Best, *Zeit. anorg. Chem.* **22**, 192 (1899).

[139] R. F. Weinland and M. Fiederer, *Ber.* **39**, 4042 (1906); **40**, 2090 (1907).

[140] R. F. Weinland and W. Friedrich, *Ber.* **38**, 3784 (1905).

[141] J. A. A. Ketelaar and E. Wegerif, *Rec. trav. chim.* **57**, 1269 (1938).

[142] O. Schmitz-Dumont and P. Opgenhoff, *Zeit. anorg. Chem.* **268**, 57 (1952).

[143] H. H. Sisler, J. D. Bush, and O. E. Accountius, *J. Amer. Chem. Soc.* **70**, 3827 (1948).

[144] H. H. Sisler, W. C. L. Ming, E. Metter, and F. Hurley, *ibid.*, **75**, 446 (1953).

[145] R. S. Drago and H. H. Sisler, *ibid.*, **79**, 1811 (1957); S. I. Tannenbaum, R. S. Drago, and H. H. Sisler, *ibid.*, **79**, 1815 (1957).

[146] P. Pascal, *Nouveau Traite de Chimie Minerale*, Vol. XIV, pp. 656–723, 823–861, 903–998, Masson et Cie, Paris (1958).

[147] J. W. Retgers, *Zeit. physik. Chem.* **10**, 548 (1892).

[148] V. Lenher and A. G. Fruehan, *J. Amer. Chem. Soc.* **49**, 3076 (1927); J. C. Bernard and G. Tridot, *Bull. Soc. Chim. France*, 810, 813, 818 (1961).

[149] M. M. Jones, *J. Amer. Chem. Soc.* **76**, 4233 (1954).

[150] G. T. Morgan and R. A. S. Casteel, *J. Chem. Soc.*, 3252 (1928).

the direct reaction of MoF_6 and the fluorides of potassium, rubidium, and cesium.[151] These have the composition M_2MoF_8 and may contain eight-coordinate molybdenum.

In the oxidation states $+4$ and $+5$, molybdenum and tungsten show coordination numbers of six and eight. With the halides one finds oxygen containing complexes such as $W(OH)Cl_5^{-2}$ and $MoOCl_5^{-2}$, all of which seem to be six-coordinate. With cyanide there are the eight-coordinate complexes $Mo(CN)_8^{-4}$, $Mo(CN)_8^{-3}$, $W(CN)_8^{-4}$, and $W(CN)_8^{-3}$. The $Mo(CN)_8^{-4}$ ion has been shown to have the ligands arranged at the apices of a dodecahedron[152] and the other complexes presumably have this same structure. This arrangement of ligands may be considered to arise from the placing of one of the cyanides perpendicular to each of the *faces* of an octahedron surrounding the central atom. These compounds may be made as follows:

$$Mo(SCN)_6^{-2} + 8KCN \rightarrow K_4Mo(CN)_8 + 4KSCN + 2SCN^- \qquad ^{153}$$

$$K_3W_2Cl_9 + 3HCN + 14KCN + H_2O \rightarrow 2K_4W(CN)_8 + NH_3 + CH_2O + 9KCl \qquad ^{154}$$

In the complex halides of Mo(III), W(III), Mo(II), and W(II) one meets polynuclear complexes in which metal-metal bonds are present.[155] For Mo(III) only the fluoride complex, $Mo_2F_9^{-3}$ appears to be of this type[156]; for tungsten the fluo complex is simple, WF_4^-, but both the chloro and the bromo complexes are polynuclear. When a solution of potassium tungstate in strong hydrochloric acid is reduced with tin, the $W_2Cl_9^{-3}$ ion results and the salt $K_3W_2Cl_9$ can be obtained from the solution.[157] Its structure has been determined by X-ray diffraction and found to consist of two WCl_6 octahedra which share a face. There are thus three bridging chloro atoms[155, 158] and the two tungsten atoms are closer to each other than tungsten atoms in the metallic state (see below). In spite of this the ion undergoes some reactions which are rather unusual, perhaps the most unexpected of these is the formation of a more highly condensed anion containing three tungsten atoms:

$$3W_2Cl_9^{-3} + Cl^- \leftrightharpoons 2W_3Cl_{14}^{-5} \qquad ^{159}$$

[151] B. Cox, D. W. A. Sharp, and A. G. Sharpe, *J. Chem. Soc.*, 1242 (1956).

[152] J. L. Hoard and H. H. Nordsiek, *J. Amer. Chem. Soc.* **61**, 2853 (1939).

[153] H. H. Willard and R. C. Thielke, *ibid.*, **57**, 2609 (1935).

[154] R. C. Young, *ibid.*, **54**, 4517 (1932).

[155] L. Pauling, *Chem. Eng. News*, 2970 (1947).

[156] A. Rosenheim and Tsu Hsun Li, *Ber.* **56**, 2228 (1923).

[157] O. Olsson, *Ber.* **46**, 566 (1913); idem, *Zeit. anorg. allgem. Chem.* **88**, 49 (1914); H. B. Jonassen, A. R. Tarsey, S. Cantor, and G. F. Helfrich, *Inorganic Syntheses*, V, 139, McGraw-Hill, Inc., New York, (1957).

[158] C. Brosset, *Nature* **135**, 875 (1935); idem, *Arkiv Kemi Mineral, Geol.* **12A**, No. 4 (1936).

[159] R. A. Laudise and R. C. Young, *J. Amer. Chem. Soc.* **77**, 5288 (1955).

At least some of the chloro groups may be replaced by heating with aniline or pyridine:

$$W_2Cl_9^{-3} + 3C_5H_5N \rightarrow [W_2Cl_6(py)_3] + 3Cl^-$$

$$W_2Cl_9^{-3} + 3C_6H_5NH_2 \rightarrow [W_2Cl_6(NH_2C_6H_5)_3] + 3Cl^- \quad [160]$$

These complexes are members of that small class of polynuclear species in which the metal atoms are close enough so the metal-metal interaction is large enough to constitute a bond. In the $W_2Cl_9^{-3}$ ion the W—W distance is 2.46 A, while in the metallic state the distance is 2.76 A.[155] The corresponding bromo complex has also been made.[161]

Of the species containing molybdenum or tungsten in oxidation states less than +3, there are some of special interest: Mo_6Cl_{12}, Mo_6Br_{12}, Mo_6I_{12}, and a complex chloro acid of tungsten of probable composition $H_2[W_6Cl_{14}(H_2O)_2] \cdot 6H_2O$. The so-called dichloride and dibromide of molybdenum have been known for over a hundred years. When dissolved in an ionizing solvent, the chloride produces the $Mo_6Cl_8^{+4}$ and Cl^- ions. The $Mo_6Cl_8^{+4}$ ions consist of six molybdenum atoms at the apices of an octahedron and eight bridging chloro groups out from each of the eight edges of the octahedron which are above or below the central square of four molybdenum atoms.[162] The $Mo_6Br_8^{+4}$ and $Mo_6I_8^{+4}$ ions probably have a similar structure. The exchange reactions are consistent with this exceptional arrangement.[163] A compound of tungsten which may be analogous to these in some respects is obtained when WCl_6 is reduced with a dilute sodium amalgam. A product may be extracted from the reaction mixture by the use of dilute hydrochloric acid which is either $H[W_3Cl_7] \cdot 4H_2O$ or $H_2[W_6Cl_{14}(H_2O)_2] \cdot 6H_2O$ as only 3/4 of the water is easily removed in a desiccator.[164] This compound is of unknown structure.

Molybdenum plays a vital role in the physiology of both plants and animals. It is a constituent of the enzymes called *xanthine oxidases* which catalyze the transformations:

$$\text{Aldehyde(hydrate?)} + O_2 \rightarrow \text{acid} + H_2O_2$$

$$\text{Xanthine(hydrate?)} + O_2 \rightarrow \text{urate} + H_2O_2 \quad [165]$$

Molybdenum compounds are essential in the fixation of atmospheric nitrogen by Azobacter in leguminous plants and also in the corresponding processes in other simple organisms. In this respect, tungsten is found to exert an antag-

[160] H. B. Jonassen and S. Cantor, *Rec. trav. chim.* **75**, 609 (1956); H. B. Jonassen, S. Cantor, and A. Tarsey, *J. Amer. Chem. Soc.* **78**, 271 (1956).

[161] R. C. Young, *ibid.*, **54**, 4517 (1932).

[162] C. Brosset, *Arkiv Kemi* **20A**, No. 7 (1945); **22A**, No. 11 (1946).

[163] J. C. Sheldon, *J. Chem. Soc.*, 3106 (1960). Some unusual derivatives are reported by this same author: *ibid.*, 750 (1961); 410 (1962).

[164] J. B. Hill, *J. Amer. Chem. Soc.* **38**, 2383 (1916).

[165] M. Dixon and E. C. Webb, *Enzymes*, Longmans, Green & Company, Ltd., London (1958), p. 204 and the references given there.

onistic action on the fixation of nitrogen, presumably because it can take the place of molybdenum in one or more of the complexes used for this process without being capable of participating in an essential step. The exact nature of the complexes which participate in this process and the detailed reactions which occur are as yet unknown.[166]

Both molybdate and tungstate undergo reactions with polyhydroxy organic compounds such as tartaric, malic, and citric acids. In some respects, these reactions are similar to the corresponding reactions of borate, though they have not been as thoroughly investigated.

MANGANESE, TECHNETIUM, AND RHENIUM. In this family we again meet a considerable variety of coordination behavior and a number of unsolved problems. These elements show such a wide variety of oxidation states that it is very difficult to summarize their behavior. Because they fall in the same general family as the halogens, it is expected that oxidation states from -1 to 7 may occur and this has been confirmed. In these elements it is easy to see the dependence of accessible oxidation states on the coordination number in certain examples. Although the oxyanions are usually considered to fall on the borderline of coordination chemistry, for purposes of consistency it is often convenient to consider them as complexes of the ligand O^{-2}. As is well known, fluorine is a much more powerful oxidizing agent than oxygen. Why then, it may be asked, should the occurrence of the very highest oxidation states be most common in species which have oxygen bound to the central atom? Thus, in this family, MnO_4^- is well known, but the highest oxidation state that manganese exhibits in a fluo complex is $+4$ in MnF_6^{-2}.[167] To a certain extent this is due to the fact that four oxygens can oxidize manganese to Mn(VII) and remain coordinated to it in the tetrahedral MnO_4^- ion. It is apparently not possible, however, for seven fluorine atoms to carry out an analogous process, as the corresponding seven-coordinate species cannot be formed by manganese. Manganese does form a seven-coordinate complex with EDTA under suitable conditions.[168] [It is certainly surprising that no manganese fluorides, either simple or complex, are known for the oxidation states Mn(V) or Mn(VI).] The same factors can be seen in several other transition elements in high oxidation states: these are usually more readily attained in oxides and oxyanions, e.g., OsO_4, FeO_4^{-2}, CrO_4^{-2}, CoO_4^{-4}, and NiO_3^{-2}.

The coordination compounds of manganese with typical ligands are found with oxidation states $+4$, $+3$, $+2$, $+1$, and 0. The complexes of Mn(IV) are

[166] G. C. Webster, *Nitrogen Metabolism in Plants*, Row, Peterson, and Co., Evanston, Ill. (1959), pp. 14–20; C. A. Lamb, O. G. Bentley, and J. M. Beattie, editors, *Trace Elements*, Academic Press, Inc., New York (1958), Chs. 19, 20.

[167] W. Klemm, *J. Inorg. Nuclear Chem.* 8, 532 (1958); H. J. Emeleus, "Nonvolatile Inorganic Fluorides" in J. H. Simons, *Fluorine Chemistry*, Academic Press, Inc., New York (1950), p. 61.

[168] J. L. Hoard, B. Petersen, S. Richards, and J. V. Silverton, *J. Amer. Chem. Soc.* 83, 3533 (1961).

few in number and include K_2MnF_6,[168a] $K_2Mn(CN)_6 \cdot 2KCN$,[169] and $K_2[Mn(C_2O_4)_2(OH)_2]$.[170] For Mn(III) there are a considerable number of complexes as this oxidation state is stabilized by coordination to several common ligands. Some typical examples are $K_3Mn(CN)_6$,[171] the acetylacetonate, $Mn(C_5H_7O_2)_3$,[172] and the complexes with oxalate, sulfate, phosphate, and several organic chelating agents.[173] Mn(III) oxalato complexes are involved in the oxidation of oxalate by permanganate and for this reason they have been studied in some detail. One preparation is:

$$5H_2C_2O_4 + KMnO_4 + K_2CO_3 \xrightarrow{\text{cold}} K_3[Mn(C_2O_4)_3] + 5H_2O + 5CO_2 \quad \text{[174]}$$

This particular complex is rather unstable, though it can be isolated and characterized. Similar complexes involving anions with two molecules of coordinated water and oxalate or malonate have also been reported[174] and may be prepared by the reactions:

$$4H_2C_2O_4 + KMnO_4 \rightarrow K[Mn(C_2O_4)_2(H_2O)_2] + 4CO_2 + 2H_2O$$

$$2KMnO_4 + 5CH_2(COOH)_2 \rightarrow 2K[Mn(C_3H_2O_4)_2(H_2O)_2] + 3CO_2 + 2H_2O$$

The realization that oxalato complexes of manganese play a role in the familiar titration of oxalate with permanganate has led to a number of studies of this reaction from both a kinetic and a mechanistic viewpoint.[175-181] The reaction proceeds through oxalato complexes of manganese in several steps; it is catalyzed by traces of Mn(III) in whose absence it proceeds rather slowly.

The coordination compounds of Mn(II) have been studied in great detail. This species shows a marked preference for coordination to oxygen, and as a result numerous complexes involving other donor atoms often undergo extensive hydrolysis in the presence of water. Other donor groups which form complexes of some stability include the halide ions (e.g., Cl^- gives $MnCl_3^-$, $MnCl_4^{-2}$), cyanide [$Mn(CN)_6^{-3}$], pyridine ($MnCl_2 \cdot 2$ pyridine), and of course, numerous organic chelating agents with oxygen containing donor groups. In many respects the coordination chemistry of Mn(II) shows similarities to that

[168a] R. F. Weinland and O. Lauenstein, *Zeit. anorg. Chem.* **20**, 40 (1899).

[169] A. Yakimach, *Compt. rend.* **190**, 681 (1930).

[170] G. H. Cartledge and W. P. Ericks, *J. Amer. Chem. Soc.* **58**, 2069 (1936).

[171] J. Meyer, *Zeit. anorg. Chem.* **81**, 385 (1913).

[172] F. Gach, *Monatsh.* **21**, 109 (1900).

[173] Abegg's *Handbuch der Anorganischen Chemie*, S. Hirzel, Leipzig (1913), Vol. IV, 2, pp. 785–814.

[174] G. H. Cartledge and W. P. Ericks, *J. Amer. Chem. Soc.* **58**, 2061, 2065 (1936).

[175] H. F. Launer and D. M. Yost, *J. Amer. Chem. Soc.* **56**, 2571 (1934).

[176] M. Polissar, *ibid.*, **58**, 1372 (1936).

[177] F. R. Duke, *ibid.*, **69**, 2885 (1947).

[178] H. Taube, *ibid.*, **69**, 1418 (1947); **70**, 3928 (1948).

[179] R. M. Noyes, *Trans. N. Y. Acad. Sci.* (2), **13**, 314 (1951).

[180] J. M. Malcolm and R. M. Noyes, *J. Amer. Chem. Soc.* **74**, 2769 (1952).

[181] S. J. Adler and R. M. Noyes, *ibid.*, **77**, 2036 (1955).

of Mg(II) including the formation of relatively weak ammines in strongly ammoniacal solutions and a common pattern of coordination with species such as oxalate and malonate, etc.

Although with technetium all studies must be carried out on synthetic material, there is a reasonable amount of information on the complexes of this rare element. In addition to the pertechnate anion, TcO_4^-, technetium also is found in complexes of a more typical sort such as [Tc(ortho(bisdimethylarsine)benzene)$_2$Cl$_2$]Cl, [Tc(ortho(bisdimethylarsine)benzene)$_2$Cl$_4$]ClO$_4$, and [Tc(ortho(bisdimethylarsine)benzene)$_2$Cl$_2$].[182] An unusual example is found in [Tc(C$_6$H$_6$)$_2$]$^+$ which was made by the neutron bombardment of the corresponding molybdenum compound: [Mo(C$_6$H$_6$)$_2$](n, β) [Tc(C$_6$H$_6$)$_2$]$^+$.[183]

The coordination chemistry of rhenium is as variegated as that of manganese, if not more so. There are a reasonable number of halide and oxyhalide complexes: K$_2$ReOCl$_5$, (NH$_4$)$_2$ReOCl$_5$, K$_3$[ReO$_2$(CN)$_4$], K$_2$ReCl$_6$, K$_2$ReF$_6$, RbReCl$_4$; a host of carbonyl derivatives;[184] complexes such as the acetylacetonate, Re(C$_5$H$_7$O$_2$)$_3$, a complex with phenylacetylene, [ReCl(C$_6$H$_5$C≡CH)$_2$],[185] and the triphenylphosphine complexes: Re(PPh$_3$)Cl$_3$ and Re(PPh$_3$)$_2$Cl$_3$.[186] Rhenium can apparently exhibit coordination numbers from four to eight, although only one example of eight-coordinate rhenium has been characterized,[187] the cyanide Re(CN)$_8^{-3}$. While it is generally accepted that the evidence for Re(−I) is conclusive,[188] the structure of the species is not determined. When the Re(−I) is produced by reduction in water a material is prepared which was originally[189] proposed to have a square planar arrangement of water molecules about the central rhenium. More recent studies have led to the belief that the structure must contain Re—H bonds[190] and may possibly be [HRe(OH)(H$_2$O)$_3$]$^-$ or [H$_3$Re(OH)$_3$(H$_2$O)]$^-$. Technetium can also be reduced polarographically to a similar state.[190].

IRON, RUTHENIUM, AND OSMIUM. These elements form many stable complexes of a variety of types. The coordination chemistry of iron and osmium is rather well understood; that of ruthenium is still imperfectly known because

[182] J. E. Ferguson and R. S. Nyholm, *Chem. and Industry*, 347 (1960).

[183] F. Baumgaertner, E. O. Fischer, and U. Zahn, *Naturwissenschaften* **48**, 478 (1961).

[184] Ref. 22, pp. 1300–1315.

[185] R. Colton, R. Levitus, and G. Wilkinson, *Nature* **186**, 233 (1960).

[186] idem, *J. Chem. Soc*, 4121 (1960).

[187] R. Colton, R. D. Peacock, and G. Wilkinson, *J. Chem. Soc.*, 1374 (1960).

[188] G. E. F. Lundell and H. B. Knowles, *J. Research Natl. Bur. Standards* **18**, 629 (1937); O. Tomicek and F. Tomicek, *Coll. Czech. Chem. Comm.* **11**, 626 (1939); J. J. Lingane, *J. Amer. Chem. Soc.* **64**, 1001, 2182 (1942); C. L. Rulfs and P. J. Elving, *ibid.*, **72**, 3304 (1950); idem, *ibid.*, **73**, 3287 (1951); E. K. Maun and N. Davidson, *ibid.*, **72**, 3509 (1950); J. Bravo, E. Griswold, and J. Kleinberg, *Science* **115**, 375 (1952); idem, *J. Phys. Chem.* **58**, 18 (1952); A. V. Grosse, *Zeit. Naturforschung* **8b**, 533 (1953).

[189] L. Pauling, *Chem. Eng. News* **25**, 2970 (1947).

[190] R. Colton, J. Dalziel, W. P. Griffith, and G. Wilkinson, *Nature* **183**, 1755 (1959); A. P. Ginsberg, J. M. Miller, J. R. Cavanaugh, and B. P. Daily, *Nature* **185**, 528 (1960).

of the variety of oxidation states which it exhibits and its considerable tendency to form polynuclear complexes.

The complexes of iron are predominantly those of Fe(II) and Fe(III), both of which form both tetrahedral and octahedral complexes. These include a large number of readily prepared species: $[FeF_6]^{-3}$, $[Fe(CN)_6]^{-3}$, $[Fe(CN)_6]^{-4}$, $[Fe(C_2O_4)_3]^{-3}$ and very stable complexes with orthophenanthroline and dipyridyl, $[Fe(ophen)_3]^{+2 \text{ or } +3}$, and $[Fe(dipyr)_3]^{+2 \text{ or } +3}$. Four-coordinate complexes are less common and generally less stable but may be illustrated by $FeCl_4^{-2}$ and $FeCl_4^{-1}$. Iron forms stable coordinate bonds with donor groups involving divalent carbon, heterocyclic nitrogen, oxygen, fluoride, sulfur, and nitrogen in NO. Hydrides are known for iron (and also osmium) and are prepared by reactions of the type:

$$[FeCl_2\{o—C_6H_4(P(C_2H_5)_2)_2\}_2] \xrightarrow{\text{LiAlH}_4} [FeH_2\{o—C_6H_4(P(C_2H_5)_2)_2\}_2] \quad [191]$$

The ammines are not stable in the presence of water but may be prepared from anhydrous salts. The simple salts dissolve in water to give aquo complexes. Incidentally, the aquo ferric ion is colorless; the usual yellow color of ferric solutions is due to hydrolytic products and can be removed by the addition of a strong acid with a noncomplexing anion such as nitric acid.

Of all the iron complexes, none is of more direct interest to human beings than hemoglobin, the iron complex by which atmospheric oxygen is picked up and transported through the blood. An enormous amount of work has been carried out on this complex and its derivatives. It is perhaps the complex on which the most attention has been lavished (with the possible exception of chlorophyll). The structure of this substance is not known exactly, but it is known to contain a high molecular weight protein part (globin) and four separate iron-porphyrin chelate systems.[192] The porphin nucleus is shown in Figure 15 and is the basic chelate structure involved. The coordination of iron by the replacement of two acidic hydrogens produces a complex of extremely great stability (an inert complex) and the ability of the iron to coordinate to two additional groups provides a mechanism by which it may interact either with simple molecules (such as O_2, CO, or NO) or with proteins which contain suitable donor groups (e.g., imidazole residues). The iron in normal hemoglobin is in the ferrous state but can be oxidized to the ferric state by a variety of reagents (e.g., ferricyanide). The four iron atoms combine reversibly with O_2 which can then be transported to parts of the body where oxygen is consumed.

The complexes of ruthenium are among the least satisfactorily character-

[191] J. Chatt, F. A. Hart, and R. G. Hayter, *Nature* **181**, 55 (1960); J. Chatt and R. G. Hayter, *J. Chem. Soc.*, 5507 (1961).

[192] *Conference on Hemoglobin*, National Academy of Sciences-National Research Council, Washington, D.C. (1958).

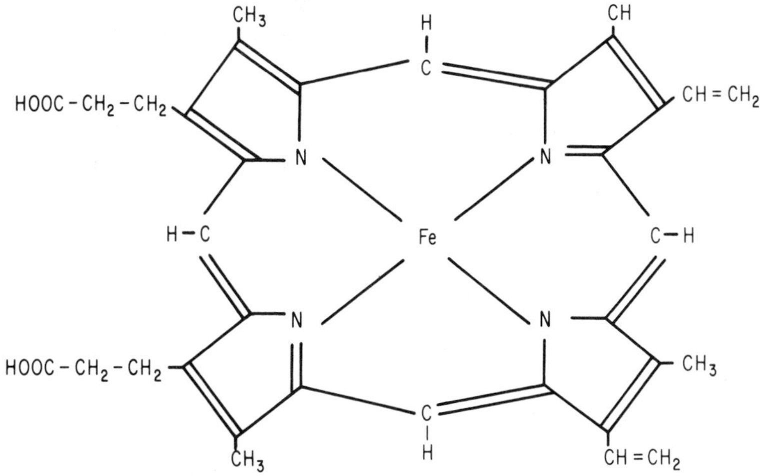

Fig. 15 The molecule "heme". The porphin nucleus is the cyclic group of four pyrrole rings bonded by the linking methine groups. This contains iron in the ferrous state. A closely related material is hemin or ferriprotoporphyrin in which the iron is in the ferric state and a chloride is coordinated to the iron.

ized of any of the complexes of the platinum metals. Since its discovery by K. K. Klaus in 1845[193] the element has never been available in large amounts. In addition there are two factors which make the elucidation of the chemical reactions of ruthenium difficult: the possible variation in oxidation states from Ru(I) to Ru(VIII) and the very considerable tendency for ruthenium to form polynuclear complexes. As a result of the general studies of fission products, much work has been carried out on the solution chemistry of ruthenium in recent years with the goal of assisting separation methods. In many cases it has been found that the earlier formulation of ruthenium compounds have erred in the direction of oversimplification. A number of mononuclear complexes of Ru(II), Ru(III), Ru(IV) and Ru(VI) are known and in these the ruthenium is generally six-coordinate and presumably octahedral. These include[194] $[Ru(CN)_6]^{-2}$, $[Ru(ophen)_3]^{+2}$, $[Ru(NH_3)_4Cl_2]^+$, $[Ru(C_2O_4)_3]^{-2}$, and $[RuO_2Cl_4]^{-2}$. A very considerable number of species appear to be present even in some solutions of relatively simple composition. Thus when ruthenium tetroxide is dissolved in nitric acid and the resultant solution is treated with nitric oxide a solution is obtained from which trinitra-tonitrosyldiaquoruthenium(III) ·2 hydrate, $[Ru(NO)(NO_3)_3(H_2O)_2]$ ·2H$_2$O

[193] K. K. Klaus, *Collected Works* together with a commentary by O. E. Zvyagintsev were published by the Izdatelstvo Akademia Nauk S.S.S.R., Moscow (1954).
[194] Ref. 22, p. 1462 ff.

may be isolated.[195] In addition there appear[196] to be a number of other species present in these solutions including nitrato complexes with from one to five nitrato groups per ruthenium. Furthermore, solutions of ruthenium may contain polynuclear species such as $[Ru_2Cl_{10}O]^{-4}$,[197] and $[Ru_2(NH_3)_8(OH)]$ $(NO_3)_6$.[198] A very elegant study of the nine complexes in the Ru(III)Cl$^-$—H_2O system, including the geometrical isomers, has recently been carried out, and it was shown that the equilibrium constants for the *cis-trans*-ratios are nearly those predicted on a purely statistical basis.[199]

It is of some interest to note that charged complex ions of large size, among which $d[Ru(ophen)_3]^{+2}$ is to be listed, have been found to exhibit curariform activity.[200] This is a property which has been found to be exhibited by a number of large positively charged complex ions and has been studied and investigated in some detail.[201] It is certainly fascinating to think that many of the common complex cations have properties initially discovered in South American Indian arrow poisons.

The coordination chemistry of osmium also exhibits some interesting peculiarities and these have been studied in some detail. Among the most unusual of these complexes are the nitrilo-halides, $[Os(N)X_4]^-$ and $[Os(N)X_5]^{-2}$, which contain what might be called a *coordinated nitride ion*. They are prepared by the following sequence of reactions:[202]

$$OsO_4 + NH_3 + KOH \rightarrow KOsO_3N + 2H_2O$$
$$KOsO_3N + 7HCl \rightarrow H_2O + Cl_2 + KH[Os(N)Cl_5]$$
$$2KH[Os(N)Cl_5] \rightarrow K_2[Os(N)Cl_5] + H_2[Os(N)Cl_5]$$

A recent infrared study of $KOsO_3N$ and $K_2[Os(N)Cl_5]$[203] confirmed Werner's structural formulation and showed that the Os—N bond had considerable multiple bond character. Another example of interest is seen

[195] J. M. Fletcher, I. L. Jenkins, F. M. Lever, F. S. Martin, A. R. Powell, and R. Todd, *J. Inorg. Nuclear Chem.* 1, 382(1955); R. M. Wallace, *J. Inorg. Nuclear Chem.* 20, 283(1961).

[196] J. M. Fletcher, P. G. M. Brown, E. R. Gardner, C. J. Hardy, A. G. Wain, and J. L. Woodhead, *J. Inorg. Nuclear Chem.* 12, 154 (1959).

[197] A. M. Mathieson, D. P. Mellor, and N. C. Stephenson, *Acta Cryst.* 5, 185 (1952); J. D. Dunitz and L. E. Orgel, *J. Chem. Soc.* 2594 (1953).

[198] A. A. Grinberg, A. M. Trofinov, and L. N. Stepanova, *Radiokhimiya* 2, 78 (1960), C.A. 54: 18033.

[199] R. E. Connick, D. A. Fine, and E. E. Mercer, "Abstracts of the American Chemical Society meeting," St. Louis, Mo. (March 21–30, 1961), p. 26M.

[200] F. P. Dwyer, E. C. Gyarfas, R. D. Wright, and A. Shulman, *Nature* 179, 425 (1957); J. H. Koch, E. C. Gyarfas, and F. P. Dwyer, *Australian J. Biol. Sci.* 9, 371 (1956).

[201] P. Trendelenberg in A. Heffer, editor, *Handbuch der Experimentellen Pharmakologie*, Springer-Verlag, Berlin (1923), Vol. I, p. 630 ff. A more recent study may be seen in D. Della-Bella and F. Rogoni, *Boll. Chim. farm.* 99, 269 (1960), C.A. 54: 19967.

[202] A. Werner and K. Dinklage, *Ber.* 34, 2702 (1901) contains data on the $[Os(N)Cl_5]^{-2}$ salts; idem, *ibid.*, 39, 500 (1906) is on $[Os(N)Br_4]^-$ and $[Os(N)Br_5]^{-2}$.

[203] J. Lewis and G. Wilkinson, *J. Inorg. Nuclear Chem.* 6, 12 (1958). See also, V. M. Valkov and M. E. Dyatkina, *Doklady Akad. Nauk S.S.S.R.*, Moscow 134, 351 (1960), *C.A.* 55: 10045.

in the products of the reaction of OsO_4 and PF_3. Here two compounds are found: $2OsF_4 \cdot PF_3$ and $OsO_4 \cdot PF_3$, the latter compound being stable at and above $70°$.[204] Ruthenium tetroxide forms similar complexes. These show how the combining power of osmium is by no means exhausted even though its formal oxidation number is $+8$.

Osmium forms a number of octahedral complexes in combination with cyanide, $[Os(CN)_6]^{-4}$; chloride, $[OsCl_6]^{-2}$; fluoride, $[OsF_6]^{-2}$; bromide, $[OsBr_6]^{-2}$; iodide, $[OsI_6]^{-2}$; thiourea, $[Os(SC(NH_2)_2)_6]^{+4}$; and ammonia, $[OsO_2(NH_3)_4]^{+2}$; as well as numerous chelating agents. A five-coordinate nitro anion, $[Os(NO_2)_5]^{-2}$, is well known and there are numerous sulfito complexes whose stereochemistry is uncertain at present: $[Os(SO_3)_5]^{-6}$, $[Os(SO_3)_6]^{-8}$, $[OsCl_2(SO_3)_4]^{-6}$, etc. Univalent osmium has been reported in the complex $[OsBr \cdot (PPh_3)]$ and some related materials.[205] The most complete series of modern studies on the coordination chemistry of osmium is seen in the work of F. P. Dwyer and his collaborators who have prepared complexes of Os(II), Os(III), Os(IV), Os(V), and Os(VI).[206] Among other items in this work are the resolution of asymmetric chelates and the first preparation of an Os(V) complex, $[Os(en—H)_2en]I_3$, where en—H signifies that a deprotonated nitrogen is present in the ethylenediamine.[207]

Although osmium and ruthenium are very similar in many of their chemical properties, there seem to be features of the chemistry of each element which are lacking in that of the other. This may be due to the incompleteness of our knowledge. There does seem to be a reluctance on the part of ruthenium to form nicely defined mononuclear complexes. There also seems to be a greater possibility of controlling the oxidation states of osmium in preparative work.

Cobalt, Rhodium, and Iridium. Even before the work of Werner, the complexes of these elements were studied by a considerable number of workers, among whom the most notable was S. M. Jorgensen.[208] After the structures of many of these compounds were established it was realized that these are among the elements with the most predictable stereochemical behavior in stable coordination compounds. This has led to a preference for their complexes in many studies where certainty on this point is desired. As a result there is an enormous amount of information available especially on the octahedral complexes of Co(III).[209]

While cobalt can exhibit oxidation states of 0, 1, 2, 3, 4, and -2, the com-

[204] M. L. Hair and P. L. Robinson, *J. Chem. Soc.* 106 (1958).

[205] L. Vaska, *Zeit. Naturforschung* **15b**, 56 (1960).

[206] This work may be traced back from F. P. Dwyer and J. W. Hogarth, *J. Amer. Chem. Soc.* 77, 6152 (1955); F. P. Dwyer and A. Sargeson, *ibid.*, 77, 1285 (1955).

[207] F. P. Dwyer and J. W. Hogarth, *loc. cit.*

[208] An excellent evaluation of the work of Jorgensen may be seen in the papers of G. B. Kauffman, cited in Ch. 1, ref. 5.

[209] A recent comprehensive summary of this may be found in an article by D. H. Busch in R. S. Young, *Cobalt*, Reinhold Publishing Corp., New York (1960), pp. 88–156.

pounds with 0 or a negative oxidation state are primarily carbonyls or their derivatives. The compounds of Co(I) are very few in number[210] and susceptible to aerial oxidation. Those of Co(II) are very numerous and have been thoroughly studied. They are generally labile and may exhibit coordination numbers of four, five, or six, though four is common for halo complexes and six is found for most ammines. The Co(II) species is readily oxidized in basic medium, especially if suitable ligands are present, e.g., NH_3. The resulting Co(III) complexes are both very numerous and sufficiently stable to allow structural determinations to be carried out by chemical methods in many cases. They are invariably six-coordinate and octahedral. The occurrence of Co(IV) in complexes is principally in the rather ambiguous form of binuclear complexes in which the assignment of formal charges leads to the possibility of both Co(III) and Co(IV) being present, i.e., in $[(NH_3)_5Co-(O-O)-Co(NH_3)_5]^{+5}$. More detailed studies have shown that the single unpaired electron interacts equally with both cobalt atoms.[211]

Simple salts of cobalt are generally those of Co(II). The behavior of Co(II) in aqueous solutions is strongly dependent on the pH of the solution and the nature of the ligands present in solution. In acidic solutions the complexes formed with halide ions, many chelating agents and water, are quite stable toward oxidation. When the solutions are rendered basic, oxidation by atmospheric oxygen or added oxidizing agents occurs readily in the presence of ammonia or its organic derivatives, carbonate or bicarbonate, and of course, cyanide. The reaction of Co(II) with cyanide in aqueous solution produces $[Co(CN)_5(OH_2)]^{-3}$. This is capable of slowly reducing hydrogen ion derived from water in the presence of more cyanide:

$$2[Co(CN)_5(OH_2)]^{-3} + CN^- + 2H^+ \rightarrow 2[Co(CN)_6]^{-3} + H_2 + H_2O \qquad {}^{212}$$

The behavior of $CoCl_2$ in the presence of water has long stimulated controversies. The pink hexahydrate, $[Co(H_2O)_6]Cl_2$, changes to an anhydrous blue material when the water is removed. The substitution of Cl^- for H_2O is responsible for the change in the color of the complex species present and this can occur in steps. In general, any change which tends to favor the replacement of water by chloride (or other halogen) results in the formation of the blue complexes. Since the octahedral configuration of the hexa-aquo ion is replaced by a tetrahedral configuration in the tetrachloro complex, the most reasonable explanation is in terms of crystal field theory as the shifts in color to longer wave length by absorption are those predicted by the sequence of

[210] [Co(Dipyr)$_3$]$^+$: G. M. Waind and B. Martin, *J. Inorg. Nuclear Chem.* **8**, 551 (1959); J. Csaszar, *Naturwissenschaften* **46**, 488 (1959); [Co(CN)$_5$X]$^{-5}$: N. Maki, *Nature* **185**, 227, 682 (1960); [Co(CNCH$_3$)$_5$]ClO$_4$: A. Sacco and M. Freni, *Gazz. chim. ital.* **89**, 1800 (1959), C.A. 55: 4226.

[211] I. Bernal, E. A. V. Ebsworth, and J. A. Weil, *Proc. Chem. Soc.* 57 (1959).

[212] D. N. Hume and I. M. Kolthoff, *J. Amer. Chem. Soc.* **71**, 867 (1949); A. W. Adamson, *ibid.*, **73**, 5710 (1951).

crystal field strengths of the ligands, i.e., $H_2O > F^- > Cl^- > Br^- > I^-$. The ease with which the color may be changed is surprising; cooling anhydrous blue $CoCl_2$ in liquid air causes it to turn red.

Although commonly six-coordinate, Co(II) may also form four- or five-coordinate complexes. Four-coordinate complexes include $[CoCl_4]^{-2}$,[213] (tetrahedral), alpha $[Co(py)_2Cl_2]$[214] ("planar") and $[Co(OPPh_3)_4]^{+2}$,[215a] (tetrahedral) and a well-characterized square planar complex with maleonitriledithiolate.[215b] A five-coordinate nitrosylacetylacetonate has also been reported whose composition is $[Co(C_5H_7O_2)_2NO]$[216] (tetragonal pyramid). The transformation of octahedral $[CoCl_2(py)_4]$ into tetrahedral $[CoCl_2(py)_2]$ is found to occur with the absorption of heat ($\triangle H = +13.4$ Kcals/mole) and a large positive entropy change ($\triangle S \sim 36.7$ e.u.).[217]

The hexacoordinate Co(III) complexes are among the most familiar of the stable coordination compounds, a fact due in no small part to the relative ease with which compounds of known structure may be prepared in this state. In general, the donor atoms found in these complexes include N, S, C, P, and O. The largest group of these which show a considerable instability toward reduction are those containing coordinated water or alcohols (e.g., ethyleneglycol). These are readily reduced in the presence of water, especially if oxygen is the only donor atom. A procedure of some generality for the preparation of Co(III) complexes is the oxidation of a cobaltous salt in the presence of the ligand in a basic solution. As an oxidizing agent one may use O_2 (or air), H_2O_2, PbO_2, NaClO, $NaClO_2$, halogens, or a large number of other materials which are effective oxidants in basic solution. In many cases such processes can be carried out in such a manner that they yield a product which is predominantly one compound, though this usually requires careful control of the experimental conditions. An alternative method in which an unstable Co(III) complex is first prepared and then reacted with the ligand (whose Co(III) complex is the desired final product) may also be used. As an example, Barbieri[218] has shown that $CoCO_3$ is oxidized by H_2O_2 in $NaHCO_3$ solutions to give the green $[Co(CO_3)_3]^{-3}$ ion which can subsequently be converted to other Co(III) complexes by treatment with the desired ligand. Thus cobalt(III) acetylacetonate is obtained when such a solution is treated with acetylacetone. This method has recently been extended[219] to a large number of other Co(III) complexes.

[213] H. M. Powell and A. F. Wells, *J. Chem. Soc.*, 359 (1935).

[214] E. G. Cox, A. J. Shorter, W. Wardlaw, and W. J. R. Way, *ibid.*, 1556 (1937).

[215a] F. A. Cotton and E. Bannister, *J. Chem. Soc.*, 1878 (1960).

[215b] H. B. Gray, R. Williams, I. Bernal, and E. Billig, *J. Amer. Chem. Soc.* **84**, 3596 (1962).

[216] R. Nast and H. Bier, *Ber*, **92**, 1858 (1959).

[217] L. E. Katzin, *J. Chem. Phys.* **35**, 467 (1961).

[218] G. A. Barbieri, *Atti accad. Lincei* (6), 7, 747 (1928).

[219] M. Mori, M. Shibata, E. Kyuno, and T. Adachi, *Bull. Chem. Soc. Japan* **29**, 883 (1956); M. Mori, M. Shibata, E. Kyuno, and H. Nakajima, *ibid.*, **29**, 887 (1956); H. F. Bauer and W. C. Drinkard, *J. Amer. Chem. Soc.* **82**, 5031 (1960).

The octahedral structure of the Co(III) complexes has been confirmed in a large number of X-ray structure determinations as well as an enormous amount of indirect chemical evidence on optical and geometrical isomerism. The numbers and types which have been obtained are those predicted for an octahedral configuration for Co(III). The reactions in which ligands are replaced may proceed with some rearrangement, though Werner originally suggested that an optically active complex that reacts to give another optically active complex does so with retention of configuration. There are even some types of reactions of optically active complexes which proceed with an inversion of configuration, a phenomenon which has been designated the *Walden Inversion* of octahedral complexes. Typical examples of this are:

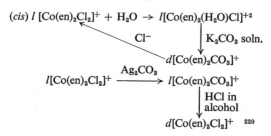

The inversion involved in the transformation of $l[Co(en)_2Cl_2]^+$ to $d[Co(en)_2 CO_3]^+$ involves the intermediate formation of the aquo complex $l[Co(en)_2 (H_2O)Cl]^{+2}$.[221] A similar inversion presumably occurs in the reaction of *cis-l-* $[Co(en)_2Cl_2]Cl$ with ammonia.[222]

In addition to the oxidations of cobaltous salts with air and hydrogen peroxide, there are many alternative preparative methods, one of which is:

$$Co^{+2}(aq.) + 3C_2O_4^{-2} \xrightarrow[\text{water slurry}]{PbO_2} [Co(C_2O_4)_3]^{-3} \quad \text{[223]}$$

When the oxidation is effected by a species whose concentration, and hence activity, is easily controlled, a wide variety of these complexes may be prepared by suitable changes in the method. Thus sodium chlorite, $NaClO_2$, can be used to prepare $[Co(NH_3)_6]Cl_3$ and a large number of related materials.[224]

There are many different complexes for Co(III). The following brief list is intended merely to indicate possible charge types:

[220] J. C. Bailar, Jr. and W. Auten, *J. Amer. Chem. Soc.* **56**, 774 (1934).

[221] J. C. Bailar, Jr., F. G. Jonelis, and E. H. Huffman, *ibid.*, **58**, 2224 (1936); J. C. Bailar, Jr. and J. P. McReynolds, *ibid.*, **61**, 3199 (1939); J. C. Bailar, Jr. and D. F. Peppard, *ibid.*, **62**, 820 (1940).

[222] J. C. Bailar, Jr., J. H. Haslam, and E. M. Jones, *ibid.*, **58**, 2226 (1940).

[223] J. C. Bailar, Jr. and E. M. Jones, *Inorganic Syntheses* **1**, 37, McGraw-Hill, Inc., New York (1939).

[224] P. Spacu, C. Gheorgiu, M. Brezeanu, and S. Popescu, *Rev. Chim. Acad. rep. populare Roumaine* **3**, 127 (1958) (in English), C.A. 54: 14812.

$[Co(CO_3)_3]^{-3}$	$[Co(NO_2)_4(NH_3)_2]^-$	$[Co(NO_2)_2Cl(NH_3)_3]$
$[Co(SO_3)_3]^{-3}$	$[Co(NO_2)_2(C_2O_4)(NH_3)_2]^-$	$[Co(NH_3)_3(NO_2)_3]$
$[Co(C_2O_4)_3]^{-3}$		$[Co(NH_3)(en)(NO_2)_3]$
$[Co(CN)_6]^{-3}$		

$[Co(H_2O)_2(NH_3)_2Cl_2]^+$	$[Co(H_2O)_3(NH_3)_2Cl]^{+2}$	$[Co(NH_2OH)_6]^{+3}$
$[Co(H_2O)(NH_3)(en)(Cl)_2]^+$	$[Co(H_2O)(NH_3)_4Cl]^{+2}$	$[Co(en)_3]^{+3}$
$[Co(NH_3)_5(SO_3)]^+$	$[Co(NH_3)_5(NO_3)]^{+2}$	$[Co(H_2O)_6]^{+3}$
$[Co(NH_3)_5(C_2O_4)]^+$	$[Co(NH_3)_5(NCS)]^{+2}$	$[Co(dipyr)_3]^{+3}$

Cobalt also forms complexes with zwitterions of the type $(CH_3)_3\overset{+}{N}CH_2COO^-$ as are found in the examples, $[(NH_3)_5Co(OOCCH_2\overset{+}{N}(CH_3)_3)](ClO_4)_3$ and $[(NH_3)_4Co(OOCCH_2\overset{+}{N}(CH_3)_3)](ClO_4)_3$.[225]

Before passing to the elements below cobalt in the periodic table, the role of cobalt in vitamin B_{12} deserves mention. In this vitamin, which strangely enough is also intimately related to the metabolism of iron, one finds Co(III) acting as a coordination center for a molecule with a grouping related to, but not identical with, a porphyrin nucleus. The two axial coordination positions in Vitamin B_{12} are occupied by a methylene group and a nitrogen in a benzimidazole ring respectively. This structure has been worked out via X-ray diffraction methods[226] and a derivative is shown in Figure 16.

The chemistry of the coordination compounds of rhodium is primarily that of Rh(III) though some Rh(II) complexes are known as well as rhodium carbonyls such as $[Rh(CO)_4]_n$. The usual coordination number is six for Rh(III) but lower coordination numbers are found in some halo complexes. As is customary with the platinum metal salts, even the simple salts are autocomplex. Thus there are isomeric forms of $Rh(CN)_3$, RhF_3, $RhCl_3$, and even Rh_2O_3 and $Rh(OH)_3$.[227]

Massive metallic rhodium is quite resistant to attack by acids but can be converted to the sulfate, $Ru_2(SO_4)_3$ by repeated fusion with $KHSO_4$. It can be chlorinated at temperatures of 250° or above to give $RhCl_3$; if this chlorination is carried out in the presence of NaCl, the product is sodium hexachlororhodate(III), Na_3RhCl_6. If the metal is alloyed by fusion with zinc, lead, bismuth, or copper, the alloy can be dissolved in aqua regia. If the alloy with zinc is dissolved in acid and the product treated with ammonia, $[Rh(NH_3)_5Cl]Cl_2$ results. By boiling this with ammonia in water, the hexammine,

[225] J. V. Quagliano, S. Kida, and J. Fujita, *J. Amer. Chem. Soc.* **84**, 724 (1962).

[226] C. Brink, D. C. Hodgkin, J. Lindsey, J. Pickworth, J. H. Robertson, and J. G. White, *Nature* 174, 1169 (1954); D. C. Hodgkin, J. Pickworth, J. H. Robertson, K. N. Trueblood, R. J. Prosen, and J. G. White, *ibid.*, 176, 325 (1955); D. C. Hodgkin, J. Kamper, M. Mackey, J. Pickworth, K. N. Trueblood, and J. G. White, *Nature* 178, 64 (1956); P. G. Lenhert and D. C. Hodgkin, *Nature*, **192**, 937 (1961). The coordination chemistry of this compound is summarized by R. J. P. Williams, *Advances in the Chemistry of the Coordination Compounds*, edited by S. Kirschner, The Macmillan Company, New York (1961), pp. 76–86.

[227] Ref. 22, p. 1511 ff.

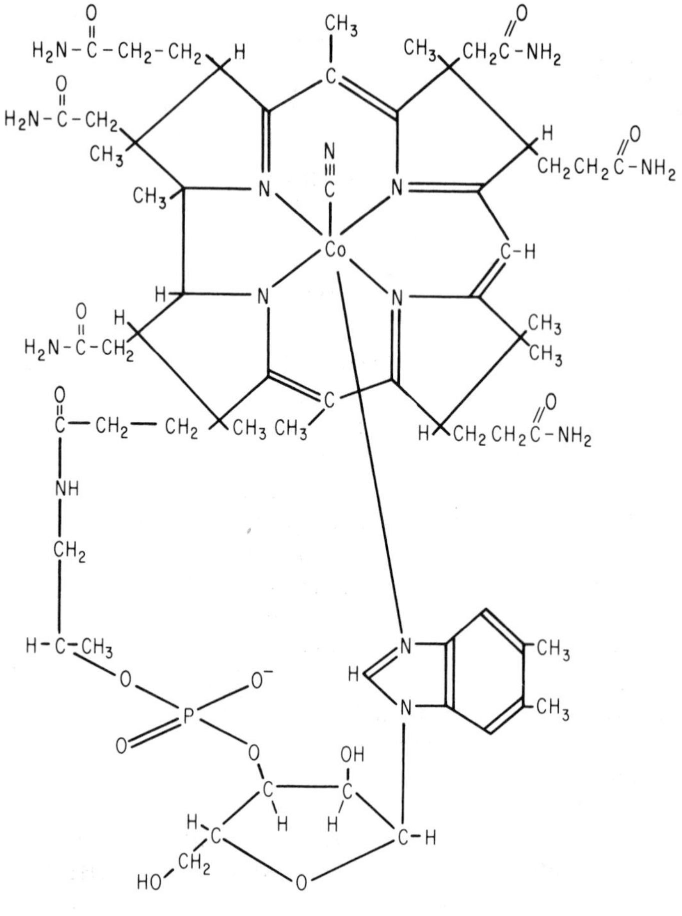

Fig. 16 The structure of the vitamin B_{12} derivative cyanocobalamin. The central planar group about the cobalt is similar to the porphyrins but differs from these in that the rings on the left are joined directly to each other, rather than through methine groups as in the true porphyrins. The naturally occurring form of vitamin B_{12} does not have a coordinated cyanide group; at that position it has an adenosine group bonded to the cobalt by a Co—C bond.

$[Rh(NH_3)_6]Cl_3$, is obtained. If the chloropentammine is digested with Ag_2O in water and the resultant base is recrystallized from water, the aquopent-ammine, $[Rh(NH_3)_5(H_2O)]^{+3}$, may be obtained as, say, the chloride $[Rh(NH_3)_5 (H_2O)]Cl_3 \cdot H_2O$ if the recrystallizing solution contains added chloride.

Although practically no information is available on bond strengths of coordinate bonds involving rhodium, these complexes are generally considered to be very stable materials from both the thermodynamic and kinetic viewpoints. The substitution reactions are known to be rather slow so that the evidence for kinetic stability is more convincing.

The trichelate complexes such as $[Rh(en)_3]^{+3}$ have been resolved and are usually racemized only under extreme conditions which result in their destruction. (Since racemization refers to a reaction in which equal amounts of the original asymmetric structure are formed and the product is a racemate, a reaction in which the original structure is destroyed should not, strictly speaking, be termed a racemization, though it is often applied to such processes for want of a suitably concise term for their description.) The complex with sulfamide, cis-$[Rh(SO_2(NH_2)_2)_2(H_2O)_2]^-$ is one of the few completely inorganic octahedral complexes which has been resolved.[228]

The analogies between the coordination chemistry of Co(III) and that of Rh(III) are very extensive as may be seen from a consideration of the various ammines of Rh(III). The following types have been prepared and characterized: $[Rh(NH_3)_3Br_3]$, $[Rh(NH_3)_5Cl]^{+2}$, $[Rh(py)_3Cl_3]$, $[Rh(py)_2Cl_4]^-$, $[Rh(NH_3)_5(H_2O)]^{+3}$, and a host of types analogous to those found for Co(III). The tetrachlorodipyridinerhodium(III) ion given above also illustrates how the Rh(III) complexes differ from those of Co(III): they are more easily obtained in anions containing halogen than those of Co(III). Other examples which show this in an even more striking manner are $[Rh(NH_3)Cl_5]^{-2}$ and $[RhCl_6]^{-3}$. Because of the greater oxidizing power of Co(III) when coordinated to halide, the Co(III) analogs are inherently unstable with respect to internal redox reactions. It is also with these complex halides that the possible exceptions to the octahedral stereochemistry for the simple Rh(III) complexes are to be found. These include complex chloro anions such as $RhCl_5^{-2}$ and $RhCl_7^{-4}$.

The coordination chemistry of iridium shows more variety than that of rhodium because both the $+3$ and the $+4$ oxidation states are reasonably stable and are found in numerous complexes. Iridium also forms compounds in the $+1$, $+2$, and $+6$ states though these are less commonly encountered. As expected by analogy with rhodium, the $+3$ state is the most important, and the massive metal is rather resistant to the action of simple acids. Finely divided iridium dissolves in aqua regia, however, and from this K_2IrCl_6 may be precipitated by the addition of potassium chloride. $[(NH_4)_2IrCl_6$ may be obtained if ammonium chloride is used.] From this complex anion a large number of iridium complexes may be obtained as is seen in the following reaction scheme:[229]

[228] F. G. Mann, *J. Chem. Soc.*, 412 (1933).

[229] Constructed from information in ref. 22, pp. 1530–1549 and M. Delepine, "Iridium" in P. Pascal, *Nouveau Traite de Chimie Minerale*, Vol. XIX, Masson & Cie, Paris (1958), pp. 465–575. This superb exposition of the chemistry of iridium by Delepine is the most extensive available in print.

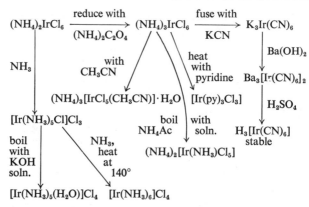

In addition to the types of complex given above, there are many others and like rhodium(III), iridium forms ammines with from one to six ammonia molecules (or equivalent) groups and halide filling the remaining coordination positions. Here again, iridium forms types *not* found with cobalt. One peculiar example is seen in $K_4H_2[N\{(H_2O)Ir(SO_4)_2\}_3]$ in which there are presumably three iridium atoms joined to the same nitrogen.[230]

Both Ir(II) and Ir(IV) are accessible in water solution, though in complex form, of course. The oxidation potentials have been determined in the hexa-halo anions and two illustrative values are:

$$IrCl_6^{-3} \rightarrow IrCl_6^{-2} + e, \qquad E° = -1.021 \text{ v}^{231}$$

$$IrBr_6^{-4} \rightarrow IrBr_6^{-3} + e, \qquad E° = -0.99 \text{ v}^{232}$$

Relatively few complexes of Ir(II) are known and these have been infrequently studied in recent years. These include $K_4[Ir(CN)_6]$, obtained by gently heating an intimate mixture of iridium and potassium ferrocyanide,[233] and a series of four-coordinate complexes: $[Ir(NH_3)_2Cl_2]$, $[Ir(NH_3)_2(SO_4)]$, $[Ir(NH_3)_4]Cl_2$, and others reported by Palmaer.[231]

Complexes of Ir(IV) can be obtained by oxidation of Ir(III) species with chlorine, aqua regia, or other strong oxidizing agents. These are all octahedral and include the ion $[Ir(C_2O_4)_3]^{-2}$ which was resolved by Delepine,[235] the hexa-halocomplexes IrF_6^{-2}, $IrCl_6^{-2}$, and $IrBr_6^{-2}$, the neutral complexes of heterocyclic bases such as $[Ir(py)_2Cl_4]$ and a few cationic ammines such as $[Ir(NH_3)_4Cl_2](NO_3)_2$.[234]

[230] C. K. Jorgensen, *Acta Chem. Scand.* **13**, 196 (1959).

[231] S. C. Woo, *J. Amer. Chem. Soc.* **53**, 469 (1931).

[232] F. P. Dwyer, H. A. McKenzie, and R. S. Nyholm, *J. Proc. Roy. Soc., New South Wales* **81**, 216 (1947).

[233] C. A. Martius, *Ann.* **117**, 357 (1861).

[234] W. Palmaer, *Ber.* **22**, 15 (1889); **23**, 3810 (1890); **24**, 2090 (1891); *Zeit. anorg. Chem.* **10**, 320 (1895); **13**, 211 (1896).

[235] M. Delepine, *Ann. Chim. Phys.*, (9) **7**, 277 (1917).

The carbonyls of iridium have been prepared from the interaction of the trichloride and carbon monoxide under pressure. Sidgwick[236] formulates them as $[Ir(CO)_3]_4$ and $[Ir(CO)_4]_2$ in accord with his effective atomic number rule. The carbonyl halides, $[Ir(CO)_2X_2]$ and $[Ir(CO)_3X]$, are also considered to be polymeric by Sidgwick.

NICKEL, PALLADIUM, AND PLATINUM. These elements show some similarities in oxidation states but the details of the chemistry of each element are different in a large number of significant ways. The complexes of nickel are usually easily dissociated while those of platinum possess a stability which has been recognized and used for many years by workers who wished to prepare complexes of known structures. Palladium falls in between these in this respect.

Nickel. The oxidation states of nickel which form well-characterized coordination compounds are 0, +1, +2, +3, and +4. Each of these has its own particular stereochemical configuration or configurations. Ni(O) is best illustrated by the tetrahedral carbonyl, $Ni(CO)_4$, or tetracyanonickelate(O), $Ni(CN)_4^{-4}$.[237] The +1 state may also be found in a cyanide, $K_4[Ni_2(CN)_6]$,[238] which may be obtained by the reduction of air-free solutions of $[Ni(CN)_4]^{-2}$. The dimeric formula is suggested by the diamagnetism of the compound.

The coordination chemistry of plus two nickel is one of reasonable complexity in which species of square planar, tetrahedral, and octahedral stereochemistries are found.[239] The most common arrangement for the four-coordinate complexes is a square planar one which is found for complexes which are usually, but not invariably, diamagnetic and generally yellow to red in color. Typical of such are $[Ni(CN)_4]^{-2}$, Ni(dimethylglyoxime)$_2$, and nickel(II)-dithiooxalate. One exception to this particular combination of properties may be seen in bis(acetylacetonato)nickel(II) which is reported to have a planar configuration in the vapor phase; the solid is paramagnetic[240] and polymeric. Much less common are the tetrahedral complexes which are paramagnetic. Typical examples are $[Ni(NH_3)_3(N(C_2H_5)_3)]^{+2}$ and $[Ni(NH_3)_3(N(CH_3)_3)]^{+2,}$ [241] in their solid salts, and $NiCl_4^{=}$.[242]

The interconversion of the diamagnetic square planar to the paramagnetic square planar configuration may occur with only slight changes in the ligand structure or environment. Thus, bis(phenylethylenediamine)nickel(II) nitrate, $[Ni(C_6H_5CHNH_2CH_2NH_2)_2](NO_3)_2$, occurs in both a yellow diamagnetic and

[236] Ref. 22, p. 1548.

[237] T. W. Estes and W. M. Burgess, *J. Amer. Chem. Soc.* **64**, 1187 (1942).

[238] The literature up to 1950 is collected in J. Kleinberg, *Unfamiliar Oxidation States and their Stabilization*, University of Kansas Press, Lawrence, Kansas (1950), pp. 90–92.

[239] A comprehensive and critical discussion is given by J. R. Miller, *Advances in Inorganic Chemistry and Radiochemistry* **4**, 133 (1962).

[240] S. Shibata, M. Kishita, and M. Kubo, *Nature* **179**, 320 (1957).

[241] E. G. Cox and K. C. Webster, *Zeit. Krist.* **92**, 478 (1935). These may be octahedral.

[242] E. Iberson, R. Gut, and D. M. Gruen, *J. Phys. Chem.* **66**, 65 (1962).

blue paramagnetic form.[243] The interconversion of one form to the other is also readily accomplished. Detailed reviews of a large number of these four-coordinate nickel complexes have been presented.[244, 239] The complexes can be classified into the following six types, depending on the combination of donor atoms:

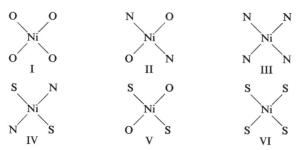

Complexes of types I and V seem to be generally paramagnetic and those of type VI appear to be generally diamagnetic; both types are usually square planar. It should be recalled that there may be a continuous transition from octahedral to square planar complexes as two axial(*trans*) groups are progressively moved out from the metal atom. Certain such changes may also be present in some of these systems. The other arrangements give rise to both types of complex, depending upon the nature of the ligand. Mellor and Craig suggest that with donor atoms of low electronegativity, covalent bonds tend to be formed and diamagnetic compounds result. Several examples of tetrahedral Ni(II) prepared in more recent years show that this is a rather approximate rule. For example, complexes of the type $[(C_6H_5)_3PNiI_3]^-$ are tetrahedral.[245] Gill and Nyholm[246] prepared a series of complex halides of nickel(II) of the general form $R_2[NiX_4]$ where R was a large cation such as tetraethylammonium ion or triphenylmethylarsonium ion and X was chloride, bromide, or iodide. The absorption spectra and magnetic data lead to the conclusion that these materials contain tetrahedral nickel(II). These authors also discuss the factors tending to stabilize such a configuration in spite of the fact that simple crystal field theory predicts that no tetrahedral complexes can exist for the Ni(II) configuration. The factors establishing the gross energy of the complex include several factors not considered in crystal field considerations; the most important of these are the manner in which the cation size affects the lattice energies of the possible arrangements and the role of covalent bonding in stabilizing structures not favored when the bonding is primarily ionic.

[243] I. Lifschitz, J. G. Bos, K. M. Dijkema, *Zeit. anorg. Chem.* **242**, 97 (1939); C.A. **33**: 9181.

[244] D. P. Mellor and D. P. Craig, *J. Proc. Roy. Soc., New South Wales* **74**, 475 (1940); D. P. Mellor, *Chem. Reviews* **33**, 137 (1943); R. S. Nyholm, *Chem. Revs.* **53**, 263 (1953).

[245] F. A. Cotton and D. M. L. Goodgame, *J. Amer. Chem. Soc.* **82**, 2967 (1960).

[246] N. S. Gill and R. S. Nyholm, *J. Chem. Soc.*, 3997 (1959).

The criterion of color, suggested by Lifschitz *et al.* (loc. cit.), runs into difficulty because of the common occurrence of octahedral Ni(II) complexes which may have similar colors and are also paramagnetic. Katzin[247] has suggested that this difficulty may be resolved by a more detailed study of the absorption spectra. He states that green paramagnetic complexes or paramagnetic complexes showing an absorption peak in the neighborhood of 4,100 A are six-coordinate; those which fail to show this peak may be assumed to be tetrahedral. In some cases, the color of the ligand may alter that of the complex, e.g., the nickel complex of ethyl 3,3′,5,5′-tetramethylpyrromethane 4,4′-dicarboxylate.[244] The magnetic susceptibility method is subject to greater limitations than the absorption spectra since a paramagnetic complex may be tetrahedral, octahedral, or square planar. The careful measurement of the magnetic susceptibility may allow some sorting out of these possibilities on the basis of the deviation from predicted values for spin-only values.[246]

The ease with which the diamagnetic square planar complexes and the paramagnetic complexes (presumably of similar structure) are interconverted is seen in the numerous reports of a change in magnetic susceptibility on solution or melting.[248] In general there is a very slight energy difference between different forms of complexes of type II.

The fact that some of the square planar complexes can be converted into octahedral ones in a suitable solvent leads to the expectation that the intermediate five-coordinate complexes should be of sufficient stability to be isolated in some cases. There appears to be little definite information on this point.

The octahedral complexes of Ni(II) are usually formed in the presence of an excess of simple ligands such as H_2O, $(Ni(H_2O)_6^{+2})$, NH_3 $(Ni(NH_3)_6^{+2})$, or with ligands which give bonds of low covalent character in general. The preparation of some of the hexammines is effected by relatively simple methods involving use of an excess of amine or ammonia:

$$Ni^{+2} + 2Br^- + 6NH_3 \xrightarrow[\text{in } H_2O]{0°} Ni(NH_3)_6Br_2 \downarrow$$

$$Ni^{+2} + 2Cl^- + 3\ o\text{-phen} \xrightarrow{\text{in } H_2O} Ni(o\text{-phen})_3Cl_2 \downarrow \quad 249$$

The tris(orthophenanthroline)nickel(II) ion is stable enough that it can be resolved via its *d*-antimonyl tartarate.[250] Similar hexamine complexes can be prepared by the interaction of Ni^{+2} with ethylenediamine, hydroxylamine,

[247] L. I. Katzin, *Nature* **182**, 1013 (1958), **183**, 1672 (1959); see also, C. Furlani and G. Morpurgo, *Zeit. phys. Chem.* **28**, 93 (1961).

[248] H. S. French, M. Z. Magee, and E. Sheffield, *J. Amer. Chem. Soc.* **64**, 1924 (1942); L. Sacconi, P. Paoletti, and R. Cini, *ibid.*, **80**, 3583 (1958) and the literature cited therein. A theoretical treatment is given by C. J. Ballhausen and A. D. Liehr, *ibid.*, **81**, 538 (1959) who also give much of the previous literature.

[249] P. Pfeiffer and F. Tappermann, *Zeit. anorg. Chem.* **215**, 273 (1933).

[250] F. P. Dwyer and E. C. Gyarfas, *J. Proc. Roy. Soc., New South Wales* **83**, 232 (1949).

simple aliphatic amines, pyridine, and similar bases. Because of the ease with which a molecule of base may be lost, numerous compounds containing less than six moles of amine per mole of nickel are known. Unfortunately, the structures of these are not known.

In addition to the complexes of a more usual sort, such as those listed above, there are some well-characterized five-coordinate complexes of Ni(II) and Ni(III). For Ni(II) a five-coordinate complex may be seen in the complex of $NiBr_2$ with one molecule of $(CH_3)_2As(CH_2)_3As(CH_3)(CH_2)_3As(CH_3)_2$.[251] This complex has a structure derived from a tetragonal pyramid. The three arsenic atoms are in a plane with the nickel; one of the bromines is depressed below the plane of this group. The apical bromine is 2.69 A from the nickel atom and is thus further away than the bromine which is depressed below the plane that is at a distance of 2.37 A. The arsenic-nickel distances are 2.27 A and the peculiar depression of the one bromine below the plane may be due to steric hindrance from the methyl groups on the arsenic atoms occupying adjacent coordination positions. The five-coordinate nickel(III) complexes are prepared by the oxidation of four-coordinate nickel(II) complexes.[252] For example:

$$2[NiBr_2(P(C_6H_5)_3)_2] + Br_2 \rightarrow 2[NiBr_3(P(C_6H_5)_3)_2]$$

This complex has been assigned a tetragonal pyramidal structure on the basis of measurements of its dipole moment. Other complexes of nickel(III) include derivatives containing orthophenylenediaminebisdimethylarsine, e.g., $[NiCl_3 C_6H_4(As(CH_3)_2)_2]$[253] which is probably octahedral, $[Ni(Arsine)_2Cl_2]Cl$, and related complexes.[254] By further oxidation of this type of complex, Nyholm has obtained complexes of Ni(IV) such as $[NiCl_2(Arsine)_2](ClO_4)_2$.[255] A final type of nickel complex worthy of mention is the organo-nickel kind reported by Chatt and Shaw.[256] These result from the reaction of nickel complexes of the type $[(PR_3)_2NiX_2]$ (where R is ethyl, *n*-propyl, or phenyl and X is a halogen) with Grignard reagents, lithium aryls or sodio-derivatives of acetylenic compounds, e.g.:

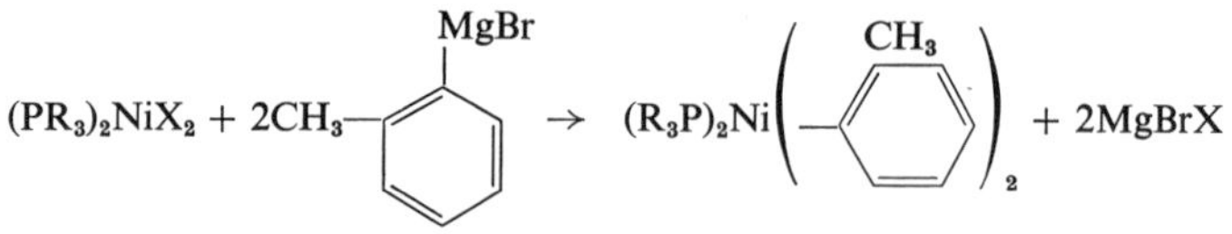

Analogous compounds of cobalt have been prepared by these same investigators.

[251] G. A. Mair, H. M. Powell, and D. E. Henn, *Proc. Chem. Soc.*, 415 (1960).

[252] K. A. Jensen, *Zeit. anorg. Chem.* **229**, 275 (1936); K. A. Jensen and B. Nygaard, *Acta Chem. Scand.* **3**, 474 (1949).

[253] R. S. Nyholm, *Nature* **165**, 154 (1950).

[254] R. S. Nyholm, *J. Chem. Soc.*, 2061 (1950).

[255] R. S. Nyholm, *J. Chem. Soc.*, 2602 (1951).

[256] J. Chatt and B. L. Shaw, *Chemistry and Industry*, 675 (1959).

PALLADIUM. The palladium complexes are mostly those of Pd(II), though some of Pd(IV) are known. Palladium(II) differs from Ni(II) in that none of its complexes are paramagnetic. When palladium dissolves in nitric acid (which it does with considerable ease) it gives rise to a diamagnetic nitrate![257]

In general a four-coordinate complex of palladium may be assumed to be square planar. Examples of these can be prepared in which the donor atoms are O, N, S, P, Cl, Br, I, Se, As, Sb, Te, or F. The tendency of groups to rearrange during substitution reactions of Pd(II) complexes is certainly not universal, but is of sufficient frequency to result in a necessity for structural proofs where the relative positions are to be known with certainty. In addition to the complexes of the type $PdCl_4^{-2}$, there are also numerous square planar complexes with bridging groups, e.g.:

$$
\begin{array}{ccccc}
OC & & Cl & & Cl \\
 & \diagdown \diagup & & \diagdown \diagup & \\
 & Pd & & Pd & \\
 & \diagup \diagdown & & \diagup \diagdown & \\
Cl & & Cl & & CO
\end{array}
$$

and it seems quite probable that the complex Pd(II) species which have been assigned a coordination number of three are also of this type.[258] Other groups which may act as bridging groups include NO_2^-, SCN^-, R_2S, and oxalate. Very few cases are known in which the Pd(II) has a coordination number of six and these are unverified.[259]

Other complex species reported for palladium include the so-called "Pd(III)" compounds such as $Cs_2(PdCl_5)$, which are mixtures of Pd(II) and Pd(IV);[260] Pd(O) compounds such as $K_4Pd(CN)_4$; Pd(I) complexes, $(K_3Pd(CN)_4)$, and the more numerous derivatives of Pd (IV). These latter are considerably less stable than the corresponding complexes of platinum. They may be prepared by the oxidation of Pd(II) complexes with chlorine or bromine.[261, 262] The following are typical of these reactions:

$$
[Pd(C_5H_5N)_2Cl_2] \xrightarrow[\text{aqueous suspension}]{Cl_2} [Pd(C_5H_5N)_2Cl_4] \quad [261]
$$

[257] R. B. Janes, *J. Amer. Chem. Soc.* **57**, 471 (1935); D. P. Mellor, *J. Proc. Roy. Soc., New South Wales* **77**, 145 (1943).

[258] A. Gutbier and C. Fellner, *Zeit. anorg. Chem.* **95**, 169 (1916) report compounds of the type tetraethylammonium tribromopalladate(II), $((C_2H_5)_4N)PdBr_3$, but provide no structural information on them.

[259] Ref. 22, p. 1572.

[260] J. Wallen, C. Brosset, and N. G. Vannerberg, *Arkiv Kemi* **18**, 541 (1962) determined the crystal structure of several examples of "Pd (III)" and "Pt(III)" compounds. These were found actually to be mixtures, e.g., $Pd(NH_3)_2Cl_3$ is $[Pd(NH_3)_2Cl_2]$ $[Pd(NH_3)_2Cl_4]$ and $Pt(NH_3)_2Cl_3$ is actually $[Pt(NH_3)_2Br_2]$ $[Pt(NH_3)_2Br_4]$. Pt(en)Br₃ similarly contains equal amounts of Pt(II) and Pt(IV); see, T. D. Ryan and R. E. Rundle, *J. Amer. Chem. Soc.* **38**, 2814 (1961).

[261] A. Rosenheim and T. A. Maass, *Zeit. anorg. Chem.* **18**, 334 (1898).

[262] A. Gutbier and C. Fellner, *ibid.*, **95**, 135 (1916).

$$[(C_2H_5)_4N]_2(PdBr_4) \xrightarrow[\text{in HBr}]{Br_2} [(C_2H_5)_4N]_2(PdBr_6) \quad {}^{262}$$

These compounds decompose with the evolution of halogen at slightly elevated temperatures. The complexes of palladium in lower oxidation states are usually prepared by careful reduction, often in a non-aqueous solvent. An example of a recent attempt may be seen in the preparation of [Pd(en)(en—H)] I and [Pd(en—H)$_2$] by the reaction of Pd(en)$_2$I$_2$ with potassium or potassium amide in liquid ammonia.[263]

PLATINUM. The coordination chemistry of platinum is unusual in many respects, perhaps most impressively so in the kinetic stability of the bonds formed with many common ligands. This stability is manifested most obviously in the slowness in many replacement reactions involving a central Pt(IV) species. Unfortunately, this inertness toward substitution is not solely a function of the central atom, but seems also to be dependent upon the nature of the ligand. For example, [Pt(en)$_3$]$^{+4}$ is very stable toward substitution or exchange of the ligand, but PtI$_6^{-2}$ undergoes complete exchange with I$^-$ in aqueous solution at 25° within 30 seconds.[264] The coordination chemistry of platinum is concerned primarily with the +2 and +4 oxidation states. As with palladium, simple ions of platinum are not known in aqueous solution and the salts and complexes commonly encountered are invariably diamagnetic.

The starting materials for the preparation of many of the Pt(II) complexes are PtCl$_2$ or K$_2$PtCl$_4$. Platinous chloride, PtCl$_2$, may be obtained by heating chloroplatinic acid to 300° or by the reaction of platinum and chlorine at 500°. Potassium tetrachloroplatinate(II), formerly called potassium chloroplatinite, may be obtained by the reduction of K$_2$PtCl$_6$ with CuCl,[265] SO$_2$,[266] N$_2$H$_4$ · H$_2$SO$_4$,[267] or most conveniently with potassium oxalate in the presence of platinum black.[268] From these compounds an enormous number of complexes may be prepared.[260, 269] The reaction of platinous chloride with Lewis bases containing N, P, S, Se, C, or halides other than F$^-$, as donor atoms, leads to square planar complexes whose stereochemistry has been repeatedly con-

[263] G. W. Watt and R. Layton, *J. Amer. Chem. Soc.* **82**, 4465 (1960). The literature cited describes more successful attempts with platinum complexes.

[264] A. J. Poë and M. S. Vaidya, *J. Chem. Soc.*, 187 (1960).

[265] G. Magnus, *Pogg. Annalen* **14**, 241 (1821) also used the thermal decomposition of Pt(IV) compounds.

[266] P. Klason, *Ber.* **37**, 1360 (1904).

[267] K. I. Gildengershel and G. A. Shagisultanova, *Zhur. Priklad. Khim.* **26**, 222 (1953), C.A. **47**: 11061; A. A. Grinberg, *ibid.*, **26**, 224 (1953), C.A. **47**: 11061 (mechanism).

[268] L. A. Tschugayev, *Ann. Inst. Platine* **7**, 207 (1929), C. Z., I, 3169 (1930). The reference in C.A. 24: 2686 is in error with respect to the details of the preparation.

[269] A. A. Grinberg, *Einführung in die Chemie der Komplexverbindungen*, VEB Verlag Technik, Berlin (1955), pp. 154–175 contains a resumé. The volumes in Gmelin's *Handbuch* are excellent.

firmed by the isolation of geometrical isomers of complexes of the types $[PtCl_2X_2]$ and $[PtCl_2XY]$. Oxygen coordinates only weakly with Pt(II). For simple complexes with the halides, the thermodynamic stability in solution (toward dissociation) increases as the halide gets heavier. The instability constants of the complexes have been measured using e.m.f. methods and the negative logarithms (pK values) of the over-all dissociation constants are $[PtCl_4]^{-2}$, 16.6; $[PtBr_4]^{-2}$, 20.4; $[PtI_4]^{-2}$, 29.6.[270] The cyano complex is even more stable, the pK value for the dissociation reaction is 41.0 for $[Pt(CN)_4]^{-4}$! This last value is certainly consistent with the observation that metallic platinum dissolves in aqueous potassium cyanide when made alternately the anode and the cathode in an electrolytic cell.

In addition to numerous four-coordinate ammines, halo complexes, and similar compounds with sulfides and other common ligands, platinum(II) forms complexes readily with nitriles and isonitriles which were once thought to be examples of six-coordinate platinum(II). Thus, $[Pt(CH_3CN)_2Cl_2]$ adds on four molecules of ammonia to give $[Pt(CH_3CN)_2(NH_3)_4]Cl_2$.[271] These are now known to be amidine complexes. Thus, $[Pt(NH_3)_4(CH_3C\equiv N)_2]Cl_2 \cdot H_2O$ is found to be actually $[Pt(NH_3)_2(NH_2-C(CH_3)=NH)_2]Cl_2 \cdot H_2O$,[272] and $[Pt(RCN)_2(RNH_2)_4]X_2$ should be $[Pt\{RC(NH)NHR'\}_2(NHR')_2]X_2$.[273] Complexes in which Pt(II) and Pd(II) have coordination numbers greater than four may be formed under favorable circumstances when ligands capable of forming double bonds are present. These include halide, thiocyanate, cyanide, and derivatives of arsine and phosphine.[272] Such an example is found in the complexes with orthophenylenebisdimethylarsine (As—As) such as $Pt(As-As)_2I_2$.[272] A five-coordinate complex is formed by Pt(II) with tris(orthodiphenylarsinophenyl)arsine (QAs) such as $[PtCl(QAs)]Cl$.[274] This ligand has four arsenic atoms capable of coordination with the platinum but they cannot be in a plane. A structure with an uncoordinated arsine grouping was ruled out by the lack of reactivity of the complex with methyl iodide. Free arsine groups undergo quaternization in an analogous environment. Platinum(II) also complexes readily with ethylenic hydrocarbons:

$$2PtCl_2 + 2C_2H_4 \rightarrow [PtCl_2(C_2H_4)]_2$$

In these the ethylene is coordinated through its double bond and the inter-

[270] A. A. Grinberg and M. I. Gelf'man, *Doklady Akad. Nauk S.S.S.R.* **133**, 1081 (1960), C.A. 54: 23632.

[271] L. A. Tschugayev, *Compt. rend.* **161**. 563 (1928).

[272] Work of N. C. Stephenson cited by C. M. Harris and S. E. Livingstone, *Revs. Pure Applied Chem.* **12**, 17 (1962).

[273] Y. Y. Khantonov, C. C. Ni, and A. V. Babaeva, *Doklady Akad. Nauk S.S.S.R.* **141**, 645 (1961), C.A. 56: 13774; V. A. Golovnya and C. C. Ni, *Zhur Neorg. Khim.* **5**, 1474 (1960); **6**, 131 (1961); C.A. 56: 15141.

[274] J. A. Brewster, C. A. Savage, and L. M. Venanzi, *J. Chem. Soc.*, 3699 (1961); G. A. Mair, H. M. Powell, and L. M. Venanzi, *Proc. Chem. Soc.*, 170 (1961).

nuclear axis through the two carbon atoms of ethylene is perpendicular to the square plane in which the other bonds of the platinum lie.[275]

The platinum(IV) complexes are usually quite stable with respect both to ligand exchange and reduction to platinum(II). In many instances reactions of the platinum(IV) complexes indicate very conclusively the great stability with which ligands are held. One good example of this is the existence of complexes containing two different ligands such as PtX_nY_m. For platinum(IV) there are several series of these where n runs from 0 to 6 and m from 6 to 0. Thus, all of the complexes in the series $[Pt(NH_3)_nCl_m]^{+4-m}$ are known, as are the members of the series $[PtCl_n(OH)_m]^{+4-n-m}$.

The octahedral configuration of the complexes of Pt(IV) has been confirmed by the resolution of a large number of asymmetric complexes among which are: $[Pt(en)_3]^{+4}$,[276] $[Pt(pn)_3]^{+4}$,[277] $[Pt(en)(NH_3)(Cl)_2(NO_2)]X$,[278] and $[Pt(en)(py)Cl(NO)_2]X$.[279]

Because of their considerable stability the complexes of platinum(IV) allow many phenomena to be studied which are difficult to separate from accompanying complications in less stable complexes. A characteristic reaction of this type is that of hydrogen atoms bonded to nitrogen atoms which are coordinated to a metal atom. The general result of the coordination act is the drawing of electrons from the nitrogen. This results in turn in the weakening of the nitrogen to hydrogen bond and the hydrogen becomes more easily ionized as an hydronium ion. This has been extensively studied and found to be a reaction of ammonia and amine ligands. It is sometimes referred to as the *imino reaction* for organic amines and the *amino reaction* when the ligand is ammonia. An example is:

$$[Pt(en)(NH_3)(Cl)_3]Cl \xrightarrow{\text{NaOH}} [Pt(en)(NH_2)(Cl)_3] + H_2O + NaCl \quad [280]$$

In several cases it is found that the platinum(IV) ammines behave as acids because of the ionization of hydrogens bound to coordinated nitrogen atoms. $[Pt(en)_3]^{+4}$ is actually capable of yielding three hydrogen ions in water:

$$[Pt(H_2NCH_2CH_2NH_2)_3]^{+4} \rightleftharpoons [Pt(H_2NCH_2CH_2NH_2)_2(HNCH_2CH_2NH_2)]^{+3} + H^+$$

or if we use the abbreviation en—H for $HNCH_2CH_2NH_2$

$$[Pt(en)_3]^{+4} \rightleftharpoons [Pt(en)_2(en-H)]^{+3} + H^+$$
$$[Pt(en)_2(en-H)]^{+3} \rightleftharpoons [Pt(en)(en-H)_2]^{+2} + H^+$$
$$[Pt(en)(en-H)_2]^{+2} \rightleftharpoons [Pt(en-H)_3]^{+} + H^+$$

[275] J. N. Dempsey and N. C. Baenziger, *J. Amer. Chem. Soc.* 77, 4984 (1955). Earlier work gave a similar structure for the ethylene-platinum bond in $[PtCl_3(C_2H_4)]$: J. A. Wunderlich and D. P. Mellor, *Acta Cryst.* 7, 130 (1954); 8, 57 (1955).

[276] A. Werner, *Naturf. Ges. Zurich* 62, 553 (1917), cited in Sidgwick, ref. 22.

[277] A. P. Smirnoff, *Helv. Chim. Acta* 3, 177 (1920).

[278] I. I. Chernyaev, *Ann. Inst. Platine* 6, 40 (1928), C.A. 23: 1583.

[279] Idem, *ibid.*, 8, 37 (1931), C.A. 26, 2131.

[280] I. I. Chernyaev, *Ann. Inst. Platine* 6, 23–39 (1928), C.A. 23: 1581–1582.

For the first two ionizations,[281] $K_1 = 3.5 \times 10^{-6}$ and $K_2 = 1.76 \times 10^{-10}$. The reactivity of amines in the coordination sphere of Pt(IV) is remarkable. They may be transformed to the corresponding chloramine and dichloramine compounds without disrupting the Pt—N bond.[282]

There are also other platinum complexes of a more unusual sort including [Pt(en)$_2$] which is obtained by the reduction of [Pt(en)$_2$]I$_2$ with potassium or potassium amide in liquid ammonia,[283] [PtH(P(C$_2$H$_5$)$_3$)$_2$Cl] which has a Pt—H bond and is remarkably stable,[284] Wolffram's red salt, Pt(C$_2$H$_5$NH$_2$)$_4$ Cl$_3$·2H$_2$O, was long thought to be an example of trivalent platinum but is actually [Pt(C$_2$H$_5$NH$_2$)$_4$Cl$_2$] [Pt(C$_2$H$_5$NH$_2$)$_4$]Cl$_4$·4H$_2$O, a mixture of divalent and tetravalent platinum,[285, 286] complexes with cyclopropane such as [(PtCl$_2$· C$_3$H$_6$)$_2$] and [PtCl$_2$(C$_3$H$_6$)(py)] which bear at least a formal resemblance to the analogous compounds with the olefins,[287] and olefinic complexes in which a molecule with two double bonds acts as a chelating agent, e.g., [Pt(1,5-hexadiene)Cl$_2$].[288]

In conclusion it must be emphasized that platinum complexes have played and continue to play an important role in the development of coordination chemistry, to a large extent because of their structural integrity. Many of the examples which will be used to illustrate points in subsequent chapters will be drawn from the information on platinum complexes and the complexes of the platinum metals.

COPPER, SILVER, AND GOLD. The chemistry of copper in all its oxidation states is intimately concerned with the coordination properties of the various species because of the slight tendency of copper to form simple ions of any sort. Copper(II) salts are generally hydrated and the presence of the [Cu(H$_2$O)$_4$]$^{+2}$ ion (or the [Cu(H$_2$O)$_6$]$^{+2}$ ion) is usually assumed in hydrated salts which do not contain anions with pronounced donor properties. The typical coordination number of Cu(II) is four and the arrangement of these four ligands is square planar. Examples are rather numerous and include [Cu(NH$_3$)$_4$]$^{+2}$, [Cu(py)$_4$]$^{+2}$, [Cu(SCN)$_4$]$^{-2}$, and complexes with many organic amines and organic acids. In the presence of an excess of a ligand such as NH$_3$ or ethylenediamine it is possible for Cu(II) to exhibit six-fold coordination with a distorted octahedral structure. In the solid Cu(II) compounds it is frequently found that the copper

[281] A. A. Grinberg and C. I. Gildengershel, *Izvest. Akad. Nauk S.S.S.R., Otdel Khim. Nauk* 479 (1948), C.A. 43: 1672.

[282] Y. N. Kukushkin, *Zhur. Neorg. Khim.* 6, 1762 (1961), C.A. 56: 4358 and other papers by this author.

[283] G. W. Watt, R. E. McCarley, and J. W. Dawes, *J. Amer. Chem. Soc.* 79, 5163 (1957).

[284] J. Chatt, L. A. Duncanson, and B. L. Shaw, *Proc. Chem. Soc.*, 343 (1957).

[285] S. Yamada and R. Tsuchida, *Bull. Chem. Soc. Japan* 29, 894 (1956).

[286] B. M. Craven and D. Hall, *Acta Cryst.* 14, 475 (1961).

[287] C. F. H. Tipper, *J. Chem. Soc.*, 2045 (1955); D. M. Adams, J. Chatt, R. G. Guy, and N. Sheppard, *J. Chem. Soc.*, 738 (1961).

[288] K. A. Jensen, *Acta Chem. Scand.* 7, 866 (1953).

is surrounded by four groups at a given distance at the corners of a square and two more, further away, at the apices of a distorted octahedron. In addition to the mononuclear complexes, Cu(II) forms a number of polynuclear complexes whose structures have been determined by X-ray diffraction. Thus $CuCl_2$ consists of chains of $(CuCl_2)_x$ units with the four Cl's in a plane surrounding the Cu(II) and each Cl acting as a bridge between two Cu(II) ions.[289] There is a distorted octahedron around each copper, however, as the next nearest neighbor of each copper atom is a bridging chloride from an adjacent chain. Thus the four closest chlorides are at 2.30 A while the two further away are 2.95 A from the Cu(II). Distorted arrangements appear to be reasonably common, thus $K_2CuCl_4 \cdot 2H_2O$ has the central copper surrounded by two oxygens at 2.01 A, two chlorides at 2.31 A and two further chlorides at 2.98 A.[289] A search [290] for the *trans*-effect in complexes of bivalent copper was unsuccessful.

In addition to these typical arrangements, copper(II) may also exhibit both three-fold and five-fold coordination. The most recently investigated three-coordinate complexes of copper(II) are those reported by Muto.[291] The procedure used by Muto to prepare these compounds involved the following sequence: (a) preparation of the Schiff base by condensation of an aldehyde or ketone with an amine, (b) reaction of the Schiff base with cupric acetate to give the corresponding copper(II) chelate, (c) preparation of the monopyridine complex of the same by reaction with pyridine, and (d) heating to remove the coordinated pyridine. Thus, in a typical experiment the Schiff base of acetyl-acetone and *o*-aminophenol was prepared and complexed as follows:

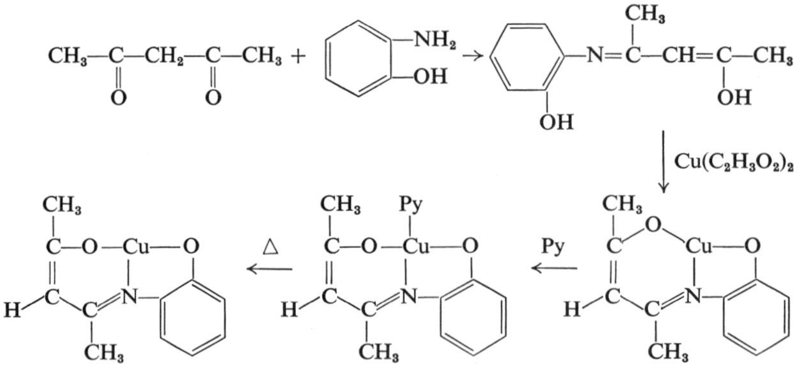

The recrystallization from pyridine is used to purify the crude material obtained from aqueous solution. The actual structure of these may be dimeric and Muto

[289] A. F. Wells, *J. Chem. Soc.*, 1670 (1947).

[290] I. I. Chernyaev, N. N. Zheligovskaya, T. M. Kanter, and A. A. Bezzubenko, *Zhur. Neorg. Khim.* 7, 472 (1962), C.A. 56:15132.

[291] Y. Muto, *Bull. Chem. Soc. Japan* 33, 1242 (1960); see also M. Kishita and M. Kubo, *ibid.*, 35, 1241 (1962) who report that Cu(II) probably attains a four-coordinate structure in these complexes via dimerization.

has also suggested a possible analogy with cupric acetate where weak copper-copper bonds are present.

A coordination number of five has also been found in several copper(II) complexes, though some of the individual cases may be subject to dispute. These include addition compounds of the chelate formed from the Schiff base of salicylaldehyde and ethylenediamine with Cu(II),[292] the complex of cupric chloride, and terpyridyl,[293] addition compounds of bis(acetylacetonato)-copper(II) and copper(II) ethylacetoacetate with heterocyclic bases,[294] and crystalline complexes such as that formed between the Schiff base of salicylaldehyde and ethylenediamine and copper(II).[295] In this last case there is a dimeric structure in the solid which results from a bond between the copper of one unit and an oxygen of the other. Here there is a pyramidal arrangement of the ligand groups about the central copper.

The coordination chemistry of the other oxidation states of copper ($+1$, $+3$, and 0) is represented by relatively few examples. For Cu(O) there is the complex $K_2[Cu(phthalocyanine)]\cdot 4NH_3$ which is obtained by the reduction of a liquid ammonia solution of copper(II) phthalocyanine with potassium.[296] This presumably is a planar complex. Cu(I), though unstable in aqueous solution against the disproportionation to copper metal and copper(II), is stabilized by coordination. Only those copper(I) complexes of considerable stability against dissociation can exist in the presence of water. Thus, $[Cu(NH_3)_4]^+$ can be obtained[297] as the sulfate, $[Cu(NH_3)_4]_2SO_4$, by dissolving cuprous oxide in a solution containing ammonia and ammonium sulfate. It is stable in the presence of an excess of ammonia but breaks down in dilute aqueous solution with disproportionation (this solid is colorless). Autocomplex salts such as the cyanide show considerable stability as well as insolubility in water. The cyanide does dissolve in solutions of the alkali cyanides to give solutions containing $Cu(CN)_3^-$ and $Cu(CN)_4^{-3}$. The typical coordination number of the cuprous ion is apparently four and the arrangement of the ligands is tetrahedral.[298] Stable cuprous complexes with both arsenic and phosphorus donors are also known and occur in several different types. Tetrameric $[CuX\cdot AsMePh_2]_4$ as well as monomeric derivatives such as $[CuX\cdot 3AsMePh_2]$ and $[Cu(AsMePh_2)_4]X$ have been isolated by the reaction of cuprous halides and methyldiphenyl-

[292] T. Tanaka, *Bull. Chem. Soc. Japan* **29**, 93 (1956).

[293] D. E. C. Corbridge and E. G. Cox, *J. Chem. Soc.*, 594 (1956).

[294] D. P. Graddon, *Nature* **183**, 1610 (1959); R. C. Traill, *ibid.*, **186**, 631 (1960). For Cu(acetylacetonate)$_2\cdot$4-methylpyridine see W. R. Walker, *Australian J. Chem.* **14**, 161 (1961).

[295] D. Hall and T. N. Waters, *J. Chem. Soc.*, 2644 (1960).

[296] G. W. Watt and J. W. Dawes, *J. Inorg. Nuclear Chem.* **14**, 32 (1960).

[297] A. Bouzat, *Compt. rend.* **146**, 75 (1908).

[298] A. F. Wells, *Structural Inorganic Chemistry*, Oxford University Press, London, 2nd ed. (1950), p. 616. Page 616 ff contain an excellent summary of the factors governing the relative stabilities of the Cu(I) and Cu(II) species.

arsine.[299] A methyl isonitrile complex may be seen in the compound [CuI · CH₃NC].[300]

Copper(III) is known in only a few compounds, two of which are the tellurate complex $Na_5H_4[Cu(TeO_6)_2]$ ·18H₂O and the iodate complex $Na_7[Cu(IO_6)_2]$ ·12H₂O. These compounds are prepared by the chemical or electrolytic oxidation of Cu(II) in a strongly alkaline medium in the presence of tellurate or iodate, respectively.[301] These complexes are square planar.[302]

SILVER. Each of the oxidation states of silver is known in a variety of complexes, the number of examples decreases with increasing oxidation number in the order Ag(I), Ag(II), Ag(III). Ag(I) forms its most stable complexes with donor atoms of carbon, sulfur, or nitrogen. It also forms complexes with unsaturated hydrocarbons and a wide variety of other donor atoms which have been less intensely studied including As(-III) and P(-III) and the heavier halides. It has no more than a minimal tendency to coordinate to fluoride and very little tendency to coordinate to oxygen except where the oxygen is incorporated into a molecule capable of forming a chelate ring. The characteristic coordination number of Ag(I) is two but its maximum coordination number is four. The maximum coordination number seems to be most readily attained when coordination is to sulfur, arsenic, phosphorus, or some other heavy donor atoms. A coordination number of two results in a linear arrangement of donor atoms while four gives rise to a tetrahedral structure. A report that the presumably tetrahedral complex with 8-hydroxyquinoline of composition $[Ag(C_9H_6ON)(C_9H_6(OH)N)]$ has been resolved has appeared.[303] More typical complexes of univalent silver include $[Ag(NH_3)_2]^+$, $[Ag(CN)_2]^-$, $[Ag(thioacetamide)_4]^+$, $[AgCl \cdot P(OEt)_3]$, $[AgI_2]^-$, $[AgI_3]^{-2}$, and $[Ag(P(C_6H_5)_3)_4]^+$.[304] A coordination number of three is quite rare in solid compounds but is found in $[AgSCN \cdot 2P(C_6H_{11})_3]$ which is also monomeric in benzene.[305] The iodide complexes may attain some degree of complexity by the formation of polynuclear complexes such as $Ag_4I_8^{-4}$.[306] Studies on the halide compounds have also revealed the presence of the types $[Ag_2X]^+$, $[Ag_3X]^{+2}$, and $[AgX_2]^-$ in solution, where X may be chloride, bromide, or iodide.[307]

Complexes of Ag(II) are usually prepared by the oxidation of Ag(I) in the presence of the coordinating agent (e.g., pyridine, orthophenanthroline, or dipyridyl). Their stoichiometry is similar to that of the corresponding Cu(II) compounds. The examples which are known include $[Ag(py)_4]^{+2}$, Ag (o-

[299] R. S. Nyholm, *J. Chem. Soc.*, 1257 (1952).

[300] H. Irving and M. Jonason, *J. Chem. Soc.*, 2095 (1960).

[301] Ref. 238, pp. 60–61.

[302] L. Jensovsky and M. Ralek, *Zeit. anorg. allgem. Chem.* **314**, 76 (1962).

[303] F. Hein and H. Regler, *Naturwissenschaften* **23**, 320 (1935); idem, *Ber.* **69**, 1692 (1936).

[304] F. A. Cotton and D. M. L. Goodgame, *J. Chem. Soc.*, 5267 (1960).

[305] A. Turco, C. Panattoni, and E. Frasson, *Ricerca Sci.* **29**, 544 (1959), C.A. 54: 148.

[306] E. Berne and M. J. Weill, *J. Phys. Chem.* **64**, 258 (1960).

[307] K. H. Leiser, *Zeit. anorg. Chem.* **304**, 296 (1960).

phen)$_2$]$^{+2}$, [Ag(dipyr)$_2$]$^{+2}$, and analogous compounds with picolinic acid and nicotinic acid.[308] These are presumably square planar complexes. Complexes of Ag(III) have also been completely characterized and include the periodates such as HK$_6$[Ag(IO$_6$)$_2$]·10H$_2$O, and tellurates such as Na$_6$H$_3$[Ag(TeO$_6$)$_2$]·18H$_2$O as well as a complex with ethylenedibiguanidine, [Ag(edibig)]X$_3$.[309] These complexes may be tentatively assumed to be square planar like those of the isoelectronic Pd(II) in the absence of more definitive information.

GOLD. Like the heaviest elements of the platinum group, gold shows very little tendency to form simple monatomic cations under any normal conditions. As a result, the chemistry of both Au(I) and Au(III) is predominantly that of coordination compounds or related covalent compounds including the organometallics. In the case of gold, it is not possible to draw an unambiguous distinction between these two classes and there is a large number of compounds which may be put into either class (or both).

Aurous complexes are formed by reactions which vary with the extent to which the ligands stabilize the +1 oxidation state. With even strong oxidizing agents, gold dissolves in solutions of alkali cyanides to give Au(CN)$_2^-$; similarly, solution of Au(OH)$_3$ in potassium cyanide gives this same complex anion! In the presence of, say chloride, the use of comparable oxidizing agents leads to the AuCl$_4^-$ species. In other cases, also, where the ligand possesses reducing properties, the aurous complexes may be produced from Au(III) starting materials, for example:

$$AuCl_3 + 2CO \rightarrow AuCl \cdot CO + COCl_2 \qquad \text{[310]}$$

$$AuCl_3 + 2PCl_3 \xrightarrow{\text{ether}} [AuCl \cdot PCl_3] + [AuCl_3 \cdot PCl_3] + \text{other products} \qquad \text{[311]}$$

$$AuCl_3 + P(OEt)_3 \rightarrow [AuCl \cdot P(OEt)_3] + \text{other products} \qquad \text{[311]}$$

$$AuCl_3 + 2P(C_6H_5)_3 \rightarrow [AuCl \cdot P(C_6H_5)_3] + P(C_6H_5)_3Cl_2 \qquad \text{[312]}$$

$$AuCl_3 + Et_2S \rightarrow [AuCl \cdot SEt_2] + \text{other products} \qquad \text{[313]}$$

In these compounds gold(I) has a coordination number of two but this is not always the case. The ammines, formed by the reaction of the aurous halides with liquid ammonia, at room temperatures, have the composition "Au(NH$_3$)$_3$Cl," "Au(NH$_3$)$_2$Br," and "Au(NH$_3$) I".[314] As is so often the case with liquid ammonia reactions, more highly ammoniated derivatives may be obtained at lower temperatures. Au(I) forms complexes in which the donor atoms are halides (other than fluoride), nitrogen, phosphorus, arsenic, oxygen, sulfur,

[308] R. Collongues in P. Pascal *Nouveau Traite de Chimie Minerale*, Masson & Cie., Paris (1957), Vol. III, pp. 641–642.

[309] P. C. Ray and K. Chakravarty, *J. Indian Chem. Soc.* **21**, 47 (1944).

[310] M. S. Kharasch and H. S. Isbell, *J. Amer. Chem. Soc.* **52**, 2919 (1930).

[311] L. Lindet, *Compt. rend.* **98**, 1382 (1884).

[312] M. Levi-Malvano, *Atti R. Accad. Lincei* **17**, 857 (1908).

[313] F. G. Mann, A. F. Wells, and D. Purdie, *J. Chem. Soc.*, 1828 (1937).

[314] F. Meyer, *Compt. rend.* **143**, 280 (1905).

selenium, and carbon. As a rule, the most stable complexes are formed with the heavier donor atoms in each group, though the complexes with CO and CN^- are also quite stable. Of the complexes of gold(I), two are of more than academic interest: $Au(CN)_2^-$ which is formed in the extraction of gold from its ores by oxidation in the presence of soluble cyanides, and $[Au(S_2O_3)_2]^{-3}$, whose sodium salt, the so-called "gold sodium thiosulfate" has been used in medicine for the treatment of tuberculosis (for which it cannot be recommended) and is presently used in the treatment of arthritis.

The complexes of gold(III) show many significant differences from those of gold(I), and among the most striking are those arising from the ability of gold(III) to form stable covalent bonds to carbon and coordinate bonds at the same time. In these compounds, gold(III) is always tetracovalent. There are again *no* simple compounds of gold(III) since the central atom is a coordination center in all of them. Even the simple halides are dimeric, e.g., Au_2Cl_6 which has a bridging structure in which two square "$AuCl_4$" groups share an edge. When gold is dissolved in aqua regia, the product is $HAuCl_4$ from which $AuCl_3$ may be obtained by careful heating. The dialkyls can be prepared by treating a pyridine solution of $AuCl_3$ with the appropriate Grignard reagent:

$$4RMgBr + Au_2Cl_6 \rightarrow [R_2AuCl_2AuR_2] + 2MgBr_2 + 2MgCl_2 \quad [315]$$

These compounds are dimeric also and the halogen atoms which act as bridging groups in the halide also serve this purpose in these derivatives. The corresponding cyanides are tetrameric, e.g., $[(C_3H_7)_2AuCN]_4$[316] and possess the structure:

$$
\begin{array}{ccc}
C_3H_7 & & C_3H_7 \\
| & & | \\
H_7C_3-Au-C\equiv N-Au-C_3H_7 \\
| & & | \\
N & & C \\
||| & & ||| \\
C & & N \\
| & & | \\
H_7C_3-Au-N\equiv C-Au-C_3H_7 \\
| & & | \\
C_3H_7 & & C_3H_7
\end{array}
\qquad \text{(planar)}
$$

Trivalent gold coordinates to oxygen when a chelate ring can be formed, as with oxalate. The attempt to prepare the nitrate of gold(III) led to a complex acid. $H[Au(NO_3)_4] \cdot 3H_2O$.[317] Oddly enough, few ammines have been prepared. $[Au(NH_3)_4]^{+3}$ salts are formed when ammonia acts on a solution of chloroauric acid in aqueous saturated ammonium sulfate,[318] but these are transformed into the explosive "fulminate of gold" in the presence of moderate amounts of chloride ion. Auric hydroxide is amphoteric and dissolves in solutions of

[315] F. H. Brain and C. S. Gibson, *J. Chem. Soc.*, 762 (1939).
[316] R. F. Phillips, and H. M. Powell, *Proc. Roy. Soc.* A173, 147 (1930).
[317] F. H. Jeffery, *Chem. News* 112, 227 (1915); idem, *Trans. Farad. Soc.* 11, 172 (1916).
[318] E. Weitz, *Ann.* 410, 117 (1915).

alkali hydroxides to give the $[Au(OH)_4]^-$ species. Numerous salts of this anion have been isolated, e.g., $Li[Au(OH)_4]$.[319] The halide complexes, AuX_4^-, are known for all the halogens. The tetrafluoroaurate(III) is rapidly hydrolyzed in the presence of water[320] while the iodo complexes are unstable thermally and lose iodine at 66° or above.[318] Salts of the type $MAuX_4$ have been characterized for all of these anions.

ZINC, CADMIUM, AND MERCURY. These elements show a few qualitative similarities in their coordination behavior with a steady trend toward more stable complexes with highly polarizable donor atoms as the atomic number of the central ion is increased. All of these elements form simple aquo ions in salts such as the perchlorate or nitrates, but their other salts, especially with the heavier halides show a considerable degree of autocomplexation (i.e., complexation with the anion). The coordination chemistry of Zn(II), Cd(II), and Hg(II) shows characteristic coordination numbers of four for all of these, and a maximum coordination number of six which is reached only for certain ligands. The arrangement of the ligands for the four-coordinate complexes is tetrahedral. This has been proven in the case of Zn(II) by the resolution of the chelate with 5-sulfo-8-hydroxy-quinoline.[321]

Zinc coordinates with donor atoms of practically all types: halides, nitrogen, oxygen, phosphorus, sulfur, carbon (in cyanides), and selenium. Zinc(II) is amphoteric in both water and ammonia:

$$Zn + 2OH^- \rightarrow Zn(OH)_2 \underset{H^+}{\overset{OH^-}{\rightleftharpoons}} Zn(OH)_4^{-2}$$

$$Zn + 2NH_2^- \rightarrow Zn(NH_2)_2 \underset{NH_4^+}{\overset{NH_2^-}{\rightleftharpoons}} Zn(NH_2)_4^{-2}$$

Anhydrous zinc chloride has been widely used as a catalyst in organic chemistry by virtue of its ability to coordinate to numerous functional groups and aid in the generation of carbonium ions. In many respects, its behavior resembles that of anhydrous aluminum chloride. Two examples of its use in this way are:

$$C_6H_{10}(cyclohexene) + CH_3OCH_2Cl \xrightarrow[10-15°]{ZnCl_2} \underset{\underset{H_2}{C}}{\overset{H_2}{\underset{H_2C}{C}}} \begin{matrix} H_2 \\ C \\ \end{matrix}^{322}$$

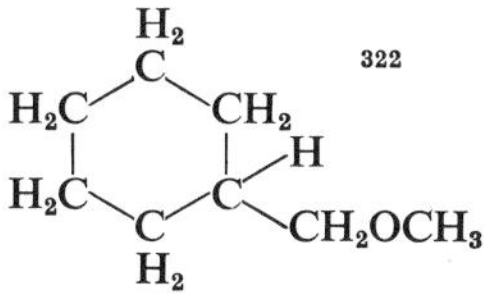

[319] G. Jander and G. Krein, *Zeit. anorg. Chem.* **304**, 165 (1960).

[320] A. G. Sharpe, *J. Chem. Soc.*, 2901 (1949); R. Hoppe and W. Klemm, *Zeit. anorg. Chem.* **268**, 364 (1952).

[321] J. C. Liu and J. C. Bailar, Jr., *J. Amer. Chem. Soc.* **73**, 5432 (1951).

[322] S. D. Mekhtiev, B. F. Pishnamazzade, S. D. Gasanova, and R. M. Mamedova, *Doklady Akad. Nauk Azerbaidzhan S.S.R.* **15**, No. 12, 1115 (1959); C.A. 54: 24450.

$$R_2O + R'COCl \xrightarrow{ZnCl_2} RCl + R'CO_2R \qquad [323]$$

A somewhat different type of reaction may be illustrated by the conversion of phenol to aniline in the presence of ammonia and anhydrous zinc chloride:

$$\langle \bigcirc \rangle\!-\!OH + NH_3 \xrightarrow[300°]{ZnCl_2} \langle \bigcirc \rangle\!-\!NH_2 + \text{other products} \quad [324]$$

The coordination chemistry of cadmium is very similar to that of the more extensively studied zinc ion in all but a few respects. The amphoteric nature of cadmium is only very slight and cadmium hydroxide will dissolve to an appreciable extent only in extremely concentrated solutions of alkali hydroxides. The stabilization of univalent cadmium in melts with aluminum chloride has been reported and the compound $Cd_2[AlCl_4]_2$ has been isolated from these melts.[325] The cadmium species here is probably the Cd_2^{+2} ion and its stabilization relative to the products of disproportionation has been interpreted in terms of the destabilization of the Cd(II) species when the chloride ion is replaced by the less basic and less readily coordinated $AlCl_4^-$ ion.

Although mercury furnishes two ionic species, Hg_2^{+2} and Hg^{+2}, the vast majority of mercury complexes are those of the second of these, the mercuric ion, Hg^{+2}. The existence of mercur*ous* complexes has either been doubted or ignored until recently, in spite of the characterization of a hydrazine complex in 1897. [326] A recent study has shown that mercurous complexes may be expected to occur with many ligands which form ionic complexes such as pyrophosphate, etc.[327]

It has been possible to characterize complexes with pyrophosphate, tripolyphosphate, oxalate, alpha dimethylmalonate, succinate, and diacethydrazide,[328] and it seems reasonable to expect that more complexes of the mercurous ion will be found with those ligands which do not form stable complexes with the mercuric ion. As Yamane and Davidson point out, the characteristic reaction of the mercurous ion with most ligands is a disproportionation to give a very stable mercuric complex and metallic mercury. This reaction can be obviated most readily using ligands which form relatively weak complexes with the mercuric ion: these will usually have oxygen or nitrogen as donor atoms.

The mercuric ion is very prone to form complexes and does so with a wide variety of donor atoms, especially those with which it can form covalent com-

[323] H. Meerwein, *Ann.* **455**, 227 (1927), a later review by this same author may be seen in *Angew. Chem.* **67**, 374 (1955).

[324] F. Beilstein, *Handbuch der Organischen Chemie, Hptwk.*, Vol. VI, 110, J. Springer, Berlin, 1923.

[325] J. D. Corbett, W. J. Burkhard, and L. F. Druding, *J. Amer. Chem. Soc.* **83**, 76 (1961).

[326] K. A. Hoffmann and E. C. Marburg, *Ber.* **30**, 2021 (1897) isolated $[Hg_2(N_2H_4)_2](NO_3)_2$.

[327] T. Yamane and N. Davidson, *J. Amer. Chem. Soc.* **81**, 4438 (1959).

[328] T. Yamane and N. Davidson, *ibid.*, **82**, 2123 (1960).

plexes. Its coordination number is almost invariably four and the stereo-chemistry is tetrahedral.[329] In a few cases a coordination number of six seems to be attained. These include the ethylenediamine complexes of composition $[Hg(en)_3]X_2$ and possibly also the hydrated ion in water.[330] A coordination number of two may possibly be found in HgS_2^{-2} which is formed when HgS dissolves in an alkaline sulfide solution and a coordination number of three is probable in some complexes with sulfides such as R_2SHgX_2.[331]

Mercuric ion tends to form its most stable complexes with large, very polarizable donor atoms such as sulfur, phosphorus, selenium, arsenic, and the heavier halides. An interesting point is that the mercuric halides (other than the fluoride which is rapidly and completely hydrolyzed in water) are present in water as the unionized molecules HgX_2 or $Hg(H_2O)_xX_2$. Such solutions possess an extremely low electrical conductivity. Because mercury electrodes are reversible it is possible to use electromotive cells to determine the stability constants of mercuric complexes in solution.[332] Some mercuric complexes have extremely small dissociation constants. The instability constants (over-all) for some typical examples are $[Hg(CN_4]^{-2}$, 4×10^{-42}; $[HgI_4]^{-2}$, 5.3×10^{-31}; $[HgBr_4]^{-2}$, 2.3×10^{-22}; $[HgS_2]^{-2}$, 1.96×10^{-55}.[333] The complexes with ligands containing oxygen or nitrogen donor atoms are generally not very stable unless chelate rings are formed.

Mercury forms bonds with carbon rather readily and in most cases the re-action of mercuric salts with unsaturated organic compounds results in organo-metallic compounds containing Hg—C bonds rather than coordinate bonds involving the double bond. An example is:

$$R—CH=CH—R + Hg(X)(OCH_3) \rightarrow RCH(OCH_3)CH(HgX)R \qquad [334]$$

Similarly, many reactive aromatic or heteroaromatic compounds are mercur-ated with mercuric acetate, rather than complexed:

[329] e.g., the HgX_4^{--} ions: J. A. A. Ketelaar, *Zeit. Krist.* **80**, 190 (1931).

[330] P. K. Gallagher, Thesis, University of Wisconsin, Madison, Wis. (1960); R. L. Carlin, J. Roitman, M. Dankleff, and J. O. Edwards, *Inorg. Chem.* **1**, 182 (1962).

[331] Ref. 22, p. 331.

[332] An early example may be seen in M. S. Sherrill, *Zeit. phys. Chem.* **43**, 705 (1903). This electrode system may also be used to determine the stability constants of complexes of other metals in some cases: G. Schwarzenbach and G. Anderegg, *Helv. Chim. Acta* **37**, 1289 (1954); J. I. Watters and J. G. Mason, *J. Amer. Chem. Soc.* **78**, 285 (1956); J. Bjerrum and E. J. Nielsen, *Acta Chem. Scand.* **2**, 297 (1948); R. W. Schmid and C. N. Reilly, *J. Amer. Chem. Soc.* **78**, 5513 (1956).

[333] W. M. Latimer, *Oxidation Potentials*, Prentice-Hall, Inc., Englewood Cliffs, N.J., 2nd ed. (1952), p. 180.

[334] H. Gilman, "Organometallic Compounds" in H. Gilman, editor, *Organic Chemistry, An Advanced Treatise*, John Wiley & Sons, Inc., New York, 2nd ed. (1943), p. 549 ff.

THE LANTHANONS (RARE EARTHS). The coordination chemistry of these elements is rendered rather simple by the slight tendency of the ions of this group to coordinate to donor atoms other than oxygen or nitrogen *when these are present in chelating agents.* In spite of this the coordination behavior of these elements is of great importance because it has provided the key to the separation of these elements from each other. The behavior of the +3 ions toward coordinating agents which are capable of forming chelate rings shows some regular trends due to the steady decrease in ionic radius in passing from Ce^{+3} to Lu^{+3}. The result of this is that there is generally a regular trend toward increased stability with increasing atomic number, though this is not without some exceptions.[335] This regularity is most easily explained on the basis of simple electrostatic interactions which may be expected to vary inversely with the ionic radii. The types of ligands with which the rare earth ions form stable complexes are limited to chelating agents such as acetylacetone, oxalate, EDTA and its derivatives, and organic hydroxy acids such as citric acid.[336] Another interesting feature is the effect of complexation on the absorption spectra of solutions of the rare earth ions. These spectra, in simple salt solutions, consist of some very sharp, almost line-like, peaks which arise from electronic transitions involving the *4f* electrons. When these ions are coordinated with many coordinating agents very little change is found in the absorption spectra.[337] This is in very great contrast to the variations in absorption spectra found for the transition metal ions. With these the absorption spectra arise from transitions involving the *d* orbitals which are also intimately involved in bonding. There has as yet been no conclusive evidence presented to show that the *f* orbitals are ever involved in bonding, though there are some coordinating agents which can effect the position and intensity of the absorption bands in the rare earth salt solutions. A number of these absorption spectra together with much of the earlier literature may be found in an article by R. C. Vickery.[338]

The stabilities of the rare earth complexes are about as much greater than those of the alkaline earths as would be predicted on the basis of simple electrostatic considerations, i.e., greater stability because of the greater ionic charge with a variation due to the changes in ionic radii superposed on this. Examples

[335] A. E. Martell and R. C. Plumb, *J. Phys. Chem.* **56**, 993 (1952); S. Chaberek and A. E. Martell, *Organic Sequestering Agents*, John Wiley & Sons, Inc., New York (1959), p. 166.

[336] Sources containing information on these complexes include Abegg's, *Handbuch der Anorganischen Chemie*, Vol. III, Part 1, pp. 129–338, S. Hirzel Verlag, Leipzig (1906) (article by R. J. Meyer and that by B. Brauner which contain scattered information on complexes); T. Moeller, *Record of Chemical Progress* **14**, 69 (1953); R. C. Vickery, *Chemistry of the Lanthanons*, Butterworth's Scientific Publications, London (1953).

[337] T. Moeller, loc. cit.

[338] R. C. Vickery, *J. Molecular Spectroscopy* **2**, 308 (1958).

of this may be seen in the pK values for the stability constants with EDTA: Ca^{+2}, 11.0; Ba^{+2}, 7.76; La^{+3}, 15.13; Lu^{+3}, 20.00.[339]

THE ACTINIDES. The coordination chemistry of the actinides has developed enormously in certain directions because of the use of selective coordination processes for the separation of these elements. Since such separations are effected on solutions, the result has been that there is much more information available on the solution behavior of these elements in the presence of various ligands than there is on even some of the much more common elements. Oddly enough, however, there is relatively little information of the traditional sort on solid complexes of these elements.[340] Unlike the lanthanons, these elements often show a considerable range of accessible oxidation states. The coordination behavior shows similarities with the lanthanons in that the most commonly encountered donor atom is oxygen, and nitrogen donor complexes are rather uncommon.[341] Other donor atoms found in these complexes are sulfur, phosphorus, and halides. The complexes formed by the anhydrous halides of the actinide elements with amines or donor atoms other than oxygen are usually completely hydrolyzed by water, though there are some exceptions useful in solvent extraction separations. Because of the large size of the ions of these elements, a coordination number of eight or even more may be possible. Thus thorium acetylacetonate is $Th(C_5H_7O_2)_4$ with eight-coordinate thorium. This compound can also add a molecule of ammonia or aniline! Complex carbonates of thorium have been reported of composition $Na_5Th(CO_3)_5 \cdot 12H_2O$ which may contain ten-coordinate thorium.[342]

A further aspect of the chemistry of some of these elements is the formation of oxycations of the type MO_2^{+x} whose stability is very great. These, like the vanadyl ion, VO^{+2}, have a typical coordination behavior of their own. The uranyl ion, UO_2^{+2}, is a linear species $O=U=O^{+2}$, which usually completes its coordination octahedron by bonding to four additional donor groups. Presumably the analogous species of the other elements (e.g., PuO_2^{+2}) have similar structures in their complexes.

Some very unusual aspects of the coordination chemistry of uranium include the occurrence of *chelated* nitrate groups in the uranyl nitrate-triethylphosphite complex whose composition is $UO_2(NO_3)_2(OP(OEt)_3)_2$[343] and the

[339] J. Bjerrum, G. Schwarzenbach, and L. G. Sillen, *Stability Constants*, Part I, The Chemical Society, London (1957), p. 77.

[340] An extensive review which contains what must be a nearly complete survey of the literature is A. E. Comyns, *Chem. Reviews* **60**, 115 (1960).

[341] One of the few examples of the common sort is a complex with orthophenanthroline, [U(ophen)$_3$] (SCN)$_6$ reported by J. A. C. Allison and F. G. Mann, *J. Chem. Soc.*, 2915 (1949).

[342] Ref. 22, p. 643.

[343] H. Lynton and J. E. Fleming, *Chemistry and Industry* (London) 1409 (1959); H. T. Evans, *Science* **141**, 154 (1963).

peculiar stereochemistry of U(VI) in $NaUO_2(C_2H_3O_2)_3$, sodium uranyl acetate.[344] In this last compound the central uranium is eight-coordinate but with the six coordinated oxygen atoms furnished by the three acetate groups forming a ring which is nearly planar. The two remaining oxygen atoms are perpendicular to this group. Such an arrangement requires the use of *f* orbitals *if* covalent bonds are formed.[345] Only a very few of the complexes of uranium or thorium have had their structures determined by X-ray methods. As a result, there is no reasonably certain procedure for guessing the structures of their complexes by analogy. As Comyns[340] notes, this has the result that though large numbers of uranium complexes have been prepared, there is not very much detailed information available on the structural coordination chemistry of the element.

The complexes of the remaining elements have been studied mostly in solution.[346] The several oxidation states of Np and Pu do lead to complexes analogous to those of the corresponding oxidation states of U, though they have not been studied in detail. The EDTA complexes of the tervalent actinides have been used to effect their separation in conjunction with ion-exchange techniques; these complexes show an increase in stability with increasing atomic number as do the corresponding lanthanon complexes.[340] It is to be anticipated that knowledge of the coordination behavior of these elements will grow very rapidly in the immediate future.

[344] W. H. Zachariasen and H. A. Plettinger, *Acta Cryst.* **12**, 526 (1959).

[345] C. A. Coulson and G. R. Lester, *J. Chem. Soc.*, 3650 (1956).

[346] Most of this is collected in J. J. Katz and G. T. Seaborg, *The Chemistry of the Actinide Elements*, Methuen & Co., Ltd., London. (1957). See also A. D. Gel'man, A. I. Moskvin, L. M. Zaitsev, and M. P. Mefod'eva, "Complex Compounds of the Transuranium Elements," Consultants Bureau, New York (1962).

5

The Nature of Bonding in Coordination Compounds

The elucidation of the factors responsible for the stability of complex ions has attracted the attention of chemists for many years. As a result there are many alternative theoretical approaches to this problem. In part, this is due to the fact that some complexes are very obviously ionic or held together by simple electrostatic interactions while others are just as obviously covalent and require a theoretical treatment which is qualitatively as well as quantitatively different. There is every reason to believe that a completely general formulation of bonding in these complexes will ultimately be achieved. The most reasonable view at present is an eclectic one in which the theories are used to describe situations in which they have had some success. We will find that radically different approaches can give very similar or identical answers to some of the fundamental questions. The most important example of this is seen in the prediction of the most probable stereochemical arrangements for complexes.

Historically, the first successful attempt to calculate the energies of formation of a complex developed from the electrostatic approach. In principle, this is much like the method of Born for the calculation of lattice energies. The constituent ions are assumed to be point charges and the change in energy associated with their movement from an initially infinite separation to their positions in the complex ion is calculated. This method is surprisingly successful in many cases, as we shall see in a more detailed consideration. The successes achieved here were pushed into the background by Sidgwick's theory of the coordinate bond and the subsequent systematic basis which it introduced into the field of coordination chemistry. Unfortunately, Sidgwick's theory was not a quantitative theory and it provided no route to the calculation of either energies of formation of complexes or coordinate bond energies. Sidgwick's assumption that the ligand species must be one which has a pair of electrons that it can share allowed a very extensive organization to be effected. This theory was (and still is) very important in stimulating further experimental work on numerous types of ligands.

At about the same time the concept of effective atomic number was introduced by Sidgwick as a guiding principle which, it was claimed, governed the formation of coordination compounds.[1] This principle states that the central atom of the complex adds on ligand molecules and takes a share in their electron pairs until the total number of electrons accommodated in its shells is the same as that found for the next inert gas. This rule is not an infallible guide by any means, but it is correct in a number of instances.[2] It seems to hold for most of the simple carbonyls and their derivatives [except $V(CO)_6$] and a large number of complexes containing central atoms in lower-than-usual oxidation states.

The use of this concept with carbonyls and carbonyl nitrosyls allows predictions to be made about the possible existence of a given compound.[3] If the effective atomic number (abbreviated E.A.N.) of the central atom is not the same as that of the next inert gas, polymerization may be expected to occur. Thus manganese carbonyl has a ratio of five carbon monoxide molecules to one manganese atom. The atomic number of the manganese is 25 and it will gain a further share in two electrons from each of the coordinated carbon monoxide molecules to give a total or effective atomic number of 35 for the manganese. The next inert gas, however, is krypton with an atomic number of 36. As a result, manganese carbonyl would be expected to undergo polymerization to allow the manganese to gain a share in an additional electron. Manganese carbonyl actually is $[Mn(CO)_5]_2$. The same behavior is observed in the carbonyl nitrosyls in which the NO group adds three electrons to the central atom on coordination. Some examples of the calculation of the effective atomic numbers are given in Table 5.1.

By 1940 the general limitations on the use of the effective atomic number concept had been clearly stated (by Blanchard, loc. cit., among others). It is quite incapable of explaining the existence of large numbers of very stable complexes. Since that time its continued use has been primarily in the discussion of complexes in which elements exhibit oxidation states lower than those customarily encountered (see the articles by Chatt and Colton cited above).

[1] N. V. Sidgwick, *Chemistry and Industry* **42**, 901 (1923); *J. Chem. Soc.* **123**, 725 (1923); *Trans. Farad. Soc.* **19**, 469 (1923).

[2] A. A. Blanchard, *Chem. Reviews* **26**, 409 (1940); *Science* **94**, 311 (1941); N. V. Sidgwick, *The Electronic Theory of Valency*, Oxford University Press, London (1927), Ch. X; J. Chatt, *J. Inorg. Nuclear Chem.* **8**, 515 (1958); E. Colton, *J. Chem. Educ.* **31**, 527 (1953).

[3] N. V. Sidgwick and R. W. Bailey, *Proc. Roy. Soc.* **A144**, 521 (1934).

TABLE 5.1

SOME TYPICAL EXAMPLES OF EFFECTIVE ATOMIC NUMBER CALCULATIONS

Complex	Atomic no. of central atom	Electron loss or gain in forming ion	Electrons gained in coordination	Total number of electrons on central atom	Inert gas
$Fe(CO)_5$	26	0	10	36	Kr
BH_3CO	5	-3	8	10	Ne
$W(CO)_6$	74	0	12	86	Rn
$Re(CO)_5Br$	75	-1	12	86	Rn
$Cr(CN)_6^{-3}$	24	-3	12	33	none
$Mn(CN)_6^{-3}$	25	-3	12	34	none
$Fe(CN)_6^{-3}$	26	-3	12	35	none
$Fe(CN)_6^{-4}$	26	-2	12	36	Kr
$Fe(CN)_5(NO)^{-2}$	26	-3	13	36	Kr
$Fe(CO)_4^{-2}$	26	$+2$	8	36	Kr
$W(CN)_8^{-4}$	74	-4	16	86	Rn
$Ru(CN)_6^{-4}$	44	-2	12	54	Xe

One of the unusual features regarding its present usage is the fact that it is most successful when the occurrence of double bonding is ignored. In general, it is found to be useful for a large class of compounds, almost all of which have one or more of the ligands joined to the central atom by double bonds! Thus in $Fe(CO)_5$, $Ni(CO)_4$, $Fe(CN)_6^{-4}$, and $[Co(CO)_3(NO)]$ it is reasonably certain that *double* and not single bonds join the central atom to some of the carbon atoms. This being the case, the use of the effective atomic number concept appears to be a convenient but extremely artificial way of systematizing information on the composition of a small class of stable complexes.

The next important development occurred when Pauling provided a quantum mechanical basis for Sidgwick's qualitative ideas. This important step resulted in new knowledge of the basis of the stereochemistry of complexes; it provided the first useful description of the magnetic behavior of these compounds and revealed a host of related information. While this was a quantum mechanical theory and capable of a complete description of these compounds, the calculation of bond energies by its use was extremely difficult and was never carried out in detail. For a period of approximately twenty years (1930–1950), this theory was the uncontested master of the field and was developed to the point where it was capable of explaining and correlating an enormous mass of data. Because it focused on the larger details of bonding it was less successful in explaining differences which were dependent on small energy variations. For examples of this, one may cite details of optical absorption spectra and details of the temperature variation of magnetic susceptibilities.

Since 1950, crystal field theory and its admixture with molecular orbital theory (called *ligand field theory*) has become more and more widely accepted as the basic explanation for the behavior of coordination compounds. A purely molecular orbital theory of coordination compounds was developed (at least in its rudiments) during the years of growth and triumph of Pauling's valence bond theory. It has never acquired either the popularity or the generality of its competitors, though it is often considered to be the source of the ultimate solution of many of the problems of bonding in coordination chemistry.

Crystal field theory considers the effect of the external electric field, due to the ligands, on the energy levels of the d orbitals of the central atom or ion. These orbitals are split into groups of different energy and the nature of the splitting determines the electronic population of the various orbitals and, by implication, the magnetic and spectral characteristics of the central atom. A further area where crystal field theory provides a very direct prediction is in the distortion of regular coordination arrangements. It predicts which electronic configurations of the central atom will be energetically favorable for distortion. Such predictions have been extensively verified from X-ray determinations of the structures of complex ions. It seems reasonable to state that this is presently the most widely used theory of bonding in this field, a situation which is due in no small measure to its demonstrated power to furnish a more sophisticated picture of the details of the behavior of coordination compounds. It is capable of dealing directly with many problems which are effectively beyond the ability of valence bond theory. The imprint of Pauling's valence bond theory upon thinking and work in this field has been so profound, however, that a large number of the concepts which he introduced have been incorporated into the thinking of even the most avid advocates of ligand field theory. As a result, many papers will be found in which there is a judicious admixture of the two theories. It should be remembered that the valence bond theory has been very productive of new *qualitative* ideas on bonding in complexes and that these have *not all* been put on a *quantitative* basis by ligand field theory.

SIMPLE ELECTROSTATIC THEORIES

In these theories the principal interactions which are considered are those which arise from simple electrostatic forces which are assumed to be adequately described by Coulomb's law in its various forms. In addition it is necessary to have some sort of repulsion forces which prevent complete collapse of the array of electric charges. The treatment is thus very strongly reminiscent of the Born theory of ionic lattices. The interactions of this sort which are available for use in treating the energy of a complex ion are: ion-ion, ion-dipole, dipole-dipole, ion-induced dipole, dipole-induced dipole, induced dipole-induced dipole, and repulsion forces between closed shells. It is not customary to include all of these in any given calculation as some of them are usually rather small. The general theories, however, do take all these into consideration and can accordingly be modified for particular cases.

Before examining the calculation of energies in detail, it should be noted that simple electrostatic theory predicts[4] symmetrical arrangements for the coordinated groups when these are in free space. This is a result of the fact that such arrangements minimize the electrostatic repulsion between the coordinated groups. If a solid forms, there is an additional condition which is generally satisfied—the arrangement will be stable only if the central ion touches each of its nearest neighbors. One result of these conditions is that the coordination number, used in the crystallographic sense to describe the number of nearest neighbors around an ion in a solid, is not always the same as the coordination number used in the sense which is customary in coordination chemistry. Fortunately, this rarely occurs with the central ions studied most frequently in complexes. In some cases the ratio of the radius of the cation to that of the anion is too small to permit the cation to touch all of its neighbors if it is to have a given coordination number in the solid. The usual consequence of this is a rearrangement to a new structure in which the central ion has a smaller coordination number. Some of the predicted configurations and the minimal values of the radius ratio, r_M^+/r_X^- are:

COORDINATION NUMBER	PREDICTED CONFIGURATION	MINIMUM r_M^+/r_X^-
3	equilateral triangle	0.155
4	tetrahedron	0.255
6	octahedron	0.414
8	cube	0.735
8	Archimedean antiprism	0.645

The Archimedean antiprism allows the electrostatic repulsion between the ligands to be minimized for eight-fold coordination.

The first calculation of the energy of a complex via the electrostatic model was carried out by Kossel,[5] but his method contained too many simplifying assumptions. Ionic radii were not known with any precision at that time and in order to carry out numerical computations Kossel assumed that all isoelectronic ions were of the same size. A later improvement on this due to Magnus[4] used the equation:

$$U = \frac{-nme\mu}{r^2} + U'$$

to calculate the energy of a complex formed by the interaction of an ion, M^m and n dipoles of moment μ with a distance r between the center of the dipole and the nucleus. U' is the mutual repulsive energy of the dipoles. In some cases this is quite sufficient to allow a rather successful calculation of the heats of forma-

[4] A. Magnus, *Zeit. anorg. Chem.* **124**, 288 (1922).
[5] W. Kossel, *Ann. Physik* (4), **49**, 229 (1916).

tion of complex ions.[6] In these calculations it is necessary to know the internuclear distances and to have a suitable model for the ligand molecules. Because of the relatively small contribution of the energy due to the repulsion (closed shell) interactions, these may be neglected in approximate calculations.

A reasonably exact analysis of the energy of formation of ionic complexes was first given by Garrick.[7] As a first approximation this treatment gives the electrostatic energy, U_E, of a complex $M(H_2O)_x^{+z}$ as

$$U_E = U_A + U_{ER} + U_p$$

Here U_A is the attractive energy due to the attraction of ions and dipoles, U_{ER} is the energy due to the mutual repulsion of the dipoles, and U_p is the energy of polarization. For an ion of charge ze surrounded by n molecules at a distance r, each of dipole moment μ, U_A is

$$U_A = \frac{-n\mu ze}{r^2}$$

If μ' is the induced dipole ($\mu = \mu_0 + \mu'$), then

$$\mu' = \alpha E$$

where α is the polarizability of the ligand and E is the electric field strength in the region where it is situated. Then

$$U_p = \frac{n\mu'^2}{2\alpha}$$

U_{ER} is the sum of a number of terms of the type

$$\frac{\mu^2}{S^3} (\sin \theta_1 \sin \theta_2 - 2 \cos \theta_1 \cos \theta_2)$$

This is the mutual potential energy of two dipoles at a distance S making angles θ_1 and θ_2 with their axes. If only those cases are considered in which there is a symmetrical distribution of the dipoles, then

$$\theta_1 = 180° - \theta_2$$

and

$$k = \frac{n(n-1)}{2}$$
$$U_{ER} = \sum_{k=1}^{k} \frac{\mu^2}{S^2} (1 + \cos^2 \theta_k)$$

These general equations can be applied to specific cases by fixing the geometry

---

[6] A good example is the calculation of the heats of hydration of ions carried out by D. D. Eley and M. G. Evans, *Trans. Farad. Soc.* **34**, 1093 (1938). This article also contains a detailed discussion of refinements in the calculations and of the entropy changes involved in such a process.

[7] F. J. Garrick, *Phil. Mag.* (7), **9**, 131 (1930) (ion hydrates); (7), **10**, 76 (1930) (correction); (7), **10**, 77 (1930) (ammines); (7), **14**, 914 (1932) (fluo and chloro complexes).

of the complex. For the three cases of most interest the constants fixed by the geometry are:

equilateral triangle: $n = 3$,

$$S_1 = S_2 = S_3 = r\sqrt{3}, \qquad \theta_1 = \theta_2 = \theta_3 = 30°$$

tetrahedron: $n = 4$,

$$S_1 = S_2 = S_3 = S_4 = S_5 = S_6 = 2r\sqrt{\tfrac{2}{3}}, \qquad \theta_1 = \theta_2 = \theta_3 = \theta_4 = \theta_5 = \theta_6 = 35°77'$$

octahedron: $n = 6$,

$$S_1 = S_2 \ldots = S_{12} = r\sqrt{2};$$
$$\theta_1 = \theta_2 = \theta_3 = \theta_4 = \theta_5 = \ldots = \theta_{12} = 45°;$$
$$\theta_{13} = \theta_{14} = \theta_{15} = 0°;$$
$$S_{13} = S_{14} = S_{15} = 2r$$

The dipole moment, μ, in the field of the other dipoles is:

$$\mu = \mu_0 + \alpha E = \frac{\mu_0 + \dfrac{\alpha z e}{r^2}}{1 + \displaystyle\sum_{k=1}^{k=n-1} \frac{\alpha}{S_k^3}(1 + \cos^2 \theta_k)}$$

where the indices for the three cases given above are:

$n = 3$, $S_1 = S_2 = S_3 = r\sqrt{3}$, $\theta_1 = \theta_2 = 30°$

$n = 4$, $S_1 = S_2 = S_3 = 2r\sqrt{\tfrac{2}{3}}$; $\theta_1 = \theta_2 = \theta_3 = 35°77'$

$n = 6$, $S_1 = S_2 = S_3 = S_4 = r\sqrt{2}$, $S_5 = 2r$, $\theta_1 = \theta_2 = \theta_3 = \theta_4 = 45°$; $\theta_5 = 0°$

Garrick also showed how the inclusion of repulsive forces allowed the calculation of the value of r and thence the total energy, U. This was done by a graphical determination of the radius at which the electrostatic attractive forces were equal to the sum of all the repulsive forces, where the noncoulombic repulsion force was of the form $\lambda r^{-\nu}$. This led Garrick to write the total energy in the form:

$$U = U_E + U_{R_1} + U_{R_2}$$

where U_E is the electrostatic term calculated earlier and U_{R_1} and U_{R_2} are terms which take into account the intrinsic repulsions between the ion and the ligand molecules (U_{R_1}) and the ligand molecules themselves (U_{R_2}). Some of the results obtained by Garrick are listed in Table 5.2. Rather similar results were obtained for ammines by the use of this same method.

A more compact version of this method has been given by Basolo and Pearson[8] which may be used when, as is usually the case, the internuclear

[8] F. Basolo and R. G. Pearson, *Mechanisms of Inorganic Reactions*, John Wiley & Sons, Inc., New York (1958), pp. 46–51.

TABLE 5.2

CALCULATED ENERGIES OF FORMATION OF HYDRATES (IN KCALS/MOL)

Ion	n	$r \times 10^8$	$-U_E$	U_{R_1}	U_{R_2}	$-U$
Na	6	2.19	138	21	3	114
K	6	2.54	106	21	1	84
Mg^{+2}	4	1.64	631	141	9	481
Mg^{+2}	6	1.78	606	93	26	487

distances are known. For an ion of charge $+q$ surrounded octahedrally by its six dipolar ligands, these authors write the potential energy as the sum of four terms which are: (a) the electrostatic interaction between the central ion and the net dipole of the ligand, (b) the repulsive interaction of the six dipoles among themselves, (c) the energy required to create the additional induced dipole in the ligand, and (d) the repulsion between the central ion and the ligands arising from "van der Waals" interactions:

$$U = \frac{-6q(\mu_0 + \mu_i)}{r^2} + \frac{6(1.19)(\mu_0 + \mu_i)^2}{r^3} + \frac{6\mu_i^2}{2\alpha} + \frac{6B}{r^9}$$

$$\text{(a)} \qquad\qquad \text{(b)} \qquad\quad \text{(c)} \quad\;\; \text{(d)}$$

Using a procedure analogous to that of Garrick, the equation may be reduced to one containing a smaller number of unknowns and then, using the fact that $(dU/dr) = 0$ at the equilibrium internuclear distance, one may obtain as a general result:

$$U = 6\left[\frac{-7\mu_0 q}{9r^2} - \frac{5q^2\alpha}{18r^4} + \frac{2.37\mu_0^2}{3r^3} - \frac{20(2.37)\mu_0 q\alpha}{18r^5}\right.$$
$$\left. - \frac{4(2.37)q^2\alpha^2}{9r^7} + \frac{(2.37)^2\alpha\mu_0^2}{2r^6}\right] \div \left(1 + \frac{2.37\alpha}{r^3}\right)^2$$

The numbers 6 and 2.37 are the coordination number and a factor arising from the geometrical arrangement, respectively. This equation contains only quantities that are experimentally accessible and so can be used as it stands in calculations on some common ligands for which these quantities are known. For a charged ligand, the corresponding equation for an octahedral complex has been given by Hamm and his co-workers[9] as:

$$U = \frac{-6qe^2}{r} - \frac{6q\mu e}{r^2} + \frac{6(1.667)e^2}{r} + \frac{6(1.19)\mu^2}{r^3}$$
$$+ \frac{6\mu_i^2}{2\alpha} + \frac{6B}{r^9} + \frac{6(1.667)\mu e}{r^2}$$

Here again, the fact that $(dU/dr)_{r=r_e} = 0$ allows B to be eliminated and an equation to be obtained which contains only variables which can be obtained experimentally.

[9] R. E. Hamm, R. Kollrack, G. L. Welch, and R. H. Perkins, J. Amer. Chem. Soc. 83, 340 (1961).

There are a number of other related procedures which can be used to carry out such calculations. These include: (a) more drastically simplified methods for calculating the energies of formation of ionic complexes,[10] (b) methods which can be used to calculate the energies and vibrational frequencies for complexes,[11] and (c) methods for calculating the shapes of simple or complex species containing lone pairs.[12] For many systems of appreciable ionic character, these calculations are quite successful. A comparison of calculated and experimental values for the energies of formation of coordinate bonds has been made by Basolo and Pearson.[8] There is surprisingly good agreement. Thus for $Fe(H_2O)_6^{+3}$ the calculated bond energy is 109 Kcals while the experimental value is 116 Kcals; for AlF_6^{-3} the corresponding values are 212 Kcals and 233 Kcals; for $Zn(NH_3)_4^{+2}$ they are 86 Kcals and 89 Kcals.

In conclusion, it should be noted that these rather unsophisticated approaches to the calculation of the *total energy of formation* of complexes have never found very much favor in the eyes of the cognoscenti of theoretical chemistry; they are unfortunately both simple and reasonably accurate. They are undoubtedly the easiest route to the estimation of the energy of formation of ionic complexes which has yet been devised and can be recommended for this purpose.

THE VALENCE BOND THEORY

As time passes, our knowledge of coordination compounds grows both in scope and detail, and it has been the case so far that no single all-inclusive theory has been able to keep up with this growth. Since this is a general feature of the development of theoretical (i.e., mathematical) physical sciences it will probably be a more or less permanent feature of this field in future years. It is thus of no small value to examine the development of a theory which held undisputed sway over coordination chemistry for over twenty years and to examine its shortcomings and the reasons why alternative treatments were developed.

Pauling's extension of the valence bond theory to coordination compounds represented a strikingly successful application of quantum mechanical ideas in a region where they had been previously unknown.[13] Furthermore, this was not a purely theoretical step, it was accompanied by the systematization of an enormous amount of experimental data in this field, much of it carried out by Pauling himself and his students. Oddly enough, this method is not suited for

[10] K. B. Jazimirsky (Yatsimirsky), *Thermochemie von Komplexverbindungen*, Akademie-Verlag, Berlin (1956), especially Chs. I, II, VI, VIII.

[11] T. A. Milne and D. Cubiciotti, *J. Chem. Phys.* **30**, 1418 (1960); H. Hartmann and E. Koenig, *Zeit. phys. Chem.* **30**, 215 (1962).

[12] A. W. Searcy, *J. Chem. Phys.* **28**, 1237 (1958); **31**, 1 (1959).

[13] The best exposition of these ideas is in L. Pauling, *The Nature of the Chemical Bond*, Cornell University Press, Ithaca, New York, 3rd ed. (1960). See especially Chs. 5, 9.

the calculation of the total energy of formation of a complex from its constituent ions and molecules, though such calculations are possible in principle.
It has been most successful in explaining and predicting stereochemistry and
lability or inertness of complexes toward substitution reactions. It also introduced a systematic treatment of magnetic moments of complexes (now largely
obsolete), the notion of double bonding in coordinate bonds, an approximate
method for estimating the strengths of the bonds formed in various stereochemistries, the electroneutrality principle, and a large number of equally
useful concepts.

The central point of the valence bond method is that each pair of bonding
electrons in the single bonds of a molecule is considered to be associated with a
single pair of atoms. For these atoms to be bonded they must each have
available orbitals which can accommodate the bonding pair. This requirement
may be stated in the alternative form: each of the bonded atoms must have
orbitals available which can be used to form an orbital that is a suitable linear
combination of the atomic orbitals. These electrons and the orbitals which they
occupy are localized to a very considerable extent between the bonded atoms
for single bonds. When a coordinate bond is formed the only difference is that
both of the electrons were originally on *one* of the bonded atoms. The orbital
in which they are put in the molecule is still a linear combination of the atomic
orbitals of the bonded species.

The chief problem which must be solved before these linear combinations
can be obtained for the bond is the selection of suitable orbitals on the central
ion (the coordination center). Soon after the initial development of the quantum theory of the covalent bond, it was realized that the relative orientation of
the orbitals available for bonding (more properly, of the simple eigenfunctions
of the hydrogen atom) were not in accord with known stereochemical facts.
Thus the *s* orbitals have no preferred direction in space, the *p* orbitals are directed along the axes of a cartesian coordinate system, and the *d* orbitals have even
more complicated and less stereochemically plausible orientations. These are
sketched out in Figure 17. Three dimensional models of these may be found in
an article by R. G. Pearson.[14]

Inasmuch as bonds are formed by the overlap of these orbitals with the orbitals of other atoms, the relative orientations of the coordinated groups would be
expected to be the same as the relative orientations of the orbitals. This leads
to the expectation that a bond formed with an *s* orbital would have no preferred
orientation, bonds formed with *p* orbitals would be oriented at 90° from each
other, etc. Since most bonds are not of this type we are faced with a dilemma—
to search for a completely new approach or to try to adapt this one. The solution of this dilemma was proposed independently by Pauling[15] and Slater.[16]

[14] R. G. Pearson, *Chem. and Eng. News,* June 29 (1959), p. 72 ff.
[15] L. Pauling, *J. Amer. Chem. Soc.* **53,** 1367 (1931).
[16] J. C. Slater, *Phys. Review* **37,** 481 (1931); **38,** 325 (1931).

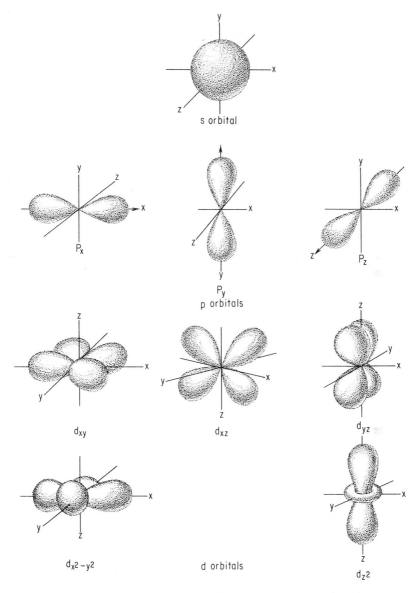

Fig. 17 The *s*, *p*, and *d* orbitals as represented by their angularly dependent parts.

This solution is an adaptation of the orbitals which were already known and is called *hybridization*. It consists of the mathematical combination of various suitable kinds of eigenfunctions (orbitals) with certain definite directional characteristics to give new, *hybridized* eigenfunctions of different, but still definite and more suitable directional characteristics. This process can be seen most readily from the following example of the hybridization of one $2s$ and one $2p$ orbital to give two equivalent sp orbitals. A $2s$ orbital has the form

$$\psi_{2s} = \frac{1}{4\sqrt{2}\,\pi} \left(\frac{Z}{a_0}\right)^{3/2} \left(2 - \frac{Zr}{a_0}\right) e^{-(Zr/2a_0)}$$

where Z is the effective nuclear charge, r is the distance from the nucleus, $a_0 = h^2/4\pi^2\mu\epsilon$, h is Planck's constant, μ is the reduced mass of the system (this ψ is for hydrogen-like atoms), and ϵ is the electronic charge. The $2s$ orbital has two concentric portions separated by a node, both portions are spherically symmetrical. The inner and smaller region is a region where ψ_{2s} is negative; in the outer portion ψ_{2s} is positive. The $2p_z$ orbital may be taken as the particular $2p$ orbital used in this hybridization; it has the form

$$\psi_{2p_z} = \frac{1}{4\sqrt{2\pi}} \left(\frac{Z}{a_0}\right)^{5/2} e^{-(Zr/2a_0)r} \cos\theta$$

where θ is the angle between the z axis and a vector from the origin to the point r. The other terms have the same significance as in the ψ_{2s} orbital. This eigenfunction is positive on one side of the nucleus (positive values of the coordinate z) and negative on the other side. In order to obtain the desired hybrid orbitals we search for suitable linear combinations of these orbitals, that is, for two new eigenfunctions, ψ_1 and ψ_2 where

$$\psi_1 = a_1\psi_{2s} + b_1\psi_{2p_z}$$
$$\psi_2 = a_2\psi_{2s} + b_2\psi_{2p_z}$$

where the a's and b's are merely numerical constants. Such linear combinations will also be solutions of Schrodinger's equation if ψ_{2s} and ψ_{2p_z} are. The restrictions which are usually used to determine the values of the a's and the b's are those of (1) normalization, (2) orthogonality, and (3) equivalence of the hybridized orbitals. These lead to the following relations among the constants:

$$\left.\begin{array}{l} \int \psi_1^2\, d\tau = a_1^2 + b_1^2 = 1 \\ \int \psi_2^2\, d\tau = a_2^2 + b_2^2 = 1 \end{array}\right\} \quad \text{normalization}$$

$$\int \psi_1 \psi_2\, d\tau = a_1 a_2 + b_1 b_2 = 0 \quad \text{orthogonality}$$

$$\left.\begin{array}{l} |a_1| = |a_2| \\ |b_1| = |b_2| \end{array}\right\} \quad \text{equivalence}$$

Solution of these equations leads to the values:

$$a_1 = 1/\sqrt{2}, \qquad a_2 = 1/\sqrt{2}$$
$$b_1 = 1/\sqrt{2}, \qquad b_2 = -1/\sqrt{2}$$

So the new hybridized orbitals have the form

$$\psi_1 = \frac{1}{\sqrt{2}}(\psi_{2s} + \psi_{2p_z})$$

$$\psi_2 = \frac{1}{\sqrt{2}}(\psi_{2s} - \psi_{2p_z})$$

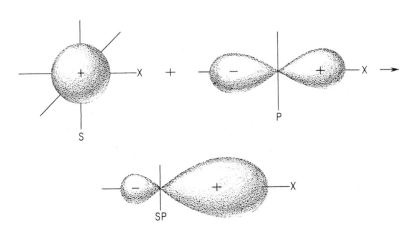

Fig. 18 Hybridization of an s and a p orbital.

TABLE 5.3

HYBRIDIZED ORBITALS AND THEIR CONFIGURATIONS[17, 18]

Hybrid	Configuration	Examples
sp	linear	$BeCl_2$
dp	linear	Fe bonds in ferrocene
sp^2	trigonal plane	BCl_3
p^3	trigonal pyramid	$NH_3(?)$
sp^3	tetrahedral	BCl_4^-
dsp^2	square planar	$PtCl_4^{-2}$
dsp^3	trigonal bipyramid	$Fe(CO)_5$
d^3sp	bipyramid	$\ldots$
d^2sp^2	tetragonal pyramid	$Ni(PEt_3)_2Br_3$
d^2sp^3	octahedron	$Co(NH_3)_6^{+3}$
d^4sp	trigonal prism	$\ldots$
d^3sp^3	pentagonal bipyramid	IF_7, ZrF_7^{-3}
d^4sp^2	face centered trigonal prism	TaF_7^{-2}
d^4sp^3	dodecahedron	$Mo(CN)_8^{-4}$
d^5p^3	Archimedean antiprism	$TaF_8^{-3}, Th(C_5H_7O_2)_4$
d^5sp^2	face centered prism	$\ldots$
d^3fsp^3	cubic	$\ldots$
d^3f^4s	cubic	$\ldots$

If this process is considered graphically, it is seen that by starting with two nonequivalent orbitals, one of which will not even form directed bonds, two new orbitals are obtained both of which are capable of forming stronger bonds (orbitals capable of greater overlap) than the initial orbitals. These new sp orbitals form two strong bonds at an angle of 180° with each other (Figure 18).

The hybridization process for other combinations of orbitals is discussed in detail in standard works on quantum chemistry.[17] Although there is a certain amount of artificiality about the use of the hybridized orbitals, they are the most widely used guide to the possible stereochemistries of inorganic compounds. Many of the most commonly invoked hybridizations are listed in Table 5.3 along with some examples in which such hybridization has been postulated.

The literature on hybridization is very extensive and is still under active development.[18] The use of f orbitals has been suggested by numerous investigators, especially for high coordination numbers,[19] but there is as yet no clear-cut case where the evidence is indisputable. It seems probable that hybridization will retain its importance in the theory of bonding in covalent molecules but it is definitely in for a period of neglect in the field of coordination chemistry.

Before passing on, it is necessary to outline a very abbreviated and convenient scheme for writing the electronic configurations of complexes which was introduced by Pauling. As an example, consider the complexes of Fe^{+3} and Fe^{+2}. Iron, with an atomic number of 26 gives rise to the ferrous ion with 24 electrons and the ferric ion with 23 electrons. The electronic configurations of these species are:

$$\begin{array}{ll} Fe & 1s^2 2s^2 2p^6 3s^2 3p^6 3d^6 4s^2 \\ Fe^{+2} & 1s^2 2s^2 2p^6 3s^2 3p^6 3d^6 \\ Fe^{+3} & 1s^2 2s^2 2p^6 3s^2 3p^6 3d^5 \end{array}$$

[17] W. Kauzmann, *Quantum Chemistry*, Academic Press, Inc., New York (1957), p. 409 ff; S. Glasstone, *Theoretical Chemistry*, D. Van Nostrand Co., Inc., Princetown, N.J. (1944), p. 98 ff; H. Eyring, J. Walter, and G. E. Kimball, *Quantum Chemistry*, John Wiley & Sons, Inc., New York (1944), p. 227 ff.

[18] J. N. Murrell, *J. Chem. Phys.* **32**, 767 (1960) contains a method for constructing hybrids for molecules of low symmetry; M. G. Shirmazan and M. E. Dyatkina, *Izvestia Akad. Nauk*, 1553, 1751 (1959) (Consultants Bureau Translation pp. 1498 and 1678) contains a rather complete reevaluation of hybrid orbitals for coordination numbers two through nine; J. H. Macek and G. H. Duffey, *J. Chem. Phys.* **34**, 288 (1961) treat twelve coordinate species as do J. R. Canon and G. H. Duffey, *ibid.*, **35**, 1657 (1961).

[19] R. L. Scott, *J. Chem. Phys.* **18**, 1420 (1950); see also, G. H. Duffey, *ibid.*, **18**, 943 (1950) for an alternative treatment based on $d^2 sp^3$ hybrids; R. L. Belford, *J. Chem. Phys.* **34**, 318 (1961); Z. Z. Hugus, *J. Amer. Chem. Soc.* **74**, 1076 (1952); R. E. Connick and Z. Z. Hugus, *ibid.*, **74**, 6012 (1952); C. Duclot, *Compt. rend.* **245**, 692 (1957) contains the most succinct and direct evidence involving $Mo(CN)_8^{-4}$; C. A. Coulson and G. R. Lester, *J. Chem. Soc.* 3650 (1956), contains a discussion of uranyl and related complexes and most of the earlier literature.

The electrons in the closed shells do not participate in bonding but the $3d$ electrons do and the empty orbitals above this in energy may also be used. Pauling's scheme for writing the electronic configurations centers attention on these orbitals. As an illustration, the examples above would be written as (circles may be used in place of the rectangles below)

	$3d$	$4s$	$4p$
Fe	⇅ ↑ ↑ ↑ ↑	⇅	☐ ☐ ☐
Fe^{+2}	⇅ ↑ ↑ ↑ ↑	☐	☐ ☐ ☐
Fe^{+3}	↑ ↑ ↑ ↑ ↑	☐	☐ ☐ ☐

The arrows represent the electrons and their directions are used to keep account of the number of unpaired electrons. When a coordinate bond is formed the central metal ion must accommodate a pair of electrons in its (hybridized) orbitals. For Fe^{+2} or Fe^{+3} this usually means an octahedral set ($3d^24s4p^3$) of orbitals, each of which can accommodate a pair of electrons from a ligand molecule. Thus $Fe(CN)_6^{-4}$ and $Fe(CN)_6^{-3}$ would be represented as:

	$3d$	$4s$	$4p$
$Fe(CN)_6^{-4}$	⇅ ⇅ ⇅ ⇅ ⇅	⇅	⇅ ⇅ ⇅
$Fe(CN)_6^{-3}$	⇅ ⇅ ↑ ⇅ ⇅	⇅	⇅ ⇅ ⇅

ligands furnish these
electrons

The two ions should show different magnetic behavior and as a matter of fact simple salts of $Fe(CN)_6^{-4}$ are diamagnetic, corresponding to no unpaired electrons, while those of $Fe(CN)_6^{-3}$ are paramagnetic (susceptibility corresponding to one unpaired electron). Complexes such as these are designated "hyperligated" by Pauling because the ligands are very firmly held. There is another class of compounds which are designated "hypoligated" and may be considered to be either "outer orbital" or ionic complexes. In these the ligands are held less tightly. As an example, consider the FeF_6^{-3} ion. This ion is paramagnetic with susceptibility corresponding to five unpaired electrons. The electronic configurations of the central iron ion may be considered to be the same as that given earlier for the free Fe^{+3} ion *or* we may consider that such complexes are outer orbital complexes in which the octahedral hybridization is made up from a $4s4p^34d^2$ combination. In this latter case the electronic configuration of the central ion in the complex would be:

sp^3d^2 hybrids

FeF_6^{-3}	↑ ↑ ↑ ↑ ↑	⇅	⇅ ⇅ ⇅	⇅ ⇅	☐ ☐

More examples of this may be seen in the standard treatises on coordination chemistry.[20]

INERT AND LABILE COMPLEXES. One of the most important notions related to valence bond theory for complexes is that of "inert" and "labile" complexes. H. Taube[21] proposed that complexes could be classified into one of two groups on the basis of the rate at which they reach equilibrium in an aqueous solution (the ideas can readily be extended to other environments). For a *labile* complex in solution it is merely necessary to specify the temperature, pressure, and gross composition to fix all of the properties of the system if these are measured on a homogeneous solution, even within a matter of minutes from the time of mixing. For an *inert* complex this is not sufficient and the previous history of the complex will also be important in fixing the properties of the solution.

A typical series of labile complexes are those formed in an acidic aqueous solution containing cupric ion and chloride ion. This system adjusts to changes in temperature or composition very rapidly and in a perfectly reproducible manner. Typical inert complexes undergo such adjustments to environmental changes more slowly, usually at a rate which can be measured experimentally without resorting to any of the specialized techniques used to follow rapid reactions. The Cr(III)—Cl$^-$ system in water furnishes an example of such inert complexes. When a solution of $Cr(H_2O)_6^{+3}$, such as that furnished by chromic nitrate or perchlorate, is saturated with HCl and cooled, $[Cr(H_2O)_6]Cl_3$ is precipitated, rather than a chloro complex of chromium(III). This same solution will undergo changes if allowed to stand and ultimately will contain $[Cr(H_2O)_4Cl_2]^+$ and $[Cr(H_2O)_5Cl]^{+2}$ if allowed to reach equilibrium. The usual "chromic chloride" of commerce is obtained by the evaporation of such solutions and is primarily $[Cr(H_2O)_4Cl_2]Cl \cdot 2H_2O$. This difference in the kinetic behavior of the Cu(II)—Cl$^-$ and Cr(III)—Cl$^-$ systems is not reflected in the thermodynamic behavior of their solutions. The dissociation constants of $[Cr(H_2O)_5Cl]^{+2}$ and $[Cu(H_2O)_xCl]^+$ at 25° and in media of moderate ionic strength are 0.2 ($\mu = 0.3$) and 1.4 ($\mu = 1.0$), respectively. Thus their relative rates of dissociation *cannot* be used to predict their relative thermodynamic stabilities!

Taube examined a large number of complexes and found that the most important single factor governing the stability (kinetic) of complex ions is the electronic structure of the central ion. Other factors which affect the stability (but in a much less obvious manner) are the bond type, size, and charge on the central ion, and the nature of the ligands. For octahedral complexes it is

---

[20] J. C. Bailar, Jr., editor, *The Chemistry of the Coordination Compounds*, Reinhold Publishing Corp., New York (1956), Ch. 4. The exact method of writing out these electronic configurations varies; in many instances circles are used to designate the orbitals, rather than the squares used above.
[21] H. Taube, *Chem. Reviews* **50**, 69 (1952).

found that inner orbital complexes using $(n-1)d^2nsnp^3$ orbitals in forming bonds are inert *when there are no other inner d orbitals completely unoccupied.* Taube designates the orbitals involved in hybridization with capital letters, S, P, D and the examples given below illustrate this convention. In Table 5.4 may be seen the application of these ideas to a number of electronic configurations found in transition element complexes.

TABLE 5.4

SOME INNER ORBITAL COMPLEXES

Electronic configuration	Class	Examples
$d^0d^0d^0$ D^2SP^3	labile	Sc(III), Ti(IV), V(V), Y(III)
$d^1d^0d^0$ D^2SP^3	labile	Ti(III), V(IV), Mo(V)
$d^1d^1d^0$ D^2SP^3	labile	Ti(II), V(III), Mo(IV)
$d^1d^1d^1$ D^2SP^3	inert	Cr(III), V(II), Mo(III), Mn(IV)
$d^2d^1d^1$ D^2SP^3	inert	Cr(II) in $Cr(CN)_6^{-4}$
$d^2d^2d^1$ D^2SP^3	inert	Fe(III), Ru(III), Ir(IV)
$d^2d^2d^2$ D^2SP^3	inert	Fe(II) in $Fe(CN)_6^{-4}$, Co(III)

To a considerable extent the lability or inertness may be modified as the ligands are varied, but these modifications are usually superimposed on a more general pattern of reactivity determined by the electronic configuration.

When outer d orbitals are used it is more difficult to arrive at a rationalization of the observed stability patterns. The general electrostatic factors of ionic charge and size may be used as a rough guide in estimating the relative stability of a series of closely related complexes. If the mechanism by which such outer orbital complexes undergo change is one involving an initial dissociation step, then it would be predicted that such a series should exhibit an increasing stability with increasing values of the charge to radius ratio. This expectation has been borne out in the few studies of these systems which are available.

A further factor which should be considered with the inner orbital complexes is the variation in bond type with changing ligand type. This can lead to a change from labile outer orbital complexes to inert inner orbital complexes for a given central ion, as the covalent nature of the bonds increases. Such a case may be seen in a comparison of the labile outer orbital complex CoF_6^{-3} with the inert inner orbital complex $Co(CN)_6^{-3}$. It should be realized that once a complex has been designated as either an inner or outer orbital complex, the electronic configuration of the central species follows directly and from this its designation as either labile or inert. This treatment is admittedly oversimplified as it ignores one of the sources of inertness in complexes, double bonding between the ligand and the central ion. This is a topic which is still under very active discussion and justifies separate treatment.

DOUBLE BONDING IN COMPLEXES (π BONDING). The original suggestion that a coordinate bond is merely a covalent bond in which both electrons come from one of the bonded atoms is generally sufficient to explain qualitatively coordinate bond formation in all but a small (but growing) number of complexes. In these there is considerable evidence that the coordinate bond is a double bond and has both a σ (sigma) component which is cylindrically symmetrical about the bond axis, and a π (pi) component, which is not. The sigma component arises from the sharing of a pair of electrons originally present on the donor (ligand) atom. The pi component usually arises from the "back-donation" of a pair of electrons of the central metal atom or ion into empty orbitals on the donor molecule or atom which possess suitable symmetry properties.

The first instances of double bonding supported by experimental evidence were reported by Pauling[22] who suggested the formation of pi bonds by back donation of electron pairs of the metal atoms in compounds such as $Ni(CO)_4$, $Fe(CO)_5$, $Ni(CN)_4^{-2}$, $[Fe(CN)_6]^{-4}$, $[Fe(CN)_5(NO)]^{-2}$, and $[Co(NO_2)_6]^{-3}$. The evidence adduced in support of this type of bonding is the unexpectedly short metal to ligand bond distance in these complexes. The bond energies are *not* known in many such compounds but in the few cases where they are available they are found to be smaller than might have been anticipated on the basis of the energies of such bonds in organic compounds. The Ni—C bond energy in $Ni(CO)_4$ is 35 Kcals![23] In addition, such pi bonding leads to reasonable charge distributions in complexes. This problem of charge distribution is a very real one as can be seen from a calculation of formal charges on the central atoms in some typical complexes. If only sigma bonding is considered, the result is an unrealistically large *negative* charge assignment to the central atom. Consider the example of the $Fe(CN)_6^{-4}$ ion as an example. In this, the central iron has initially a $+2$ charge. Formation of six-coordinate sigma bonds with the twelve electrons furnished by the cyanide ions gives the iron a half share in each of six pairs of electrons or "complete control" over six more electrons. The central iron then has a net charge of -4 insofar as the formal charge assignment is concerned. Back donation of electrons via pi bonding allows the iron atom to reduce this formal charge considerably and it is generally accepted that it actually approaches a state of electroneutrality rather closely.

It is important to realize that present theory allows us to draw few analogies with the sigma and pi bonds of carbon compounds, other than those of symmetry of the orbitals involved. Thus it is quite common to find that pi bonding is assigned an importance greater than sigma bonding in many specific compounds. As an example, examination of the paramagnetic resonance of single crystals of copper(II) acetylacetonate shows that there are strong pi bonds and

[22] L. Pauling, *The Nature of the Chemical Bond*, Cornell University Press, Ithaca, New York, 2nd ed. (1940), p. 250 ff, 3rd ed., p. 331 ff.

[23] D. R. Stull and G. C. Sinke, *Thermodynamic Properties of the Elements*, American Chemical Society, Washington, D.C. (1956).

weak sigma bonds. In this particular case, the valence bond electron configuration is demonstrably in error.[24]

The whole problem of pi bonding in coordination compounds is presently under active investigation and will be considered again later in this chapter. The metal orbitals useful for pi bonding have been tabulated[25] and are used whatever the nature of the theoretical treatment, be it valence bond, ligand field, or molecular orbital.

NON-BONDING PAIRS AND STEREOCHEMISTRY. In 1940, Sidgwick and Powell[26] pointed out how the total number of electron pairs in the outermost shell of an atom can be used as a reliable guide to the stereochemistry of many systems. The chief restriction on the use of this method is that no inner d orbitals must be invoked in the bonding. This means that the method is most suitable for the complexes of the regular families of the periodic table. Where this restriction is met, the arrangements are those given in Table 5.5.

TABLE 5.5

PREDICTED STEREOCHEMISTRIES

Number of electron pairs	Stereochemistry
Two	Linear
Three	Trigonal Plane
Four	Tetrahedron
Five	Trigonal Bipyramid
Six	Octahedron

Where lone pairs are present, the resultant shape of the *molecule* (ignoring the actual distribution of these lone pairs) can be predicted to be one arising from the positioning of the atoms in some of the allowed directions. Thus with four pairs of electrons, of which only three are involved in bonding, a trigonal pyramid (rather than a tetrahedron) would be the expected shape of the molecule. This is derived from the tetrahedron by having the apex occupied by the electron pair.

Atoms which are connected by double bonds to a central atom may be assumed to occupy two of the positions when predicting structures.[27] Further refinements in the predictions can be effected by consideration of the variation

[24] B. R. McGarvey, *J. Phys. Chem.* **60**, 71 (1956). See further discussion of this in A. D. Liehr, *J. Chem. Ed.* **39**, 135 (1962); L. Pauling, *ibid.*, **39**, 461 (1962).

[25] H. Eyring, J. Walter, and G. Kimball, *Quantum Chemistry*, John Wiley & Sons, Inc., New York (1944); G. Kimball, *J. Chem. Phys.* **8**, 188 (1940). A more explicit discussion of pi bonding in tetrahedral complexes is given by F. A. Cotton, *J. Chem. Soc.*, 5269 (1960).

[26] N. V. Sidgwick and H. M. Powell, *Proc. Roy. Soc*, **A176**, 153 (1940).

[27] R. J. Gillespie and R. S. Nyholm, *Progress in Stereochemistry* **2**, 261 (1958); R. J. Gillespie, *Canadian J. Chem.* **39**, 318 (1961); *J. Chem. Ed.* **40**, 295 (1963).

in the repulsion between electron pairs of different types. This is found to decrease in the order:

lone-pair:lone-pair > lone-pair:bond-pair > bond-pair:bond-pair

The consideration of these variations allows deviations from regular configurations to be predicted.

Most of the theoretical treatments of stereochemistry find their ultimate justification in the Pauli exclusion principle.[27] In general, electrons whose spins are identical avoid each other as much as they can. The ideas of electron correlation as well as hybridization have their common basis in this principle. It is of interest to note that the Pauli principle is essentially a statement about the symmetry properties of the wave functions which are allowable (the total wave function must be antisymmetric with respect to the exchange of any electron pair).[28]

CRYSTAL FIELD THEORY AND LIGAND FIELD THEORY

The most significant theoretical advance in coordination chemistry in recent years has been the renewed interest in the development of crystal field theory and its modification, ligand field theory. Crystal field theory centers its attention on the effect of the electrical field due to the ligands on the energy levels of the central ion. It dates back to the 1930's when the fundamental theoretical basis was developed by Bethe[29] and exploited by Van Vleck.[30] From then until about 1950 it was used almost exclusively by physicists in such problems as the interpretation of the properties of ions trapped in regular ionic lattices. At the beginning of the 1950's it was applied to the spectra of complexes by H. Hartmann and his students[31] and by Orgel[32] to explain variations in the stabilities of the transition metal aquo complexes. In the years which followed it has been used in the interpretation of a great number of

---

[28] See, for example, R. Daudel, R. Lefebvre, and C. Moser, *Quantum Chemistry*, Interscience Publishers, Inc., New York (1959), p. 144.

[29] H. Bethe, *Ann. Physik* (5), **3**, 133 (1929).

[30] J. H. Van Vleck, *The Theory of Electric and Magnetic Susceptibilities*, Oxford University Press (1932).

[31] The initial papers are H. Hartmann and H. L. Schläfer, *Zeit. physik. Chem.* **197**, 116 (1951) and F. E. Ilse and H. Hartmann, *ibid.*, **197**, 239 (1951). Subsequent work has been summarized in H. Hartmann and H. L. Schläfer, *Angew. Chem.* **66**, 768 (1954); **70**, 155 (1958).

[32] L. E. Orgel: *J. Chem. Soc.*, 4756 (1952); *An Introduction to Transition Metal Chemistry: Ligand Field Theory*, Methuen & Co., Ltd., London (1960) very ably presents an over-all qualitative account of the work of both Orgel and other investigators; C. J. Ballhausen's, *Introduction to Ligand Field Theory*, McGraw-Hill, Inc. (1962) presents an excellent quantitative account.

facets of coordination chemistry and a large number of excellent reviews are available.[33]

The most appropriate starting point for a description of crystal field theory is the examination of the results of bringing a symmetrical group of ligands up to a central charged ion. There will be a distinct difference in the effect of such an act on the relative energies of the various d orbitals of the central atom and it is with these differences that crystal field theory is primarily concerned.

Consider the effect of forming an octahedral complex on the relative energies of the $3d$ orbitals of a first row transition element. Let the ligands be brought up to the central atom or ion along the cartesian axes. Then the repulsion between the electrons of the filled orbitals of the ligand and the electrons in the d orbitals of the central ion will vary with the particular d orbitals under consideration. For an octahedral complex, the d_{z^2} and $d_{x^2-y^2}$ orbitals are found to point directly at the ligands along the z axis and the x and y axes, respectively. The other three d orbitals, d_{xy}, d_{yz}, and d_{xz} are found to be directed between the ligands. As a result, electrons in the d_{z^2} and $d_{x^2-y^2}$ orbitals are repelled more strongly by the ligand electrons than are those in the d_{xy}, d_{yz}, or d_{xz} orbitals and hence are of a higher energy. Thus, under the influence of the electrical field of the ligands, the five $3d$ orbitals which originally were all of the same energy (degenerate) are split into two groups. One group, which consists of the d_{xy}, d_{yz}, and d_{xz} orbitals, has a lower energy than the other group, while the other group, containing the d_{z^2} and $d_{x^2-y^2}$ orbitals, has a higher energy. The actual value of this energy difference is determined by the ligand species and the internuclear distances. The situation is that depicted in Figure 19.

[33] Ref. 31 and 32 can be highly recommended. See also (a) J. S. Griffith, *The Theory of Transition-Metal Ions*, Cambridge University Press, London (1961) contains a very comprehensive and sophisticated theoretical treatment; (b) F. Basolo and R. G. Pearson, *Mechanisms of Inorganic Reactions*, John Wiley & Sons, Inc. (1958) contains numerous applications of the theory to problems of stability and reaction mechanisms, etc.; (c) J. Lewis and R. G. Wilkins, editors, *Modern Coordination Chemistry*, Interscience Publishers, Inc., New York (1960) contains a very detailed application of this theory to problems of the interpretation of spectroscopic (Ch. 4) and magnetic (Ch. 6) data as well as information on other applications. Review articles on this theory are fairly numerous and include: (d) P. George and D. S. McClure, *Progress in Inorganic Chemistry* **1**, 381 (1959); (e) J. D. Dunitz and L. E. Orgel, *Advances in Inorganic Chemistry and Radiochemistry* **2**, 1 (1960); (f) L. E. Sutton, *J. Chem. Educ.* **37** 498 (1960); (g) R. G. Pearson, *ibid.*, **38**, 164 (1961); (h) W. Manch and W. C. Fernelius, *ibid.*, **38**, 192 (1961); (i) R. J. Gillespie and R. S. Nyholm, *Quarterly Reviews* **11**, 339 (1957); (j) idem, *Progress in Stereochemistry* **2**, 290 (1958); (k) H. Hartmann, *Zeit. Elektrochem.* **61**, 908 (1957); (l) D. S. McClure, *Solid State Physics* **9**, 400 (1959); (m) "Discussions of the Faraday Society," No. 26 (1958); (n) C. Furlani, *Atti accad. nazl. Lincei, Rend. Classe sci. fis. mat., e nat.* **25**, 488 (1958); (o) *Supplement, Progress of Theoretical Physics*, No. 14 (1960), "Properties of d-electrons in Complex Salts," by M. Kotani, Y. Tanabe and S. Sugano; (p) C. M. Herzfeld and P. H. E. Meijer, *Solid State Physics* **12**, 1–91 (1961); C. K. Jorgensen, *Solid State Physics* **13**, 375 (1962).

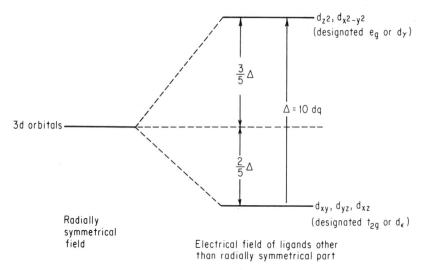

Fig. 19   The splitting of the 3*d* orbitals in an octahedral complex.

The electric field of the ligands increases the energies of all the *d* orbitals and also, because of its spatial arrangement, splits the degenerate *d* orbitals.

For a transition metal ion in such a field there will be then, different energy levels available than otherwise and the distribution of electrons among these levels will determine the details of the magnetic behavior of the complexes and the possible transitions which can be responsible for the absorption of light. That energy levels may be split in electric or magnetic fields has been known for many years. Van-Vleck[34] referred to the splitting described above as an "electrical Paschen-Back effect" many years ago; the Paschen-Back effect arises when an atom is in a magnetic field of such strength that the usual rules governing the interaction of the spin and the orbital angular momentum begin to break down. When the spectrum of an atom is excited while it is in a strong magnetic or electrical field, it is found to contain far more lines than when it is observed in the absence of such a field. Both the Zeeman effect (in a magnetic field) and the Stark effect (in an electric field) have been studied for many atoms and are general phenomena. The effect of the field is to separate some of the energy levels which are normally coincident into two or more levels. This is also termed *removing the degeneracy* as coincident levels are called *degenerate levels.*

The theoretical basis of crystal field theory lies in quantum mechanics and is hence of general validity, but there is an important restriction which applies to its customary use. This is the fact that it centers its attention on the splitting of the *d* orbitals and not on a description of the total energy picture of the com-

[34] J. H. Van Vleck, *J. Chem. Phys.* **3**, 807 (1935).

plex.[35, 36] Within this scope it can provide a detailed picture of how and why the electrons in the d orbitals distribute themselves among the available orbitals.

The splitting of the orbitals for a given central ion is found to be dependent on the ligand in a very definite manner. This splitting is determined by the strength of the field produced by the ligand. Furthermore, common ligands can be arranged in serial order of decreasing ability to split the two sets of orbitals for octahedral complexes. This order is almost, but not quite, independent of the cation involved and is the same for complexes of other symmetries, though the actual splitting produced varies with symmetry.[32,33] This order is:

cyanide > dipyridyl > 1,10-orthophenanthroline > nitrite

ethylenediamine > ammonia > pyridine > thiocyanate > water >

fluoride > carboxyl > hydroxide > chloride > bromide > iodide

This is also the order of decreasing polarizability except for the halides. The exact factors responsible for this order are not yet completely known and the order is determined from experimental evidence such as shifts in the absorption spectra, etc. It should be noted that the ligands which tend to form covalent bonds are here classed as ligands with high field strengths though a simple electrostatic justification of this is lacking.[37]

The degree of splitting of the d orbitals is important in determining the electronic distribution in a complex when it changes the pattern in which the orbitals are filled. When the separation of the t_{2g} and e_g orbitals is small (i.e., when the ligand field is weak), the electrons will tend to follow Hund's rule and remain unpaired if this is possible. Hund's rule simply states that when adding electrons to a set of p, d, or f orbitals, the electrons will tend not to pair up until each of these orbitals is at least singly occupied. When the separation of the t_{2g} and the e_g orbitals is large enough (i.e., when the ligand field is strong), then the energy required to keep the electrons unpaired by putting them in the higher energy orbitals may be greater than that required to pair them up. In this case Hund's rule is no longer followed and the resultant central ion will have fewer unpaired electrons and correspondingly, a lower magnetic moment than it possesses in a weak ligand field. These two cases of high spin and low spin are roughly analogous to the valence bond designations "ionic" and "covalent" complexes or "outer orbital" and "inner orbital" complexes, though the details of the interpretations are quite different. Figure 20 shows how the behavior of the $3d$ orbitals of the ferric ion is interpreted for the two cases of low and high ligand field. The ferric ion has five electrons in the $3d$ orbitals and is termed a d^5 system.

[35] W. Moffitt and C. J. Ballhausen, *Annual Reviews of Physical Chemistry* **7**, 107 (1956).
[36] E. A. Magnusson, *Reviews Pure Applied Chem.* **7**, 195 (1957).
[37] J. Chatt and R. G. Hayter, *J. Chem. Soc.*, 772 (1961), for the ligand field strengths of the halide, methyl, phenyl, and hydride anions.

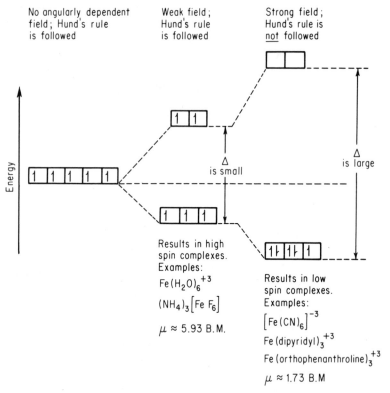

Fig. 20 Occupation of the $3d$ orbitals of Fe^{+3} in weak and strong crystal fields.

The presence of the octahedral field in such complexes results in a stabilization of the ground state of the ion in comparison to the ground state of the free ion. For a strong field this depends on the atomic configuration (i.e., the number of electrons in the d orbitals) and can be expressed in terms of the splitting of the energy levels when a single d electron is involved. By convention the splitting between the t_{2g} and the e_g levels is designated Δ or $10Dq$. The meaning of this stabilization energy is more clearly seen when it is realized that the splitting occurs so that there is no net change in energy for the fully occupied orbitals. Thus the three t_{2g} orbitals are stabilized by an amount $4Dq$ while the two e_g orbitals are destabilized by $6Dq$. The octahedral stabilization energies given below are the amount by which the *ground state* (low spin) is stabilized:[35]

Configuration:	d^1	d^2	d^3	d^4	d^5	d^6	d^7	d^8	d^9	d^{10}
Stabilization energy in Dq	4	8	12	16	20	24	18	12	6	0

A factor which opposes this stabilization energy is the energy of repulsion between the paired electrons. This represents the price that we must pay in energy if we are to violate Hund's rule. Two kinds of repulsion are present, the electrostatic repulsion between like charges and a quantum mechanical exchange interaction which favors parallel spins for electrons in the same set of d orbitals. Following Sutton[33f.] we can designate these as π_c and π_e per interaction. Thus for each pair of electrons in a single d orbital there will be contribution π_c from their electrostatic interaction (repulsion) and a contribution of the exchange type which is dependent upon the number and distribution of the other electrons. Each possible combination of two electrons with the same spin will contribute π_e to the stabilization. To show how this last is computed, consider the case of a d^3 ion where all the spins are parallel. If the electrons are designated 1, 2, and 3, the possible pairs of interactions are (1,2), (1,3), and (2,3), so there are three different pairings possible and the exchange stabilization energy is $3\pi_e$. For the d^4 ion of low spin, two of the electrons, say 1 and 2, must have opposite spins. The interactions of this sort are then (1,3), (1,4), and (3,4) and the exchange stabilization energy is $3\pi_e$. For the d^4 ion of high spin the corresponding pairs of interactions are (1,2), (1,3), (1,4), (2,3), (2,4), and (3,4) which gives an exchange stabilization energy of $6\pi_e$. For the general case, the number of such interactions may be calculated from the equation:

$$- \left\{ \frac{(n)(n-1)}{(1)(2)} + \frac{(p)(p-1)}{(1)(2)} \right\} \pi_e$$

where n is the number of electrons with one spin and p is the number with the opposite spin.

A simple case shows how these terms can be evaluated for the possible electronic arrangements for a given number of d electrons. Consider the example of a d^5 ion for the cases of both low field and high field. For a low field, each of the orbitals will be singly occupied. The total splitting due to the ligand field is $10Dq$ and the t_{2g} orbitals are $4Dq$ below the reference state of the free atom and the e_g orbitals are $6Dq$ above this same reference state. The stabilization due to the crystal field will be: (Crystal Field Stabilization Energy)

$$\text{CFSE} = -3 \times 4Dq + 2 \times 6Dq = 0$$

For the electrostatic repulsion energy, we also have no net term as all the electrons are in different orbitals. For the exchange interaction there is the term:

$$- \left\{ \frac{(5)(4)}{(1)(2)} \right\} \pi_e = -10\pi_e$$

as there are five electrons, all with the same spin. The total stabilization energy is thus $-10\pi_e$. For the low spin case each of these contributions is different. There are now five electrons in the t_{2g} orbitals so the stabilization due to the crystal field will be:

$$\text{CFSE} = -(5)(4Dq) = -20Dq$$

The electrostatic repulsion term will include contributions from both of the doubly occupied t_{2g} orbitals and will be $2\pi_c$. The exchange interaction may be calculated as before:

$$- \left\{ \frac{(3)(2)}{(1)(2)} + \frac{(2)(1)}{(1)(2)} \right\} \pi_e = -4\pi_e$$

The total energy for these interactions is then $-20Dq + 2\pi_c - 4\pi_e$ as opposed to $-10\pi_e$ for the high spin case. Obviously the question as to which configuration will be adopted cannot be answered until the relative magnitudes of Dq, π_c, and π_e are known. Since Dq is dependent upon the ligand it can be seen that in the present case a low spin complex will result when $-20Dq + 2\pi_c - 4\pi_e$ gives a lower energy than $-10\pi_e$, i.e., for ligands with a sufficiently high ligand field. A similar calculation can be carried out for other configurations and it is found that such a choice of configurations for octahedral complexes is possible only with d^4, d^5, d^6, and d^7 states. For the d^1, d^2, and d^3 configurations all of the electrons will go into the t_{2g} orbitals regardless of the strength of the ligand field, while for the d^8 and d^9 configurations vacancies can occur only in the e_g orbitals.

As mentioned before, the actual order of splitting of the d orbitals is very dependent upon the symmetry of the ligand field which surrounds the central atom. For a regular tetrahedral arrangement of the ligands, the splitting of the d orbitals is the exact reverse of that found for an octahedral arrangement. Here the d_{z^2} and the $d_{x^2-y^2}$ orbitals are directed between the ligands while the d_{xy}, d_{yz} and d_{xz} orbitals point directly toward the ligands. The actual amount of the splitting in a tetrahedral environment is less than that for an octahedral one at the same internuclear distance by a factor of about $\frac{4}{9}$.[33b] For the equally important case of a square planar arrangement (usually considered to be a case of extreme distortion of an octahedron) the order of the d orbitals going from the lowest energy is $d_{xz} = d_{yz} < d_{z^2} \ll d_{xy} \ll d_{x^2-y^2}$. Here again the d_{z^2} or d_{xz} or d_{yz} orbitals which are the lowest in energy obviously allow the electrons of the central atom to be concentrated furthest from the electrons of the ligands. Tetrahedral complexes of the transition metal ions are not so common as the octahedral ones and those which have been found are invariably labile; they include $FeCl_4^-$, $CoCl_4^{-2}$, some $NiCl_4^{-2}$ complexes, and other less thoroughly characterized examples. Square planar complexes are more common in the second half of each of the transition series. Examples may be found in the four-coordinate complexes of Cu(II), Ni(II), Pd(II), Pt(II), and Au(III).

THE JAHN-TELLER EFFECT. It is a fundamental idea of crystal field theory that those electrons in orbitals which point directly at the ligands possess a higher energy (are destabilized) because of the electronic repulsion between them and the electrons of the ligand. It might be suspected that one result of such interaction may be a slight irregularity in the structure in order to attain a lower energy. There is a considerable body of evidence which indicates that such distortions do occur. One of the experimental *facts* which is known about the structures of *some* types of octahedral complexes is that the octahedron *is* distorted. Often such complexes will have four groups in a plane at one distance from the central ion and two axial groups at a greater distance. This distorted octahedral structure has a lower symmetry than a regular octahedron with the result that there will be a further loss of degeneracy among the groups of d orbitals of the central ion. This will allow a redistribution of the electrons into the orbitals of lowest energy. This is called the *Jahn-Teller effect* and was predicted by a theorem due to Jahn and Teller.[38] In effect, this states that when a complex which might be expected to be a perfect octahedron (or tetrahedron, etc.) has several energy levels which are degenerate, this degeneracy will generally be removed by a distortion of the octahedron which leads to a new distribution of the electrons which has a lower energy.[39]

An example of the configurational distortion may be seen in the "octahedral" complexes of Cu(II) discussed by Sutton.[40] Here there are a total of nine electrons to be put into the $3d$ orbitals. Of these, six go into the low energy $3d$ orbitals which point away from the ligands, that is the d_{xy}, d_{yz}, and d_{xz}. The remaining three electrons must then go into the $d_{x^2-y^2}$ and the d_{z^2} orbitals which are degenerate and which point toward the ligands. The resultant system can be stabilized if the octahedron is distorted so that the total interaction between these three electrons of the central ion and those of the ligand is reduced. This can be accomplished by moving the ligands on the z axis out and moving those on the x and y axes in. Then two electrons can be put into the stabilized d_{z^2} orbital and only one electron is then put into the $d_{x^2-y^2}$ orbital which is destabilized by the movement of the ligands. The fundamental idea here is that characteristic of ligand field theory as a whole: the d electrons on the central metal ion will go into orbitals in which they can be as far as possible from the electrons of the ligands. If a slight geometrical rearrangement allows this process to proceed to a more stable situation, such a rearrangement will occur.

The Jahn-Teller effect has been examined in detail and more comprehensive accounts of such work are available.[33e,33j] Actually, the only electronic configurations which will not be expected to show this effect are those giving a distribution of electrons which is the same along each axis. For a weak ligand

[38] H. A. Jahn and E. Teller, *Proc. Roy. Soc.*, London **A161**, 220 (1937).

[39] A. D. Liehr and C. J. Ballhausen, *Annals of Physics* **3**, 304 (1958) have given a theoretical exposition of this for octahedral complexes of the configurations d^1, d^4, d^6, and d^9. F. A. Cotton and M. D. Meyers, *J. Amer. Chem. Soc.* **82**, 5023 (1960) have shown that CoF_6^{-3} in its salts shows behavior which indicates that there is a dynamic Jahn-Teller effect in the electronic excited states. The dynamical Jahn-Teller effect refers to the direct coupling of the electronic and vibrational motions which may occur without great distortion. It is discussed in ref. 33a, and in B. Weinstock and H. H. Claasen, *J. Chem. Physics* **31**, 262 (1959) also, may be found a discussion of cases where the Jahn-Teller effect need not show itself by a configurational distortion but may appear as a special vibronic coupling. This latter has been less thoroughly studied than the configurational distortion.

[40] L. E. Sutton, *J. Inorg. Nuclear Chem.* **8**, 27 (1958). This interpretation is not universally accepted.

field these nondistorting configurations are d^3, d^5, and d^8; for a strong ligand field they are d^3 and d^6. The configurations which are expected to show the greatest distortions are for a weak field: $d^4(d_{xy}, d_{yz}, d_{xz}, d_{z^2}$ with the z axis lengthened) and $d^9(d_{xy}^2, d_{yz}^2, d_{xz}^2, d_{z^2}^2$, and $d_{x^2-y^2}$ also with the z axis lengthened); for a strong field the most pronounced distortions will be expected for the systems: $d^7(d_{xy}^2, d_{yz}^2, d_{xz}^2, d_{z^2}$ with the z axis lengthened), $d^8(d_{xy}^2, d_{yz}^2, d_{xz}^2, d_{z^2}^2$ with the z axis lengthened), and $d^9(d_{xy}^2, d_{yz}^2, d_{xz}^2, d_{z^2}^2, d_{x^2-y^2}$ with the z axis lengthened). The distortions given here are those predicted for complexes in which six identical ligands surround the central ion. Usually the distortions involving the movement of groups in the x and y planes are smaller. There are many recent studies of this effect in specific complexes where the interested reader may find further details.[41]

The application of the ideas of ligand field theory to the transition metal complexes can best be appreciated by a consideration of the behavior of specific ions with the different possible numbers of d electrons. Since the elements of the first transition period have been most intensively studied, most of the examples cited come from this group. This should not be interpreted as meaning that the theory is not applicable to other species.

d^1: Examples of d^1 ions are Ti^{+3}, V^{+4}, Cr^{+5}, and Mn^{+6}. The case of Ti^{+3} has been studied by Hartmann and his students.[42] In an octahedral field such as that found in the $Ti(H_2O)_6^{+3}$ ion the $3d$ orbitals split into a lower level and a higher one as described earlier. A calculation of this difference using reasonable assumptions shows that the energy levels are separated by an amount roughly equal to 18,000 cm^{-1} which corresponds to the energy found in light with a wave length of 5,500 A or 550 millimicrons. Aqueous solutions of titanous perchlorate show absorption of visible light reasonably close to this value, the maximum actually being found at 4,900 A. Such absorption then corresponds to the energy needed to transfer an electron from the lower t_{2g} level to the upper e_g level. Such a transition is forbidden in the free Ti^{+3} ion, but occurs in the complex as a result of the vibration of the water molecules about the central Ti^{+3} ion which destroy the perfect octahedral symmetry. Since the differences are generally cited in units of cm^{-1} ($\tilde{v} = 1/\lambda = $ cm^{-1}) it is useful to note the relationship between the commonly used units for energy and these units: 1 ev = 8067.5 cm^{-1} and 1000 cm^{-1} = 2.8575 Kcals/mole. The observed absorption for the $Ti(H_2O)_6^{+3}$ ion at 4,900 A corresponds to $\frac{1}{4,900} \times 10^{-8}$ cm^{-1} = 20,400 cm^{-1}. This is the 10Dq value for this ion so Dq for the ion $Ti(H_2O)_6^{+3}$ is 2,040 cm^{-1}.[43]

[41] A. Forman and L. E. Orgel, *Molecular Physics* 2, 362 (1959); this is concerned primarily with the Jahn-Teller effect in manganese(III) acetylacetonate but also discusses the corresponding complexes of Cr(III), Fe(III), and Al(III).

[42] H. Hartmann, *Theorie Der Chemischen Bindung*, Springer Verlag, Berlin (1954), pp. 226–231 summarize this work.

[43] F. E. Ilse and H. Hartmann, *Zeit. phys. Chem.* 197, 239 (1951).

d^2: Ti^{+2}, V^{+3}, Cr^{+4}, Mn^{+5}, and Fe^{+6} are the chemical species which are of this type. The V^{+3} system is the most easily studied under a variety of experimental conditions and has been the subject of a theoretical study by Hartmann and his students.[44] The ground state of this ion has both of the electrons in t_{2g} orbitals (or d_ϵ in Hartmann's terminology). The absorption of light by the V^{+3} ion is found to occur in two absorption bands when this ion is present in octahedral complexes with ligands having oxygen donor atoms. One of these bands is around 16,000 cm^{-1} (6,250 A) and the other is around 24,000 cm^{-1} (4,100 A). Hartmann assigns these to the transitions:

$$(t_{2g})^2 \rightarrow (t_{2g})(e_g)$$
and
$$(t_{2g})^2 \rightarrow (e_g)^2, \text{ respectively.}$$

For the $[V(OC(NH_2)_2)_6]^{+3}$ ion, the calculated frequencies for these absorptions are 12,400 cm^{-1} and 26,200 cm^{-1}; the experimental values are 16,250 cm^{-1} and 24,200 cm^{-1}. This agreement must be considered to be quite good. The value of Dq suggested by Orgel for $V(H_2O)_6^{+3}$ is 1,900 cm^{-1}; a somewhat lower value of about 1,700 cm^{-1} seems not unreasonable in the light of this work.[45] The detailed analyses[44] of these systems are more complicated than would be suggested by the simple picture of crystal field theory presented earlier.

d^3: The ions with this configuration include the very important Cr^{+3}, and the less important Ti^+, V^{+2}, and Mn^{+4} species. The analysis of the Cr^{+3} case has been carried out by Hartmann and Kruse[46] for complexes of the types CrX_6, CrX_5Y, and *cis-* and *trans-*CrX_4Y_2.

For octahedral complexes with identical ligands, it is predicted that the ground state of the d^3 system (for $Cr(NH_3)_6^{+3}$, for example,) will have the configuration $(t_{2g})^3$ and there will be two higher levels: $(t_{2g})^2(e_g)$ at about 21,000 cm^{-1} and $(t_{2g})(e_g)^2$ at about 28,000 cm^{-1} for the hexamminechromium(III) ion. This is in excellent agreement with the experimental values of 21,500 cm^{-1} and 28,500 cm^{-1}. For complexes of lower symmetry these bands may be split into further components and are always shifted to longer wave lengths. A further difference between *cis-* and *trans-*isomers is that the long wave length bands for the *cis-*isomers are more intense (higher extinction coefficients) than those of the *trans-*isomer, a result of the lower symmetry of the *cis-*isomer.[46, 47]

[44] H. Hartmann, C. Furlani, and A. Burger, *Zeit. phys. Chem.* **9**, 62 (1956); H. Hartmann and C. Furlani, *ibid.*, **9**, 162 (1956).

[45] L. E. Orgel, *J. Chem. Phys.* **23**, 1820 (1955).

[46] H. Hartmann and H. H. Kruse, *Zeit. phys. Chem.* **5**, 9 (1955); R. E. Hamm, R. Kollrack, G. L. Welch, and R. H. Perkins, *J. Amer. Chem. Soc.* **83**, 340 (1961). The experimental data available are due largely to M. Linhard and his co-workers, *Zeit. Elektrochem.* **50**, 244 (1944); *Zeit. anorg. allgem. Chem.* **262**, 328 (1950); *ibid.*, **263**, 233 (1950); *ibid.*, **264**, 321 (1951); *ibid.*, **266**, 49 (1951); *ibid.*, **266**, 73 (1951); *ibid.*, **267**, 113 (1951); *ibid.*, **267**, 121 (1951), and subsequent papers in this same journal.

[47] M. Linhard and M. Weigel, *Zeit. phys. Chem.* **5**, 20 (1955). The analysis of the bands has since been refined: *ibid.*, **11**, 308, 318 (1957).

The analysis of the Mo(III) system has also been carried out.[48] The value of Dq for octahedral complexes of a given ligand with successively heavier members of an inner transition group is found to increase with increasing atomic number. Thus Dq is greater for Mo(III) complexes than it is for the corresponding Cr(III) complexes. The ions V^{+2} and Mn^{+4} have been examined in the solid state and it is found that $10Dq$ for V^{+2} in $V(H_2O)_6^{+2}$ is 12,350 cm^{-1}, [49] while for Mn^{+4}, $10Dq$ is 21,750 cm^{-1}, [50] in MnF_6^{-2}. The corresponding $10Dq$ value for CrF_6^{-3} is 15,200 cm^{-1}. [51] These values illustrate the general trend for the values of $10Dq$ to increase as one passes to isoelectronic ions of greater charge.

d^4: The ions with this configuration are the less commonly encountered Cr^{+2} and Mn^{+3}. For a low ligand field a high spin configuration, $(t_{2g})^3(e_g)$, is the expected one. For both Mn^{+3} and Cr^{+2} in water, absorption bands corresponding to the transition $(t_{2g})^3(e_g) \rightarrow (t_{2g})^2(e_g)^2$ are found.[33a] An appreciable Jahn-Teller effect is anticipated for this configuration. Griffith[33a] gives $10Dq$ as 13,900 cm^{-1} for the Cr^{+2} ion and as 21,000 cm^{-1} for Mn^{+3}. These values are based upon the distorted ions.[52]

d^5: The important ions Fe^{+3} and Mn^{+2} are of this type as well as the rarer Co^{+4}. For the case of the weak ligand field the expected configuration is $(t_{2g})^3(e_g)^2$ and there are no low energy transformations involving electron promotion from the lower to the higher level which have high probabilities of occurrence for the symmetrical ions $Fe(H_2O)_6^{+3}$ or $Mn(H_2O)_6^{+2}$. As a result, aqueous solutions of the salts of these ions are very pale in color, e.g., $Fe(H_2O)_6^{+3}$ and $Mn(H_2O)_6^{+2}$. These cases have been studied in some detail.[53, 54, 55, 56] The very weak bands have been analyzed and the $10Dq$ values found to be 25,000 cm^{-1} for manganese and 24,450 cm^{-1} for ferric iron. For Mn(II) the detailed analysis requires that some allowance for a variable ligand environment be made in such cases as $Mn(H_2O)_6^{+2}$. For both of the ions of this type a comparison of the octahedral splittings with some tetrahedral splittings is possible. For $FeCl_4^-$, $10Dq$ is 18,800 cm^{-1}, for $MnBr_4^{-2}$ it is 22,300 cm^{-1}, while for Mn^{+2} present in MnS—ZnS mixtures in an octahedral environment it is about 20,000 cm^{-1}. The Jahn-Teller distortion should be absent for weak field d^5 complexes.

[48] H. Hartmann and H. J. Schmidt, *ibid.*, **11**, 234 (1957).

[49] C. K. Jorgensen, *Acta Chem. Scand.* **12**, 1537 (1958) for $V(H_2O)_6^{+2}$ dissolved in solid $(NH_4)_2 [Zn(H_2O)_6] (SO_4)_2$.

[50] C. K. Jorgensen, *ibid.*, **12**, 1539 (1958) for solid K_2MnF_6.

[51] C. K. Jorgensen, *J. Chim. Phys.* **56**, 892 (1959).

[52] The Cr^{+2} case is treated by H. L. Schlafer and H. Skoludek, *Zeit. phys. Chem.* **11**, 277 (1957).

[53] H. L. Schlafer, *Zeit. phys. Chem.* **4**, 116 (1955), **6**, 201 (1956).

[54] C. K. Jorgensen, "Discussions of the Faraday Society" **26**, 110 (1958).

[55] L. E. Orgel, *J. Chem. Phys.* **23**, 1004 (1955).

[56] R. Pappalardo, *ibid.*, **31**, 1050 (1959); **33**, 613 (1960).

For d^5 ions there should be considerable differences between strong field and weak field complexes. The strong field complexes should be of the type $(t_{2g})^5$. The analysis of the splitting is rendered difficult by simultaneous processes based upon other absorptions. Potassium ferricyanide is ruby red and photosensitive and the orthophenanthroline and dipyridyl complexes are also strongly colored. The photosensitivity has apparently precluded a complete analysis of these compounds as the charge transfer responsible for the absorption of visible light arises from the transfer of an electron from the ligand to the central ion.[33b] In cases such as these it is possible to estimate $10Dq$ using a procedure due to Jorgensen.[54] Jorgensen showed that $10Dq$ could be factored into two terms:

$$10Dq = f(\text{ligand}) \times g(\text{central ion})$$

where f is a constant characteristic of a ligand for an octahedral complex and g is a constant for a given central ion in such an environment. For 6 cyanides, f is 1.7 while g for Fe(III) is 14,000 cm^{-1}. Thus $10Dq$ is $1.7 \times 14,000$ cm^{-1} or 23,800 cm^{-1}(4,200 A); the charge transfer spectra are superposed on this absorption. Jorgensen also showed that β, the ratio between the interelectronic repulsion parameters in the complex and the free(gaseous) ion could be correlated by the equation:

$$(1-\beta) = h(\text{ligand}) \times k(\text{central ion})$$

Some typical values for these constants are: $6H_2O: f = 1.0, h = 1.0$; $6NH_3$: $f = 1.25, h = 1.4$; three oxalate anions: $f = 0.98, h = 1.5$; Mn(II): $g = 8,000$ cm^{-1}, $k = 0.07$; Cr(III): $g = 19,000$ cm^{-1}, $k = 0.21$; Ir(III): $g = 32,000$ cm^{-1}, $k = 0.3$. Values for other ligands and central ions may be found in the original article by Jorgensen or Griffith's book.[33a]

d^6: This configuration is of especial interest for its occurrence in Co(III). However, the spectrum of the free gaseous ion has not yet been completely analyzed. The complexes have been very intensively studied, however, and tentative assignments have been made.[57] The bands found in the region 16,000 cm^{-1} to 21,000 cm^{-1} for these complexes are assigned to a transition of the type $(t_{2g})^6 \to (t_{2g})^5(e_g)$ and $10Dq$ is approximately 21,000 cm^{-1}. The second band which arises around 25,000 cm^{-1} is assigned to a transition $(t_{2g})^6 \to (t_{2g})^4(e_g)^2$. It is known from the work of Linhard[46,47] that Co(III) complexes exhibit absorption spectra very similar to those of the corresponding Cr(III) complexes with similar changes occurring in the case of geometrical isomerism. The lower symmetry of *cis*-isomers causes a shift in absorption bands to the red in

---

[57] The literature may be found in the superb article by T. M. Dunn, "The Visible and Ultra-Violet Spectra of Complex Compounds" in J. Lewis and R. G. Wilkins, editors, *Modern Coordination Chemistry*, Interscience Publishers, Inc., New York (1960), pp. 229–300. This article contains a rather complete, if extremely succinct, account of the work in this field.

both cases and may be assumed to have a similar theoretical basis. An examination of the case of Fe(II) has been carried out by Furlani.[58,59]

d^7: This configuration is found in Co(II) and the rather uncommon Ni(III). Of these, only Co(II) has been thoroughly studied in octahedral complexes. These are mostly low field (high spin) complexes with the configuration $(t_{2g})^5(e_g)^2$ and the transitions observed have been assigned as follows: $(t_{2g})^5(e_g)^2 \rightarrow (t_{2g})^4(e_g)^3$ at about 8,000 cm^{-1}; $(t_{2g})^5(e_g)^2 \rightarrow (t_{2g})^6(e_g)$ at about 11,000 cm^{-1} and $(t_{2g})^5(e_g)^2 \rightarrow (t_{2g})^3(e_g)^4$ at about 17,000 cm^{-1}. The tetrahedral ion $CoCl_4^{-2}$ has been examined and its spectra interpreted on this basis.[57]

d^8: Ni(II) and Cu(III) are ions of this sort, but only the nickel complexes have been studied in detail. The complexes of nickel have a rather interesting history and it is only in the last few years that the peculiar color changes found with these materials has found a sound explanation.[60] For octahedral fields which are weak, there is generally a band at 8,600 cm^{-1} assigned to a transition of the type $(t_{2g})^6(e_g)^2 \rightarrow (t_{2g})^5(e_g)^3$ and a close pair of bands at 14,000 cm^{-1} corresponding to a transition $(t_{2g})^6(e_g)^2 \rightarrow (t_{2g})^4(e_g)^4$ and further transitions at 15,400 cm^{-1}, 18,500 cm^{-1}, and 25,500 cm^{-1}.[57] For $Ni(H_2O)_6^{+2}$, Jorgensen[51] reports $10Dq$ as 8,500 cm^{-1}; for $Ni(NH_3)_6^{+2}$, $10Dq$ is 10,800 cm^{-1}; for $Ni(en)_3^{+2}$ it is 11,500 cm^{-1}. This assignment is based on a band in the near infrared, as 8,500 cm^{-1} corresponds to a wave length of 11,750 A.

With the d^8 configuration in the ground state, $(t_{2g})^6(e_g)^2$, a very considerable Jahn-Teller distortion is expected and found. This distortion is so great that Ni(II) forms characteristically four-coordinate square planar complexes with many ligands. It was formerly thought that[60a] four-coordinate complexes of Ni(II) could be either square planar (and diamagnetic and red in color) or tetrahedral (and paramagnetic and blue in color). Maki[51d] showed how both of these types of behavior may arise in square planar complexes and also what type of absorption spectra might be expected for tetrahedral Ni(II) complexes. With a few exceptions then the four-coordinate complexes of nickel are square planar. These square planar complexes may pass over into octahedral complexes by the addition of two more ligands to the axial positions and numerous examples of this are known.[60b,c] Also known are cases where a diamagnetic square planar complex becomes a paramagnetic square complex on solution in an unreactive solvent such as chloroform. The explanation for this is based on the fact that the energy separation of the diamagnetic and paramagnetic states for square planar nickel(II) complexes is small. This is in good accord with the several instances where heating a solution of a diamagnetic yellow or

[58] C. Furlani, *Gazz. chim. ital.* **87**, 371 (1957).

[59] C. Furlani and G. Sartori, *ibid.*, **87**, 380 (1957).

[60] For the literature on the spectra see ref. 57. For the chemistry see: (a) D. P. Mellor, *Chem. Reviews* **33**, 137 (1943) on square planar complexes; (b) R. S. Nyholm, *ibid.*, **53**, 263 (1953) (general); (c) W. Manch and W. C. Fernelius, *J. Chem. Educ.* **38**, 192 (1961). The theoretical papers of importance are: (d) G. Maki, *J. Chem. Phys.* **28**, 651 (1958); **29**, 1129 (1958); (e) C. J. Ballhausen and A. D. Liehr, *J. Amer. Chem. Soc.* **81**, 538 (1959).

red nickel(II) complex (in an inert solvent) results in a blue paramagnetic solution. The magnetic susceptibility of these complexes does not always correspond to an integral number of unpaired electrons if it is assumed that the spin-only formula is adequate.[61]

d^9: Cu(II) and the rare Ni(I) possess this configuration. It is one which is subject to a very considerable Jahn-Teller effect with the result that the complexes of these central species are predominantly "square planar" rather than tetrahedral. These square planar complexes are found frequently to have an additional two axial ligands at a greater distance in the crystalline solid. As a result of such X-rays studies as are available, it is very probable that square planar Cu(II) complexes will complete their coordination octahedra by some sort of weak bonding to an additional two donor atoms, possibly from ligand atoms in adjacent molecules. In the case of cupric acetate there are bonds to adjacent copper atoms.[62] In solution, molecules of solvent may complete the coordination octahedra. With several chelating agents copper can also attain a coordination number of six.[63] Though the type of distortion present is not known, it may be somewhat different than when each donor group can move independently.

The spectrum of a d^9 ion is expected to show certain similarities to that of a d^1 ion as a d^n ion shows behavior analogous in some respects to that of a d^{10-n} ion. There is thus an analogy between electrons and "holes" in orbitals.[57] The hole in a square planar d^9 complex is in the $d_{x^2-y^2}$ orbital as this is the orbital of highest energy. The spectra of such complexes generally contain two bands when they are dissolved in a non-polar solvent, one at about 18,000 cm^{-1} and one at about 15,000 cm^{-1}; in coordinating solvents they contain a further band at about 12,500 cm^{-1}. The assignment of these bands in the case of copper(II) acetylacetonate[64] has been made on the basis of shifts observed on changing the solvent. The 18,000 cm^{-1} band arises from the transfer from a d_{xz} or d_{yz} (degenerate) orbital to the $d_{x^2-y^2}$ orbital; the band at 15,000 cm^{-1} to a d_{xy} to $d_{x^2-y^2}$ transfer, and the band at 12,000 cm^{-1}, which is found only in coordinating solvents, is assigned to a d_{z^2} to $d_{x^2-y^2}$ transfer.

[61] The spin-only formula assumes that only the intrinsic angular momentum of the unpaired electrons contributes to the magnetic moment; in such cases $\mu = \sqrt{n(n+2)}$. The literature is collected in R. H. Holm, "Spectral and Magnetic Studies in Substituted Ni(II) Salicylaldimine Complexes" in S. Kirschner, editor, *Advances in the Chemistry of Coordination Compounds*, The Macmillan Company, New York (1961), p. 341 ff. which also presents much new experimental data.

[62] I. G. Ross, *Trans. Faraday Soc.* **55**, 1057 (1959); I. G. Ross and J. Yates, *ibid.*, **55**, 1064 (1959).

[63] The older literature may be followed back from P. Pfeiffer *et al.*, *Zeit. anorg. allgem. Chem.* **192**, 346 (1930). See also, Ch. V.

[64] R. L. Belford, A. E. Martell, and M. Calvin, *J. Inorg. Nuclear Chem.* **2**, 340 (1956); R. L. Belford, M. Calvin, and G. Belford, *J. Chem. Phys.* **26**, 1165 (1957). Data of the same sort on cupric ethylacetoacetate may be found in D. P. Graddon, *J. Inorg. Nuclear Chem.* **14**, 161 (1960).

The extensive geometrical distortions found in copper(II) complexes have caused much comment.[33e] The distortions may result in different internuclear distances within the square plane. Thus, in $CuCl_2 \cdot 2$pyridine there are two nitrogens at 2.02 A from the copper, two chlorides at 2.28 A, and two more chlorides at 3.05 A. Furthermore, in $Cu(NH_3)_2Cl_2$ there are two nitrogens at 1.95 A and four chlorides at 2.76 A! There are a few truly square planar copper(II) compounds; these include the oxide, CuO, and bis(salicylaldimine) copper(II).[65] A further peculiarity of copper salts of aliphatic carboxylic acids and possibly some other compounds is the occurrence of metal to metal δ bonds in the solid state.[62] A further peculiarity in the nature of the Jahn-Teller effect with Cu(II) apparently requires that the electron cloud should oscillate with respect to the nucleus.[66]

d^{10}: In the d^{10} system none of the phenomena intimately related to incompletely filled d orbitals are present. Ions such as Cu(I) and Zn(II) which have this configuration show no visible absorption and any color developed in their solid compounds arise from other sources. The stereochemistry of these ions is determined by the repulsion between the ligands and both Cu(I) and Zn(II) have a characteristic coordination of four and have a tetrahedral stereochemistry in such complexes.

APPLICATIONS OF CRYSTAL FIELD THEORY AND LIGAND FIELD THEORY TO CHEMICAL PROBLEMS

Crystal field theory is most successful in the prediction of properties of ionic complexes. For such complexes it can predict with considerable confidence properties such as the energy of formation, spectra of the ions in various environments and the effect of the crystal field on properties which are also determined in part by other parameters. Since most chemical properties fall in this last class, the chemical potentialities of crystal field theory are not capable of full development until it is coupled with molecular orbital theory. This joint treatment incorporating molecular orbital and crystal field is designated ligand field theory.[32c, 67]

Two examples of correlations which are possible by consideration of the energy changes arising from the effects of the ligand field on the central ion d energy levels may be seen in the heats of formation of the hydrated transition metal ions and in the most commonly observed stability order for complexes of a given ligand with a series of such ions.

The variations in the heats of hydration for the ions of the first row of transi-

[65] J. M. Stewart and E. C. Lingafelter, *Acta Cryst.* **12**, 242 (1959).

[66] V. I. Avvakumov, *Soviet Physics JETP* **37**, 723 (1960), p. 1017 in the original; A. Abragam and M. H. L. Pryce, *Proc. Physical Soc.* **A63**, 409 (1950).

[67] W. Moffitt and C. J. Ballhausen, *Annual Reviews of Physical Chemistry* **7**, 107 (1957); R. J. P. Williams, "Discussions of the Faraday Society" **26**, 123 (1958).

tion elements can best be explained by variations in the crystal field stabilization energy (C.F.S.E.). If the heats of hydration of the divalent or trivalent ions of this series are considered, they would be expected to vary in a smooth fashion with atomic number except for the irregularities caused by the varying C.F.S.E.[68] This is found to be the case. The experimental curve of the hydration energy vs. atomic number for the divalent ions Ca^{+2} through Zn^{+2} shows two "humps" superimposed on a continual increase as one passes to elements of greatest atomic number. The low point between the maxima is at Mn^{+2} for this series. For the similar plot involving trivalent cations the low point is at Fe^{+3}. When it is recalled that water is a ligand with a low ligand field and that the resultant aquo complexes are high spin complexes it is realized that these low points in the hydration energy curve correspond to the d^5 configurations which have the minimum C.F.S.E. for each series. When the C.F.S.E. is subtracted from the heats of hydration, a smooth curve is obtained for both the $+2$ and $+3$ ions.[69]

Predictions of the stabilities of complexes is also an area in which this theory has shown some utility. It would be expected that the C.F.S.E. terms would allow a prediction to be made about: (a) the relative tendency of the various metal ions toward complex formation and (b) the order of stabilities of complexes of a given metal ion with various ligands. The first of these problems was solved empirically by Irving and Williams[70] who found the order of stabilities of complexes of a large number of ligands to be such that a maximum is reached at copper(II) and we have smaller values for the divalent ions on either side of copper in the periodic table:

$$Cr^{+2} < Mn^{+2} < Fe^{+2} < Co^{+2} < Ni^{+2} < Cu^{+2} > Zn^{+2}$$

Irving and Williams explained this order on the basis of the variation in ionization potentials of the atoms involved. This has also been explained by George and McClure[33d] as the result of the superposition of C.F.S.E. effects on a regular trend of increasing heat of complex formation. This includes a not inconsiderable contribution resulting from the distortion found in copper(II) complexes. The difficulties involved in assessing the contributions of these various factors have not all been overcome.[69]

The relative stabilities of complexes formed with various ligands follows the crystal field values to some extent. This relative order is also dependent on such factors as double bonding and the availability of suitable orbitals for this on both the central atom and the ligands. Because of the specificity of such

[68] L. E. Orgel, *J. Chem. Soc.*, 4756 (1952); O. G. Holmes and D. S. McClure, *J. Chem. Phys.* **26**, 1686 (1957); P. George and D. S. McClure, *Progress in Inorganic Chemistry* **1**, 381 (1959).

[69] R. J. P. Williams, *Annual Reports Chem. Soc.* LVI, 87 ff. (1959) for a discussion of some more complicated cases of this sort.

[70] H. Irving and R. J. P. Williams, *Nature* **162**, 746 (1948); idem, *J. Chem. Soc.*, 3192 (1953).

interactions, generalizations are often only very rough guides to behavior.[71]

Crystal field theory has also been used in the interpretation of electron-transfer processes in cobalt complexes. Adamson[72] noted that there are two large classes of redox processes for cobalt complexes: (a) a group of relatively rapid reactions where the oxidation is carried out by the addition of the oxidizing agent to the cobalt complex:

$$[Co(CN)_5]^{-3} + \tfrac{1}{2}X_2 \rightarrow [Co(CN)_5X]^{3-}; \quad (X = Br_2 \text{ or } I_2)$$

$$2[Co(C_2O_4)_2]^{-2} + H_2O_2 \rightarrow [(C_2O_4)_2Co \overset{\overset{\displaystyle H}{\displaystyle O}}{\underset{\underset{\displaystyle H}{\displaystyle O}}{\diagup\diagdown}} Co(C_2O_4)_2]^{-4}$$

$$2[Co(C_2O_4)_2]^{-2} + ClO^- + H_2O \rightarrow [(C_2O_4)_2Co \overset{\overset{\displaystyle H}{\displaystyle O}}{\underset{\underset{\displaystyle H}{\displaystyle O}}{\diagup\diagdown}} Co(C_2O_4)_2]^{-4} + Cl^-$$

and (b) a group of relatively slow reactions in which an electron transfer process is involved:

$$Co(CN)_5^{-3} + Fe(CN)_6^{-3} + H_2O \rightarrow [Co(CN)_5(OH_2)]^{-2} + Fe(CN)_6^{-4}$$

$$Co(C_2O_4)_3^{-4} + Ce(IV) \rightarrow Co(C_2O_4)_3^{-3} + Ce(III)$$

$$Co(Y)^{-2} + Fe(CN)_6^{-3} \rightarrow Co(Y)^{-1} + Fe(CN)_6^{-4} \, (Y = EDTA^{-4})$$

$$\overset{*}{Co}(C_2O_4)_3^{-4} + Co(C_2O_4)_3^{-3} \rightarrow \text{exchange}$$

$$Co(Y)^{-2} + \overset{*}{Co}(Y)^{-1} \rightarrow \text{exchange}$$

An explanation for the difference in rates observed here was given by Adamson in terms of effects of crystal field stabilization energies of the different intermediate configurations. Libby[73] has shown that in an electron transfer process the intermediate must be symmetrical in the species exchanging the electrons. The oxidation of an ionic cobalt(II) complex by an exchange process would correspond to the sequence: Co(II), weak field → Co(III), weak field → Co(III), strong field and would be expected to have a high activation energy because of the high energy of the Co(III) weak field configuration. For the direct oxidation (e.g., of the pentacyanocobaltate(II) ion by bromine) the process would correspond to the sequence:

[71] For a less enthusiastic description of the powers of crystal field theory see R. J. P. Williams, *J. Chem. Soc.*, 8 (1956); idem, "Discussions of the Faraday Society" **26**, 123 (1958). The most comprehensive review of the spectra of ions in crystals, where this theory has had its most striking successes, is by D. S. McClure, *Solid State Physics* **9**, 400 (1959).

[72] A. W. Adamson, *Rec. trav. chim.* **75**, 809 (1956).

[73] W. L. Libby, *J. Phys. Chem.* **56**, 863 (1958).

Co(II), strong field → Co(III), strong field

or in other cases to

Co(II), weak field → Co(III), intermediate field → Co(III), strong field

These processes go through activated complexes which require much less energy for their formation. The electron transfer processes will be slow because of the requirements which are placed on the geometry of the activated complex for the necessary rapid adiabatic transfer of the electron.

In view of the great interest which has been centered on the *trans*-effect in recent years, it should be no surprise that a ligand field interpretation of these systems should be proposed. A detailed explanation of the *trans*-effect for platinum(II) complexes has been suggested by Orgel.[74] The *trans*-effect is the term used to describe the ability of groups in the square planar complexes of platinum(II) to labilize groups *trans* to themselves toward replacement reactions. The starting point is the observation that those ligands with the greatest *trans*-effect have vacant orbitals suitable for pi bonding.[75] These can accommodate electrons from the d_{xz} orbital of the central atom. This d_{xz} orbital is the critical one because it has its maximum concentration along the directions which the entering group must take. The order of increasing *trans*-effect is known from experimental studies to be:

$$H_2O < OH^- < NH_3 \lessapprox F^- < Cl^- < Br^- < I^- \lessapprox R_3P \lessapprox R_2S < SC(NH_2)_2 < NO_2^- < CO \lessapprox$$
$$C_2H_4 < CN^-$$

This is also roughly the order of increasing ability to pi bond with the central ion. Inasmuch as these substitution reactions occur with the retention of configuration (in most cases), the entering group takes the place of the group which is replaced. A reasonable assumption is that the reaction takes place when the entering group approaches the plane of the molecule from above or below the group which is to be replaced. If the group *trans* to this position forms strong pi bonds with the d_{xz} orbital, its electronic density will be more concentrated in the direction of that ligand and hence less concentrated on the other side. This will render attack by the entering group subject to less electrostatic repulsion. The reaction may then proceed through a distorted trigonal bipyramidal intermediate. This mechanism is shown in Figure 21. The d_{xz} orbital in platinum contains a pair of electrons and it is by back donating this pair of electrons that the pi bond is formed. This orbital is also directed along the bond directions for the Pt—E and Pt—D bonds in the intermediate so any process which reduces its electron density in this direction will facilitate the reaction.

[74] L. E. Orgel, *J. Inorg. Nuclear Chem.* **2**, 137 (1956).

[75] J. Chatt and A. A. Williams. *J. Chem. Soc.* 3061 (1951). A theory similar in most respects to Orgel's was proposed somewhat earlier by J. Chatt, L. A. Duncanson, and L. M. Venanzi, *ibid.*, 4456 (1955).

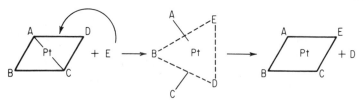

Fig. 21   Mechanism proposed for the trans effect in substitution reactions
of Pt(II).

The rise of crystal field theory has resulted in a renewed interest in the magnetic properties of complex compounds and the use of such data to furnish structural information. The magnetic behavior of these materials varies over wide limits and the detailed interpretation of such measurements is often very complicated. The general types of behavior which may be found are summarized below:[76]

NAME	MAGNITUDE (c.g.s. units)	TEMP. DEPENDENCE	EXAMPLE
Diamagnetism	~-1 to -10×10^{-6}	None	KCl, Na_3AlF_6
Normal Paramagnetism	$\sim10 \times 10^{-6}$	$1/T$ or $1/(\varDelta+T)$	$K_3Fe(CN)_6$
Van Vleck Paramagnetism	$\sim1 \times 10^{-6}$	None	$KMnO_4$
Anti-Ferromagnetism[77]	~0.1 to 100×10^{-6}	Increase with T below Transition temperature	$KNiF_3$

The simple ideas which are commonly used in interpreting magnetic moments can be seen to require a thorough revision when a large number of such compounds are examined. There are a number of extensive discussions of this.[78] Complexes which contain no unpaired electrons are usually diamagnetic (i.e., they are repelled by magnetic fields) with a susceptibility increasing with the total number of electrons per ion or molecule. In some important cases, however, these may be found to exhibit a small, temperature independent paramagnetism, e.g., $KMnO_4$, CrO_4^{-2}, VO_4^{-3} and some cobalt(III) ammines. For many of the transition element ions, the magnetic moment is rather simply related to the number of unpaired electrons and can be estimated using the spin-only formula:

$$\mu = \sqrt{n(n + 2)} \quad \text{Bohr magnetons}$$

where n is the number of unpaired electrons. It should be recalled that correc-

[76] Adapted from R. S. Nyholm, *Record of Chemical Progress* **19**, 46 (1958).

[77] V. Scatturin, L. Corliss, N. Elliott, and J. Hasting, *Acta Cryst.* **14**, 19(1961).

[78] B. N. Figgis and J. Lewis, "The Magnetochemistry of Complex Compounds", Ch. 6 in J. Lewis and R. G. Wilkins, editors, *Modern Coordination Chemistry*, Interscience Publishers, Inc., New York (1960), pp. 400–454; Ref. 27a, Ch. 10; P. W. Selwood, *Magnetochemistry*, Prentice-Hall, Inc., Englewood Cliffs, N.J., 2nd ed. (1956).

tions are applied to the experimental susceptibility before the magnetic moment of the paramagnetic species is computed. These correct for the inherent dia-magnetism which arises from the mere presence of electrons in the orbitals of the atoms composing the solid. When the measured magnetic moment of an ion such as MnO_4^- is used to determine the value of n, a small fractional value results. This behavior is characteristic of a situation in which there are atoms in two states present in the sample, usually a ground state in which all the spins are paired and an excited state in which at least some of them are unpaired.

The occurrence of antiferromagnetic behavior in polynuclear complexes is another source of difficulty. The general shape of the magnetic susceptibility curve for such a substance shows a rise in susceptibility up to a certain transition temperature (Neél temperature). Beyond this temperature the susceptibility decreases. The sharp change in temperature coefficient means that the inter-pretation of the measurements requires data over a wide temperature range. The antiferromagnetic state is characterized by an ordered antiparallel arrange-ment of electron spins in the solid and is an indication that there is a very con-siderable interaction between different metal atoms in the solid. The possibility of its occurrence is one reason why measurements of magnetic susceptibilities should be made over as wide a range of temperatures as is feasible.

The magnetic susceptibilities of complexes depend primarily upon the state of the central ion and its energy levels. Since, for transition metal ions, this means that the crystal field effects which determine the orbital populations will also determine the state of the central ion, this theory should be useful in describing the details of magnetic behavior. Historically, this was one of the first applications of the theory. Nyholm (loc. cit.) lists the following factors which may determine the actual magnitude of the paramagnetic susceptibility:

1. The number of unpaired electrons

2. The spin (S) and orbital(L) angular moments and the manner in which they are coupled to give the total angular momentum (J) of the atom

3. The nature of the energy levels and the separations of the ground state from the higher states

4. The arrangement of the ligands (their symmetry) and the strength of the field which they produce

An example can be seen in the various stereochemistries met in the com-plexes of Co(II).[79] The ground state of the Co^{+2} ion is $^4F_{9/2}$. Here the super-script 4 designates the multiplicity of the state which is $(2S+1)$ where S is the sum of the unpaired electron spins with each unpaired electron contributing $\frac{1}{2}$. F is the symbol used to designate the total orbital angular momentum and indi-cates that L is 3 where L is the orbital angular momentum. The subscript 9/2

[79] B. N. Figgis and R. S. Nyholm, *J. Chem. Soc.*, 12 (1954); 338 (1959); B. S. Chiswell and S. E. Livingston, *ibid.*, 97 (1960).

TABLE 5.6

STEREOCHEMISTRY AND MAGNETIC BEHAVIOR OF SOME COBALT(II) COMPLEXES*

Stereochemistry	Configuration	Type of bonding	Unpaired electrons	Magnetic moment		
				calcd. from $\mu=\sqrt{L(L+1)+4S(S+1)}$	calcd. from $\mu=\sqrt{n(n+2)}$	observd. μ
Square planar	$(t_{2g})^6(e_g)^1$	Spin-paired	1	3.00	1.73	2.1–2.9
Tetrahedral	$(e_g)^4(t_{2g})^3$	Spin free	3	5.21	3.87	4.3–4.8
Octahedral	$(t_{2g})^5(e_g)^2$	Spin free	3	5.21	3.87	4.8–5.3
Sexicovalent (tetragonal)	$(t_{2g})^6(e_g)^1$	Spin-paired	1	3.00	1.73	1.7–2.0

*Adapted from ref. 79

refers to the J value of this state, the vector sum of L and S. The possible magnetic moments for the various stereochemistries may or may not include an appreciable contribution from L. The possible arrangements are given in Table 5.6 which is adapted from Chiswell and Livingston, loc. cit.

In the case of these complexes, the observed magnetic moments show that the orbital contribution is generally of importance and the magnetic moments should be estimated using a slightly more general relation than the spin-only formula. This relationship is:

$$\mu = \sqrt{L(L+1) + 4S(S+1)}$$

which in the present case gives:

$$\mu = \sqrt{(3)(4) + 4(3/2)(5/2)} = 5.196$$

For octahedral complexes, the distribution of electrons is $(t_{2g})^5(e_g)^2$ and the effect of the magnetic field is to remove the degeneracy of the t_{2g} orbitals (Jahn-Teller effect) and to allow a larger contribution to the orbital moment by altering the electron density in these orbitals. For the tetrahedral complexes, the distribution of electrons is $(e_g)^4(t_{2g})^3$. Since there is one electron in each t_{2g} orbital, the magnetic field has little effect on the electronic density (spin-pairing will not occur) and there will be only a slight contribution from the orbital angular momentum. A similar argument leads to the prediction of a large orbital contribution from the configurations $(t_{2g})^1$, $(t_{2g})^2$, $(t_{2g})^4(e_g)^2$, and $(t_{2g})^5(e_g)^2$ but only a small one from $(t_{2g})^3$, $(t_{2g})^3(e_g)^1$, $(t_{2g})^3(e_g)^2$, $(t_{2g})^6(e_g)^2$ and $(t_{2g})^6(e_g)^3$ (for octahedral complexes).

A further feature which is found with the heavier transition elements results in very low moments in many cases. With these ions, fields tend to orient the L and S vectors in opposite directions and to result in moments less than those predicted by the spin-only formula. This is especially common with the platinum metals where it has been extensively studied.

MOLECULAR ORBITAL THEORY

Molecular orbital theory is only recently gaining popularity with coordination chemists. The reason for this is *not* that it has been unsuccessful in treating important problems, but rather because each type of compound requires a separate theoretical development. This has mitigated against the use of the theory by those lacking in the special techniques required for this development. Much of the small body of work using this method has been concerned with the elucidation of the details of the absorption spectra of complexes. Examples include the treatment of the charge transfer spectra of the halogeno-pentamminecobalt(III) ions by Yamatera,[80] the calculation of the changes in

[80] H. Yamatera, *J. Inorg. Nuclear Chem.* **15,** 50 (1960).

the absorption spectra of dipyridyl and orthophenanthroline upon chelation,[81] the absorption spectra of copper(II) complexes with beta-diketones,[82] the energy levels in ferrocene,[83] and the bonding in dicobalt hexacarbonyldiphenyl-acetylene.[84] Short general reviews have been given by Linnett[85a] and Gray.[85b]

The common goal in molecular orbital calculations is the set of orbitals describing the electron distribution in the molecule as a whole; these are obtained by combining the orbitals of the constituent atoms or molecules. In treating complexes this is carried out by combining orbitals of the central atom with n ligand orbitals of the n ligands to obtain the molecular orbitals responsible for holding the complex together. These molecular orbitals will be of three types: (a) bonding orbitals or orbitals stabilized by the formation of the complex; in these an electron will have a lower energy than it possessed prior to coordination, (b) non-bonding orbitals or orbitals in which electrons have the same energy as they possessed prior to coordination, and (c) anti-bonding orbitals or orbitals in which an electron will have a higher energy than it possessed prior to coordination. The over-all distribution of electrons in these orbitals must be such that complexation results in a situation in which the energy gained by putting electrons into bonding orbitals more than offsets any loss due to the placing of any electrons into anti-bonding orbitals.

The theoretical treatments of this problem may be seen in the work of Van Vleck,[86] Stevens,[87] or Owen.[88,89] The ligand and metal orbitals which are used to build up the molecular orbitals are combined to form new linear combinations which satisfy certain symmetry requirements. The d orbitals of the central atom which do not point toward the ligands become non-bonding molecular orbitals. Thus, the d_{xz}, d_{yz}, and d_{xy} are non-bonding orbitals for an octahedral complex, while for a square planar complex the non-bonding orbitals are p_z, d_{xz}, d_{yz}, d_{xy}, and d_{z^2}. For an n coordinated central ion there will be found n bonding orbitals and n anti-bonding orbitals. Thus, for the octahedral case there will be twelve orbitals in all and these are given by expressions of the type:[86]

$$\psi(E_g) = \alpha\psi(3d_{\gamma_1}) + (1-\alpha^2)^{\frac{1}{2}}(1/12)^{\frac{1}{2}}(2\psi_3 + 2\psi_6 - \psi_1 - \psi_4 - \psi_2 - \psi_5)$$

where $\psi(3d_{\gamma_1})$ is an atomic $3d$ orbital of the central ion and the ψ_1's, ψ_2's, etc.,

[81] H. L. Schlafer, *Zeit. phys. Chem.* **8**, 373 (1956) and the later papers in this series. Perturbation theory is used here.

[82] R. L. Belford, M. Calvin, and G. Belford, *J. Chem. Phys.* **26**, 1165 (1957); R. L. Belford, "Report No. UCRL–3051" (June 1955).

[83] J. P. Dahl and C. J. Ballhausen, *Det. Kgl. Danske Videns. Selskab.* **33**, No. 5 (1961).

[84] D. A. Brown, *J. Chem. Phys.* **33**, 1037 (1960).

[85a] J. W. Linnett, "Discussions of the Faraday Society" **26**, 8 (1958).

[85b] H. Gray, *J. Chem. Educ.* **41**, 2 (1964).

[86] J. H. Van Vleck, *J. Chem. Phys.* **3**, 803, 807 (1935).

[87] K. W. H. Stevens, *Proc. Roy. Soc.* **A219**, 542 (1953).

[88] J. Owen, *Proc. Roy. Soc.* **A227**, 183 (1955).

[89] Idem, "Discussions of the Faraday Society" **19**, 127 (1955).

refer to orbitals of the six ligands. The value of α determines the degree of transfer of the electron. For the wave functions of different symmetry the coefficients are denoted β or γ and these play a similar role in determining the charge distribution in the complex. It is to be noted that values of these coefficients may be obtained from paramagnetic resonance experiments under favorable circumstances. Thus, in $IrCl_6^{-2}$ there is a single unpaired electron in a π orbital, designated $\pi*$ in recent literature. This is of the form:

$$\pi_{xy}^* = \beta d_{xy} - (1 - \beta^2)^{\frac{1}{2}}(\tfrac{1}{2})(p_1 + p_2 - p_4 - p_5)\pi$$

From experiments $\beta^2 = 0.66$ so the electron is β^2 on the iridium atom and $1/6(1-\beta^2)$ on each chlorine. Several other examples of this technique for the determination of the coefficients may be seen in the survey presented by Owen.[88] This flexibility in describing electronic distributions is a very obvious advantage of the molecular orbital theory. The fact that molecular orbital theory does not assign values to the parameters α, β, or γ on an arbitrary basis means that it is capable in principle of describing the entire gamut of polarities which may be met in coordinate bonds. This can also be achieved, though far less readily, by the other theories of the coordinate bond. In molecular orbital theory the transfer of electrons in either direction can be accommodated by adjusting the relative importance of the donor and acceptor orbitals in the molecular orbitals. This is true of both sigma and pi bonding.[89] It is possible to write the molecular orbital electronic configurations for complexes using a procedure analogous to that given by Mulliken for diatomic molecules. The order of the orbitals is determined by the stereochemistry of the complex. For an octahedral complex of a first row transition element which uses $4s$, $4p$, and $3d$ orbitals of the central metal and six ligand orbitals the order of the molecular orbitals in increasing energy is:

$$(a_{1g})_b(t_{1u})_b(t_{1u})_b(t_{1u})_b(e_g)_b(t_{2g})_n(t_{2g})_n(t_{2g})_n(e_g)_a(e_g)_a(a_{1g})_a(t_{1u})_a(t_{1u})_a(t_{1u})_a$$

The subscripts b, n, and a indicate whether the orbitals are bonding, non-bonding, or anti-bonding. Each orbital can accommodate two electrons. As an example one may consider the molecular orbital configuration for the FeF_6^{-3} ion. Here the central ion has five electrons which are to be put into the molecular orbitals. These are the five electrons in the $3d$ orbitals which are taken in combinations to form the molecular orbitals. There are also twelve electrons from the six ligand ions which are to be put into molecular orbitals. The actual distribution will be determined by the separations between the energies of the groups of degenerate orbitals. It should be noted that the orbitals upon which crystal field centers its attention are the non-bonding orbitals designated $(t_{2g})_n$ here and the anti-bonding orbitals designated $(e_g)_a$. The effect of the ligand field here is also to split these orbitals so the gross results of crystal field theory can be rather readily incorporated into the molecular picture. In the case of FeF_6^{-3}, the separation between these levels may be taken as small, so the molecular orbital electronic configuration may be written as:

$$(a_{1g})_b^2(t_{1u})_b^6(t_{1u})_b^6(e_g)_b^2(e_g)_b^2(t_{2g})_n^1(t_{2g})_n^1(t_{2g})_n^1(e_g)_a^1(e_g)_a^1$$

Here the relative energies of $(t_{2g})_n$ and $(e_g)_a$ determine whether the pairing up of electrons is energetically favored over promotion. An alternative way of presenting these orbitals[85] is shown in Figure 22. This allows the electrons to

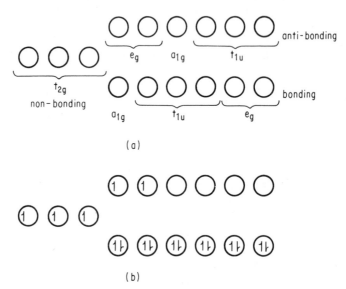

Fig. 22 (a) The molecular orbitals of an octahedral complex. (b) Electron distribution in the molecular orbitals of FeF_6^{-3}.

be sorted out in a more obvious graphical method. Figure 22(a) shows the general arrangement for an octahedral complex. The order of the anti-bonding orbitals may change if there is a large overlap of ligand and metal orbitals,[89] but a simple illustration of the use of this diagram will show how the electron distribution is written and how the molecular orbital treatment is just as successful as crystal field theory is in describing both magnetic behavior and absorption spectra. The diagram for FeF_6^{-3} is shown in Figure 22(b). As can be seen FeF_6^{-3} should have a magnetic moment corresponding to five unpaired electrons. The absorption spectra can be interpreted only if one has more detailed knowledge of the spacings of the energy levels. As with crystal field theory, the experimental evidence of this sort is usually used to estimate the spacings of the energy levels. In this case there are no allowed transitions between orbitals close in energy so the lack of a significant visible absorption spectra has the same basis as with crystal field theory. With an example such as this the bonding orbitals would have very large contributions from the ligand orbitals, i.e., they would form the most important part of the molecular orbital and would appear in the expression for the molecular orbital with large coefficients.

The sharing of electrons in the non-bonding molecular orbitals with empty orbitals of the ligands results in pi bonding, and the analogies with the valence bond picture are quite apparent.[86] Less common, but still easily incorporated into the framework of molecular orbital theory, are pi bonds which arise from the donation of pi electrons from the ligand to the central metal or from *d* electrons from ligand to metal. These presumably occur in complexes with chloride or heavier halides as ligands. A listing of the metal and ligand orbitals which may be combined to form sigma and pi bonds has been given by Orgel.[31b]

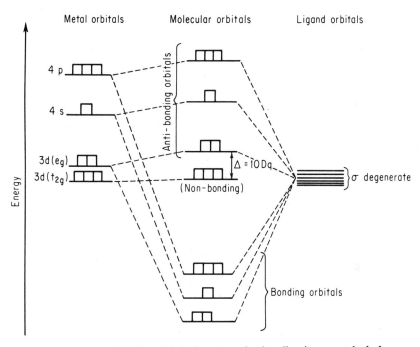

Fig. 23 The molecular orbitals for non-polar bonding in an octahedral complex. (Redrawn by permission of the Reinhold Publishing Corp.)

The whole question of pi bonding presupposes a rather detailed picture of the electronic distribution in complexes such as is presently available only in small part. A more empirical approach to this problem may be seen in a discussion of how sigma and pi bonding affect the stabilities of complex ions.[90]

A somewhat different qualitative presentation of the use of molecular orbital theory with both typical complexes and metal cyclopentadienyls has

[90] R. J. P. Williams, "Discussions of the Faraday Society" **26**, 123 (1958).

been presented by Richardson.[91] The diagrams presented are a more detailed picture of the relative energy levels and also can be modified easily to show pi bonding effects. Here again n metal orbitals are combined with n ligand orbitals to give n bonding molecular orbitals and n anti-bonding molecular orbitals. For non-polar bonding there will be nearly equal contributions of both metal and ligand orbitals to the bonding orbitals. Such a situation is presented in Figure 23. The six bonding orbitals can hold twelve ligand electrons and form the basis of six sigma bonds. The energy levels in Figure 23 are for octahedral complexes.

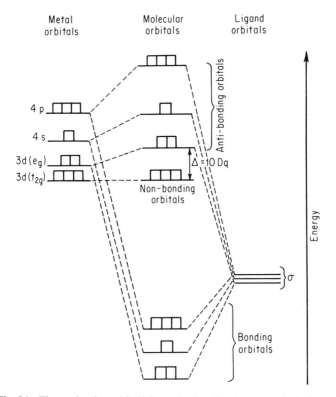

Fig. 24 The molecular orbitals for polar bonding in an octahedral complex. (Redrawn by permission of the Reinhold Publishing Corp.)

For an octahedral complex in which strongly polar bonds are formed, the ligand orbitals will be correspondingly more important in their contributions to the bonding orbitals. For such a case the molecular orbitals can be presented as in Figure 24.

[91] J. W. Richardson in H. Zeiss', *Organometallic Chemistry*, Reinhold Publishing Corp., New York (1960), pp. 1–35.

It is easy to see from the diagram that the separation Δ or $10Dq$ here will determine whether electrons in the non-bonding or anti-bonding orbitals derived from the $3d$ orbitals will tend to pair up or not, as in crystal field theory. The drawings are not to scale and it should be recalled the Δ or $10Dq$ will be larger for non-polar bonding. When pi bonding is of importance, an accurate energy level diagram can be drawn only if the spacing and types of orbitals in the ligand are known. In an octahedral complex these will combine with the $3d(t_{2g})$ orbitals and the $4p$ orbitals of the central metal to give molecular pi orbitals which are the basis of the pi component of the double bond between metal and ligand in cyanides, carbonyls, and similar complexes.

Molecular orbital treatments for complexes of other stereochemistries have also been developed. It is necessary to have information on bond energies and internuclear distances to work out a detailed molecular treatment of a given complex. The lack of such precise data for many compounds of special interest is a factor which limits the development of a generalized molecular treatment of coordination compounds at the present time. The carbonyls are perhaps the only class of compounds for which enough detailed information of this sort is available.[91]

FUTURE DEVELOPMENTS

The quantitative treatment of the coordinate bond is as yet in a rudimentary stage. The major problems of charge distribution, bond energies, and bond distances and their relation to the contributions of sigma and pi bonds in a given molecule are yet to be solved in a general manner. It seems increasingly unlikely that any simple theory will be adequate. The diversity of chemical behavior which must be encompassed will probably necessitate the use of more powerful, but also unfortunately more sophisticated, mathematical technique. The reader who is interested in the quantitative treatment of these problems can find no better introduction than that given in F. A. Cotton, *Chemical Applications of Group Theory*, Interscience Publishers, Inc., N.Y. (1963).

EXERCISES

1. Write the valence bond electronic configurations for the following species:
   $Ag(CN)_2^-$, $Fe(CN)_6^{-3}$, $MoCl_6^{-3}$, $W(CN)_8^{-4}$, $Cu(NH_3)_4^{+2}$, $Ti(H_2O)_6^{+3}$, $V(C_2O_4)_3^{-3}$, $FeCl_4^-$, $AlCl_4^-$.

2. Describe how you would use crystal field theory in discussing the V(IV) ion. Consider both the tetrahedral and octahedral arrangements of ligands. Tell how you would use the absorption spectra of V(IV) in a suitable environment to help in determining its coordination number. Would you expect octahedral complexes of this species to show a Jahn-Teller effect?

3. Reformulate Taube's rules for predicting the lability of complexes in terms of molecular orbital terms. Can you provide an analogous rationalization in terms of crystal field theory concepts?

4. How is the square pyramidal structure of IF_5 accommodated by the general principle that the electron pairs of a central atom will assume an average position in which they are as far apart as is consistent with their retention at a fixed distance from the central atom?

5. Calculate the effective atomic number of the central atoms in the following complexes: $Ag(NH_3)_2^+$, $AuCl_4^-$, $Co(NH_3)_6^{+2}$, $Pd(NH_3)_2Cl_2$, $MoCl_6^{-3}$, $V(CN)_6^{-4}$, and $Os(CO)_5$. Indicate which atoms achieve the E.A.N. of an inert gas.

6. Predict which of the following species would be expected to be inert: $NiBr_3 \cdot 2P(Et)_3$, TaF_7^{-2}, ZrF_7^{-3}, $Cu(CN)_3^{-2}$, and $W(CN)_8^{-3}$.

7. How do the results of S, Sugano and R. G. Shulman, *Phys. Rev.* **130**, 12(1963) affect the explanation given for the order of ions in the series of increasing crystal field strengths?

6

Some General Aspects of the Behavior of Complexes

There are a number of features of the chemistry of coordination compounds which are the result of particular conditions of stereochemistry or stability rather than specific factors found only with a given species. Several of these are discussed in this chapter. Though the discussion of these is in terms of specific compounds of a given element, it should be remembered that the notions are of more general applicability. This is true even of the *trans*-effect which is found in its most obvious form in the compounds of platinum(II).

RESOLUTION OF ENANTIOMORPHS[1]

Under normal circumstances, a reaction which is used to synthesize a molecule which is asymmetric will result in the production of equal amounts of the *d* and *l* forms. The subsequent separation of these enantiomorphs is termed *resolution* and may, in principle at least, be effected by a large number of processes. Very rarely, it is possible to isolate one of the enantiomorphs by a spontaneous (but presumably nonequilibrium) process in which one of the forms crystallizes from solution *before* the other. A process which occurs with somewhat greater frequency (but is still comparatively rare) is one in which the crystallization of each form proceeds separately to give a mixture of asymmetric crystals, each of which contains only one isomer. The classical resolu-

[1] A general review of the techniques used for the resolution of organic compounds is given by W. Theilacker in Houben-Weyl, *Methoden der Organischen Chemie*, G. Thieme Verlag, Stuttgart, 4th ed. (1955), Vol. 4, Part 2, p. 505. The most complete discussion concerned exclusively with octahedral complexes is that of F. Basolo in J. C. Bailar, Jr., *The Chemistry of the Coordination Compounds*, Reinhold Publishing Corp., New York (1956), p. 331 ff.

tion of tartaric acid by Pasteur is a typical example. In this case if the tartaric acid is crystallized from solution at a temperature less than 27°, two kinds of crystals (*d* and *l*) separate which can be sorted by hand. This method has been used[2] to separate *d* and *l* $K_3Co(C_2O_4)_3 \cdot H_2O$ above 13.2° and by Jaeger and Bijkerk to separate *d* and *l* [Rh(cyclopentanediamine)$_3$](ClO$_4$)$_3 \cdot 12H_2O$ below 48°.[3] The basis for this kind of separation lies in the solubility-temperature curves for the active forms and the racemate.[4] Two types of behavior which would allow such a separation to be achieved are shown in Figures 25 and 26.

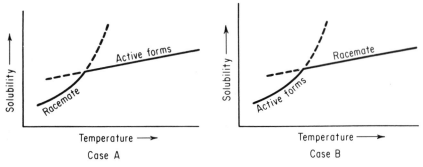

Fig. 25 Solubility curve observed for a racemic mixture when the active forms crystallize out separately above a certain temperature.

Fig. 26 Solubility curve observed for a racemic mixture when the active forms crystallize out separately below a certain temperature.

The basis for this kind of a separation can be seen from the solubility curves for the active forms and the racemate. If there is a temperature at which the stable solid in equilibrium with the solution is the two active solids rather than the racemate, such a process is possible. The solubility diagram for $K_3Co(C_2O_4)_3 \cdot H_2O$ is an example of Case A, Figure 25. The fact that this is a rather inconvenient method of resolution has militated against its widespread use.

The other methods which are available all require the use of an asymmetric environment to effect the resolution. These methods are:

1. The formation of diastereoisomers

2. The action of bacteria or enzymes upon racemic mixtures

3. Kinetic methods of resolution, e.g., esterification of a racemic acid with an optically active alcohol

[2] F. M. Jaeger and W. Thomas, *Rec. Trav. Chim.* **38**, 171 (1919); F. M. Jaeger, *ibid.*, **38**, 250 (1919).

[3] F. M. Jaeger and L. Bijkerk, *Proc. Konik. Akad. Weten. Amsterdam* **40**, 116 (1937), C.A. 32: 446.

[4] H. W. B. Roozeboom, *Zeit. Physik. Chem.* **2**, 513 (1888).

4. Absorption on an optically active surface or absorption in an optically active network

5. Diffusion in a solution of an optically active compound (e.g., in a solution of sucrose in water)

6. Preferential solution in an optically active solvent

7. Preferential induced crystallization

8. Diffusion through asymmetric membranes

9. Use of configurational activity

10. Any process in which enantiomorphs exhibit different behavior due to an asymmetric environment can conceivably be used to effect at least a partial resolution

FORMATION OF DIASTEREOISOMERS. The most widely used method for resolving enantiomorphs makes use of the formation of diastereoisomers. Thus a *d* and *l* acid mixture will react with an *l* base to give two products which are not enantiomorphs, but diastereoisomers, and which differ in solubility and other physical properties:

$$d \text{ acid} + l \text{ base} \rightarrow \text{salt} (d \text{ anion plus } l \text{ cation})$$

$$l \text{ acid} + l \text{ base} \rightarrow \text{salt} (l \text{ anion plus } l \text{ cation})$$

Solubility differences are usually used to effect the separation of diastereoisomers. Subsequently, a reaction is carried out to remove the resolving agent and to obtain the optical isomers in pure form. The following procedure from the literature shows how this method is used. A. Werner[5] resolved $Rh(en)_3^{+3}$ via this method. The complex is prepared by the reaction:

$$Na_3[RhCl_6] \cdot 12H_2O + 3en \rightarrow [Rh(en)_3]Cl_3 + 3NaCl + 12H_2O$$

The resolution is then effected by forming diastereoisomers using sodium nitrocamphorsulfonate:

$$d, l[Rh(en)_3]^{+3} + \text{sodium nitrocamphorsulfonate} \rightarrow$$

$$\begin{cases} l[Rh(en)_3] \text{ (nitrocamphorsulfonate)} \downarrow \text{ (as a precipitate)} \\ d \ Rh(en)_3^{+3} \text{ in solution} \end{cases}$$

The resolving agent is then removed from the less soluble diastereoisomer by grinding with a little water and sodium iodide:

$$l[Rh(en)_3] \text{ (nitrocamphorsulfonate)} + NaI \rightarrow$$

$$l[Rh(en)_3]I_3 + \text{sodium nitrocamphorsulfonate}$$

The enantiomorph which forms the more soluble diastereoisomer may often be recovered from the mother liquor in a state of reasonable purity. The use of several resolving agents is generally possible in any given case and the final

[5] A. Werner, *Ber.* **45**, 1228 (1912).

choice is made upon the basis of effectiveness of the separation. In this case *d*-tartaric acid acts equally well as a resolving agent.

The requirements of a good resolving agent vary but it must be a *stable* optically active anion or cation or easily converted into such. Generally (but not necessarily) these are naturally occurring materials. Their solubility properties are important for they must be capable of forming diastereoisomers with solubility characteristics *different* from their own and yet be readily removable from such diastereoisomers by gentle chemical reaction (usually a metathetical one). Several of the common resolving agents are listed below:

RESOLVING AGENT	CHARACTER
d-tartaric acid	anion
nitrocamphorsulfonate	anion
bromcamphorsulfonate	anion
cinchonine	cation
quinine	cation
strychnine	cation
brucine	cation
d or *l*[Co(en)$_3$]$^{+3}$	cation
d-antimonyl tartarate	anion

There is apparently no necessity that the compound formed with the two enantiomorphic forms be one of the usual sort with literal chemical bonds. An early report of the use of "molecular compounds" (charge-transfer compounds) may be seen in the resolution of *d*, *l*-terpineol via its molecular compound with digitonin.[6]

ACTION OF BACTERIA OR ENZYMES UPON RACEMIC MIXTURES. The fact that microorganisms preferentially attack one of a pair of enantiomorphs was known to Pasteur by 1860. This is a general feature of biological processes and many enzymatic reactions as well. Thus the functioning of most enzymes is *stereospecific* to a greater or lesser extent. The naturally occurring amino acids all have the same spatial configurations relative to the alpha carbon atom[7] and this is the form which is attacked initially by microorganisms in the racemic mixture. This method of resolution has not been used very much with complexes. Actually many metal activated enzymes are complexes but the effect of a large concentration of metal ions, such as would be encountered in the racemic mixtures of complexes, has a deleterious effect on the activity of both bacteria and enzymes in many cases.

KINETIC METHODS OF RESOLUTION. Marckwald and McKenzie[8] found that *d*-mandelic acid reacted more rapidly with *l*-menthol than did *l*-mandelic acid. This method could possibly be used for the resolution of complexes which have

---

[6] A. Windaus, F. Klanhardt, and R. Weinhold, *Zeit. Physiol. Chem.* **126**, 308 (1923).

[7] D. L. Lloyd, *Biol. Reviews* **7**, 254 (1932).

[8] W. Marckwald and A. McKenzie, *Ber.* **34**, 469 (1901).

functional groups not bound up by coordination. It is not widely used by organic chemists.

Asymmetric Adsorption and Absorption. Perhaps the earliest observations on a preference for one enantiomorph in such a process are those of R. Magini.[9] This worker found that natural textile fibers such as cotton, wool, and silk, which possess an asymmetric structure, take up different enantiomorphic forms of a substance at different *rates*. Subsequent studies have been concerned primarily with differences in the *equilibrium* behavior in such processes. W. Porter [10] found that in at least one case wool specifically absorbed (or adsorbed?) one enantiomorphic form of a dye from solution and left the other form in solution. While this method has not found widespread use it is of interest to note that a wide variety of optically active solids have been used in attempts to resolve inorganic complexes. Finely ground, optically active quartz,[11] starch, lactose,[12] and numerous other materials have been used. In a few cases a complete resolution has been effected but the method has resulted in partial resolution in many cases.[13,14]

Diffusion in a Solution of an Optically Active Solute. V. Carassiti[15] demonstrated that the d and l forms of $Co(en)_3^{+3}$ could be separated by utilizing the differences in their rates of free diffusion in a concentrated aqueous sucrose solution. The resolution was only a partial one.

Preferential Solution in an Optically Active Solvent. In earlier efforts, little success was encountered in attempts to use optically active solvents in resolution. Recent work [16] has shown that partial resolutions may be effected with organic compounds. The zone melting techniques as applied by Kirschner and Doron[17] to inner complex salts may also be considered to be a successful application of this type of technique.

Preferential Induced Crystallization. If a seed crystal of one antipode (or even another optically active substance) is added to a solution of the racemate and then precipitation is started (by the addition of another solvent) sometimes the solid which separates consists of only one of the two enantiomorphs. An example of this is provided by the work of Werner and Bosshart[18] who added seed crystals containing only $d[Co(en)_2(C_2O_4)]^+$ to an aqueous solu-

[9] R. Magini, *J. Chim. Physique* **2**, 403 (1904).

[10] W. Porter, *J. Amer. Chem. Soc.* **45**, 1990 (1923).

[11] R. Tsuchida, M. Kobayashi, and A. Nakamura, *Bull. Chem. Soc. Japan* **11**, 38 (1936).

[12] T. Moeller and E. Gulyas, *J. Inorg. Nuclear Chem.* **5**, 245 (1958) (contains earlier literature), T. M. Hseu, D. F. Martin, and T. Moeller, *Inorg. Chem.* **2**, 587 (1963).

[13] W. Bradley, R. A. Brindley, and G. C. Casty, "Discussions of the Faraday Society", No. 16, 152 (1954): absorption of enantiomorphs by wool.

[14] H. Irving, J. B. Gill, and W. R. Cross, *J. Chem. Soc.* 2087 (1960).

[15] V. Carassiti, *J. Inorg. Nuclear Chem.* **8**, 227 (1958).

[16] A. Luttringhaus and D. Berrer, "Tetrahedron Letters", No. 10, p. 10 (1959).

[17] Work reported in *Chem. Eng. News* (July 10, 1961), p. 38; see also, *Inorganic Chemistry* **1**, 539 (1962).

[18] A. Werner and J. Bosshart, *Ber.* **47**, 2171 (1914).

tion containing the *d* and *l* forms and then added alcohol. The precipitate which formed contained only the $d[Co(en)_2(C_2O_4)]^+$. Delepine used an analogous idea in developing his method of "active racemates".[19] He added, say, $d K_3[Rh(C_2O_4)_3]$ to a solution of *d, l* $K_3[Ir(C_2O_4)_3]$ and obtained crystals containing $d K_3[Rh(C_2O_4)_3]$ and $l K_3[Ir(C_2O_4)_3]$. This method can be used when the compounds used are very similar in structure.

MISCELLANEOUS METHODS. There are several other possible methods of resolution some of which have proven useful in specific cases. These include stereospecific reactions with inclusion compounds,[20] diffusion through an asymmetric membrane, use of an optically active ion exchange resin,[21] electrophoresis in a strong centrifugal or magnetic field,[22] gas chromatography,[22a] paper chromatography, and preferential photochemical decomposition of a racemic mixture by means of circularly polarized light.[23] The use [23a] of diastereoazeotropes has been tried without success.

ENUMERATION OF ISOMERS. The problem of determining the number and types of isomers which are possible for various compounds is one which has been attacked in two ways. The first way is to write out all the possible isomers using structural formulas or suitable equivalent symbols. This is the method which has been used most commonly by chemists and is easily appreciated. The second method is to determine the rules governing the occurrence of such isomers and to express this in some general mathematical form. One of the commonest rules of this sort is the one which states that *n* dissimilar asymmetric atoms in a molecule give rise to 2^n isomers arranged in enantiomorphous pairs. Much more general treatments have been given and the whole problem can be broken down into fairly tractable portions. Lunn and Senior[24] divided the general problem into the determination of the number of skeletons or basic structures and the determination of the number of substitution isomers possible with each structure. (They also give a review of much of the earlier work in this field.) When dealing with coordination compounds the skeleton is generally known and the second part of the problem is the one of greater interest. Lunn and Senior treated the second problem in detail using the methods of group theory. With every skeleton (or basic molecular kind of arrangement) there is associated a permutation group whose properties suffice to determine the number and types of univalent substitution isomers possible for that skeleton.

[19] M. Delepine, *Bull. Soc. Chim. France* (4), **29**, 656 (1921); (5), **1**, 1256 (1934).

[20] F. Cramer and W. Dietsche, *Ber.* **92**, 1739 (1959).

[21] S. Tsuboyama and M. Yanagita. *Sci. Papers Inst. Phys. Chem. Res.* (Tokyo) **53**, 245 (1959), C.A. 54:14173.

[22] F. C. Lendrum, *Nature* **192**, 499 (1958). (a) R. E. Sievers, R. W. Moshier, and M. L. Morris, *Inorg. Chem.* **1**, 966 (1962).

[23] R. Tsuchida, A. Nakamura, and M. Kobayashi, *J. Chem. Soc. Japan* **56**, 1335 (1935); F. M. Jaeger, *Optical Activity and High Temperature Measurements*, McGraw-Hill, Inc., New York (1930), p. 210 ff. (a) C. J. McGinn, *J. Phys. Chem.* **65**, 1896 (1961).

[24] A. C. Lunn and J. K. Senior, *J. Phys. Chem.* **33**, 1027 (1929).

Lunn and Senior have tabulated some of the types of functions needed for such an examination of many of the commonly encountered groups. Since little work has been done on isomerism for coordination numbers other than four and six this treatment is of considerably greater generality than is required at present.

The method of Lunn and Senior was used by Marchi, Fernelius, and McReynolds[24a] in determining the number of isomers possible with various eight-coordinate structures, but has otherwise been little used.

THE BAILAR-MAYPER SCHEME FOR OCTAHEDRAL COMPLEXES. A convenient scheme for determining the numbers and types of positional isomers of *octahedral* complexes has been given by J. C. Bailar, Jr.[25] and extended to enantiomorphic forms by S. A. Mayper.[26]

The method starts with a complex with six monodentate ligands, all different which are arranged as in Figure 27. The configuration is then represented by the composite symbol:

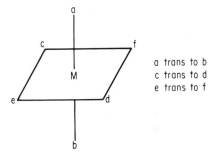

a trans to b
c trans to d
e trans to f

Fig. 27 The designation of the octahedral coordination positions used by Bailar in his scheme for enumerating isomers.

$$ab$$
$$cd$$
$$ef$$

If the isomers which are *not* enantiomorphs are first considered, it is found that there are fifteen which are represented by the tabulation:

	L	M	N
1	ab cd ef	ab ce df	ab cf de
2	ac bd ef	ac be df	ac bf de
3	ad bc ef	ad be cf	ad bf ce
4	ae bc df	ae bd cf	ae bf cd
5	af bc de	af bd ce	af be cd

[24a] L. E. Marchi, W. C. Fernelius, and J. P. McReynolds, *J. Amer. Chem. Soc.* **65**, 329 (1943).

[25] J. C. Bailar, Jr., *J. Chem. Ed.* **34**, 334, 626 (1957).

[26] S. A. Mayper, *ibid.*, **34**, 623 (1957).

If we define an *interchange* operation as one in which two *trans*-pairs are exchanged *or* one *trans*-pair is reversed, such an operation forms the symbol which is the mirror image of the starting symbol. For *optically active* structures any odd number of such interchanges will give the symbol of the enantiomorph and any even number the original symbol. If the structure is its own mirror image any number of interchanges will yield an equivalent symbol. As an example consider 4-M

$$\left\{\begin{array}{l} ae \\ bd \\ cf \end{array}\right\} \text{ gives } \left\{\begin{array}{l} ea \\ bd \\ cf \end{array}\right\} \qquad \text{or} \qquad \left\{\begin{array}{l} ae \\ bd \\ cf \end{array}\right\} \text{ gives } \left\{\begin{array}{l} ae \\ cf \\ bd \end{array}\right\}$$

reversal of a trans-pair   exchange of two pairs
                                      of trans-symbols

These are shown in Figure 28. Each of the symbols listed in the table above is

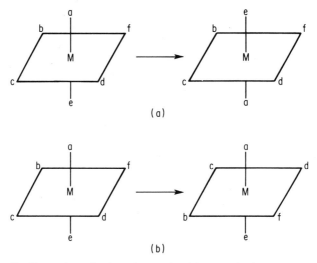

Fig. 28 Formation of mirror images by (a) reversal of a *trans*-pair of ligands and (b) by exchange of two pairs of *trans*-ligands.

that of an isomer which is not superposable on its mirror image so there is a total of 30 isomers in all. This is the largest possible number of isomers which needs to be considered for simple substituents and the number of isomers in other cases (in which there is no asymmetric ligand) will always be less. Most of the other cases of isomerism of interest can be enumerated by the same kind of a process, as will be shown below.

When the complex contains six groups, some of which are identical, this scheme easily allows the sorting out of the isomers. Since the maximum number of isomers results when all of the groups are different, we can consider how the results are changed when some of the groups are the same by writing the same symbol for the identical ligands. For a compound such as $[Co(NH_3)_2(NO_2)_2Br(H_2O)]$, a and b are the same, and c and d are the same. For this compound the table becomes:

	L	M	N
1	aa cc ef	aa ce cf	$\begin{bmatrix} aa \\ cf \\ ce \end{bmatrix}$
2	ac ac ef	ac ae cf	ac af ce
3	$\begin{bmatrix} ac \\ ac \\ ef \end{bmatrix}$	$\begin{bmatrix} ac \\ ae \\ cf \end{bmatrix}$	$\begin{bmatrix} ac \\ af \\ ce \end{bmatrix}$
4	$\begin{bmatrix} ae \\ ac \\ cf \end{bmatrix}$	$\begin{bmatrix} ae \\ ac \\ cf \end{bmatrix}$	ae af cc
5	$\begin{bmatrix} af \\ ac \\ ce \end{bmatrix}$	$\begin{bmatrix} af \\ ac \\ ce \end{bmatrix}$	$\begin{bmatrix} af \\ ae \\ cc \end{bmatrix}$

Identical configurations are:

1M and 1N
2L and 3L
2M, 3M, 4L, and 4M
2N, 3N, 5L, and 5M
4N and 5N

In the table, brackets are placed around duplicated structures. The result is six positional isomers of which two exist in enantiomorphous forms to give a total of eight isomers.

When chelating groups are present, a slight modification allows the present scheme to be extended to cover isomerism in such compounds. If the coordinating portions of the chelating agent are indicated by capital letters (e.g., AA for $H_2NCH_2CH_2NH_2$, AB for $H_2NCH_2CH_2SH$, etc.) and it is remembered that adjacent coordinating positions of a chelating agent must occupy *cis*-positions in the coordination sphere, the scheme can be used in the same manner as with simple ligands. Thus a table for a compound of the type [M(AA)cdef] is:

	L	M	N
1	$\begin{bmatrix} AA \\ cd \\ ef \end{bmatrix}$	$\begin{bmatrix} AA \\ ce \\ df \end{bmatrix}$	$\begin{bmatrix} AA \\ cf \\ de \end{bmatrix}$
2	Ac Ad ef	Ac Ae df	Ac Af de
3	$\begin{bmatrix} Ad \\ Ac \\ ef \end{bmatrix}$	Ad Ae cf	Ad Af ce

4	$\begin{bmatrix} Ae \\ Ac \\ df \end{bmatrix}$	$\begin{bmatrix} Ae \\ Ad \\ cf \end{bmatrix}$	$\begin{matrix} Ae \\ Af \\ cd \end{matrix}$
5	$\begin{bmatrix} Af \\ Ac \\ de \end{bmatrix}$	$\begin{bmatrix} Af \\ Ad \\ ce \end{bmatrix}$	$\begin{bmatrix} Af \\ Ae \\ cd \end{bmatrix}$

Here there are six pairs of antipodes. The extension of the method to multidentate ligands is quite straightforward. It is relatively easy to keep track of the similar arrangements if the same symbol is used for identical coordinating groups in the chelating agent. A listing of the isomers possible with tetradentate or higher ligands is also available.[27]

There are further types of isomerism which are possible in chelate complexes which arise from the various possible conformations which the ligand atoms may assume. This has been discussed thoroughly by Corey and Bailar[28] in an important paper. These authors showed how the conformations of chelate ligands can be worked out on the basis of the general methods of conformational analysis used for organic compounds. They also showed how this method and the known conformation of optically active organic ligands can be combined to provide information on the *absolute* configuration of asymmetric chelate complexes.

DETERMINATION OF THE ABSOLUTE CONFIGURATIONS OF ENANTIOMORPHS. While the *existence* of optical isomerism establishes the fact that pairs of mirror images give rise to such behavior, *none* of the possible chemical methods allows the determination of *which structure* corresponds to a given isomer. All that chemical information can establish is the existence of such structures. Naturally, the problem of the absolute configuration of enantiomorphs has interested chemists for many years. At present many discussions about "absolute" configurations are based upon ideas derived from Emil Fischer. Fischer made an *arbitrary* assumption by assigning a configuration to dextro-rotatory glucose and then showed the genetic relation between this and numerous other molecules, including simpler compounds. At present dextro-rotatory glycerose is assigned a D-configuration by convention.[29] Acids with substituents are given the prefix D if the alpha substituted group points to the right when the COOH group is written at the top and the COOH and R groups point backward. This is shown in Figure 29 (a) and (b). The configurations of other active molecules are generally related to that of D-glycerose which is shown in Figure 29 (c). There is *no* necessary identity between the sign of the optical rotation and the D- or L-configuration. Malic acid has a rotation which changes *sign* with changes in concentration.

[27] W. C. Fernelius and B. E. Bryant, *J. Amer. Chem. Soc.* **75**, 1735 (1953).
[28] E. J. Corey and J. C. Bailar, Jr., *J. Amer. Chem. Soc.* **81**, 2620 (1959).
[29] C. S. Hudson, *J. Chem. Ed.* **18**, 353 (1941).

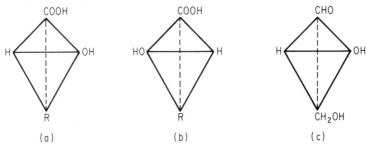

Fig. 29 Absolute configurations of some simple organic molecules: (a) D form of RCH(OH)COOH, (b) L form of RCH(OH)COOH, (c) D-glycerose.

In inorganic chemistry the problem of generic relationships of enantiomorphous forms has never been developed in any systematic experimental fashion, though the general principles have been presented. The reasons for this are the relatively few systematic studies on generically related compounds and the frequency of the Walden inversion. One finds some examples of the use of the general principle that very closely related compounds of the same absolution configuration should exhibit a similarity in the dependence of the rotation on the wavelength of light (rotatory dispersion curves). A few configurations have been shown to be the same on the basis of rotatory dispersion studies.[30]

In very recent years an attack upon the problem of absolute configurations using X-ray techniques has achieved some measure of success. The X-ray studies are based upon differences in the intensities of the diffraction patterns obtained with certain types of enantiomorphs.[31,32] The basic notion here is that of anomalous diffraction. Thus, the phase difference between the waves diffracted by two atoms depends not only on the path difference, but also upon the nature of the atoms. This difference can be made large if the X-rays used are of a suitable frequency to excite the electrons in the K shell of one of the atoms in the substance under study. This idea was developed by Bijvoet to the point where the intensity patterns for D- and L-configurations could be calculated on an a priori basis for anomalous diffraction. These are found to be different as Table 6.1 shows.

In this case the K shell electrons of the rubidium atom absorb energy furnished by the Zr-K radiation. The determination of configuration was carried

[30] F. M. Jaeger, *Optical Activity and High Temperature Measurements*, McGraw-Hill, Inc., New York (1930); Ch. VI, J. P. Mathieu, *Bull. Soc. Chim. France* (5), **3**, 476 (1936); (5), **4**, 687 (1937); Ref. 28 contains references to some more recent studies; B. E. Douglas, R. A. Haines, and J. G. Brushmiller, Inorg. Chem. **2**, 1194 (1963).

[31] J. M. Bijvoet, *Endeavor* **14**, 71 (1955) contains an account of the first such investigation which was successful.

[32] R. Pepinsky, *Record of Chemical Progress* **17**, 145 (1956).

TABLE 6.1

DATA FOR RUBIDIUM HYDROGEN TARTARATE (FROM REF. 31)

	Calculated intensities		
Indices of reflection plane	D-form anomalous diffr.	Normal diffr.	L-form anomalous diffraction
113	281	313	351
114	412	385	369
123	371	420	482
125	63	55	52
151	359	333	316
135	227	250	278

out by matching intensities and fair agreement was found. Bijvoet and his co-workers determined the configurations of dextrorotatory tartaric acid and found the structure to be *in agreement* with that assigned using the convention of Fischer mentioned above. Bijvoet first determined the structure, except for the "Handedness" of the molecule and then determined the absolute configuration using the anomalous diffraction pattern. Pepinsky has since combined these two operations into a single more rapid procedure.

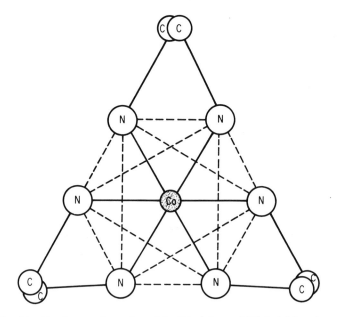

Fig. 30 Absolute configuration of the D(+) form of [Co(en)₃]⁺³ as determined by Saito and his co-workers.

The use of this method with coordination compounds may be seen in the fundamental studies of Saito and his co-workers. The structure of D and L $Co(en)_3^{+3}$ were determined using Cu-K radiation (wave length = 1.542 A) which can just excite the cobalt electrons (wave length = 1.608 A). The D and (+) forms were found to be the same where D represents the absolute configuration and (+) the sign of the rotation for the sodium light wave length. This ion has the structure shown in Figure 30. The five-membered rings are not planar; each ethylenediamine ligand assumes the gauche form.[33] These general structural features of ligand conformation are also found in complexes containing optically active ligands such as *trans*-[Co(*l*-propylenediamine)₂Cl₂]Cl ·HCl · $2H_2O$.[34] It is reassuring to note that the detailed development of our knowledge of the stereochemistry of coordination compounds is adding new facets to the classical theory, rather than replacing it.

KINETICS OF DISPLACEMENT REACTIONS OF COMPLEXES

In recent years kinetic studies of the displacement reactions of complexes have appeared in increasing number. If we restrict our considerations to octahedral complexes we find that a considerable amount of effort has been expended in efforts to elucidate the mechanisms of such changes. While such studies can never lead unequivocally to a single mechanism they can very frequently lead to a mechanism which is very highly probable. This being the case, it should be no surprise that this field is presently one in which there is considerable controversy. For convenience, it is preferable to discuss the work of various groups in this field in terms of the types of approach which they take to such problems.[35]

The first group of investigations to be considered is due to C. K. Ingold and his co-workers.[36] Ingold takes the concept of *edge displacement* as his

[33] Y. Saito, K. Nakatsu, M. Shiro, and H. Kuroya, *Acta Cryst.* **8**, 729 (1955). Further details are given in K. Nakatsu, M. Shiro, Y. Saito, and H. Kuroya, *Bull. Chem. Soc. Japan* **30**, 158 (1957); **30**, 795 (1957).

[34] Y. Saito and H. Iwasaki, in S. Kirschner, editor, *Advances in the Chemistry of the Coordination Compounds*, The MacMillan Company, New York (1961), p. 557 which also lists earlier work.

[35] There are a number of excellent treatments of this very active field which are available. The most comprehensive of these is F. Basolo and R. G. Pearson, *Mechanisms of Inorganic Reactions*, John Wiley & Sons, Inc., New York (1958). Others are: C. K. Ingold, *Substitution at Elements other than Carbon*, The Weizmann Science Press of Israel, Jerusalem (1959); R. G. Stranks, " The Reaction Rates of Transitional Metal Complexes" in J. Lewis and R. G. Wilkins, editors, *Modern Coordination Chemistry*, Interscience Publishers, Inc., New York (1960), pp. 78–173. Reviews on many special types of compounds are also available, e.g., that on the oxalato complexes by K. V. Krishnamurty and G. M. Harris, *Chem. Reviews* **61**, 213 (1961).

[36] C. K. Ingold, *et al.*, *J. Chem. Soc.*, 2674, 2680, 2696 (1953); *ibid.*, 1691, 1707, 2862 (1956) and numerous papers by his students and associates in *The Journal of the Chemical Society*.

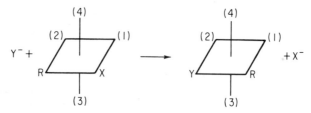

Fig. 31 The edge displacement mechanism for octahedral complexes. (Redrawn by permission of The Chemical Society, London.)

starting point. This is illustrated schematically in Figure 31. If the result of such a reaction is described from the position of a fixed group A we shall give a different description and name to the process depending upon the position of A. Some of these descriptions are

A at 1	*cis-trans*
A at 2	*trans-cis*
A at 3 or 4	*d-l* or *l-d*

Yet this is the same reaction for all of these varying descriptions. The inevitable conclusion is that there may be no essential difference between a reaction which results in a *cis-* to *trans*-change and one which results in a *d* to *l* change. If the groups are not all different (e.g., if 1 and 2 and also 3 and 4 are superposable by rotation) a *cis-cis*-reaction is also possible. Further variations are also possible; the only process which is *not* compatible with the edge displacement mechanism is a *trans-trans*-reaction which occurs in one step. While some processes of this kind are known, it is not certain that they proceed in one step. The following diagram illustrates the relation of these two classes of mechanism to the various stereochemical changes (stereochanges) in reactions:

		Substitution without Edge displacement		
Stereochange		No Stereochange		
cis ⇌ *trans*	*d* ⇌ *l*	*D* ⇌ *D* *L* ⇌ *L*	*cis* ⇌ *cis*	*trans* ⇌ *trans*
Substitution with Edge Displacement				

The frequency with which stereochange is observed in inorganic complexes led Ingold to limit "legitimate" configurations to those which have been established by one of the following three methods:

   1. X-ray analysis where this is accompanied by additional evidence that no rearrangement takes place on solution

   2. A distinction based upon optical resolvability

3. A chain of genetic reactions which does not involve the breaking of a metal-ligand bond

Ingold *et al.* then proceed to examine the problem of mechanism in more detail. For substitution by OH^- in $[Co(NH_3)_5X]^{+2}$ second order kinetics are found, first order in each reactant:

$$[Co(NH_3)_5X]^{+2} + OH^- \rightarrow [Co(NH_3)_5(OH)]^{+2} + X^-$$

The kinetic data for this reaction are unfortunately consistent with *three* mechanisms:

S_N2: substitution, nucleophilic, second order

S_N1CB: substitution, nucleophilic, first order, conjugate base

S_N2CB: substitution, nucleophilic, second order, conjugate base

For the second and third mechanisms, a proton would first be removed from one of the ammonias coordinated to the cobalt. The second step would then involve the loss of a halide ion by the conjugate base with the subsequent (S_N1CB) or simultaneous (S_N2CB) uptake of a molecule of water:

$$[Co(NH_3)_5X]^{+2} + OH^- \rightleftharpoons [Co(NH_3)_4(NH_2)X]^+ + H_2O$$

$$\text{then} \left. \begin{array}{l} [Co(NH_3)_4(NH_2)X]^+ \rightleftharpoons [Co(NH_3)_4(NH_2)]^{+2} + X^- \\ [Co(NH_3)_4(NH_2)]^+ + H_2O \rightarrow [Co(NH_3)_5(OH)]^{+2} \end{array} \right\} S_N1CB$$

$$\left. \begin{array}{l} \text{or} \\ S_N2CB \end{array} \right\} [Co(NH_3)_4(NH_2)X]^+ + H_2O \rightarrow [Co(NH_3)_5(OH)]^{+2} + X^-$$

In many other cases experimental evidence favors a unimolecular mechanism with first order kinetics (S_N1). An example is the exchange of radioactive cyanide with $[Mn(CN)_6]^{-3}$ which is zero order in $[Mn(CN)_6]^{-3}$. The result of a general survey was the conclusion that a "duplexity" of mechanisms may be observed and that there should be a discontinuous break in type of mechanism as we vary the attacking nucleophilic group. Furthermore, this variation should occur in a manner which is predictable using certain specific properties of the systems.

The work of Ingold and his collaborators revealed other aspects of these reactions which are also of importance. The displacement of chloride in *l* cis-$[Co(en)_2Cl_2]^+$ by various ions was studied in methanol solution. For the ions NO_3^-, Cl^-, Br^-, and NCS^- the rate of replacement was found to be first order in the concentration of the complex and *independent* of the concentration of the entering group. This is consistent with an S_N1 (substitution, nucleophilic, first order) mechanism of the type:

$$l\,cis\text{-}[Co(en)_2Cl_2]^+ \xrightarrow{\text{slow}} \underset{\substack{(\text{optically} \\ \text{inactive})}}{[Co(en)_2Cl]^{+2}} + X^- \xrightarrow{\text{fast}} [Co(en)_2XCl]^+$$

For three other ions NO_2^-, N_3^- and CH_3O^- substitution was found to occur in whole or in part by a second order reaction, first order in the complex, and first order in the entering group. These rates were greater than those found for the first order reactions. The reasonableness of the proposed S_N1 mechanisms is confirmed by the fact that the observed first order rate is the same as the rate of racemization of the resolved *cis*-complex and *also* the same as the rate at which this complex exchanges with radioactive chloride. It was then proposed that if the base strength of the entering group is great enough, the more rapid second order process can occur. For weaker bases, the rate of replacement of chloride is limited to the rate of dissociation of the parent complex. A more detailed course for the sequence of reactions may also be given[37] for the S_N1 reaction:

$$l\text{-}cis\text{-cation} \xrightarrow{\text{slow}} \left\{ \begin{array}{c} \text{cobaltium ion} \\ + \\ \text{chloride ion} \end{array} \right\} \begin{array}{l} \xrightarrow{\text{fast}} trans\text{-cation} \\ \xrightarrow[\text{fast}]{} \text{racemic mixture} \\ \quad\quad \text{of } cis\text{-cations} \end{array}$$

One of the significant results of the further work was the discovery that a stereochange need not necessarily occur even in some instances where it might be expected. Thus in the reaction with hydroxide, the following results were obtained:

$$trans\text{-}[Co(en)_2Cl(NCS)]^+ \xrightarrow{OH^-} \begin{array}{l} 76\% \ \ cis\text{-}[Co(en)_2(OH)(NCS)]^+ \\ 24\% \ \ trans\text{-}[Co(en)_2(OH)(NCS)]^+ \end{array}$$

$$trans\text{-}[Co(en)_2Br(NCS)]^+ \xrightarrow{OH^-} \begin{array}{l} 81\% \ \ cis\text{-}[Co(en)_2(OH)(NCS)]^+ \\ 19\% \ \ trans\text{-}[Co(en)_2(OH)(NCS)]^+ \end{array}$$

$$cis\text{-}[Co(en)_2Cl(NCS)]^+ \xrightarrow{OH^-} \begin{array}{l} 82\% \ \ cis\text{-}[Co(en)_2(OH)(NCS)]^+ \\ 18\% \ \ trans\text{-}[Co(en)_2(OH)(NCS)]^+ \end{array}$$

Unfortunately, an equilibrium exists between the *cis*- and *trans*-forms so a correction for this had to be made in interpreting the results. The product ratios were determined for other reactions of this type. Some of these are listed below. The diversity of results indicates the difficulties which any mechanism must face. Consider the products for reactions of the type: *d-cis-*, *l-cis-* or *trans*-$[Co(en)_2(NH_3)(X)]^{+2} + OH^- \rightarrow d\text{-}cis\text{-}, \ l\text{-}cis,$ or $trans\text{-}[Co(en)_2(NH_3)(OH)]^{+2} + X^-$:

Displaced Group	Temp.	Product ratio %		trans
		d-cis	*l-cis*	
trans-Cl	0°	76		24
trans-Cl	10.5°	79		21
trans-Cl	25.0°	83		17
d-cis-Cl	0°	60	24	16
d-cis-Br	0°	59	26	15
l-cis-Br	0°	27	58	15
d, l-cis-NO₃	0°	86		14

[37] D. D. Brown, C. K. Ingold, and R. S. Nyholm, *J. Chem. Soc.*, 2699 (1953).

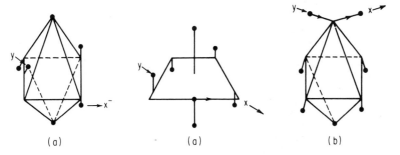

Fig. 32 Transition states for the displacement reactions of octahedral complexes according to Ingold, (a) with edge displacement, (b) without edge displacement. (Redrawn by permission of The Chemical Society, London.)

Finally, it was found that *trans*-chloronitrobis(ethylenediamine)cobalt(III) gives the *pure trans*-nitroaquobis(ethylenediamine)cobalt(III) on aquation. The *cis*-isomer also gives the *cis*-product. This evidence then definitely proves that stereochange definitely does *not* occur in at least some cases *and* that the concept of edge displacement has its limitations. Possible transition states may be described which either incorporate or do not incorporate the edge displacement concept; these are shown in Figure 32.

In order to delineate the possible steric course of these reactions, Asperger and Ingold[38] compare the possible routes for substitution reactions in octahedral complexes. An attack on a *face* of an octahedron violates the principles of microscopic reversibility and also the ideas of crystal field theory. The principle of microscopic reversibility requires that, in the transition state, the attacking and the displaced groups have a similar geometrical relationship to the rest of the molecule. One intermediate which meets this requirement is a pentagonal bipyramid in which the entering and leaving groups are symmetrically located.[39]

The symmetry requirements can be satisfied more easily by the molecule in two other ways. In the first of these, shown in Figure 32(a), neither edge displacement nor stereochange are involved. An alternative transition state in which edge displacement is involved is shown in Figure 32(b). These transition states can then be used, in principle, to explain all of the observed types of reaction given earlier. It is to be noted that edge displacement is *not* involved in *trans* → *trans*-reactions.

In brief the views of Ingold are centered in the alternative possibilities of either S_N1 or S_N2 mechanisms for these displacement reactions and the duplexity of mechanism which may arise as the base strength of the substituent species is varied.

[38] S. Asperger and C. K. Ingold, *J. Chem. Soc.*, 2875 (1956).
[39] F. Basolo, B. D. Stone, and R. G. Pearson, *J. Amer. Chem. Soc.* **75**, 819 (1953).

Another school of thought is found in the work of F. Basolo, R. G. Pearson, and their co-workers.[40] These workers prefer to describe the majority of the basic hydrolysis reactions of cobalt(III) ammines in terms of the S_N1CB (substitution, nucleophilic, first order, conjugate base) mechanism which was first proposed by Bronsted[41] on the basis of kinetic studies of aquation reactions (replacement of a ligand by water). Bronsted noted that the reaction of $[Co(NH_3)_5(NO_3)]^{+2}$ with water was first order *and slower* than the corresponding reaction of $[Co(NH_3)_4(H_2O)(NO_3)]^{+2}$. The reactions examined were:

(a) $[Co(NH_3)_5(NO_3)]^{+2} + H_2O \rightarrow [Co(NH_3)_5(H_2O)]^{+3} + NO_3^-$

and

(b) $[Co(NH_3)_4(H_2O)(NO_3)]^{+2} + H_2O \rightarrow [Co(NH_3)_4(H_2O)_2]^{+2} + NO_3^-$

The rate of reaction (a) is strictly unimolecular and independent of the concentration of added acid. This is probably an example of an S_N1 reaction. Reaction (b) has a rate expression:

$$\text{Rate} = \left\{1.60 \times 10^{-3} + \frac{3.2 \times 10^{-5}}{[H^+]}\right\} [Co(NH_3)_4(H_2O)(NO_3)]^{+2}$$

and must exhibit a duplexity of mechanism. Bronsted proposed that this reaction could proceed via an S_N1 mechanism which was relatively slow and an S_N1CB mechanism which was much faster except when high concentrations of acid were present. The over-all scheme is:

$$
\begin{array}{ccc}
 & S_N1 & \\
[Co(NH_3)_4(H_2O)(NO_3)]^{+2} + H_2O & \longrightarrow & [Co(NH_3)_4(H_2O)_2]^{+3} + NO_3^- \\
\Updownarrow & S_N1CB & \Updownarrow \\
[Co(NH_3)_4(OH)(NO_3)]^+ + H_2O & \longrightarrow & [Co(NH_3)_4(OH)(H_2O)]^{+2} + NO_3^- \\
+ H^+ & & + H^+
\end{array}
$$

Bronsted reasoned that the conjugate base of the complex, $[Co(NH_3)_4(OH)(NO_3)]^+$, would hold the nitrate anion less firmly because of the decrease in its charge which resulted from splitting off the proton. His kinetic data supported this reaction scheme and he was able to estimate that the aquation of the conjugate base proceeded more rapidly than that of the original complex by a factor of about 10^6! He also showed that such a mechanistic dualism was found for the aquation of $[Co(NH_3)_4(H_2O)Cl]^{+2}$.

Basolo (*loc. cit.*) sums up the evidence in support of this type of mechanism for some reactions which he and his colleagues studied:

"1. The rates of hydrogen exchange of Co(III) ammines with water in alkaline solutions are sufficiently fast to permit such a reaction path.

[40] F. Basolo and R. G. Pearson, *Mechanisms of Inorganic Reactions*, John Wiley & Sons, Inc., New York (1958); F. Basolo, *Record of Chemical Progress* **18**, 1 (1957).
[41] J. N. Bronsted, *Zeit. phys. Chem.* **122**, 383 (1926).

2. Base-hydrolysis rates generally increase with increasing acid strength of analogous complexes.

3. Very rapid rates of base hydrolysis suggest pi bonding of the amido group to enhance the stability of the five-coordinated transition state.

4. The basic hydrolysis of complexes which do not contain acidic hydrogen is not accelerated by alkali even when acid hydrolysis is relatively slow.

5. The rate of basic hydrolysis of $[Co(ND_3)_5Cl]^{2+}$ with OD^- is about 50% slower than that for the corresponding hydrogen system.

6. The stereochemical results are explained almost quantitatively on the basis of a trigonal bipyramidal intermediate."

The bonding is illustrated by the mechanism shown in Figure 33.

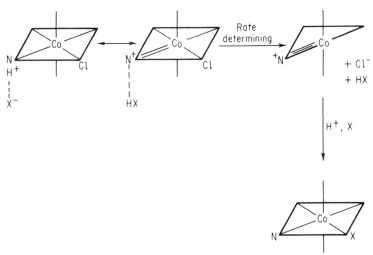

Fig. 33 Basolo's reaction sequence for an S_N1CB mechanism with pi bonding. (Redrawn from *Record of Chemical Progress*, vol. 18, p. 5, 1957, F. Basolo, by permission of the Wayne State University Press. Copyright 1957 by Kresge-Hooker Science Library Associates.)

For methanol solution, Basolo and Pearson suggest an S_N1IP (substitution, nucleophilic, unimolecular, ion-pair) mechanism. The typical S_N1IP mechanism is:

$$[Co(en)_2Cl_2]^+ + X^- \rightleftharpoons [Co(en)_2Cl_2]^+, X^-$$
$$[Co(en)_2Cl_2]^+, X^- \rightleftharpoons [Co(en)_2ClX]^+ + Cl^-$$

Evidence in favor of this has been obtained by studies of ion-pair formation in methanol. Thus *cis*-$[Co(en)_2Cl_2]^+$ forms ion pairs with both Cl^- and Br^-.

Ingold's reply to these claims may be found in his Weizmann Memorial Lectures cited above. They are based on a detailed analysis of the kinetic data presented by his critics. For the present it must be conceded that the evidence favoring the S_N1CB mechanism is conclusive in some cases but *not* in all for which it has been claimed. For many reactions there is simply not enough detailed information. In the case of aquation reactions—Ingold, Nyholm, and Tobe[41a] have shown that the analogies of aquation reactions with similar organic reactions strongly favor the S_N1 or S_N2 mechanism as opposed to the S_N1CB mechanism. The reactions considered are of the general type:

$$[Co(en)_2AX]^+ + H_2O \rightarrow [Co(en)_2A(H_2O)]^{++} + X^-$$

where A and X were varied. On the basis of these studies they propose "the first stereokinetic rule applicable to octahedral substitutions", namely:

"In octahedral aquations which replace X in filled-sub-shell complexes MR_4AX of a transition metal, M, configuration will be totally preserved unless A and X are *trans*, and A but not R has unshared electrons adjoining M."

The restriction to "filled-sub-shell" ions drastically limits this rule and it is intended for Co(III) complexes.

RACEMIZATION AND EXCHANGE REACTIONS

RACEMIZATION REACTIONS. When the detailed information on racemization reactions is examined, it is obvious that our previous classification of complexes as "labile" and "inert" provides only a very general guide to such phenomena. Complexes of some cations which usually give labile complexes have been resolved, e.g., Ni(II), Ti(IV), and Al(III). In these cases the nature of the *ligand* seems to be the chief factor governing the resolvability. Secondly, it is found that many inert complexes racemize at a fairly rapid rate, e.g., hexol-cobaltic ion. The range of half-lives for racemization (at room temperature) runs from a few seconds or less to at least centuries. The racemization of such ions as $Co(en)_3^{+3}$, $Pt(en)_4^{+4}$, and $Rh(en)_3^{+3}$ does not occur to a measurable extent in boiling water over a period of several days. A further factor, often of great importance, is the pH of the solution in which the complex is manipulated. *d* or *l*[As(catechol)_3]^{-1} can be boiled in a solution of barium hydroxide without suffering very much racemization, but in acidic solutions at room temperature the complex is completely destroyed in a matter of minutes. The study of racemization processes is carried out polarimetrically by simply following the angle through which the plane of polarized light is rotated as a function of time. Thus if a racemization occurs as a unimolecular process where there are no intermediates:

$$d\text{-A} \underset{k_2}{\overset{k_1}{\rightleftharpoons}} l\text{-A}$$

[41a] C. K. Ingold, R. S. Nyholm, and M. L. Tobe, *Nature* **187**, 477 (1960); see, however, M. Green and H. Taube, *Inorg. Chem.* **2**, 948 (1963).

and the rate of disappearance of d-A is:

$$- \frac{d(d\text{-A})}{dt} = k_1(d\text{-A}) - k_2(l\text{-A})$$

if C_0 is the concentration of d-A at $t = 0$, then C_t is the concentration of d-A at $t = t$ and $C_0 - C_t$ is the concentration of l-A at $t = t$. So

$$- \frac{dC_t}{dt} = k_1C_t - k_2(C_0 - C_t)$$

If now, the reasonable assumption is made that $k_1 = k_2$, then

$$- \frac{dC_t}{dt} = k_1(2C_t - C_0)$$

or

$$- \frac{dC_t}{2C_t - C_0} = k_1 dt$$

on integration this becomes:

$$\tfrac{1}{2}\ln(2C_t - C_0) + \text{const} = -k_1 t$$

when $\quad t = 0$

$$\tfrac{1}{2}\ln C_0 = -\text{const, so}$$

$$\tfrac{1}{2}\ln(2C_t - C_0) - \tfrac{1}{2}\ln C_0 = k_1 t$$

now $\quad C_0 = K\alpha_0$ and $C_t = K\alpha_t + \tfrac{1}{2}(\alpha_0 - \alpha_t)$

Here α_0 is the rotation observed at $t = 0$, α_t is the rotation at $t = t$, and α_∞ is that observed at $t = \infty$. Rearrangement and substitution leads to:

$$\tfrac{1}{2}\ln \frac{C_0}{(2C_t - C_0)} = k_1 t = \tfrac{1}{2}\ln \left|\frac{\alpha_0}{\alpha_t}\right|$$

Here the rate constant k is one-half the slope of the $\ln(\alpha_0/\alpha_t)$ plot. A different situation arises in racemizations of the type:

$$d\text{-A} \underset{k_2}{\overset{k_1}{\rightleftharpoons}} \text{inactive products} \underset{k_1}{\overset{k_3}{\rightleftharpoons}} l\text{-A}$$

Here the rate expression is:

$$- \frac{d(d\text{-A})}{dt} = k_1(d\text{-A}) - k_2 \text{ (inactive products)}$$

if $k_2 \ll k_1$, and (inactive products) $\ll (d\text{-A})$ then for the initial rate:

$$- \frac{d(d\text{-A})}{dt} = k_1(d\text{-A})$$

$$\ln \frac{(d\text{-A})_0}{(d\text{-A})_t} = k_1 t$$

$$(d\text{-A})_0 = K(\alpha_0 - \alpha_\infty); \quad (d\text{-A})_t = K(\alpha_t - \alpha_\infty)$$

so $\qquad\qquad kt = \ln \dfrac{\alpha_0 - \alpha_\infty}{\alpha_t - \alpha_\infty}$

Since α_∞ is generally zero, k's determined by the second method will be *twice* as large as those determined by the first method. The solution to this dilemma must be sought in another independent measurement which will allow a choice to be made between the two mechanisms. For example, if the formation of the intermediate is one in which a dissociation occurs, the rate of this dissociation can be determined separately and should be equal to the rate of racemization.

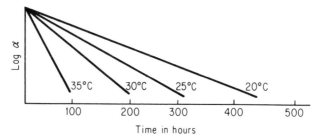

Fig. 34   Rate data on the loss of optical activity by $[Cr(en)_3]^{+3}$. (Redrawn by permission of Pergamon Press Ltd.)

An example of the kind of data obtained may be seen in Figure 34 which presents a graph for $0.01 M [Cr(en)_3](ClO_4)_3$ in aqueous solution at pH 1.0.[42]

There are two general classes of mechanisms which have been suggested for the racemization of octahedral complexes: (a) intramolecular and (b) intermolecular. The present consensus favors intermolecular mechanisms of one kind or another for most complexes, but intramolecular processes are not excluded in some cases.[40a] It is of interest to consider some of the proposed mechanisms and the evidence used to support or discredit them.

Thomas[43] proposed that $[Cr(C_2O_4)_3]^{-3}$ racemized by a process in which one of the oxalate groups was first split off to produce a symmetrical intermediate with a square planar configuration. This then added an oxalate group to re-form the octahedral complex. Since the last step will give equal amounts of both enantiomorphs, racemization will result. The over-all scheme can be summarized as

$$[Cr(C_2O_4)_3]^{-3} \rightleftharpoons [Cr(C_2O_4)_2]^{-1} + C_2O_4^{=} \rightleftharpoons [Cr(C_2O_4)_3]^{-3}$$
asymmetric   square planar   octahedral,
octahedral   symmetrical   equal amounts
                                           d, l forms

This mechanism for *this anion* was subsequently shown to be untenable by three pieces of experimental evidence:

1. The rate of exchange of $[Cr(C_2O_4)_3]^{-3}$ with radioactive oxalate is much *slower* than the rate of racemization.[44]

[42] H. L. Schlafer and O. Kling, *J. Inorg. Nuclear Chem.* **8**, 327 (1958).

[43] W. Thomas, *J. Chem. Soc.* **121**, 196 (1922).

[44] F. A. Long, *J. Amer. Chem. Soc.* **61**, 570 (1939).

2. Solutions of this complex ion contain no detectable traces of free oxalate anion.[45]

3. The rate of racemization is unaffected by the addition of oxalates to the solution.[46]

Alternative mechanisms for the racemization of such complexes as $Cr(C_2O_4)_3^{-3}$ and $Co(en)_3^{+3}$ were suggested by Werner, Ray and Dutt, Bailar, and Bushra and Johnson. These may be used with minor variations to explain several types of such processes.

Werner[47] proposed a mechanism for intramolecular racemizations in which one end of a chelate group breaks free of the central ion to give a five-coordinate intermediate in which there is either a plane of symmetry or at least a reasonable probability of forming *either* enantiomorph when the free end of the ligand reforms a coordinate bond with the central atom. Another intramolecular mechanism is that proposed by Ray and Dutt.[48] These authors proposed the reaction sequence shown in Figure 35. It consists of distortion of

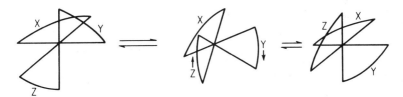

Fig. 35   The racemization mechanism of Ray and Dutt.

the octahedron, without the release of ligands, until a position is achieved from which either enantiomorph may be regenerated by a relaxation of the distortion. Since bonds are more readily bent than they are broken or stretched, this mechanism is attractive for many intramolecular racemizations.

Bushra and Johnson[49] proposed that in complexes such as $[Cr(C_2O_4)_3]^{-3}$, two different bidentate ligands could each free *one* of their donor atoms to form an intermediate from which each of the enantiomorphs could subsequently be reformed. Such a path should be one of higher activation energy than the analogous mechanism of Werner.

A final mechanism for intramolecular isomerizations or racemizations may be seen in a proposal by Bailar.[50] This involves a trigonal prism as an intermediate. This is formed by a relatively slight distortion of the octahedron. For a complex such as $[Co(en)_3]^{+3}$ a trigonal prism is a symmetrical structure which

[45] N. W. D. Beese and C. H. Johnson, *Trans. Farad. Soc.* **31**, 1635 (1935).

[46] E. Bushra and C. H. Johnson, *J. Chem. Soc.*, 1941 (1939).

[47] A. Werner, *Ber.* **45**, 3061 (1912).

[48] P. Ray and N. Dutt, *J. Indian Chem. Soc.* **20**, 81 (1943).

[49] E. Bushra and C. H. Johnson, *J. Chem. Soc.*, 1937 (1939).

[50] J. C. Bailar, *J. Inorg. Nuclear Chem.* **8**, 171 (1958).

can then form the octahedral complex of either d or l configuration when the distortion is relieved.

The mechanisms by which a given complex loses optical activity may vary with the environment. Thus Brown and Ingold[51] found that the loss of optical activity of l-cis-$[Co(en)_2Cl_2]^+$ in methanol could be explained by a mechanism in which the complex first loses a Cl^- to form a five-coordinated symmetrical intermediate. This then recoordinates with a Cl^- to give a mixture of the *trans*- (82%) and d- and l-cis (18%) forms. In water, the same complex racemizes by a completely different path. In this case an initial rapid hydration reaction occurs with retention of configuration. This is followed by a slow racemization reaction in which the trans chloroaquo complex is formed:

$$l\text{-}cis\text{-}[Co(en)_2Cl_2]^+ + H_2O \xrightarrow{\text{fast}} l\text{-}cis\text{-}[Co(en)_2(H_2O)Cl]^{+2} + Cl^-$$
$$\downarrow \text{slow}$$
$$trans\text{-}[Co(en)_2(H_2O)(Cl)]^{+2}$$

The rate of loss of optical activity is ten times slower than the rate of acid hydrolysis.[52]

An intramolecular mechanism seems operative in the racemization of $[Cr(C_2O_4)_3]^{-3}$, $[Co(C_2O_4)_3]^{-3}$, and $Fe(dipyr)_3^{+2}$.

THE WALDEN INVERSION. The Walden inversion usually calls to mind an organic reaction in which an attacking species Y reacts with an asymmetric organic compound CLMNO to produce another compound CLMNY with an *inversion* of configuration. This proceeds by a mechanism in which the groups remaining around the carbon are rearranged in a manner reminiscent of the way an umbrella is blown inside out in a windstorm. The fact that some reactions of optically active complexes apparently proceed with a change in sign of rotation was first noted by Werner[53] and was commented on by Pfeiffer[53a, 54] and Wittig.[55] Werner, however, was misled by certain properties of the complexes he studied and came to the conclusion that displacement reactions occur with retention of configuration. The specific reactions involved the *least* soluble diastereoisomers with bromcamphorsulfonate (X) of the ions $[Co(en)_2 Cl(NCS)]^+$ and $[Co(en)_2Cl(NO_2)]^+$. These are levorotatory and dextrorotatory respectively and undergo the reactions:

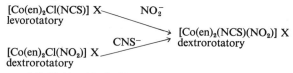

[51] D. D. Brown and C. K. Ingold, *J. Chem. Soc.*, 2680 (1953).

[52] J. Mathieu, *Bull. Soc. Chim.* (5), **4**, 687 (1937).

[53] A. Werner, *Ber.* **44**, 873 (1911); Ann. **386**, 65 (1912); (a) P. Pfeiffer, Ann. **383**, 123 (1911); *Zeit. anorg. Chem.* **87**, 240 (1914).

[54] P. Pfeiffer, "Komplexverbindungen" in K. Freudenberg's, *Stereochemie*, F. Deuticke, Leipzig and Vienna (1932), Vol. III, p. 1284.

[55] G. Wittig, *Stereochemie*, Akademische Verlags, Leipzig (1930), p. 267.

On the basis of these reactions Werner came to the correct conclusion that both of the initial cations had the *same* absolute configuration. It remained for Bailar and his students[56] to establish the occurrence of such a phenomenon in the field of complex compounds.

The following reaction sequence illustrates this:

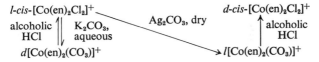

Thus these reactions occur both with and without the retention of configuration. The reaction with aqueous K_2CO_3 passes through an optically active hydrated intermediate. While the use of the term, Walden Inversion, for such reactions has been deprecated, it seems that the configurational changes involved *are* analogous though the *mechanisms* of such changes need not be.

EXCHANGE AND ELECTRON TRANSFER REACTIONS. Exchange reactions are reactions in which atoms or ions of a given element replace identical species in a more complex substance or reactions in which there is exchange between identical species in two or more complex substances. Both types of reactions have been studied with various types of coordination compounds. Such processes may be followed by tracer techniques if radioactive atoms of the element involved are available. Except for the lightest elements, the chemical properties of the isotopes of a given element are sufficiently alike that they may usually be assumed to possess *identical* behavior. For hydrogen, nitrogen, and carbon very slight differences have been observed between the behavior of different isotopes. Such behavior is termed the *isotope effect* and will be ignored in the following discussion.

There are three types of exchange reactions of great interest in coordination chemistry:

1. Reactions in which the central metal ion is exchanged:

$$Fe(phen)_3^{+2} + Fe^{*+2} \rightleftharpoons Fe^* (phen)_3^{+2} + Fe^{+2}$$

$$Cr(CN)_6^{-3} + Cr^*(H_2O)_6^{+3} \rightleftharpoons Cr^*(CN)_6^{-3} + Cr(H_2O)_6^{+3}$$

2. Reactions in which the ligand species is exchanged:

$$W(CN)_8^{-4} + C^*N^- \rightleftharpoons [W(CN)_7(C^*N)]^{-4} + CN^-$$

$$PtCl_4^{-2} + Cl^{*-} \rightleftharpoons [PtCl_3Cl^*]^{-2} + Cl^-$$

3. Reactions in which hydrogen on donor atoms is exchanged with solvent hydrogens or deuterium:

$$[Cr(H_2O)_6]^{+3} + D_2O \rightleftharpoons [Cr(H_2O)_5(D_2O)]^{+3} + H_2O$$

[56] The work is collected by F. Basolo in J. C. Bailar, Jr., *The Chemistry of The Coordination Compounds*, Reinhold Publishing Corp., New York (1956), pp.344–348.

Thus complete exchange occurs between the hydrogen atoms of ammino and aquo groups of cobalt complexes and the deuterium of heavy water.[57]

The rate at which such processes occur is given by an equation due to McKay.[58] A general equation for these processes is:

$$AX + BX^* \rightleftharpoons AX^* + BX$$

Let us call the gross rate of exchange R and then this will also be equal to the rate of appearance of AX^*. Then let:

$$a = (AX) + (AX^*), \qquad b = (BX) + (BX^*)$$
$$x = (AX^*), \qquad (AX) = a\text{-}x$$
$$y = (BX^*), \qquad (BX) = b\text{-}y$$

Then the net rate of exchange of the radioactive species will be equal to the gross rate of the forward reaction times the fraction of such exchange which occurs between proper species minus the gross rate of the reverse reaction times the fraction of such reactions which occur between proper species. All of the gross exchange rate is not effective in promoting the exchange of radio-active isotopes.

$$\frac{dx}{dt} = R\left(\frac{y}{b}\right)\left(\frac{a\text{-}x}{a}\right) - R\left(\frac{x}{a}\right)\left(\frac{b\text{-}y}{b}\right)$$

$$\frac{dx}{dt} = R\left(\frac{ay\text{-}bx}{ab}\right)$$

Now $y = x_\infty + y_\infty - x$ and $x_\infty/y_\infty = a/b$ so:

$$\frac{dx}{dt} = \frac{R}{ab}[(a + b)(x_\infty - x)]$$

on integration this gives:

$$\ln\left(\frac{x_\infty}{x_\infty - x}\right) = \frac{R}{ab}(a + b)t = -\ln\left(\frac{x_\infty - x}{x}\right) = -\ln(1 - F)$$

if we set:

$$\frac{x}{x_\infty} = F; \qquad Rt = -\frac{ab}{a + b}\ln(1 - F)$$

or converting to $\log_{10}$:

$$R = -\frac{2.303}{t}\left(\frac{ab}{a + b}\right)\log_{10}(1 - F)$$

x_i is the specific activity or percentage isotopic abundance excess at time i. The equation for R is valid as long as the radioactive isotope is used in tracer amounts.[59]

---

[57] F. W. James, J. S. Anderson, and H. V. A. Briscoe, *Nature* **139**, 109 (1937); J. Horiuti and G. Okamoto, *Sci. Papers Inst. Phys. Chem. Res.* (Tokyo) **31**, 205 (1937); G. Okamoto, *J. Fac. Sci. Hokkaido Imp. Univ.* **2**, III, 81a (1937); J. S. Anderson, N. L. Spoor, and H. V. A. Briscoe, *Nature* **139**, 508 (1937).

[58] H. A. McKay, *Nature* **142**, 997 (1938).

[59] For macroscopic amounts of exchanging species see C. A. Bunton, D. P. Craig, and E. A. Halevi, *Trans. Farad. Soc.* **51**, 196 (1955).

R can conveniently be determined from the slope of a $\log_{10} (1 - F)$ vs. time plot or from the half-time of exchange:

$$R = \frac{0.693}{t_{\frac{1}{2}}} \frac{(ab)}{(a + b)}$$

The R is then related to the chemical reactions occurring through the usual equation

$$R = \sum k_i [A]^a [B]^b [C]^c \dots$$

The actual application of these considerations to specific cases has been carried out with a large number of complexes. An excellent review, from which most of the material given below was obtained, is that of Stranks and Wilkins.[60] An extended treatment of the theory underlying the use of isotopes in the investigation of chemical reactions has been given by Roginskii.[61]

The interpretation of the resultant data is least complicated when dealing with simple inert complexes. With labile complexes the concentrations must be so adjusted so that the species present in solution are definitely known, preferably with only a single complex present. With a labile complex it is often possible to decrease the rate of exchange by simply increasing the concentration of ligand in the solution. This makes the equilibrium conditions such that exchange is not favored but can result in misleading conclusions about the *lability* of the complex.

Since exchange processes ultimately result in a statistical distribution of marked atoms, rate studies can be used to establish the equivalence or non-equivalence of such atoms. With PCl_5, for example, three chlorines are exchanged rapidly and then two more slowly. This is consistent with our picture of a trigonal bipyramidal structure for PCl_5 with two types of chlorine atoms.

EXCHANGE RATES AND REACTIONS OF FOUR-COORDINATE COMPLEXES

In an early study of exchange reactions of copper chelates with radioactive copper (as acetate) in pyridine, Duffield and Calvin[62] found that for reactions of the type given below:

$$Cu(II)Ke_2 + Cu^*(II) \rightleftharpoons Cu^*(II)Ke_2 + Cu(II)$$

the rate of exchange was inversely proportional to the thermodynamic stability of the chelate used. In this case the rate of exchange was represented by a second order rate law. (The relationship between the thermodynamic and kinetic

[60] D. R. Stranks and R. G. Wilkins, *Chem. Reviews* **57**, 753 (1957).

[61] S. Z. Roginskii, *Theoretical Principles of Isotope Methods for Investigating Chemical Reactions*, translated by Consultants Bureau, U.S. Atomic Energy Commission, AEC-tr-2855.

[62] R. B. Duffield and M. Calvin, *J. Amer. Chem. Soc.* **68**, 557 (1946).

properties found here is *not* a general feature of exchange reactions.) Other copper complexes generally undergo rapid exchange of either metal or ligand. One exception is copper phthalocyanine which, with almost all other phthalocyanines, is very resistant to the exchange of the metal.

The complexes of nickel(II) exhibit a wide variety of behavior with respect to exchange reactions involving the nickel. Bis(N-methylsalicylaldimine)-nickel(II) exchanges very rapidly with radioactive nickel chloride in pyridine solutions. Bis(salicylaldehydeethylenediimine)nickel(II) undergoes no measurable exchange under similar conditions after 48 h. Here the differences in rate are probably related to the fact that the exchange process involves the disruption of a bidentate chelate in one instance and a more stable tetradentate chelate in the other. Some studies on the exchange of nickel between complexes have been carried out by Long.[63] These results are summarized below:

Exchange pair	$t_{\frac{1}{2}}$
$Ni^*(NH_3)_x^{+2} - Ni(CN)_4^{-2}$	<1 min
$Ni^*(C_2O_4)_2^{-2} - Ni(CN)_4^{-2}$	3 hr
$Ni^*(tartarate) - Ni(CN)_4^{-2}$	46 hr

Ligand exchange reactions usually involve more than mere exchange. For most of the four-coordinate systems where kinetic information is available there is good evidence that the reaction sequence is: (a) aquation and then (b) anation. Thus for the system $PtBr_4^{-2} - Br^*$ the rate was found[64] to be first order in the concentration of the complex and *independent* of the bromide ion concentration. However, the rate of exchange was found to *increase* as the tetrabromoplatinate(II) solutions aged. The kinetics allow two mechanisms:

S_N1:

$$PtBr_4^{-2} \underset{fast}{\overset{slow}{\rightleftharpoons}} PtBr_3^- + Br^-$$

$$PtBr_3^- + Br^{*-} \underset{slow}{\overset{fast}{\rightleftharpoons}} [PtBr_3Br^*]^{-2}$$

or S_N2:

$$PtBr_4^{-2} + H_2O \underset{fast}{\overset{slow}{\rightleftharpoons}} [PtBr_3(H_2O)]^- + Br^-$$

$$[PtBr_3(H_2O)]^- + Br^{*-} \underset{slow}{\overset{fast}{\rightleftharpoons}} [PtBr_3Br^*]^{-2} + H_2O$$

The effect of ageing on the rate of exchange indicates that the S_N2 mechanism is the most probable. With $PtCl_4^{-2}$ aquation also proceeds anation, but the

[63] F. A. Long, *J. Amer. Chem. Soc.* **73**, 537 (1951).

[64] A. A. Grinberg, L. E. Nikolskaya, and G. A. Shagisultanova, *Doklady Akad. Nauk S.S.S.R.* **101**, 1059 (1955), C.A. 49: 12094; A. A. Grinberg and G. A. Shagisultanova, *Izvest. Akad. Nauk S.S.S.R., Otdel Khim Nauk* 981 (1955), C.A. 55: 7813.

aquo complex, $[PtCl_3H_2O]^-$, can apparently exchange by an S_N1 process. For $AuCl_4^-$, exchange with Cl^- is quite rapid and the rate is given by

$$R = 0.20[AuCl_4^-] + 11.0[AuCl_4^-][Cl^-] \quad [65]$$

The second term indicates that an S_N2 mechanism plays an important role in the reaction. Presumably a trigonal bipyramidal intermediate is involved. This would give a reaction sequence as follows:

$$AuCl_4^- + Cl^{*-} \rightarrow [AuCl_4Cl^*]^{-2} \rightarrow [AuCl_3Cl^*]^- + Cl^-$$

$AuCl_4^-$	Cl^{*-}	$[AuCl_4Cl^*]^{-2}$	$[AuCl_3Cl^*]^-$
(square planar)	(radioactive)	(trigonal bipyramid)	(square planar)

The exchange of ligands may occur within a very short period of time if conditions are suitable. Thus for ions of the type HgX_4^{-2}, where X is Cl^-, Br^-, I^-, or SCN^-, complete exchange with the corresponding anions in aqueous solution occurs within 3 to 5 sec over the temperature range 2 to 25°C.[66] The rate at which a given central ion exchanges a ligand is dependent on the nature of the central ion, the nature of the ligand, the solvent, the temperature, and whether chelate rings are formed. An example of this may be seen in the complexes of zinc. In aqueous solutions, ligand exchange reactions of zinc complexes involving simple ligands are quite rapid. When chelates are examined in non-aqueous solvents it is found that exchange rates are less and that exchange occurs more rapidly (a) with more concentrated solutions[67] or (b) when the species into which the zinc may move forms a much more stable chelate. In illustration[68] of this last point, zinc acetylacetonate exchanges with zinc oxinate in dioxane. The fact that this exchange is suppressed by the addition of free acetylacetone to the solution indicates a mechanism in which the chelates break down to a greater or lesser extent. When zinc is present in a very stable fused ring chelate, as is found in zinc phthalocyanine, the exchange is very slow, an observation in accord with a prediction made earlier that metals in phthalocyanines or porphyrin systems will undergo exchange rather slowly.[69]

The exchange reactions of many square planar complexes of Pt(II) and Pd(II) have also been studied. These show that the Pd—X bond is quite labile and readily exchanges[70] X where X is Cl^-, Br^-, I^-, SCN^-, or NO_2^-. A detailed study of the much slower rate of chloride exchange in *trans*-$[Pt(py)_2Cl_2]$ showed that strong interaction between the metal ion and solvent was important. Nitromethane and dimethylsulfoxide[71] were the solvents in which this exchange

[65] R. L. Rich and H. Taube, *J. Phys. Chem.* **58**, 1, 6 (1954).

[66] A. A. Grinberg and V. E. Mironov, *Radiokhimiya* **2**, 249 (1960), C.A. 54: 17140d.

[67] D. C. Atkins, Jr., and C. S. Garner, *J. Amer. Chem. Soc.* **74**, 3527 (1952).

[68] K. Saito and M. Tamura, *Bull. Chem. Soc. Japan* **32**, 533 (1959).

[69] S. Ruben, M. D. Kamen, M. B. Allen, and P. Nahinsky, *J. Amer. Chem. Soc.* **64**, 2297 (1942). These workers based their prediction on a lack of exchange of iron in hemoglobin and its derivatives as well as related complexes.

[70] F. Basolo, H. B. Gray, and R. G. Pearson, *J. Amer. Chem. Soc.* **82**, 4203 (1960).

[71] R. G. Pearson, H. B. Gray, and F. Basolo, *J. Amer. Chem. Soc.* **82**, 787 (1960).

occurred rapidly; in glacial acetic acid the exchange was too rapid to be measured. The solvents in which the exchange was most rapid all had available potentially empty orbitals which could form bonds with the d_{yz} or d_{xz} orbitals of the platinum atom. Since they can also donate a pair of electrons they are capable of accelerating reactions in which either type of behavior (or both) is required and the special designation *biphilic* reagent is proposed for such species. This particular study presents several points of very general interest concerning the reactions of square planar complexes which should also prove useful in formulating mechanisms for reactions of a more typical sort.

EXCHANGE REACTIONS OF SIX-COORDINATE COMPLEXES

With six-coordinate complexes we have a situation in which inert inner orbital complexes generally undergo slow exchange reactions and outer orbital complexes undergo exchange reactions at rates which are at least partly dictated by the nature of the ligand. Thus while $Fe(EDTA)^-$ is ionic, its rate of exchange with $Fe(H_2O)_6^{+3}$ is slow enough to be measured. Here again the role of water, the customary solvent, is often of paramount importance. In many exchange reactions of unidentate ligands aquation *preceeds* anation. Thus *cis-* and *trans-*$[Co(en)_2Cl_2]^+$ apparently do not exchange directly with radioactive chlorine but do in an indirect manner through $[Co(en)_2(H_2O)Cl]^{+2}$ and $[Co(en)_2(H_2O)_2]^{+3}$.

When exchange of bidentate ligands is considered additional complications may arise. For the complexes $[Co(NH_3)_4CO_3]^+$, $[Co(NH_3)_5CO_3]^+$, and $[Co(en)_2CO_3]^+$ the rates of exchange are given by

$$R = k_1(\text{complex})(\text{total carbonate}) + k_2 K(\text{complex})(H^+)$$

The first term covers direct ligand exchange and the second term accounts for aquation. K here is the equilibrium constant for the reaction

$$[Co(NH_3)_5CO_3]^+ + H_3O^+ \rightleftharpoons [Co(NH_3)_5HCO_3]^{+2} + H_2O$$

For aquation reactions of carbonato complexes, H_2O^{18} exchange studies indicate that the process is one in which the C—O bond is broken rather than the Co—O bond.

A comparison of exchange and racemization processes indicates that they may proceed at identical rates or that either *may* be faster. Data on some systems where such information is available are summarized below:

System	Relation between the rates of exchange and racemization
$[Co(C_2O_4)_3]^{-3}$	Rate of exchange < Rate of Racemization
$[Cr(C_2O_4)_3]^{-3}$	Rate of exchange < Rate of Racemization
$[Co(en)_2Cl_2]^+$ in methanol	Rate of exchange = Rate of Racemization
$[Ni(phen)_3]^{+2}$	Rate of exchange = Rate of Racemization
$[Co(en)_2CO_3]^+$	Rate of exchange > Rate of Racemization

Inasmuch as the last system in water contains the carbonato group as a monodentate ligand the character of the exchange reactions involved differs from those reactions listed above it.

All in all, exchange reactions are capable of providing much information on the intimate details of a reaction even if they do not allow us to resolve the ever-present dilemma of mechanism in a final fashion.

A few examples will show how such studies may provide details of behavior not otherwise available.

The complexes of platinum(IV) are generally considered to be quite stable and, as a rule, they undergo ligand exchange only slowly in the absence of platinum(II). This stability is also dependent to a certain extent on the nature of the ligand. $PtCl_4^=$ and $PtCl_6^=$ undergo a fairly rapid exchange reaction with chloride which is sensitive to the presence of both light and a wide variety of reagents. The exchange[72] of Pt between $PtCl_4^=$ and $PtCl_6^=$ is also much more rapid than would be expected when the considerable stability of d and $l[Pt(en)_3]^{+4}$ is recalled. In the case of the chloro complexes an intermediate chloro complex of Pt(III) has been postulated and a sequence of steps is involved which is not open to a complex such as $[Pt(en)_3]^{+4}$. In general halo groups of the transition element complexes are *more* labile than ammine groups. In the case of PtI_6^{-2} exchange with radioactive iodine is immeasurably fast.[73]

A comprehensive study of the exchange of coordinated water with several ions has been carried out by Taube and his co-workers[74] using water enriched in O^{18}. $[Cr(H_2O)_6]^{+3}$ exchanges very slowly with a half-life for exchange of about 40 h. The experiments carried out also allowed the coordination number of Cr(III) *in water* to be determined and it was shown that six molecules of water are firmly bound. For more labile complexes a special flow method was used to determine the exchange rates. The half-time for exchange of water with $Al(H_2O)_6^{+3}$ was greater than 0.02 sec while for Ni^{+2} and Fe^{+3} it was *less* than 0.02 sec! Since so many complexes are studied in aqueous solution, these studies provide information on the nature of the systems which must be taken into consideration if a full understanding of the possible reactions is to be achieved.

ELECTRON TRANSFER PROCESSES

The subject of electron transfer is very closely related to that of exchange as electron transfer represents one mechanism by which an ostensible exchange

[72] R. L. Rich and H. Taube, *J. Amer. Chem. Soc.* **76**, 2608 (1954).

[73] A. J. Poe and M. S. Vaidya, *J. Chem. Soc.*, 187 (1960).

[74] J. P. Hunt and H. Taube, *J. Chem. Phys.* **19**, 602 (1951); H. W. Baldwin and H. Taube, *ibid.*, **33**, 206 (1960); W. Kruse and H. Taube, *J. Amer. Chem. Soc.* **83**, 1280 (1961).

of ligands may occur between two ions of the same central atom which are in different oxidation states. In brief an electron transfer process may be written:

$$[M(L)_z]^{+x} + [N(P)_w]^{+y} \rightarrow [M(L)_z]^{+v} + [N(P)_w]^{+u}$$

Here M and N, L and P, and z and w may be the same or different and $x + y = v + u$.[75]

The recent theories of electron transfer processes in aqueous solution favor the formation of either ion pairs or coordination compounds as intermediates in many reactions. There are several reasons for this, one of which involves simple electrostatic considerations. If we look at the process:

$$Fe^{+2} + Fe^{*+3} \rightleftharpoons Fe^{*+2} + Fe^{+3},$$

the coulombic repulsion between the similarly charged ions at small separation distances will be very large. Thus if an Fe^{+2} ion comes within 2 A of a Fe^{+3} ion the coulombic potential would result in an activation energy of 994 kcals/mole for the system.[75a] If, however, we consider the system $Fe^{+2} - Cl - Fe^{*+3}$ in which each separation distance is 2 A, the potential energy for a linear complex is now negative (-308 kcals/mole) and results in a net attraction! It can be easily appreciated that such intermediates will provide much more convenient paths for electron transfer processes than any involving the direct confrontation of two similarly charged species.

The possible mechanisms which are usually considered for electron transfer processes are the following:[75a]

1. Reaction between oppositely charged particles:

$$A^+ + B^- \rightarrow [A^+ \ldots B^-] \rightarrow A + B$$

Such reactions are generally rapid, especially if the transfer of only one electron is involved.

2. Reactions between a neutral species and an ion:

$$A^+ + B \rightarrow [A^+ \ldots B] \rightarrow A + B^+$$
$$A + B^- \rightarrow [A \ldots B^-] \rightarrow A^- + B$$

These reactions are called charge transfer reactions and are frequently encountered in photochemical work.

3. Reactions between ions of similar charges:

$$A^p + B^q \rightarrow [A^p \ldots B^q] \rightarrow A^{p-1} + B^{q+1}$$

[75] General refs. on this topic are: B. J. Zwolinski and H. Eyring, *Chem. Reviews* **55**, 157 (1955); C. B. Amphlett, *Quarterly Reviews* **8**, 219 (1954); H. Taube, *Advances In Inorganic Chemistry and Radiochemistry* **1**, 1(1959); J. Halpern and L. E. Orgel, "The Discussions of the Faraday Society" No. 29, 32 (1960); R. T. M. Fraser, *Reviews of Pure and Applied Chem.* **11**, 64 (1961); J. Halpern, *Quarterly Reviews* **15**, 207 (1961).

When $p = q$, reactions of this type are found to be strongly *endothermic*. When A is identical with B and $p \neq q$ we have examples such as were considered earlier as exchange reactions.

4. Electron Solvation:

$$A + S \rightarrow A^+ + S^-$$

$$S^- + B \rightarrow [S^- \ldots B] \rightarrow S + B^-$$

Reactions of this type probably occur in solvents such as liquid ammonia where electron solvation is a well-established phenomenon. They are not expected to be common in water as this solvent is too readily reduced.

A further observation which should be kept in mind is that only one electron is usually transferred at a time. Processes which *require* the transfer of two electrons will generally be *slow* in the absence of some other species which can act as an intermediate.

One of the guides to the nature of the possible transition states is the Franck-Condon principle. According to this principle, the electron transfer process occurs so rapidly that no nuclear motion can occur during the short time it requires. This and the principle of microscopic reversibility require that the transfer process in the activated complex occur adiabatically. The restrictions which these two requirements place on the activated complex allow us to obtain plausible explanations for several different types of behavior found with the complexes undergoing electron transfer reactions. It is also claimed that electron "tunnelling" occurs through potential barriers in such reactions. A possible objection to the picture above is that the lifetime of the activated complex may well be shorter than the time required for the electron transfer, i.e., that the special character of the activated complex precludes the strict application of the Franck-Condon principle to the electron transfer process.[76]

For an exchange process such as that involving $Fe^*(CN)_6^{-3}$ and $Fe(CN)_6^{-4}$, the activated complex must have a symmetrical structure in which both species have undergone reorganization to achieve this condition. It is this reorganization process which may account for large entropies of activation and hence slow electron transfers in cases where such reorganization is difficult to achieve. Thus electron transfer reactions between species with the same arrangement of ligands and very similar internuclear distances are very rapid. Examples of this may be seen in the following reactions:

$MnO_4^{-2} - MnO_4^-$ complete exchange in about 5 sec

$Fe(CN)_6^{-4} - Fe(CN)_6^{-3}$ complete exchange in less than 1 min

$Mo(CN)_8^{-4} - Mo(CN)_8^{-3}$ complete exchange in about 5 sec

$Os(dipyr)_3^{+2} - Os(dipyr)_3^{+3}$ complete exchange in less than 15 sec

[76] K. K. Innes, private communication.

A somewhat unexpected result is found in the system $Co(NH_3)_6^{+2}$ – $Co(NH_3)_6^{+3}$ where the exchange is slow. Here the deciding factor seems to be the great difference in the Co—N bond distances in the two species. The Co^{+3} – N distance is reported as 1.9 A and the Co^{+2} – N as 2.5 A.[77] The amount of reorganization necessary in this case is *very* large and would account for the slow rate observed.[78]

There are many examples where anions such as OH⁻, F⁻, Cl⁻, etc., catalyze such electron transfer reactions. A qualitative explanation of the effectiveness of such reagents is given above in purely electrostatic terms. Taube and his students have developed the idea of a "bridge transfer" mechanism in some detail. In essence, a group is coordinated in a symmetrical fashion between the two species undergoing electron exchange and provides a bridge for the flow of electrons. Thus such a process for the Fe^{+2} – Fe^{*+3} system in water would be:

$$Fe^{+2} + Fe^*(OH)^{+2} \to [Fe^{+2} \cdots \overset{-}{\underset{H}{O}} \cdots Fe^{+3}] \to Fe(OH)^{+2} + Fe^{*+2}$$

Very elegant evidence supporting this mechanism may be seen in the work of Taube and Myers[79] who used oxidizing agents of the type $[Co(NH_3)_5X]^{+2}$ and the chromous ion as a reducing agent. (The X groups are called "electron mediators" by Taube.) Since the Cr^{+3} complexes produced are inert, one would expect the bridging group to be retained and be present as such in the chromic complexes produced by these reactions. Taube and Myers found that such was indeed the case. In the reaction:

$$Cr^{+2} + [Co(NH_3)_5Cl]^{+2} \to [CrCl(H_2O)_5]^{+3} + [Co(NH_3)_5(H_2O)]^{+2}$$

the Cl was transferred to the chromium and *no* exchange with chloride ion present in solution occurred. Similar results were obtained using $[Co(NH_3)_5 Br]^{+2}$ as the oxidizing agent. The activated complex in these reactions is given by Taube and Myers as:

$$[(NH_3)_5Co \cdots X \cdots Cr]^{+4}$$

These authors also called attention to the exchange in the system $Co(en)_3^{+3}$ – $Co(en)_3^{+2}$ where direct atom bridges are probably *not* involved in the electron transfer process.

When X is an organic acid, the electron transfer can take place through the carboxylate grouping. If it is a dibasic acid in which the carboxylate groups are connected by a conjugated system (as in fumaric or terephthalic acid), the elec-

[77] H. C. Brown, *J. Phys. Chem.* **56**, 862 (1952).
[78] K. J. McCallum, and S. A. Hoshowksi, *J. Chem. Phys.* **16**, 254 (1948); W. B. Lewis, C. D. Coryell, and J. W. Irvine, *J. Chem. Soc.* Suppl. Issue, No. 2, 5386 (1949).
[79] H. Taube and H. Myers, *J. Amer. Chem. Soc.* **76**, 2103 (1954).

tron transfer process may occur through this system.[80,81] If the uncoordinated carboxyl group in such a system is initially esterified, electron transfer
via the conjugated system leads to hydrolysis of the ester. The same system
may also undergo an electron transfer process involving the *coordinated*
carboxyl group. In this latter case hydrolysis of the ester does not accompany
electron exchange.[82,83] When $[(NH_3)_5CoC_2O_4]^+$ is attacked by Ce(IV) a somewhat different process occurs. Here the oxalate is oxidized to CO_2, and the
Ce(IV) and Co(III) are reduced to Ce(III) and Co(II), respectively.[84] The rate
is slower than the oxidation of free oxalate by Ce(IV). The oxalate catalysis
of electron exchange need not involve the oxidation of the oxalate, an example
of such a case where the oxalate serves to bring the two ions together (in a
complex in which electrostatic repulsion is reduced) may be seen in the
Fe(II) − Fe(III) electron exchange.[85]

A more detailed physical analysis of electron-exchange reactions has been
given by Zwolinski, Marcus, and Eyring. These authors propose a structure
for the activated complex in such reactions which is shown in Figure 36. Here

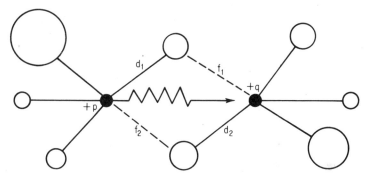

Fig. 36 Model of the activated complex proposed for electron transfer
processes by Zwolinski, Marcus, and Eyring. (Redrawn by permission of *Chemical Reviews.*)

the two central atoms may share two or more groups by forming bonds f_2 and
f_1. When the activated complex breaks down, bonds d_1 and d_2 break and the
products are formed.

In both of these mechanisms the *inner* coordination sphere of the ions is

[80] H. Taube, *J. Amer. Chem. Soc.* **77**, 4481 (1955).

[81] H. Taube, *Can. J. Chem.* **37**, 129 (1959).

[82] R. T. M. Fraser, D. K. Sebera, and H. Taube, *J. Amer. Chem. Soc.* **81**, 2906 (1959).

[83] R. T. M. Fraser in S. Kirschner, editor, *Advances in the Chemistry of the Coordination
Compounds*, The Macmillan Company, New York (1961), p. 287.

[84] P. Saffir and H. Taube, *J. Amer. Chem. Soc.* **82**, 13 (1960).

[85] R. A. Horne, *J. Phys. Chem.* **64**, 1512 (1960).

involved in a reorganization of bonds. Thus neither of them is satisfactory to explain such changes as are found in systems where no such process seems necessary, e.g., $Fe(CN)_6^{-3} - Fe(CN)_6^{-4}$, $Os(dipyr)_3^{+2} - Os(dipyr)_3^{+3}$, $IrCl_6^{-3} - IrCl_6^{-2}$, etc., since these systems consist of inert complexes. For reactions like these the activated complex must involve some outer coordination sphere complex. In all of these cases electron transfer occurs *more* rapidly than substitution reactions. It would seem possible that these complexes can achieve the activated complex configuration with relative ease, in expectation with predictions based upon the Franck-Condon principle. Marcus[86] has developed a detailed theoretical treatment which allows the calculation of the rates of some processes of this sort if enough information is available.

Many of the studies in this field have used isotopic exchange techniques but this is not absolutely necessary. Several cases have shown themselves susceptible to polarimetric study. Dwyer and Gyarfas[87] examined the process:

$$d\text{Os(dipyr)}_3^{+2} + l\text{Os(dipyr)}_3^{+3} \rightleftharpoons d\text{Os(dipyr)}_3^{+3} + l\text{Os(dipyr)}_3^{+2}$$

by mixing d-tris(2,2-dipyridyl)osmium(II) perchlorate (with a value of $[\alpha]_{5,461}^{25} = 2,200°$) with l-tris(2,2-dipyridyl)osmium(III) perchlorate (which has a value of $[\alpha]_{5,461}^{25} = 200°$). For solutions 5×10^{-4} M in both ions the exchange was complete in less than 15 sec at 25° but required 65 sec at 10° and 95 sec at 5°. The reaction results in a *complete* loss of optical activity and hence can be readily examined polarimetrically. This general method has also been applied to ethylenediaminetetraacetatocobaltate(III) and propylenediaminetetraacetatocobaltate(III); the former has been shown to undergo electron transfer in a reaction in which the absolute configuration is not conserved[88] while in the latter case electron transfer occurs with the complete retention of configuration.[89]

A final feature for this type of reaction which seems well supported empirically but whose theoretical basis is unknown, is the correlation between the magnetic susceptibilities and the half-times for exchange. Adamson[90] has drawn attention to the relation between the product of the sum and the difference of the magnetic susceptibilities (K_A and K_B) and the rates. In general as the factor $(K_A + K_B)(K_A - K_B)$ increases, the half-life of the electron transfer between A and B also increases. The following data from Adamson's paper are illustrative:

[86] R. A. Marcus, *J. Chem. Phys.* **24**, 966, 979 (1956); *ibid.*, **26**, 867, 872 (1958). This has been applied to the kinetics of oxidation of Fe(II) and other species by B. M. Gordon, L. I. Williams, and N. Sutin, *J. Amer. Chem. Soc.* **83**, 2061 (1961).

[87] F. P. Dwyer and E. C. Gyarfas, *Nature* **166**, 480 (1950).

[88] Y. A. Im and D. H. Busch, *J. Amer. Chem. Soc.* **83**, 3357 (1961).

[89] Y. A. Im and D. H. Busch, *J. Amer. Chem. Soc.* **83**, 3362 (1961).

[90] A. W. Adamson, *J. Phys. Chem.* **56**, 858 (1952).

Electron exchange pair	$(K_A + K_B)(K_A - K_B)$	$t_{\frac{1}{2}}$
Eu(II)-Eu(III)	52	100 hr
Co(en)$_3^{+2}$-Co(en)$_3^{+3}$	24	10 hr
Mn(II)-Mn(III)	10	less than 1 min
Fe(II)-Fe(III)	6	20 sec
Fe(CN)$_6^{-3}$-Fe(CN)$_6^{-4}$	3	very fast
Co^{+2}-Co^{+3}	24	1 min

The correlation is not an absolute one, but seems to be one of fair generality.

HYDROLYSIS REACTIONS AND RELATED PROCESSES

Hydrolytic processes occur in solutions of almost all cations. They are most obviously present in aqueous solutions of salts which have a small, highly charged cation. Because of the participation of the solvent in these reactions, they are difficult to study quantitatively. There are some terms used to discuss this behavior which have a special meaning which emphasize its basis in coordination phenomena. The general background of experimental behavior is in accord with this, as we shall see.

Hydrolysis is a general term used to cover almost any reaction in which water is involved. We will use it to cover reactions in which water is involved as a reacting coordinated group or in which water furnishes species which become coordinated, e.g., OH, $-O-$, or H_2O. Some typical hydrolysis reactions are:

$$SiCl_4 + 4H_2O \rightleftharpoons Si(OH)_4\downarrow + 4HCl$$

$$Zn^{+2} + 4H_2O \rightleftharpoons Zn(H_2O)_4^{+2} \overset{H_2O}{\rightleftharpoons} [Zn(H_2O)_3(OH)]^+ + H_3O^+$$

Most frequently a reaction of the second type is implied when discussing the hydrolysis of a metallic ion.

A related process is *olation*, which is a reaction in which a polynuclear complex is formed through bridging OH groups. Olation may be followed by *oxolation*, a process in which the bridging OH group is converted to a bridging $-O-$ group.

All of these reactions are found with both inert and labile complexes. Their nature is more firmly established with the inert complexes where intermediates may be isolated and characterized. Much of the recent work has also found considerable support from X-ray determinations of the crystal structures of solid basic salts.

For many years it was the custom to consider hydrolysis reactions to be reactions in which a simple cation with coordinated water split off successive protons and acted as an acid in the Bronsted-Lowry sense. The first reaction for such systems was written as:

$$M(H_2O)_x^{+y} + H_2O \rightleftharpoons [M(H_2O)_{x-1}(OH)]^{+y-1} + H_3O^+$$

and subsequent reactions as:

$$[M(H_2O)_{x-1}(OH)]^{+y-1} + H_2O \rightleftharpoons [M(H_2O)_{x-2}(OH)_2]^{+y-2} + H_3O^+$$

and a final reaction which led to the precipitation of the hydroxide:

$$[M(H_2O)_{x-y+1}(OH)_{y-1}]^+ + H_2O \rightleftharpoons M(OH)_y\downarrow + H_3O^+ + (x-y)H_2O$$

For the most part the formation of polynuclear complexes was ignored in spite of several types of evidence which indicated their presence. It now seems very probable that hydrolysis via mononuclear species is the exception rather than the rule. Sillen[91] and his co-workers have made detailed *quantitative* studies of such processes and found polynuclear complexes to be an almost inevitable component of the hydrolysed system. Of the numerous ions whose hydrolysis has been investigated by Sillen and his students, the mercuric ion and the thallic ion are apparently the only ones which fit into this simple pattern. For the mercuric ion, there are two steps:

$$Hg(H_2O)_2^{+2} + H_2O \rightleftharpoons [Hg(H_2O)(OH)]^+ + H_3O^+, \qquad K_1 = 10^{-3.70}$$

$$[Hg(H_2O)(OH)]^+ + H_2O \rightleftharpoons Hg(OH)_2\downarrow + H_3O^+, \qquad K_2 = 10^{-2.60}$$

Before proceeding to a consideration of more recent work in this field it is to be noted that polynuclear complexes were recognized as constituents of some systems for many years. Among these are the products of hydrolysis of Be^{+2} (where polynuclear complexes offer the only explanation of the data), with systems such as those derived from $Cr(H_2O)_6^{+3}$ where polynuclear complexes have been isolated and characterized, for anions such as CrO_4^-, MoO_4^-, VO_4^{-3}, etc., and some cobaltic complexes where well-defined solids have been characterized.

BERYLLIUM(II) COMPLEXES. The ion Be^{+2} is the smallest of the alkaline earth ions and shows the greatest differences from the typical behavior expected for ions of this type. These include the following idiosyncrasies:

1. $Be(OH)_2$ is a weak base.

2. BeO is quite soluble in aqueous solutions of beryllium salts.

3. Beryllium salts of weak acids either cannot be prepared or are decomposed by water.

4. $Be(OH)_2$ is amphoteric in nature.

5. Aqueous solutions of beryllium salts show all the signs of very extensive hydrolysis such as acidity, etc.

6. Beryllium forms the largest number and the most stable complexes of any element in its group in the periodic table.

7. Aqueous solutions of beryllium salts have high viscosities such as would be expected for solutions containing polynuclear species.

[91] L. G. Sillen, *Quarterly Reviews* **13**, 146 (1959); *Rec. trav. Chim.* **75**, 705 (1956).

Renewed attempts to place the hydrolytic behavior of beryllium upon a quantitative basis have been a prominent feature of recent studies.[91]

CHROMIC COMPLEXES. The hydrolytic processes which occur in solutions of chromium(III) salts are frequently slow and difficult to study under reversible conditions. Pfeiffer[92] and Bjerrum[93] demonstrated the occurrence of polynuclear species in the hydrolytic products of chromic solutions. Pfeiffer interpreted the results on the basis of the reaction which $[Cr(en)_2(OH)(H_2O)]^{+2}$ underwent when heated:

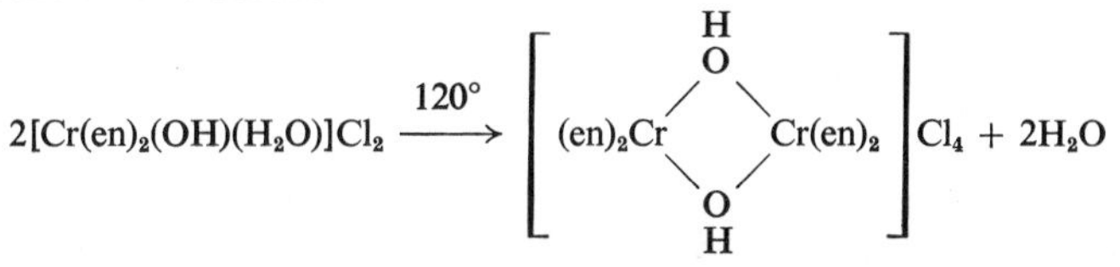

$$2[Cr(en)_2(OH)(H_2O)]Cl_2 \xrightarrow{120°} \left[(en)_2Cr \begin{smallmatrix} H \\ O \\ \diagup \diagdown \\ \diagdown \diagup \\ O \\ H \end{smallmatrix} Cr(en)_2 \right] Cl_4 + 2H_2O$$

Subsequent studies on chromium complexes have generally been interpreted on a similar basis but in many instances the products were *much less carefully characterized*.[93a] The case of the various chromium(III) sulfates illustrates some of these difficulties. The solutions undergo slow changes with time which are not understood completely. H. Erdmann[94] concluded from conductometric titrations that both OH and SO_4 groups act as bridging groups in the polynuclear complexes formed during the titration of aged chromic sulfate solutions with base. During this reaction H^+ is split off as the OH bridges form. The following scheme was proposed to cover the observations noted:

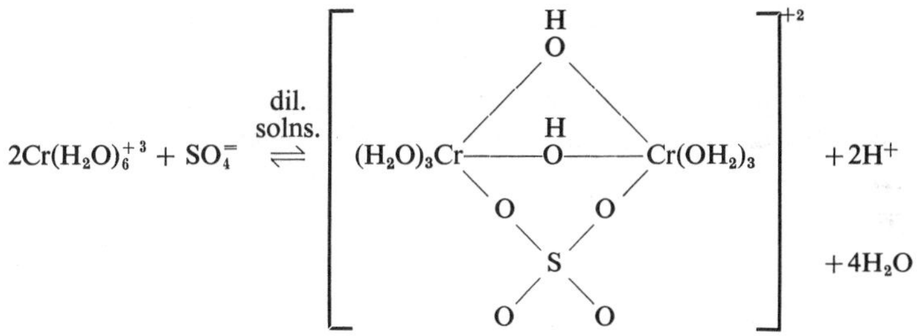

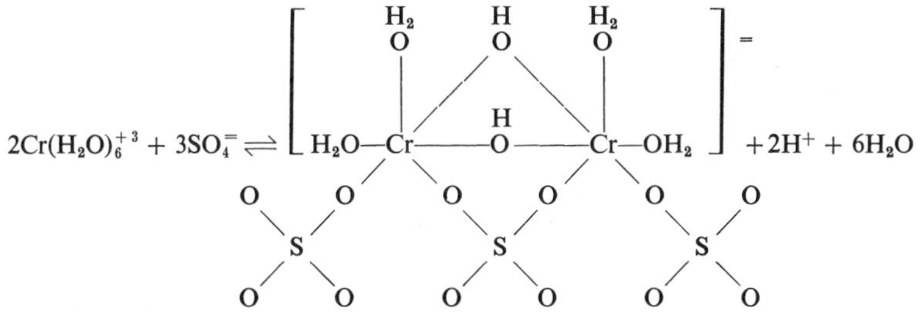

$$2Cr(H_2O)_6^{+3} + SO_4^- \underset{\text{solns.}}{\overset{\text{dil.}}{\rightleftharpoons}} \left[(H_2O)_3Cr \begin{smallmatrix} H \\ O \\ \diagup \diagdown \\ \diagdown \quad \diagup \\ O \quad O \\ \diagdown \diagup \\ S \\ \diagup \diagdown \\ O \quad O \end{smallmatrix} Cr(OH_2)_3 \right]^{+2} \begin{array}{l} +2H^+ \\ \\ +4H_2O \end{array}$$

$$2Cr(H_2O)_6^{+3} + 3SO_4^- \rightleftharpoons \left[H_2O{-}Cr \cdots Cr{-}OH_2 \right]^= +2H^+ + 6H_2O$$

[92] P. Pfeiffer, *Zeit. anorg. Chem.* **56**, 261 (1907).

[93] N. Bjerrum, *Zeit. physik. Chem.* **59**, 336 (1907); **73**, 724 (1910); **110**, 656 (1924).

[93a] The literature is collected in J. C. Bailar, Jr., *The Chemistry of The Coordination Compounds*, Reinhold Publishing Corp., New York (1956), Ch. 13.

[94] H. Erdmann, *Angew. Chem.* **64**, 500 (1952).

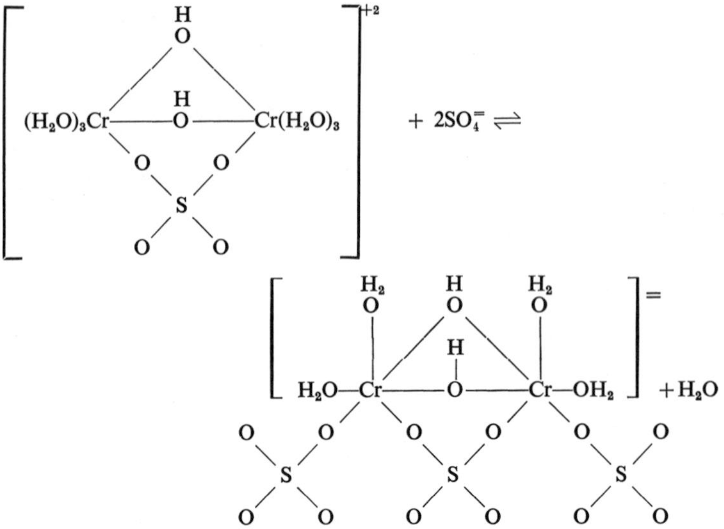

$$\left[(H_2O)_3Cr \begin{array}{c} \overset{\displaystyle H}{\underset{\displaystyle O}{}} \\ \diagup \quad \diagdown \\ \overset{\displaystyle H}{O} \end{array} Cr(H_2O)_3 \right]^{+2} + 2SO_4^{=} \rightleftharpoons$$

$$\left[H_2O\text{—}Cr \overset{H_2O}{\underset{\diagup\diagdown}{|}} \overset{\overset{H}{O}}{\diagup} \overset{H_2O}{\underset{\diagdown\diagup}{|}} Cr\text{—}OH_2 \right]^{=} + H_2O$$

This interpretation is consistent with the known complexing power of sulfate ion for chromium(III),[95] but it is quite possible that alternative schemes would be as satisfactory.

The nature of the species present in solutions of even the simplest of chromium(III) compounds is still a subject of active investigation. A recent study of these ions which generated them in situ by oxidation of chromous ions with various oxidizing agents indicates[96] that higher oxidation states of chromium are present during such a process. Ardon and Plane investigated the generation of polynuclear chromium(III) species by the oxidation of chromous ions and concluded that the following reaction sequences are probable:

$$Cr^{+2} + \text{one electron oxidizing agent} \rightarrow Cr^{+3} \text{ (mononuclear)}$$
$$Cr^{+2} + \text{two electron oxidizing agent} \rightarrow Cr(IV)$$
$$Cr^{+2} + Cr(IV) \rightarrow \text{dinuclear species}$$

The mononuclear species can also be converted to the polynuclear species by boiling the solutions.

An independent approach to the investigation of these processes is provided by ultracentrifuge studies. These are capable of providing information on some types of aggregation in solution.[97] In the case of Pb(II) and Sn(IV) such studies showed that mononuclear species were present in strongly basic solutions. This method has been applied to a number of other systems by Kraus and his co-workers.

[95] F. Krauss, H. Querengasser, and P. Weyer, *Zeit. anorg. Chem.* **179**, 413 (1929), see also M. Harmelin, Ph.D.Thesis, Univ. of Paris, 1963.

[96] M. Ardon and R. A. Plane, *J. Amer. Chem. Soc.* **81**, 3197 (1959).

[97] J. S. Johnson and K. A. Kraus, *J. Amer. Chem. Soc.* **81**, 1569 (1959).

The effects of hydrolysis occurring during titrations carried out to determine stepwise formation constants has been examined by Martell and his associates.[98]

A further example of hydrolytic behavior where the products are well characterized may be found in the polynuclear complexes of cobalt(III). These reactions have served to give a pattern for many interpretations of less stable systems because the products are isolatable solids. The general type of reaction which occurs may be written as:

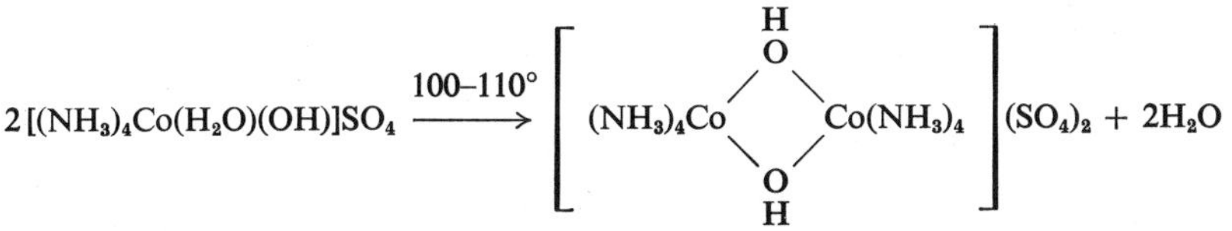

$$2\,[(NH_3)_4Co(H_2O)(OH)]SO_4 \xrightarrow{100\text{--}110°} \left[(NH_3)_4Co \underset{\underset{H}{O}}{\overset{\overset{H}{O}}{\diamond}} Co(NH_3)_4 \right](SO_4)_2 + 2H_2O \quad \text{[99]}$$

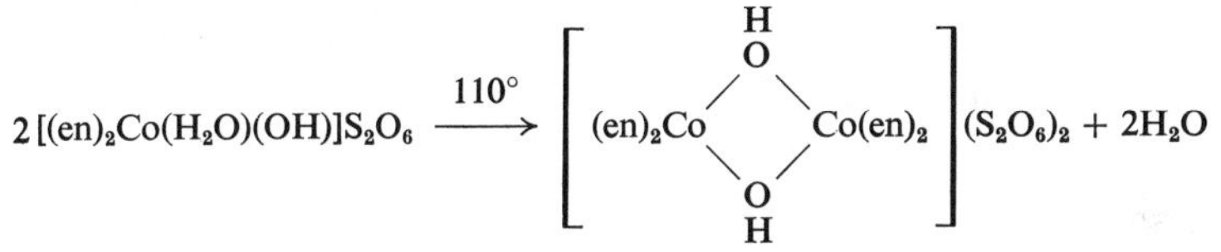

$$2\,[(en)_2Co(H_2O)(OH)]S_2O_6 \xrightarrow{110°} \left[(en)_2Co \underset{\underset{H}{O}}{\overset{\overset{H}{O}}{\diamond}} Co(en)_2 \right](S_2O_6)_2 + 2H_2O \quad \text{[100]}$$

An unusual method for studying the hydrolysis of chromic salts in aqueous solution is that of Hall and Eyring.[101] Starting with the equation:

$$6(NH_4)_6Mo_7O_{24} + 7[Cr(H_2O)_6](NO_3)_3 \rightarrow$$
$$7(NH_4)_3[Cr(MoO_4H)_6] + 15NH_4NO_3 + 6HNO_3 + 18H_2O,$$

they argued that the water coordinated directly to the chromium was replaced by coordinated $HMoO_4^-$ groups when ammonium paramolybdate solutions were added to chromium(III) solutions. Using principally conductometric titrations, they were able to show that for freshly prepared solutions of chromium(III) nitrate, six molybdates were coordinated by each chromium ion. For boiled solutions which contained hydrolyzed and polymerized species, the number of molybdate groups taken up per chromium(III) decreased. It is of some interest that their results are consistent with the presence of *no* nitrate in the coordination sphere of the chromium even when a large excess of nitrate ion was present. They found that equilibrium in these solutions was usually attained after about *sixty hours* refluxing! The coordination of molybdate did not appear to disrupt ol or oxo bridges in these complexes. While the molybdate group is not commonly considered to be a good coordinating agent, a chromium(III) complex with six such groups, $(NH_4)_3[Cr(MoO_4H)_6]$ · $7H_2O$, has been isolated and characterized.[102]

[98] A. E. Martell *et. al.*, *J. Am. Chem. Soc.* **79**, 3036 (1957); **81**, 519, 525 (1959) and the references cited therein.

[99] A. Werner, *Ber.* **40**, 4437, 4440, 4820 (1907).

[100] A. Werner and J. Rapiport, *Ann.* **375**, 84 (1910).

[101] H. T. Hall and H. Eyring, *J. Amer. Chem. Soc.* **72**, 782 (1950).

[102] R. D. Hall, *J. Amer. Chem. Soc.* **29**, 692 (1907).

WORK OF L. G. SILLEN AND HIS COLLABORATORS. Sillen (*loc. cit.*) considers that the hydrolyzed cation gives rise to species of the general form $B\{(OH)_tB\}_n$ where the initial B is the *core* and the $\{(OH)_tB\}$ groups are the *links* in the polynuclear complex. By using an ingenious development of the potentiometric method for studying complexes in solution, Sillen has examined numerous hydrolyses. The work reported by Sillen is based upon the direct application of the law of mass action to the equilibria in a medium which contains a high concentration of an inert salt such as sodium perchlorate. A typical result is that found with the ferric ion. Here the equilibria involved are reported as:

$$Fe^{+3} + H_2O \rightleftharpoons Fe(OH)^{+2} + H^+$$

$$Fe(OH)^{+2} + H_2O \rightleftharpoons Fe(OH)_2^+ + H^+$$

$$2Fe^{+3} + 2H_2O \rightleftharpoons Fe_2(OH)_2^{+4} + 2H^+$$

These equilibria suffice to explain the pH of solutions of ferric ion when diluted or when titrated with a base, so long as precipitation does not occur. With other cations a variety of species are reported. Some of these are:

Beryllium:

$$3Be^{+2} + 3H_2O \rightleftharpoons Be_3(OH)_3^{+3} + 3H^+$$

$$2Be^{+2} + H_2O \rightleftharpoons Be_2OH^{+3} + H^+$$

$$Be^{+2} + 2H_2O \rightleftharpoons Be(OH)_2 + 2H^+$$

Tin(II):

$$3Sn^{+2} + 4H_2O \rightleftharpoons Sn_3(OH)_4^{+2} + 4H^+$$

$$2Sn^{+2} + 2H_2O \rightleftharpoons Sn_2(OH)_2^{+2} + 2H^+$$

$$Sn^{+2} + H_2O \rightleftharpoons SnOH^+ + H^+$$

Bismuth:

$$6Bi^{+3} + 12H_2O \rightleftharpoons Bi_6(OH)_{12}^{+6} + 12H^+$$

$$Bi^{+3} + H_2O \rightleftharpoons Bi(OH)^{+2} + H^+$$

Information on other systems studied may be found in the references cited earlier. The same methods have been applied to systems where anionic polymerization occurs, such as molybdate, vanadate, etc.

In addition to studies based on pH determination, other methods have been used to study this type of reaction. Thus the hydrolysis of zirconium has been studied by solvent extraction methods.[103] In these particular studies two reactions are examined simultaneously one of which is an extraction process:

$$Zr(IV) + nHX^{+(-z)} \rightleftharpoons Zr(X)_n^{+(4-zn)} + nH^+$$

where X is any anion

$$Zr(IV)(aq.) + 4HK(org.) \rightleftharpoons ZrK_4(org.) + 4H^+(aq.)$$

[103] E. M. Larsen, *J. Chem. Educ.* **28**, 529 (1951) contains previous literature also.

Studies of the hydrolysis of zirconium in perchlorate solutions led to the estimation of species such as $Zr(OH)^{+3}$ and $Zr(OH)_2^{+2}$ as well as polynuclear complexes. In perchlorate solutions the reactions do not have the complication of involving anion coordination. Thus in sulfuric acid solutions, zirconium is present in *anionic* complexes.[104]

FORMATION AND PROPERTIES OF POLYNUCLEAR COMPLEXES

Numerous examples of polynuclear complexes are well recognized and many different types have had their structures determined by X-ray diffraction studies. Some of the commonly encountered classes are:

1. Complexes with —OH or —O— bridging groups

2. Complexes with —NH$_2$— or —NH— (or more rarely —NH$_2$NH$_2$—) bridging groups

3. Complexes with —O—O bridging groups

4. Complexes with multidentate ligands such as proteins, synthetic polymers, or structures such as found in hemoglobin

5. Complexes in which halide ions or other anions such as sulfate, acetate, or cyanide act as bridging groups

6. Complexes with metal to metal bonds

7. Polynuclear carbonyls

1. Complexes with —OH or —O— bridges are extremely common in the water solvent system and several examples have already been cited. It is generally believed that the processes of olation and oxolation are of almost universal occurrence in the formation of hydroxides and hydrous oxides from aqueous solutions of the parent metallic cations. A typical example of this is seen in the hydrolysis scheme for Th^{+4} presented by Hietanen and Sillen.[105]

$$2Th^{+4} + 2H_2O \rightleftharpoons Th_2(OH)_2^{+6} + 2H^+$$
$$2Th^{+4} + H_2O \rightleftharpoons [Th_2(OH)]^{+7} + H^+$$

where the OH groups are shared by the two thorium ions. Studies on solid basic salts support this formulation in a general way *but* the formulation of solid basic salts in a manner which presumes them to be Werner complexes of the usual sort is definitely *not* in accord with the experimental evidence.

Processes analogous to olation and oxolation are probably of general occurrence in protonic solvents of all sorts and may be found in numerous

---

[104] J. Lister, *J. Chem. Soc.*, 4315 (1952).
[105] S. Hietanen and L. G. Sillen, *Acta Chem. Scand.* **13**, 533 (1959).

systems of this sort. While such reactions have not been subjected to extensive study, the following pieces of evidence support such a presumption:

(a) Cobalt(III) complexes containing —NH_2— and —NH— bridging groups are common and well characterized.

(b) Many alkoxides are polymeric materials of much higher molecular weight than expected, especially those of elements which readily undergo olation in aqueous systems.

(c) Polynuclear acetates are well known for Fe(III) and Cr(III).

(d) Such processes as ammonolysis reactions and the existence of amphoteric behavior in non-aqueous solvents indicates that the general sequence of such reactions is similar to that in the water system. Thus the addition of KNH_2 solution to a solution of a zinc(II) salt in liquid ammonia results in the precipitation of zinc amide which redissolves in an excess of potassium amide.[106]

(e) Such other solvents that show general coordination properties which are similar to those of water and exhibit solvation can be the bridging species in polynuclear species.

2. Complexes with NH_2 and NH bridges are especially common among the polynuclear complexes of cobalt (III). As an example, consider the complex mixture designated as Vortmann's sulfate. This is prepared by the aerial oxidation of ammoniacal cobaltous nitrate solutions followed by subsequent neutralization with dilute sulfuric acid in the cold.[107] The two chief constituents of the brown product obtained here are:

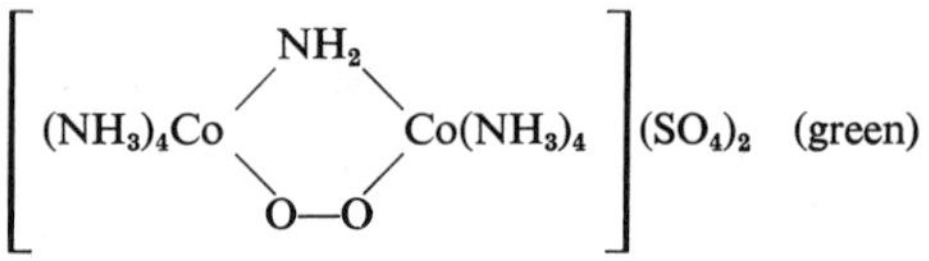

$$\left[(NH_3)_4Co \underset{O-O}{\overset{NH_2}{\diagup\diagdown}} Co(NH_3)_4 \right] (SO_4)_2 \quad \text{(green)}$$

and

$$\left[(NH_3)_4Co \underset{\underset{H}{O}}{\overset{NH_2}{\diagup\diagdown}} Co(NH_3)_4 \right] (SO_4)_2 \quad \text{(red)}$$

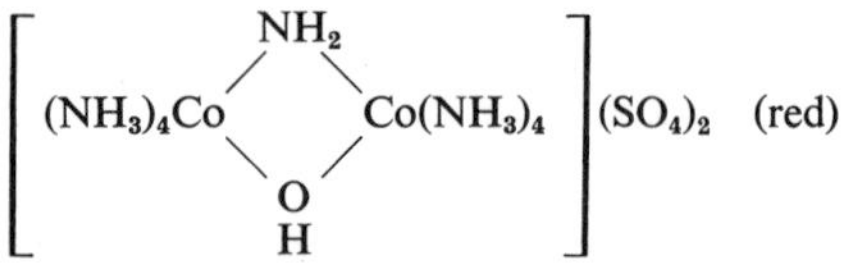

Cations of the first type are of interest as examples of complexes containing "cobalt(IV)". Paramagnetic resonance spectra show that the single unpaired electron present interacts equally with both nuclei and has an equal probability of being on either cobalt atom.[108] It is thus impossible to assign integral oxidation numbers to the two cobalt atoms in such complexes.

[106] E. C. Franklin, *Zeit. anorg. Chem.* **55**, 195 (1907).

[107] A. Werner, *Ber.* **40**, 4609 (1907).

[108] I. Bernal, E. A. V. Ebsworth and J. A. Weil, *Proc. Chem. Soc.*, p. 57 (Feb. 1959). For related studies on cobalt complexes containing peroxo bridges see E. A. V. Ebsworth and J. A. Weil, *J. Phys. Chem.* **63**, 1890 (1959).

Complexes with bridging amido groups may sometimes be prepared by treating those containing amino groups with base or by driving off acid with heat. The following sequence of reactions illustrates these processes:

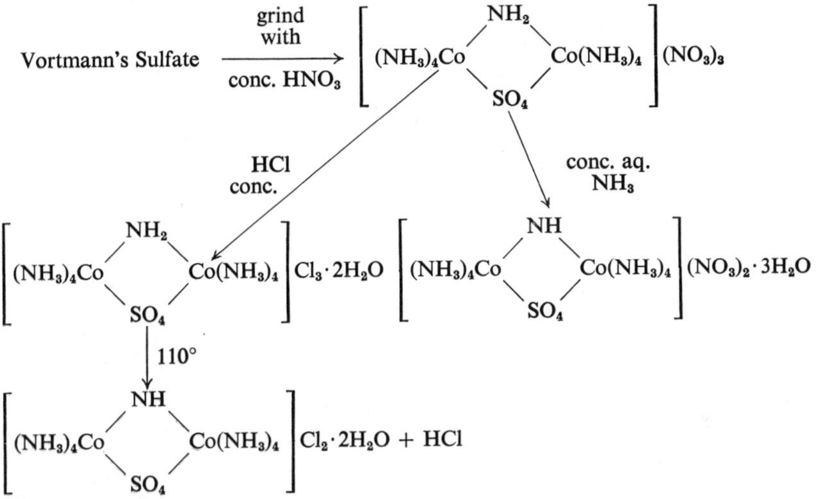

$$\text{Vortmann's Sulfate} \xrightarrow[\text{conc. HNO}_3]{\substack{\text{grind} \\ \text{with}}} \left[(NH_3)_4Co \underset{SO_4}{\overset{NH_2}{\diagdown\diagup}} Co(NH_3)_4 \right](NO_3)_3$$

$$\left[(NH_3)_4Co \underset{SO_4}{\overset{NH_2}{\diagup\diagdown}} Co(NH_3)_4 \right]Cl_3 \cdot 2H_2O \qquad \left[(NH_3)_4Co \underset{SO_4}{\overset{NH}{\diagup\diagdown}} Co(NH_3)_4 \right](NO_3)_2 \cdot 3H_2O$$

$$\downarrow 110°$$

$$\left[(NH_3)_4Co \underset{SO_4}{\overset{NH}{\diagup\diagdown}} Co(NH_3)_4 \right]Cl_2 \cdot 2H_2O + HCl$$

The existence of N_2H_4 bridges has been reported for some complexes of ruthenium. Thus a complex $[(Cl)_3(N_2H_5)_2Ru—(NH_2)_2Ru(N_2H_5)_2Cl_3]^{+4}$ has been *proposed*.[109] When this compound is heated it loses four molecules of HCl to give a compound which is formulated as containing two molecules of hydrazine chelated to each of two ruthenium atoms which are themselves joined by a hydrazine bridge:

$$[Cl(NH_2NH_2)_2Ru—NH_2NH_2Ru(NH_2NH_2)_2Cl]^{+4}$$

3. Complexes with —O—O bridges play a prominent part in many metal-complex catalyzed oxidations involving molecular oxygen. One of the easiest of these to prepare is the pentamminocobalt(III)-μ-peroxopentamminocobalt(III) cation formed by the action of oxygen on ammoniacal solutions of cobaltous salts.[110]

$$2Co(NH_3)_6^{+2} + O_2 \rightarrow [(NH_3)_5Co—(O—O)—Co(NH_3)_5]^{+4} + 2NH_3$$

(The use of cobaltous nitrate results in the corresponding nitrate.) These ions undergo a further oxidation when warmed with dilute (1:1) nitric acid:

$$[(NH_3)_5Co—(O—O)—Co(NH_3)_5]^{+4} \xrightarrow{HNO_3} [(NH_3)_5Co—(O—O)—Co(NH_3)_5]^{+5}$$

4. Any organic species which has a large number of ligand groups may

[109] L. F. Audrieth and B. J. Ogg, *The Chemistry of Hydrazine* John Wiley & Sons, Inc., New York (1951), Ch. 9 contains a discussion of this and related complexes.

[110] A. Werner and A. Mylius, *Zeit. anorg. Chem.* **16**, 262 (1898).

form polynuclear complexes with metal ions. This type of polynuclear complex is of a type quite different from the kinds mentioned above. In such a complex there may be many atoms intervening between two metal ions. The general properties of this kind of polynuclear complex are determined primarily by the structure of the coordinating agent. Here the coordination agent supplies the structure to which the metallic ions are added at various (usually) chelating sites.[111]

Typical examples include complexes with polymeric acids, amines, etc., as well as proteins. These materials, especially the calcium complexes, are of considerable importance from a biological viewpoint as being important in an understanding of the role of calcium in the body fluids.

5. Complexes in which halide ions act as bridging groups are known in the solid state but such bridges are often destroyed on solution in water. Other anions are also capable of forming stable bridges. Acetato, sulfato, and cyanido bridges are known in several transition metal complexes which are stable in aqueous solution. Bridging structures of this general type are known in many anhydrous chlorides, bromides, and iodides. Some examples are: (a) ferric chloride which is dimeric in the gaseous state, $(FeCl_3)_2$—each iron is in the center of a tetrahedron and two tetrahedra share an edge and correspondingly, two chlorides;[112] (b) aluminum chloride is also dimeric and has a similar structure in the gas phase; and (c) palladium(II) chloride in the solid state consists of infinite chains of square planar $PdCl_4$ groups in which each chloride is shared by adjacent Pd(II) species.

Often the structure of such compounds in the solid state is quite different from that found for the gaseous species. Thus with Fe(III) chloride, four chlorine atoms surround each iron in the gaseous state but six surround each iron atom octahedrally in the solid state.

Complexes containing acetato bridging groups were studied by Weinland, Krauss, and others in the 1920's. Ferric salts of monocarboxylic acids are generally *not* simple.[113] In ferric acetate the composition corresponds to $Fe(C_2H_3O_2)_3$, but the properties correspond to $[Fe_3(C_2H_3O_2)_6](C_2H_3O_2)_3$, as the ionizable acetates may be replaced without destroying the polynuclear complex ion.[114] N. V. Sidgwick[115] formulates these complexes as containing rings such as:

---

[111] The relation of these materials to more conventional complexes is quite close. Thus the methods used for studying complexation equilibria of simple ligands may be extended to polymeric chelates: G. K. Hoeschele, J. B. Andelman, and H. P. Gregor, *J. Phys. Chem.* **62**, 1239 (1958).

[112] A. F. Wells, *Structural Inorganic Chemistry* Oxford University Press (1960).

[113] R. Abegg, *Handbuch der Anorganischen Chemie* IV Bd., 3 Abt., Z. Teil B., pp. 362–373.

[114] A. Krauss, *Zeit. anorg. Chem.* **169**, 273 (1928).

[115] N. V. Sidgwick, *The Chemical Elements and Their Compounds*, Oxford University Press (1950), p. 1363.

$$
-C\begin{array}{c} \diagup O\text{---}Fe\leftarrow\text{---}O \diagdown \\ \diagdown O\text{---}\rightarrow Fe\text{---}O \diagup \end{array}C-
$$

Weinland and Holtmeir[116] found three types of cations in this kind of poly-nuclear ferric complex ring:

$$[Fe_3(C_2H_3O_2)_6]^{+3}, \qquad [Fe_3(C_2H_3O_2)_6(OH)]^{+2}, \text{ and } [Fe_3(C_2H_3O_2)_6(OH)_2]^{+}$$

Analogous phenomena are encountered in the study of chromium(III) acetate. Here complexes of the types $[Cr_3(C_2H_3O_2)_6XY]^{+z}$ are found with X and Y being either —OH or H_2O.

Complexes in which the cyano groups act as bridging groups are fairly common among the transition metals. One finds such bridging groups in the Prussian or Turnbull's blues, whose structures in the solid state are very similar, consisting of a network of iron atoms held together by cyano bridging groups. The nickel complex $K_2[Ni(CN)_3]$ is presumably $K_4[Ni_2(CN)_6]$ containing bridging cyano groups.

Another example may be seen in the gold compounds of the type R_2AuCN which are presumably tetrameric:

$$
\begin{array}{ccc}
C_2H_5 & & C_2H_5 \\
| & & | \\
C_2H_5\text{---}Au\text{------}C\equiv N\text{------}Au\text{---}C_2H_5 \\
| & & | \\
N & & C \\
||| & & ||| \\
C & & N \\
| & & | \\
C_2H_5\text{---}Au\text{------}N\equiv C\text{------}Au\text{---}C_2H_5 \\
| & & | \\
C_2H_5 & & C_2H_5
\end{array}
$$

Suggested structures for the cyanides of Pd(II), Pt(II), Ni(II), and Cu(I) cyanides have similar bridging cyano groups.

6. Complexes in which metal to metal bonds occur are apparently more common than generally believed. Such a bond is possible when the distance separating the metal atoms is rather small and recent opinion favors the notion that appreciable interaction of this type may occur without the intervention of any special chemical process. This phenomenon may range from the weak interaction found between the nickel atoms in solid nickel(II) dimethylgly-oxime (where the nickel atoms are close enough to exhibit noticeable inter-action) to complexes such as $Mo_6Cl_8^{+4}$ where very stable metal-metal bonds hold the structure together even in aqueous solutions. Several structures where metal-metal bonds are present are listed below, together with their structures where these are known.

[116] R. F. Weinland and H. Holtmeir, *Zeit. anorg. Chem.* **173**, 49 (1929).

COMPLEX	STRUCTURE
$Mo_6Cl_8^{+4}$	An octahedron with Mo atoms on each apex and 8Cl's on the 8 vertical edges of the octahedron
$Nb_6Cl_{12}^{+2}$	An octahedron with Nb atoms on each apex and 12Cl's on the 12 edges of the octahedron
$Ta_6Cl_{12}^{+2}$	Same as $Nb_6Cl_{12}^{+2}$
$W_2Cl_9^{-3}$	Two WCl_6 octahedra share a face and hence three bridging Cl's; W in center of each octahedron

Weak, but still definite, metal to metal interactions are found in a number of solids where their existence was previously unsuspected. In solid cupric acetate[117] and in chromous acetate[118] the metal atoms are sufficiently close to each other that a weak but definite interaction is present and the metal ions may be considered to have metal ions in their coordination sphere.

7. Polynuclear carbonyls were discovered soon after the simple carbonyls. *All* transition elements of *odd* atomic number which form carbonyls form only polynuclear carbonyls. Polynuclear carbonyls of the other transition elements may sometimes be prepared from the simple carbonyls by photochemical reactions or by thermal decomposition, e.g.:

$$Fe(CO)_5 \xrightarrow{h\nu} Fe_2(CO)_9 + Fe_3(CO)_{12}$$

$$2Re + 10CO \xrightarrow{pressure} Re_2(CO)_{10}$$

In these complexes it is generally considered that the bridging group is a CO group and this is supported by the observation that two different C—O absorption bands are found in the infrared spectra of these polynuclear carbonyls.[119]

A final aspect of the importance of bridging complexes is their role in many ligand and electron exchange reactions. In the oxidation of Cr^{+2} by $[(NH_3)_5Co(OH_2)]^{+3}$ there is a *quantitative* transfer of the oxygen in the coordinated water from the cobalt to the chromium.[120] This same study showed that in the oxidation of Cr^{+2} by *cis*-$[(en)_2Co(OH_2)_2]^{+3}$ only *one* oxygen is transferred so there is no need to postulate a double bridging in such a reaction even though it is possible. Such reactions involving ligand exchange via intermediates in-

[117] J. N. Van Niekerk and F. R. L. Schoening, *Acta Cryst.* **6**, 230 (1953).

[118] B. Bleaney and A. Bowers, *Proc. Roy. Soc.* **A214**, 451 (1952). J. N. Van Niekerk and F. R. L. Schoening, *Nature* **171**, 36 (1952); *idem, Acta Cryst.* **6**, 501 (1953).

[119] J. W. Cable and R. K. Sheline, *Chem. Reviews* **56**, 1 (1956); for earlier work see F. G. Mann, *Annual Reports Progress Chem.* **35**, 148 (1938).

[120] W. Kruse and H. Taube, *J. Amer. Chem. Soc.* **82**, 526 (1960).

volving bridging groups are very common; the bridge intermediate often allows such reactions to proceed via mechanisms in which the coordination numbers of the reactant species are not drastically altered.

THE TRANS-EFFECT[121]

Most of the substitution reactions of the numerous square planar complexes of Pt(II) proceed in such a manner that the entering group takes the place of the group which is replaced. The considerable structural stability of these Pt(II) complexes has allowed a systematic study of their substitution reactions to be carried out. The result of these studies has been a realization that a given ligand in the complex has a considerable influence in determining the replaceability of the group which is *trans* to it in the complex. The detailed theoretical explanation of the substitution reactions of these complexes is *not* complete at present.

The general significance of this directive effect as well as its use in synthetic work were first explored by Chernyaev in 1926. The order of increasing labilization of the *trans*-group is:[121g]

$$H_2O < OH^- < NH_3 \sim RNH_2 < Py < Cl^- < Br^- < NCS^- \sim I^- \sim NO_2^- \sim SO_3H^-$$
$$\sim PR_3 \sim R_2S \sim SC(NH_2)_2 < NO \sim CO \sim C_2H_4 \sim CN^-$$

This *trans*-effect has proven itself useful in synthetic work. The preparation of the three geometrical isomers of [PtNH₃PyClBr] illustrates how the *trans*-effect can be used in such work.[122] The order of the *trans*-effect for the ligands concerned is:

$$NH_3 < Py < Cl < Br$$

The three isomers desired are:

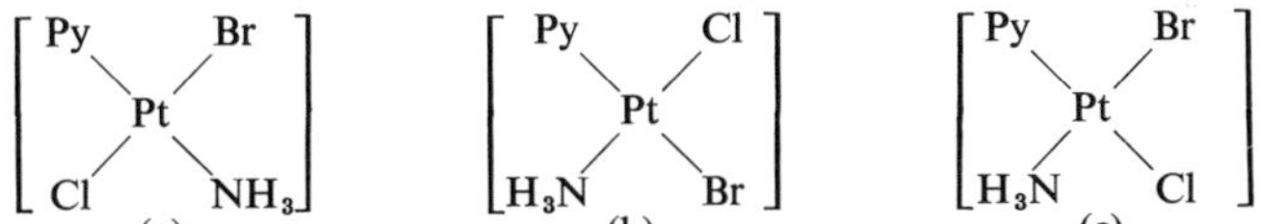

(a) (b) (c)

[121] General references are (a) J. V. Quagliano and L. Schubert, *Chem. Reviews* **50**, 201 (1952); (b) A. A. Grinberg, *Einführung in die Chemie der Komplexverbindungen*, VEB Verlag, Berlin (1955), p. 240 ff., 261 ff.; (c) J. C. Bailar, Jr., *Chemistry of the Coordination Compounds*, Reinhold Publishing Corp. New York (1956), pp. 146, 195, 204, 294, 490; (d) F. Basolo and R. G. Pearson, *Mechanisms of Inorganic Reactions*, John Wiley & Sons, Inc., New York (1958), pp. 6, 172–192; (e) A. A. Grinberg, *Chem. Zvesti* **13**, 201–223 (1959), C.A. **53**: 17646; (f) F. Basolo, H. B. Gray, and R. G. Pearson, *J. Amer. Chem. Soc.* **82**, 4200 (1960); (g) J. Chatt, L. A. Duncanson, and L. M. Venanzi, *J. Chem. Soc.* 4456 (1955); (h) S. S. Batsanov, *Refractometry and Chemical Structure* translated by P. P. Sutton, Consultants Bureau, New York (1961), pp. 211–229, (i) F. Basolo and R. G. Pearson, Progress in Inorganic Chem. **4**, 381 (1962).

[122] A. D. Helman, E. F. Karandaschowa, and L. E. Essen, *Ann. Sec. Plat.* **24**, 60 (1949), C.A. **45**: 2810.

The preparations may start from $PtCl_4^{-2}$.

(a)

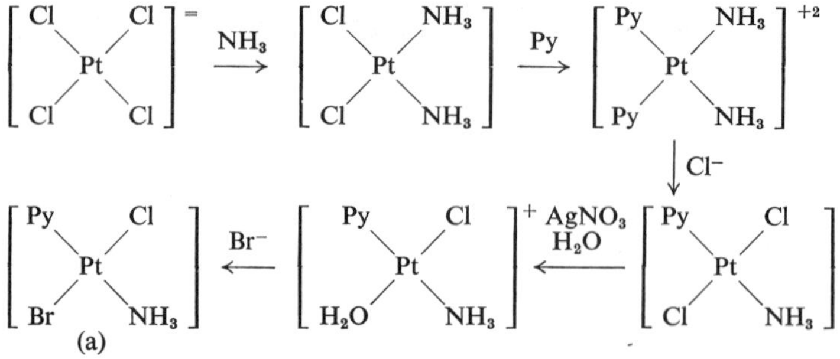

$$\begin{bmatrix} Cl & Cl \\ & Pt & \\ Cl & Cl \end{bmatrix}^{=} \xrightarrow{NH_3} \begin{bmatrix} Cl & NH_3 \\ & Pt & \\ Cl & NH_3 \end{bmatrix} \xrightarrow{Py} \begin{bmatrix} Py & NH_3 \\ & Pt & \\ Py & NH_3 \end{bmatrix}^{+2}$$

$$\downarrow Cl^-$$

$$\begin{bmatrix} Py & Cl \\ & Pt & \\ Br & NH_3 \end{bmatrix} \xleftarrow{Br^-} \begin{bmatrix} Py & Cl \\ & Pt & \\ H_2O & NH_3 \end{bmatrix}^{+} \xleftarrow[H_2O]{AgNO_3} \begin{bmatrix} Py & Cl \\ & Pt & \\ Cl & NH_3 \end{bmatrix}$$
(a)

(b) 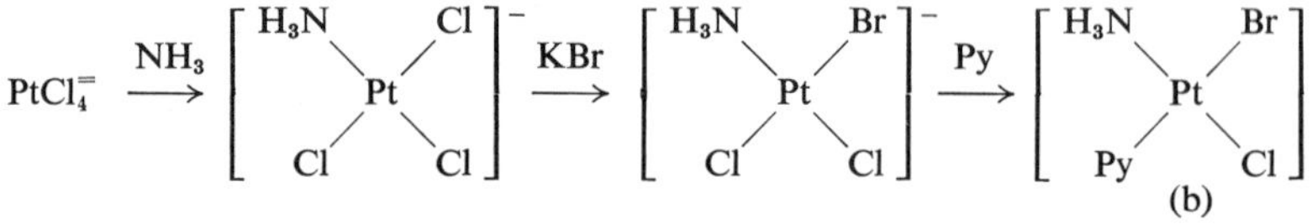 $PtCl_4^{=} \xrightarrow{NH_3} \begin{bmatrix} H_3N & Cl \\ & Pt & \\ Cl & Cl \end{bmatrix}^{-} \xrightarrow{KBr} \begin{bmatrix} H_3N & Br \\ & Pt & \\ Cl & Cl \end{bmatrix}^{-} \xrightarrow{Py} \begin{bmatrix} H_3N & Br \\ & Pt & \\ Py & Cl \end{bmatrix}$
(b)

(c) $PtCl_4^{=} \xrightarrow{Py} \begin{bmatrix} Py & Cl \\ & Pt & \\ Cl & Cl \end{bmatrix}^{-} \xrightarrow{KBr} \begin{bmatrix} Py & Br \\ & Pt & \\ Cl & Cl \end{bmatrix}^{-} \xrightarrow{NH_3} \begin{bmatrix} Py & Br \\ & Pt & \\ H_3N & Cl \end{bmatrix}$
(c)

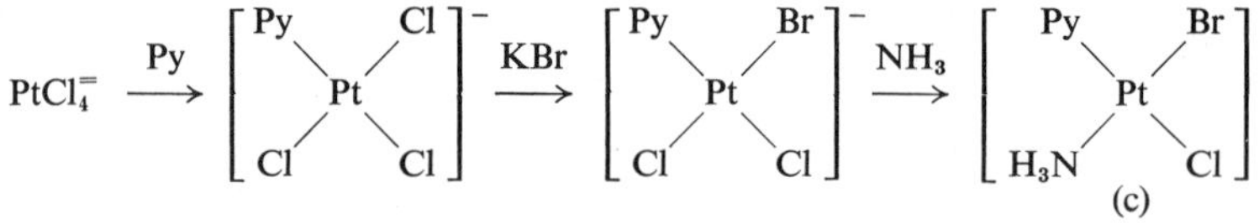

Two rules based upon the *trans*-effect are the following:

1. Peyrone's Rule: The action of ammonia or amines on tetraacidoplatinate(II) ions leads to diacidodiammines with a *cis*-configuration, e.g.,

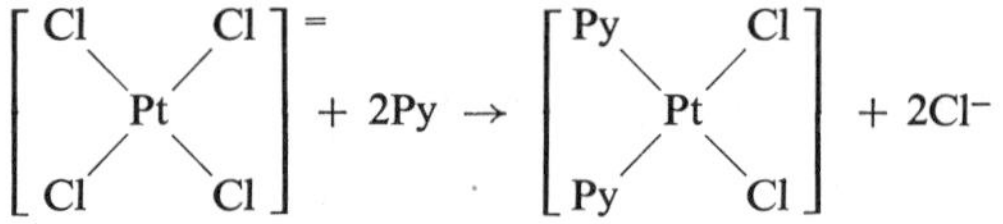

$$\begin{bmatrix} Cl & Cl \\ & Pt & \\ Cl & Cl \end{bmatrix}^{=} + 2Py \rightarrow \begin{bmatrix} Py & Cl \\ & Pt & \\ Py & Cl \end{bmatrix} + 2Cl^-$$

2. Jorgensen's Rule: Thermal decomposition of tetramines of the type $[Pt(Am)_4]X_2$ leads to the formation of diacidodiammines with the *trans*-configuration, e.g.,

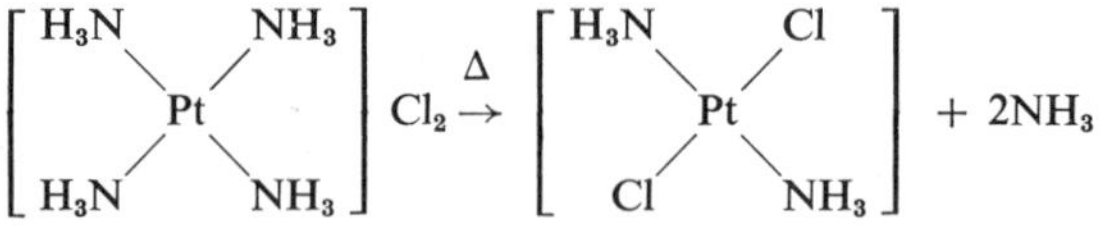

$$\begin{bmatrix} H_3N & NH_3 \\ & Pt & \\ H_3N & NH_3 \end{bmatrix} Cl_2 \xrightarrow{\Delta} \begin{bmatrix} H_3N & Cl \\ & Pt & \\ Cl & NH_3 \end{bmatrix} + 2NH_3$$

These rules must be used with discretion. They are commonly used as guides in designing preparative methods. The difficulties which arise with Peyronne's rule may be seen in the attempt to extend it to the reactions with tertiary phosphines. Here the great *trans*-effect of the tertiary phosphines results in the production of the *trans*-compound when a tertiary phosphine reacts with, say K_2PtI_4:

$$\left[\begin{array}{c} I \quad\quad I \\ \diagdown \diagup \\ Pt \\ \diagup \diagdown \\ I \quad\quad I \end{array}\right]^{=} \xrightarrow{R_3P} \left[\begin{array}{c} R_3P \quad I \\ \diagdown \diagup \\ Pt \\ \diagup \diagdown \\ I \quad\quad I \end{array}\right]^{-} \xrightarrow{R_3P} \left[\begin{array}{c} R_3P \quad I \\ \diagdown \diagup \\ Pt \\ \diagup \diagdown \\ I \quad\quad PR_3 \end{array}\right]$$

The same kind of difficulties arise when any system capable of pi bonding to the central platinum atom acts as a ligand. In this case there is a back donation of a pair of electrons from the platinum atom to empty orbitals of the ligand. Ligands which commonly show the characteristic features expected from such bonding include R_3P, R_2S, CN^-, isonitriles, NO, CO, C_2H_4, etc. For platinum(II), two such d_π-p_π bonds can be formed with the ligands using the d_{yz} orbitals of the metal and p_z orbitals of the ligand. This type of bonding is shown in Figure 37.

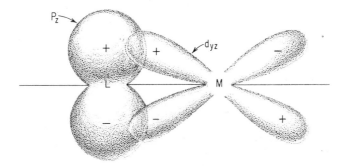

Fig. 37 Back bonding involving the overlap of the filled metal d_{yz} orbital with an empty p_z orbital of the ligand.

The orbitals usable for these square planar complexes are the d_{yz} and the d_{xz} orbitals. (With octahedral complexes the three orbitals d_{yz}, d_{xz} and d_{xy} may be used in this manner.) Ligands capable of forming such double bonds invariably have a *high trans*-effect.

One aspect of the chemistry of these platinum(II) complexes which must be kept in mind is the ability of certain of them to undergo *cis-trans*-isomerization, e.g.

$$\left[\begin{array}{c} (C_2H_5)_2S \quad\quad Cl \\ \diagdown \diagup \\ Pt \\ \diagup \diagdown \\ (C_2H_5)_2S \quad\quad Cl \end{array}\right] \overset{\Delta}{\rightleftharpoons} \left[\begin{array}{c} (C_2H_5)_2S \quad\quad Cl \\ \diagdown \diagup \\ Pt \\ \diagup \diagdown \\ Cl \quad\quad S(C_2H_5)_2 \end{array}\right]$$

Fortunately, isomerization reactions of this kind are not common.[123]

QUALITATIVE THEORY OF THE TRANS-EFFECT. At present two complementary ideas suffice to explain most of the available data on the *trans*-effect:

1. For simple ligands the *trans*-effect is in the order of the polarizability

[123] J. Chatt and R. G. Wilkins, *J. Chem. Soc.*, 2308 (1950); 273 (1952); J. Chatt and F. A. Hart, *Nature* **169**, 673 (1952), *idem, J. Chem. Soc.*, 2363 (1953); 2807 (1960).

of the ligands. This idea has been exploited by Nekrasov and Grinberg. It gives the correct order for most monatomic ligands. The effect is illustrated qualitatively in Figure 38.

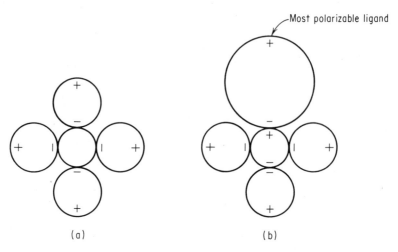

Fig. 38 Polarization effects in square planar complexes. (a) In the case of four identical ligands there is no resultant dipole induced in the central ion and no ligand is stabilized by an electrostatic effect of a special sort. (b) When one of the ligands is much more polarizable than the others (here assumed to be identical) a dipole is induced in the central ion which presents its negative end to the negative end of the ligand dipole and hence labilizes the group *trans* to the most polarizable ligand.

2. For ligands capable of pi bond formation this pi bonding will generally govern their *trans*-effect. As mentioned earlier, such ligands have high *trans*-effects.

As might be expected, negatively charged ligands have a higher *trans* effect than neutral species which cannot participate in pi bonding.

QUANTITATIVE THEORIES OF THE TRANS-EFFECT. Nekrasov and Grinberg worked out a theory of the *trans*-effect based upon electrostatics with an emphasis on polarization effects. They showed that the presence of *any trans*-partner weakened the bond. The assumptions necessary for this theoretical treatment were primarily ones that allowed the reduction of the problem to one involving the interaction of charged particles only. A more thorough electro-static treatment has apparently not yet been carried out but it is believed that the experimental results are not explicable using a theory that considers only classical electrostatic interactions (Ref. 121d, p. 180).

One further item which supports Grinberg's theory is that it gives the correct order for the two dissociation constants of *cis*- and *trans*-

$[Pt(NH_3)_2(H_2O)_2]$.[124] The polarizabilities involved are NH_3 (5.61), H_2O (3.76), and OH^- (5.1).

$$\left[\begin{array}{c} H_3N \quad\quad OH_2 \\ \diagdown\;\diagup \\ Pt \\ \diagup\;\diagdown \\ H_3N \quad\quad OH_2 \end{array}\right]^{+2} + H_2O \rightleftharpoons \left[\begin{array}{c} H_3N \quad\quad OH \\ \diagdown\;\diagup \\ Pt \\ \diagup\;\diagdown \\ H_3N \quad\quad OH_2 \end{array}\right]^{+} + H_3O^+, \quad pK_1 = 5.56$$

$$\left[\begin{array}{c} H_3N \quad\quad OH \\ \diagdown\;\diagup \\ Pt \\ \diagup\;\diagdown \\ H_3N \quad\quad OH_2 \end{array}\right]^{+} + H_2O \rightleftharpoons \left[\begin{array}{c} H_3N \quad\quad OH \\ \diagdown\;\diagup \\ Pt \\ \diagup\;\diagdown \\ H_3N \quad\quad OH \end{array}\right] + H_3O^+, \quad pK_2 = 7.32$$

$$\left[\begin{array}{c} H_3N \quad\quad OH_2 \\ \diagdown\;\diagup \\ Pt \\ \diagup\;\diagdown \\ H_2O \quad\quad NH_3 \end{array}\right]^{+2} + H_2O \rightleftharpoons \left[\begin{array}{c} H_3N \quad\quad OH \\ \diagdown\;\diagup \\ Pt \\ \diagup\;\diagdown \\ H_2O \quad\quad NH_3 \end{array}\right]^{+} + H_3O^+, \quad pK_1 = 4.32$$

$$\left[\begin{array}{c} H_3N \quad\quad OH \\ \diagdown\;\diagup \\ Pt \\ \diagup\;\diagdown \\ H_2O \quad\quad NH_3 \end{array}\right]^{+} + H_2O \rightleftharpoons \left[\begin{array}{c} H_3N \quad\quad OH \\ \diagdown\;\diagup \\ Pt \\ \diagup\;\diagdown \\ HO \quad\quad NH_3 \end{array}\right] + H_3O^+, \quad pK_2 = 7.38$$

Thus the larger displacement of charge on the central Pt(II) by the NH_3 makes the *cis*-isomer a weaker acid than the *trans*-isomer, insofar as the *first* dissociation constant is concerned.

An important assumption in all of Grinberg's work is that the *trans*-effect has a *thermodynamic* rather than a *kinetic* basis. Alternative theories based upon kinetic notions have also been presented.[121 d, f] Since the energy of activation may be related to the same factors as those used in determining thermodynamic stability only rate data can be used to decide between these alternatives. From recent kinetic studies [121f] it appears that the *rates* of displacement of groups from Pt(II) are slower for those groups with a greater *trans*-effect. (These are also the groups in which the bond strengths are presumably greater.) This order of lability in the kinetic sense is:

$$NO_3^- > Cl^- > Br^- > I^- > N_3^- > SCN^- > NO_2^- > CN^-$$

For cobalt(III) complexes[121d] the order of lability is slightly different; it is:

$$NO_3^- > I^- > Br^- > Cl^- > SCN^- > NO_2^-$$

It must be noted that the *trans*-effect order is not inevitably followed in the reactions of Pt(II) complexes. In a survey of over 120 reactions of Pt(II), where the structure of the products were known,[125] about 80 reactions followed the *trans*-effect rule rigidly. The remaining reactions fell into several categories:

1. reactions which occur in several steps most of which individually follow the *trans*-effect generalization

[124] K. A. Jensen, *Zeit. anorg. Chem.* **242**, 87 (1939).
[125] S. G. Tilford, private communication.

2. reactions in which the expected products are formed initially but then undergo rearrangements

3. reactions in which a neutral group replaces another neutral group in preference to the replacement of an anion in a "more labile" position

4. reactions in which an anion replaces another anion in preference to the replacement of a nitrogen donor

5. reactions in which the products are mixtures because of the nearly equal labilizing tendency of two different ligands

6. reactions in which peculiar circumstances of mechanism or ligand behavior lead to unexpected products

The *trans*-effect has been extended to other central atoms with varying success. Thus with Pd(II) complexes the notion of the *trans*-effect has had both successes[126] and failures[127a] as might be expected for a central ion for which the establishment of configurations is rendered difficult by the tendency of certain ligands to be loosely coordinated.

THE STABILIZATION OF OXIDATION STATES BY COORDINATION

That elements may exhibit very unusual oxidation states in coordination compounds has been known for half a century and more. The systematic exploitation of coordination compounds to obtain these unusual oxidation states with a few elements has a long history but the general principles involved and their deliberate application to a large number of elements are relatively recent phenomena.

The stabilization which occurs is generally a stabilization with respect to the aquated ion of the same oxidation number, though in some cases it will refer to another environment such as a particular non-aqueous solvent or molten salt solvent.[127a-135] Thus the aquated nickel(O) species is not known but

[126] H. B. Jonassen and N. L. Cull, *J. Amer. Chem. Soc.* **73**, 274 (1951).

[127a] D. Banerjea and K. K. Tripath, *J. Inorg. Nuclear Chem.* **7**, 78 (1958).

[127b] B. C. Douglas, *J. Chem. Ed.* **29**, 119 (1952).

[128] J. Kleinberg, *Unfamiliar Oxidation States and Their Stabilization*, University of Kansas Press, Lawrence, Kansas (1950).

[129] M. J. Copley, L. S. Foster, and J. C. Bailar, Jr., *Chem. Reviews* **30**, 227 (1942).

[130] J. Kleinberg, *J. Chem. Educ.* **29**, 324 (1952).

[131] S. Herzog, *J. Inorg. Nuclear Chem.* **8**, 557 (1958).

[132] J. Chatt, *J. Inorg. Nuclear Chem.* **8**, 515 (1958).

[133] (a) W. Klemm, *J. Inorg. Nuclear Chem.* **8**, 532 (1958); (b) W. Klemm, W. Brandt, and R. Hoppe, *Zeit. anorg. u. allgem. Chem.* **308**, 179 (1961).

[134] J. Kleinberg, *J. Chem. Educ.* **33**, 73 (1956).

[135] (a) R. J. P. Williams, *Chem. Reviews* **56**, 299 (1956); *idem*, in P. D. Boyer, H. Lardy, and K. Myrback, editors, *The Enzymes*, Academic Press, Inc., 2nd ed. (1959), Vol. 1, p. 391; (b) J. C. Bailar, Jr., *The Chemistry of the Coordination Compounds*, Reinhold Publishing Corp., New York (1956), Chs. 4, 11. A set of rules for making predictions of such changes is given here.

such compounds as $Ni(CO)_4$ and $K_4Ni(CN)_4$ are known. In these cases we talk about the stabilization of Ni(O) through coordination to carbon monoxide or the cyanide ion. In cases where the aqueous ion is known the stabilization consists of a shifting of the oxidation potential to a more negative value when complexation occurs. This can be seen in the following data on the Fe(II)-Fe(III) system in water:

Coordinating agent	$E°$
H_2O	-0.77 v
CN^-	-0.36 v
ortho-phenanthroline	-1.14 v

These data indicate that complexation does not always result in the stabilization of the same one of a pair of oxidation states. Cyanide ion stabilizes the Fe(III) oxidation state relative to Fe(II) in water, but with ortho-phenanthroline the reverse result is found with the ferrous phenanthroline complex being more stable with respect to oxidation than the aquated Fe(II) species.

The broad problem of the stabilization of unusual oxidation states is more readily attacked by dividing it into two portions:

1. the stabilization of high oxidation states

2. the stabilization of low oxidation states

There are known, at present, an enormous number of compounds containing elements in peculiar oxidation states which owe their stability to their coordination environment. The future promises a continuous sequence of complexes in adjacent oxidation states for most of the transition elements and possibly some of the elements in the regular families as well. At present such sequences are known in part or whole for a number of transition elements, e.g., V, Cr, Mn, Fe, Co, Ni, Mo, W, Re, Tc, Ru, Os, Ir, Pd, Pt, and Ti.

The preparation of high oxidation states in an environment in which their coordination behavior results in their stabilization generally is carried out by one of two general methods. The first method is to oxidize the species in a medium where it will remain surrounded by oxide or fluoride ions (i.e., oxidation with O_2, F_2, or an electric current in a melt). Such a process can be used to obtain higher than usual oxidation states with many elements. The following list contains some compounds prepared in this manner:[133]

$CsRuF_6$	$CsOsF_6$	Li_2FeO_3	Na_4FeO_4
$CsIrF_6$	K_2CrF_6	Ba_3FeO_5	K_2FeO_4
K_2MnF_6	Cs_2CoF_6	Na_2CoO_4	K_2NiO_3
Rb_2NiF_6	K_2RhF_6	$KCuO_2$	$CsCuO_2$
K_3NiF_6	K_3CuF_6	$KBiO_3$	Ba_2TeO_5
K_2PdF_6	$KAgF_4$	$Ba_5(ReO_6)_2$	

In general such compounds are more readily formed if large cations such as

Cs^+, Ba^{+2} etc., are present. In several instances the corresponding Li^+ salts *cannot* be prepared.

The second method of stabilizing a high oxidation state is to incorporate it in a complex with a very polarizable ligand. These are ligands of high negative charge or considerable basicity, which in many cases are capable of forming double bonds with the metal ion. In such complexes the sharing of electrons by the ligand occurs in such a manner as to neutralize to a very large extent the high positive charge ostensibly on the central metal ion. Examples of such behavior may be seen in the following complexes of nickel(IV) and nickel(III):

$$\left(C_6H_5-C\overset{S}{\underset{S}{\diagdown}}\right)_2 Ni\overset{S}{\underset{S}{\diamondsuit}}Ni\left(\overset{S}{\underset{S}{\diagup}}C-C_6H_5\right)_2 \quad {}^{136}$$

$$\left(C_6H_4\overset{S}{\underset{\underset{H_2}{N}}{\diagdown}}\right)_2 Ni\overset{O}{\underset{O}{\diamondsuit}}Ni\left(\overset{S}{\underset{\underset{H_2}{N}}{\diagup}}C_6H_4\right)_2 \quad {}^{10}$$

$$[NiCl_2(o\text{-}(CH_3)_2As-C_6H_4-As(CH_3)_2)_2]Cl \quad {}^{137}$$

$$[NiCl_2(o\text{-}(CH_3)_2As-C_6H_4-As(CH_3)_2)_2](ClO_4)_2 \quad {}^{137}$$

The number of examples of stabilized oxidation states falling in this second group is large and growing rapidly. An older example of the same sort may be seen in the Ag(II) complexes with heterocyclic nitrogen bases, e.g.,

$$[Ag(dipyr)_2]S_2O_8, \quad [Ag(o\text{-}phenanthroline)_2]S_2O_8$$

The stabilization of low oxidation states is effected primarily by the use of coordinating species capable of accepting a pair of electrons from the central metal atom with the concurrent formation of a pi bond. The simple species which do this include CN^-, CO, NO, and PH_3. The earliest known examples of the stabilization of very low oxidation states are complexes in which these simple ligands are present: $Ni(CO)_4$, $Fe(CO)_5$, and $K_4Ni(CN)_4$. In recent years it has been found that some chelating agents such as α, α'-dipyridyl and orthophenanthroline can stabilize low oxidation states in a similar manner. Thus it was found that these chelating agents could partially replace CO from carbonyls:

$$M(CO)_x + o\text{-}phen \rightleftharpoons [M(CO)_{x-2}(o\text{-}phen)] + 2CO$$

but only in recent years have complexes of the type $M(o\text{-}phen)_3$ been prepared. The isocyanides, RNC, are also excellent stabilizers of very low oxidation states:

[136] W. Hieber and R. Bruch, *Zeit. Naturforsch* **3b**, 312 (1949).

[137] R. S. Nyholm, *J. Chem. Soc.*, 2061 (1950); 2602 (1951).

$$C_6H_5NC + Ni(CO)_4 \xrightarrow[\text{ether}]{\text{dry}} [Ni(CNC_6H_5)_4] + 4CO \uparrow \quad \text{[138]}$$

Similar complexes with PCl_3, PBr_3, and PF_3 have been prepared by analogous methods:

$$Ni(CO)_4 + 4PF_3 \rightarrow Ni(PF_3)_4 + 4CO \quad \text{[139]}$$

The recent work of S. Herzog on the preparation of complexes of lower oxidation states of the transition elements, especially Cr and V represent a very elegant demonstration of the use of dipyridyl in stabilizing these lower oxidation states. Starting with the complexes $Cr(dipyr)_3^{+2}$ and $V(dipyr)_3^{+2}$, Herzog has prepared and characterized all the lower oxidation states of chromium down to $Cr(O)$ in $Cr(dipyr)_3$ and those of vanadium down to $V(-I)$ in[140] $V(dipyr)_3^-$. Herzog has exploited the reduction of these complex ions to produce well-characterized examples of oxidation states previously unknown. The reactions used to obtain $Cr(dipyr)_3$ were:

$$[Cr(dipyr)_3]Br_2 \xrightarrow[\text{THF*}]{\substack{\text{Na suspension} \\ \text{in}}} Cr(dipyr)_3 + 2NaBr$$

*THF = tetrahydrofuran

$$Cr(C_2H_3O_2)_2 \cdot H_2O \xrightarrow[\text{air-free water}]{\text{dipyridyl in}} Cr(dipyr)_3 + Cr(III)$$

subsequently $Cr(dipyr)_3^+$ can be obtained by disproportionation or oxidation. For vanadium the sequence of reactions used is:

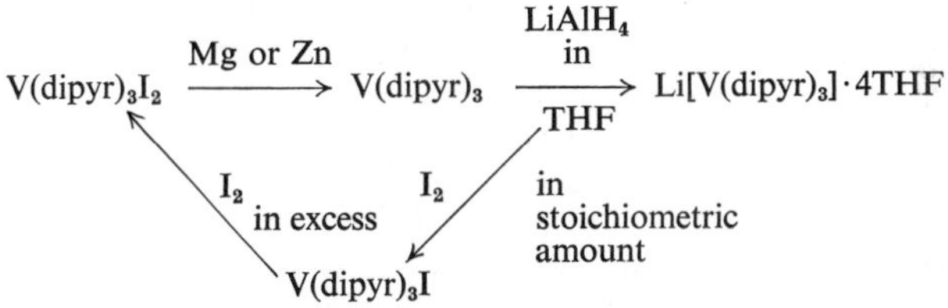

Herzog explains these reactions as processes in which the ultimate limit is set by the attainment of the configuration of the next inert gas by the central metal atom. On this basis, the filling up of the orbitals for chromium or vanadium may be pictured as:

[138] W. Heiber, *Zeit. Naturforsch* **5b**, 129 (1950); W. Hieber and E. Bockly, *Zeit. anorg. allgem. Chem.* **262**, 344 (1950).

[139] J. W. Irvine and G. Wilkinson, *Science* **113**, 742 (1951); G. Wilkinson, *J. Amer. Chem. Soc.* **73**, 550 (1951).

[140] F. Hein and S. Herzog, *Zeit. anorg. allgem. Chem.* **267**, 337 (1952); S. Herzog and W. Schon, *ibid.*, **297**, 323 (1958); S. Herzog, *J. Inorg. Nuclear Chem.* **8**, 557 (1958); S. Herzog, *Zeit. anorg. allgem. Chem.* **294**, 155 (1958).

	3d					4s	4p		
V(dipyr)$_3^{+2}$ or Cr(dipyr)$_3^{+3}$	↑	↑	↑	↑↓	↑↓	↑↓	↑↓	↑↓	↑↓
V(dipyr)$_3^{+1}$ or Cr(dipyr)$_3^{+2}$	↑↓	↑	↑	↑↓	↑↓	↑↓	↑↓	↑↓	↑↓
V(dipyr)$_3^{0}$ or Cr(dipyr)$_3^{+1}$	↑↓	↑↓	↑	↑↓	↑↓	↑↓	↑↓	↑↓	↑↓
V(dipyr)$_3^{-1}$ or Cr(dipyr)$_3$	↑↓	↑↓	↑↓	↑↓	↑↓	↑↓	↑↓	↑↓	↑↓

One is thus lead to expect a lower limit of zero for the oxidation state of chromium and -1 for that of vanadium. Such a picture may be of considerable use in the rationalization of this particular group of complexes; it appears also to be capable of a general explanation of the lower oxidation states of chromium such as Cr($-$II) which is known in Na$_2$[Cr(CO)$_5$]

$$Cr(CO)_6 + 2Na \xrightarrow[\text{soln.}]{\text{liq. NH}_3} Na_2[Cr(CO)_5] + CO \qquad [141]$$

Here the additional two electrons can be accommodated only if fewer groups are coordinated. It appears that another consideration of importance is the presence of low lying empty molecular orbitals capable of receiving the additional electrons. Such orbitals may be characteristic of the molecule as a whole or, more usually, determined primarily by ligand structure. Where such is the case, the electronic structure of the central metal atom will not be capable of setting a limit to the lowest possible oxidation state.

Low oxidation states of several elements have also been obtained by L. Malatesta who has explored the use of isonitriles as stabilizing ligands. When an aryl isonitrile reacts with a chromous compound such as chromous acetate, a disproportionation reaction occurs with the resulting production of a hexaarylisonitrilochromium(O) compound and the acetate of the corresponding hexaarylisonitrilochromium(III) ion:

$$3Cr(C_2H_3O_2)_2 + 18RNC \rightarrow Cr(NCR)_6 + 2[Cr(NCR)_6](C_2H_3O_2)_3 \qquad [142]$$

Malatesta has also prepared Pd(O) and Pt(O) complexes with isonitriles as well as mixed complexes of low oxidation states using isonitriles and analogous ligands.[143]

In addition to direct chemical methods, indirect methods such as polarography may be used to characterize lower oxidation states in a solvent. Waind and Martin [144] studied the polarographic reduction of Co(dipyr)$_3^{+3}$ in water and found it to proceed via the ions Co(dipyr)$_3^{+2}$ and Co(dipyr)$_3^{+}$.

[141] H. Behrens, *Angew. Chem.* **69**, 716 (1957); H. Behrens and J. Kohler, *Zeit. anorg. allgem. Chem.* **300**, 51 (1959).

[142] L. Malatesta, A. Sacco, and S. Ghielmi, *Gazz. Chim. ital.* **82**, 516 (1952).

[143] L. Malatesta and C. Cariello, *J. Inorg. Nuclear Chem.* **8**, 561 (1958). A general review of these complexes may be found in L. Malatesta, *Progress in Inorganic Chemistry* **1**, 283 (1959).

[144] G. M. Waind and B. Martin, *J. Inorg. Nuclear Chem.* **8**, 551 (1958).

They later prepared solid [Co(dipyr)$_3$]ClO$_4$ by the reduction of Co(dipyr)$_3^{+3}$ or Co(dipyr)$_3^{+2}$ with sodium amalgam.

In addition to the compounds discussed above, there are a large number of derivatives, mixed and simple, of cyclopentadiene, benzene, thiophene, carbon monoxide and similar ligands, containing elements in unusual oxidation states. These will be discussed separately because of their great importance.

In summary, a list can be prepared of ligands known to stabilize high and low oxidation states. The following lists are incomplete:

Ligands which stabilize high oxidation states:

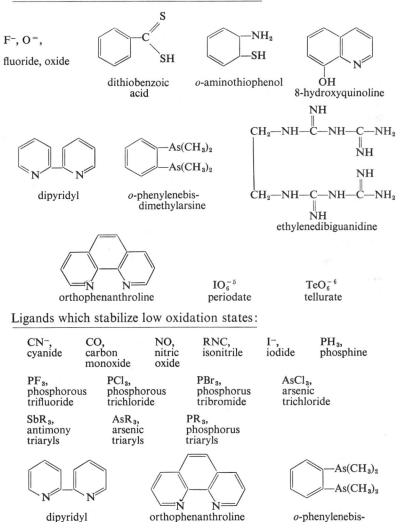

F^-, $O^=$,

fluoride, oxide

dithiobenzoic acid

o-aminothiophenol

8-hydroxyquinoline

dipyridyl

o-phenylenebis-dimethylarsine

ethylenedibiguanidine

orthophenanthroline

IO_6^{-5}
periodate

TeO_6^{-6}
tellurate

Ligands which stabilize low oxidation states:

CN^-,	CO,	NO,	RNC,	I^-,	PH_3,
cyanide	carbon monoxide	nitric oxide	isonitrile	iodide	phosphine

PF_3,	PCl_3,	PBr_3,	$AsCl_3$,
phosphorous trifluoride	phosphorous trichloride	phosphorus tribromide	arsenic trichloride

SbR_3,	AsR_3,	PR_3,
antimony triaryls	arsenic triaryls	phosphorus triaryls

dipyridyl

orthophenanthroline

o-phenylenebis-dimethylarsene

EXERCISES

1. Using the Bailar-Mayper scheme, determine the number and types of isomers which are possible for the compound: [Co(dien)(Br)Cl(NO$_3$)] where dien is diethylenetriamine (H$_2$NCH$_2$CH$_2$NCH$_2$CH$_2$NH$_2$).

$$\underset{\underset{H}{|}}{}$$

2. Show how a *trans-trans*-reaction of an octahedral complex which occurs in one step is incompatible with the concept of edge displacement. What kind of an edge-displacement sequence would be required to explain a *trans-trans*-reaction?

3. Predict the relative rates of the following paired reactions. Indicate clearly which one you think will be the slower of each pair and explain the grounds for your prediction.

(a) $\begin{cases} V(H_2O)_6^{+3} + V^*(NH_3)_6^{+3} \rightleftharpoons V^*(H_2O)_6^{+3} + V(NH_3)_6^{+3} \\ V(H_2O)_6^{+2} + V^*(NH_3)_6^{+2} \rightleftharpoons V^*(H_2O)_6^{+2} + V(NH_3)_6^{+2} \end{cases}$

(b) $\begin{cases} Cr(H_2O)_6^{+3} + H_2O^{18} \rightleftharpoons Cr(H_2O)_5(H_2O^{18})^{+3} + H_2O \\ Ti(H_2O)_6^{+3} + H_2O^{18} \rightleftharpoons Ti(H_2O)_5(H_2O^{18})^{+3} + H_2O \end{cases}$

(c) $\begin{cases} Cr^{+2} + \overset{*}{Cr}^{+3} \rightleftharpoons Cr^{*+2} + Cr^{+3} \\ Cr^{+2} + \overset{*}{Cr}Cl^{+2} \rightleftharpoons \overset{*}{Cr}^{+2} + CrCl^{+2} \end{cases}$

(d) $\begin{cases} W^*(CN)_8^{-4} + W(CN)_8^{-5} \rightleftharpoons W^*(CN)_8^{-5} + W(CN)_8^{-4} \\ Pt^*Cl_4^- + PtCl_6^- \rightleftharpoons PtCl_4^- + Pt^*Cl_6^- \end{cases}$

4. Suggest a method with which you might have a reasonable basis for expecting success in the resolution of an uncharged complex such as Cr(oxine)$_3$. The desired goal is pure samples of both enantiomorphs. Do you know of any instances in which such a non-ionic species has been resolved?

5. Set out a detailed plan which might be used to obtain both *d* and *l* forms of Ir(en)$_3^{+4}$. How would you go about putting such a plan into practice in the laboratory? (Describe the laboratory operations involved.) Check your answer in the literature, if possible.

6. If the absolute configurations of D- and L-Co(en)$_3^{+3}$ are known, how could you make a scientific guess about the absolute configuration of *d* and *l* Cr(en)$_3^{+3}$ using any data other than anomalous diffraction?

7. What kind of a mechanism (inter- or intra-molecular) would you favor for the racemization of a complex ion if the racemization showed no dependence on the pH (i.e., had a constant measureable rate) over a fair range of pH?

8. Using the *trans*-effect as a guide, tell how the following platinum(II) complexes may be prepared. Start with a material whose preparation from elemental platinum may be effected without difficulty.

$$\left[\begin{array}{c} Et_3P \qquad I \\ Pt \\ I \qquad Br \end{array} \right]^-, \quad \left[\begin{array}{c} I \qquad I \\ Pt \\ Et_3P \qquad Br \end{array} \right]^-, \quad \left[\begin{array}{c} I \qquad I \\ Pt \\ Cl \qquad Br \end{array} \right]^=,$$

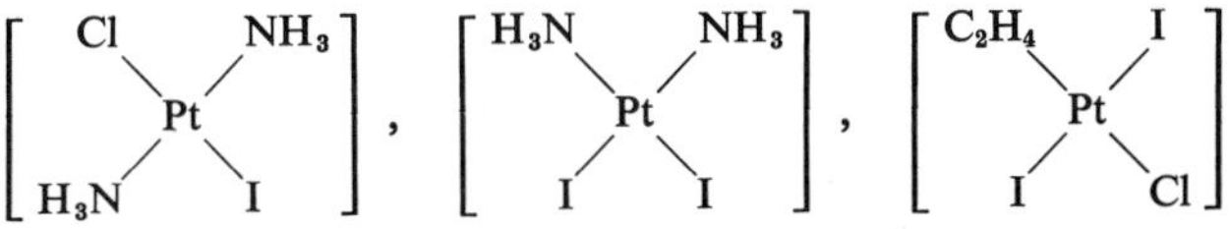

$$\begin{bmatrix} Cl & NH_3 \\ & Pt & \\ H_3N & I \end{bmatrix}, \begin{bmatrix} H_3N & NH_3 \\ & Pt & \\ I & I \end{bmatrix}, \begin{bmatrix} C_2H_4 & I \\ & Pt & \\ I & Cl \end{bmatrix}$$

9. Using the theory of the *trans*-effect as given by Grinberg, predict whether the *cis*- or *trans*-form of diaquobis(ethylenediamine)cobalt(III) would be the stronger acid. [J. Bjerrum and S. E. Rasmussen, *Acta Chem. Scand.* **6**, 1265 (1952)]. Which geometrical isomer of nitroaquobis(ethylenediamine)cobalt(III) would be expected to be the stronger acid if the prediction is based upon the same theory?

10. Describe in detail how you could use studies of the acid strengths of Pt(II) complexes to provide a test which would furnish information on the validity of the theory of the *trans*-effect as given by Grinberg.

11. Why would you expect data on the *trans*-effect in Cu(II) complexes (which are square planar) to be much scarcer and more difficult to obtain than such data for platinum(II) complexes?

12. Would you expect Jorgensen's rule to be followed in the thermal decomposition of tetraphosphinoplatinum(II) chloride? If not, why?

13. Describe some simple measurements which you would consider necessary (in addition to elemental analysis) for the characterization of ruthenium(III) propionate? What type of compound would you expect this to be if your expectations are based on the similarity to iron(III) carboxylates?

14. One form of chromium(III) sulfate prepared by F. Krauss, H. Querengasser, and P. Weyer, *Zeit. anorg. Chem.* **179**, 413 (1929) gave no immediate precipitate with barium chloride solution when its aqueous solution was treated with this reagent. Write a reasonable structure for the species present in this solution.

15. Describe how the following polynuclear complexes can be prepared from readily available starting materials:

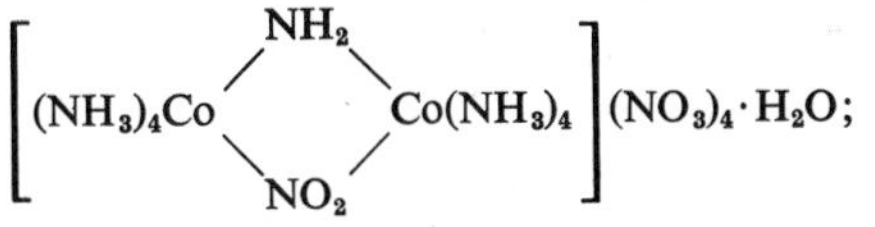

$$\begin{bmatrix} & NH_2 & \\ (NH_3)_4Co & & Co(NH_3)_4 \\ & NO_2 & \end{bmatrix}(NO_3)_4 \cdot H_2O;$$

$$[Cl_2(NH_3)_3Co-NH_2-Co(NH_3)_3(OH_2)Cl]Cl_2$$

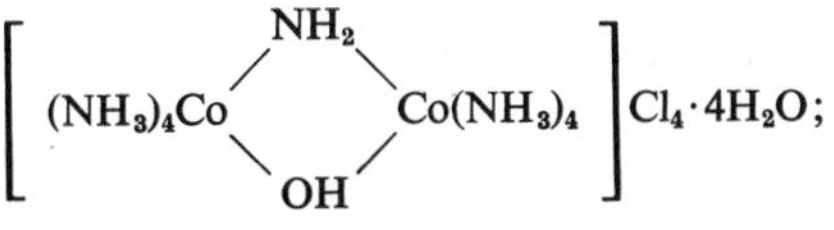

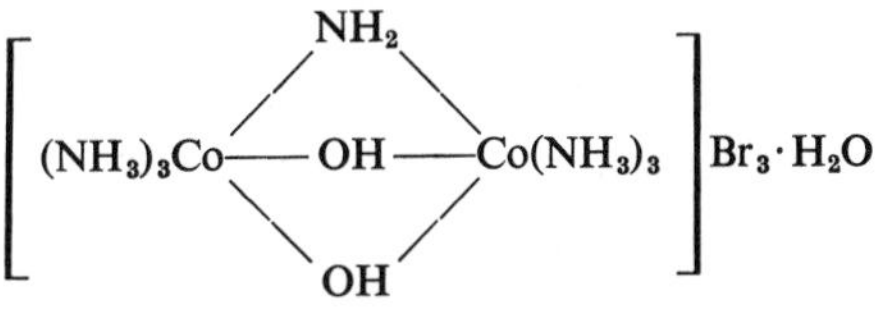

$$\begin{bmatrix} & NH_2 & \\ (NH_3)_4Co & & Co(NH_3)_4 \\ & OH & \end{bmatrix}Cl_4 \cdot 4H_2O;$$

$$\begin{bmatrix} & NH_2 & \\ (NH_3)_3Co & -OH- & Co(NH_3)_3 \\ & OH & \end{bmatrix}Br_3 \cdot H_2O$$

$$[(NH_3)_5Cr-OH-Cr(NH_3)_5]Cl_5 \cdot H_2O$$

7

Determination of the Structures of Coordination Compounds

The structures of coordination compounds may be determined by a large number of methods of variable precision and dependability. These range from intuitive guesses based upon scattered pieces of purely chemical information to detailed descriptions of bond angles and internuclear distances obtained from studies of the patterns produced when the compounds diffract X-rays, electrons, or neutrons.

Of the available methods, one occupies a special position by virtue of its wide applicability and the exact information which it is capable of furnishing; this is the X-ray diffraction technique. It is the ultimate method for the determination of the positions of the atoms (other than hydrogen) in a complex.

RESULTS OF X-RAY STUDIES OF COORDINATION COMPOUNDS

One of the most gratifying aspects of the growth of knowledge of the structure of coordination compounds is the manner in which the intuitive reasoning of Werner has been confirmed. The structures of hundreds of such compounds have been determined and the ideas of Werner have required revision in only a few instances.

One of the first complexes studied by X-ray methods was K_2PtCl_4. This consists of discrete K^+ and $PtCl_4^-$ ions with a square planar arrangement of the chlorides about the central platinum.[1] Similar structures are found with

---

[1] R. G. Dickinson, *J. Amer. Chem. Soc.* **44**, 2404 (1922).

K_2PdCl_4 and $(NH_4)_2PdCl_4$. In the years which followed, the number of such structural determinations has increased steadily. Because of the exact nature of the information which they supply, these results are fundamental to discussions of bond types, bond energies, stereochemistry, and reaction mechanisms.

A number of complexes whose structures have been determined by X-ray methods are collected in Table 7.1.

TABLE 7.1

Complex	Structure	Literature
$Mn(C_5H_5N)_2Cl_2$	*trans*-planar	2
$\alpha Co(C_5H_5N)_2Cl_2$	*trans*-planar	2
$CoCl_4^{-2}$	tetrahedral in Cs_3CoCl_5	3
$[Ni(NH_3)_3(N(C_2H_5)_3)]^{+2}$	tetrahedral	4
$[Ni(NH_3)_3(N(C_3H_7)_3)]^{+2}$	tetrahedral	4
Mn phthalocyanine	square planar	5
$M(tripyridyl)Cl_2$	trigonal bipyramidal when $M = Zn^{+2}$, Cu^{+2}, or Cd^{+2}. $Zn-N = 2.2$ A; $Zn-Cl = 2.29$ A	6
$SnCl_6^{-2}$	octahedral in K_2SnCl_6	7
bis(salicylaldoxime) nickel(II)	planar	8
$[M(dithiooxalate)_2]^=$	planar for $M = Ni(II), Pd(II), Pt(II)$	8
$[M(C_5H_5N)_2Cl_2]$	*trans*-planar for $M = Cu(II), Ni(II)$	9
$PtCl_6^{-2}$	octahedral in K_2PtCl_6	10
$Cu(CN)_4^{-3}$	tetrahedral	11
$[Cu(SC(NH_2)_2)_4]^+$	tetrahedral	11
bis(dimethylglyoximato) nickel (II)	square planar, long Ni-Ni bonds	12
$[Ni(N(CH_2CH_2-NH_2)_3)(NCS)_2]$	octahedral, *cis*-NCS groups	13
$[M(H_2O)_6]^{+2}$	octahedral for $M = Zn(II), Mg(II)$	14
$[Co(H_2O)_4Cl_2]2H_2O$	octahedral, *trans*-Cl groups	15
$Co(CN)_6^{-3}$	octahedral in $K_3Co(CN)_6$, $Co-C = 1.89$ A; $C-N = 1.14$ A	16
$SeOCl_2 \cdot 2C_5H_5N$	distorted tetragonal pyramid (O at apex) about Se, $Se-Cl = 2.57$ A; $Se-N = 2.39$ A	17
$[Cr(H_2O)_6]^{+3}$	octahedral in $[Cr(H_2O)_6]Cl_3$	18
$[Ag(SC(CH_3)(NH_2))_4]^+$	tetrahedral	11
$[Ag(picolinate)_2]$	square planar Ag(II)	11
$AuBr_4^-$	square planar	19
$[Cr(NCS)_4(NH_3)_2]^-$	octahedral, *trans*-diammino	20
$UO_2(NO_3)_2 \cdot 2(C_2H_5O)_3PO$	eight-coordinated uranium, linear OUO group perpendicular to six nearly planar coordinated O's, two each from two chelated nitrate groups and two from the phosphites	21
KMF_3	octahedral when $M = Cu(II), Cr(II)$	22
I_3^-	linear	23
trans-$[Co(en)_2Cl_2]Cl$	octahedron	24

(Table 7.1 continued)

Complex	Structure	Literature
trans-[MCl$_4$(Py)$_2$]	trans-octahedral for M = Si, Ge, Ti, Ge—Cl = 2.27 A; G—N = 2.02 A	25
[Zn(acetylacetonate)$_2$H$_2$O]	trigonal bipyramidal Zn, H$_2$O in trigonal plane, Zn—O = 2.11 A, 1.96 A; Zn—H$_2$O = 2.02 A	26
Ag(C$_8$H$_8$)NO$_3$	Ag$^+$ interacts with two nonadjacent pi bonds of each cyclooctatetraene molecule, Ag$^+$—C = 2.46, 2.51, 2.78, and 2.84 A. Slightly longer Ag$^+$—C interactions at 3.17 and 3.29 A join these units into infinite chains. Ag$^+$—O distances 2.36 and 2.43 A	27
[Cd(SC(NH·CH$_2$)$_2$)$_2$(NCS)$_2$]	octahedral Cd, SCN acts as bridging group, each Cd^{+2} coordinated to two S atoms from thioimidazolidine, two S atoms from SCN, and two nitrogens from SCN	28
[Co(NH$_3$)$_3$(NO$_3$)$_2$Cl]	trans-dinitro structure; Co—NH$_3$ = 1.90, Co—Cl = 2.30, Co—NO$_3$ = 1.99 A; Co—NH$_3$ in plane with nitrate group is also 1.99 A	29
[Co(NH$_3$)$_3$(NO$_2$)$_2$Br]	octahedral Co(III); Br trans to a NO$_2$ group	30
[Co(NH$_3$)$_2$(NO$_2$)$_4$]$^-$	octahedral cobalt, trans-diammine, Co—N = 2.00 A	31, 43
[Co(NH$_3$)$_3$(NO$_2$)$_3$]	octahedral cobalt, trans-NO$_2$ group	32
[Co(NH$_3$)$_3$(H$_2$O)Cl$_2$] Cl	octahedral Co; trans-Cl groups; Co—N = 1.96; Co—O = 1.96; Co—Cl = 2.33 A	33
CoCl$_4^{-2}$	slightly distorted tetrahedra, Co—Cl = 2.23 A	34
NH$_4$[Co(NH$_3$)$_2$(NO$_2$)$_4$]	trans-NH$_3$ groups, Co—NH$_3$ = 2.00 A; Co—NO$_2$ = 1.96 A	35
α[Cu(NH$_3$)$_2$Br$_2$]	trans-planar; Cu—N = 1.93 A, Cu—Br = 2.54 A	36
[ZnBr$_4$]$^=$	distorted tetrahedron, Zn—Br = 2.377 to to 2.410 A	37
Co(C$_5$H$_7$O$_2$)$_2$·2H$_2$O	distorted octahedron, Co—OH$_2$ = 2.23 A, Co—O(of acetylacetonate) = 2.05 A, trans-H$_2$O	38
Au(CN)$_2^-$	linear Au(CN)$_2^-$ ions, Au—C = 2.12 A	39
PtCl$_6^{-2}$	octahedral Pt; Pt—Cl = 2.35 A	40
CuCl$_2$·2H$_2$O	square planar Cu	41
K$_2$[M(CN)$_4$]	tetrahedral for M = Zn, Cd, Hg; Zn—C = 2.61; Cd—CN = 2.67; Hg—CN = 2.65 A	42
[M(NH$_3$)$_4$]$^{+2}$	square planar for M = Pt, Pd	44

(Table 7.1 continued)

Complex	Structure	Literature
K_2CuF_4	distorted octahedron about Cu, axial $Cu—F = 1.95$ A, other $Cu—F = 2.08$ A	45
$[Ru(NO)(OH)(NH_3)_4]Cl_2$	octahedral ruthenium, *trans*-NO, OH groups	46
NN'-disalicylidenepropane-1,2 diaminecopper(II) monohydrate	pyramidal configuration about Cu(II) four planar bonds; $Cu—N = 1.78$ A, $Cu—O = 1.94$ A, $Cu—H_2O = 2.53$ A	47
K_2SbF_5	tetragonal pyramid but Sb displaced *below* the plane of the base	48, 49
N,N'-disalicylidene-ethylenediaminezinc(II) monohydrate	tetragonal pyramid: $Zn—N = 2.08$; $Zn—O = 1.94$; $Zn—H_2O = 2.13$ A, Zn above plane of large ligand groups; water above zinc	50
$SnCl_2 \cdot 2H_2O$	$Sn(H_2O)Cl_3$ units; Sn at center of tetrahedron of which one position is vacant; $Sn—Cl = 2.59$; $Sn—O = 1.99$ A	51
$[Co(dimethylglyoximato)_2 \cdot (NH_3)_2]NO_3$	*trans*-octahedral cobalt	52
$SbCl_5 \cdot S_4N_4$	octahedral Sb surrounded by 5Cl's and one N; $Sb—Cl = 2.40$; $Sb—N = 2.17$ A	53
trans-$[Pt(C_2H_4)(NH(CH_3)_2)Cl_2]$	planar, ethylene perpendicular to this plane, $Pt—N = 2.02$; $Pt—Cl = 2.30$; Pt to middle of ethylene = 2.09 A	54
$[Pt(SCN)_2Cl_2(P(C_3H_7)_3)_2]$	planar binuclear complex with bridging NCS groups, each Pt linked to two bridging SCN groups by one S and one N. $Pt—N = 2.05$; $Pt—S = 2.44$; $Pt—Cl = 2.37$; $Pt—P = 2.16$ A	55
$[Zn(H_2O)_6](BrO_3)_2$	$[Zn(H_2O)_6]^{+2}$ is a nearly regular octahedron, $Zn—O = 2.12$ A	56
$[M(NO_2)_6]^{-3,4}$	octahedral when $M = Co^{+3} Ni^{+2}$; $Co—N = 2.03$ A; $Ni—N = 2.15$ A	57
$LiCuCl_3 \cdot 2H_2O$	contains planar $Cu_2Cl_6^=$ groups; $Cu—Cl = 2.30$ (bridging); $Cu—Cl = 2.26$ A, (non-bridging); has coordination octahedron completed by O from H_2O and Cl from adjacent planar group	58
$SnCl_4 \cdot 2SeOCl_2$	Sn at center of distorted octahedron of 4Cl's and 2 O's. $Sn—Cl \sim 2.38$ A; $Sn—O = 2.12$ A; Se at apex of pyramid	59

(Table 7.1 continued)

Complex	Structure	Literature
$[Ni(en)_3](NO_3)_2$	Ni at center of distorted octahedron: $Ni-N = 2.12$ A; ethylenediamines are gauche and $Ni(en)_3^{+3}$ are D-*lll* or L-*ddd*	60
$[FeF_2(H_2O)_4]$	octahedral, Fe—F and Fe—O are equal, 1.94—1.97 A	61
$CuBr_4^{-2}$	distorted tetrahedron in Cs_2CuBr_4; Cu—Br approx. 2.37 A	62
$GdCl_3 \cdot 6H_2O$	contains $[GdCl_2 \cdot 6H_2O]$ units with eight-coordinate Gd, Gd—Cl = 2.76 A, Gd—O ranges from 2.39 to 2.42A; Cl's are *trans* in a plane containing four other coordinated O's. Two other coordinated oxygens are perpendicular to this plane.	63
$KCuF_3$	distorted octahedron of F about Cu; Cu—F values are 2.25, 1.96, and 1.89 A	64
FeF_6^{-3}	regular octahedron	65
ZrF_6^{-2}	almost regular octahedron in Li_2ZrF_6; Zr—F = 2.00 A	66
$[Cu(IO_6)_2]^{-3}$	two O's from each periodate coordinated to central Cu(III) to give a square planar stereochemistry	67
$[M_4(OH)_8(H_2O)_{16}]X_8$	M = Zr or Hf; Cl or Br may be X; metal atoms at corners of a square connected by double OH bridges along each edge. Each metal coordinates four additional H_2O's to achieve a square Archimedian antiprismatic stereochemistry	68
$SbCl_6^=$, $SbBr_6^=$	octahedral $SbX_6^=$ groups, Sb—Cl = 1.23 A; Sb—Br = 1.30 A	69
$CuI \cdot CH_3NC$	nearly regular tetrahedral Cu(I) coordinated to two I and 2C; I's act as bridging groups. Possible Cu—Cu bonds	70
$[Pd(SC(NH_2)_2)_4]Cl_2$	planar, rectangular, Pd—S = 2.33 A and 2.35 A	71
$[Ag(SCN)(P(C_3H_7)_3)]$	very distorted tetrahedron about Ag(I); SCN act as bridging groups and are coordinated at both ends to different Ag atoms; each S of SCN is coordinated to two Ag. Ag—P = 2.52 A; Ag—S = 2.74 A	72
bis(salicylaldehydemethylimine)-copper(II)	square planar Cu, molecules stacked upon each other; Cu—O = 1.92 A; Cu—N = 1.97 A	73

(Table 7.1 continued)

Complex	Structure	Literature
bis(acetylacetonato)-nickel(II)	trimeric in solid state; each Ni surrounded by a distorted octahedron of O atoms; Ni—O = 2.00 A for those O's bonded to single Ni and 2.12 A for those bonded to two	74
Rb[Fe(OH$_2$)EDTA] · H$_2$O	seven-coordinate Fe	74^a

[2] E. G. Cox, A. J. Shorter, W. Wardlaw, and W. J. R. Way, *J. Chem. Soc.*, 1556 (1937).

[3] H. Powell and A. F. Wells, *J. Chem. Soc.*, 359 (1935).

[4] E. G. Cox and K. C. Webster, *Zeit. Krist.* **92**, 478 (1935).

[5] R. P. Linstead and J. M. Robertson, *J. Chem. Soc.*, 1736 (1936).

[6] D. E. C. Corbridge and E. G. Cox, *J. Chem. Soc.*, 594 (1956).

[7] R. G. Dickinson, *J. Amer. Chem. Soc.* **44**, 276 (1922).

[8] E. G. Cox, W. Wardlaw, and K. C. Webster, *J. Chem. Soc.*, 1475 (1935).

[9] E. G. Cox, E. Sharrott, W. Wardlaw, and K. C. Webster, *J. Chem. Soc.*, 129 (1936).

[10] R. Wyckoff and E. Posnjak, *J. Amer. Chem. Soc.* **43**, 2292 (1921).

[11] E. G. Cox, W. Wardlaw, and K. C. Webster, *J. Chem. Soc.*, 775 (1936).

[12] L. E. Godycki and R. E. Rundle, *Acta Cryst.* **6**, 487 (1959).

[13] D. Hall and M. D. Woulfe, *Proc. Chem. Soc.*, 346 (1959).

[14] A. Ferrari and A. Brabianti, *Ann. Chim.* (Rome) **48**, 1232 (1958).

[15] J. Mizuno, M. Ukei, and T. Sugawara, *J. Phys. Soc. Japan* **14**, 383 (1959).

[16] N. A. Curry and W. A. Runciman, *Acta Cryst.* **12**, 674 (1959).

[17] I. Lindqvist and G. Nahringbauer, *Acta Cryst.* **12**, 638 (1959).

[18] K. Andress and C. Carpenter, *Zeit. Krist.* **87**, 446 (1934).

[19] E. G. Cox and K. C. Webster, *J. Chem. Soc.*, 1635 (1936).

[20] Y. Takeuchi and Y. Saito, *Bull. Chem. Soc. Japan* **30**, 319 (1957).

[21] J. E. Fleming and H. Lynton, *Chem. and Ind.*, 1409 (1959).

[22] A. J. Edwards and R. D. Peacock, *J. Chem. Soc.*, 4126 (1959).

[23] R. Allman and E. Hellner, *Naturwissenschaften* **46**, 557 (1959).

[24] K. A. Becker, G. Grosse, and K. Plieth, *Zeit. Krist.* **112**, 375 (1959).

[25] R. G. Hulme, G. J. Leigh, and I. R. Beattie, *J. Chem. Soc.*, 366 (1960).

[26] E. L. Lippert and M. R. Truter, *J. Chem. Soc.*, 4996 (1960).

[27] F. S. Mathews and W. N. Lipscomb, *J. Phys. Chem.* **63**, 845 (1959).

[28] L. Cavalca, M. Nardelli, and G. Fava, *Proc. Chem. Soc.*, 159 (1959).

[29] Y. Tanito, Y. Saito, and H. Kuroya, *Bull. Chem. Soc. Japan* **26**, 420 (1953).

[30] Y. Komiyama, *Bull. Chem. Soc. Japan* **31**, 26 (1951).

[31] Y. Komiyama, *Bull. Chem. Soc. Japan* **29**, 300 (1956).

[32] Y. Tanito, Y. Saito, and H. Kuroya, *Bull. Chem. Soc. Japan* **25**, 188 (1952).

[33] Y. Tanito, Y. Saito, and H. Kuroya, *Bull. Chem. Soc. Japan* **25**, 328 (1952).

[34] M. A. Porai-Koshits, *Trudy Inst. Krist., Akad. Nauk S.S.S.R.* **10**, 117–135 (1954), C.A. 50: 1406 h.

[35] Y. Komiyama, *Bull. Chem. Soc. Japan* **29**, 300 (1956); *idem, ibid.*, **30**, 13 (1957).

[36] F. Hanic, *Acta Cryst.* **12**, 739 (1959).

[37] B. Morosin and E. C. Lingafelter, *Acta Cryst.* **12**, 744 (1959).

[38] G. J. Bullen, *Acta Cryst.* **12**, 703 (1959).

[39] A. Rosenzweig and D. T. Cromer, *Acta Cryst.* **12**, 709 (1959).

[40] M. L. Huggins, *Phys. Rev.* **27**, 638 (1926).
[41] D. Harker, *Zeit. Krist.* **93**, 136 (1936).
[42] R. G. Dickinson, *J. Amer. Chem. Soc.* **44**, 774 (1922).
[43] A. F. Wells, *Zeit. Krist.* **95**, 74 (1936).
[44] E. G. Cox and G. H. Preston, *J. Chem. Soc.*, 1089 (1933).
[45] K. Knox, *J. Chem. Phys.* **30**, 991 (1959).
[46] N. A. Parpiev and G. B. Bokii, *Zhur. Neorg. Khim.* **4**, 2452 (1959), C.A. 54: 14861.
[47] F. J. Llewellyn and T. N. Waters, *J. Chem. Soc.*, 2639 (1960).
[48] A. Bystrom and K. A. Wilhelmi, *Arkiv. Kemi.* **3**, 461 (1951).
[49] D. Grdenic and S. Scavnicar, *Proc. Chem. Soc.*, 147 (1960).
[50] D. Hall and F. H. Moore, *Proc. Chem. Soc.*, 256 (1960).
[51] D. Grdenic and B. Kamenar, *Proc. Chem. Soc.*, 312 (1960).
[52] N. R. Kunchur and K. S. Viswanathan, *Zeit. anorg. allgem. Chem.* **302**, 289 (1959).
[53] D. Neubauer and J. Weiss, *Zeit. anorg. allgem. Chem.* **303**, 28 (1960).
[54] P. R. H. Alderman, P. G. Owston, and J. M. Rowe, *Acta Cryst.* **13**, 149 (1960).
[55] P. G. Owston and J. M. Rowe, *Acta Cryst.* **13**, 253 (1960).
[56] S. H. Yu and C. A. Beevers, *Zeit. Krist.* **95**, 431 (1936).
[57] M. van Driel and H. J. Verweel, *Zeit. Krist.* **95**, 308 (1936).
[58] P. H. Vossos, L. D. Jennings, and R. E. Rundle, *J. Chem. Phys.* **32**, 1590 (1960).
[59] Y. Hermodsson, *Acta Cryst.* **13**, 656 (1960).
[60] L. N. Swink and M. Atoji, *Acta Cryst.* **13**, 639 (1960).
[61] B. R. Penfold and M. R. Taylor, *Acta Cryst.* **13**, 953 (1960).
[62] B. Morosin and E. C. Lingafelter, *Acta Cryst.* **13**, 807 (1960).
[63] M. Marezio, H. A. Plettinger, and W. H. Zachariasen, *Acta Cryst.* **14**, 234 (1961).
[64] A. Okazaki and Y. Suemune, *J. Phys. Soc. Japan* **16**, 176 (1961).
[65] W. Minder, *Zeit. Krist.* **96**, 15 (1937).
[66] R. Hoppe and W. Dahne, *Naturwissenschaften* **47**, 397 (1960).
[67] I. Hadinec, L. Jensousky, A. Linek, and V. Synecek, *Naturwissenschaften* **47**, 377 (1960).
[68] G. M. Muha and P. A. Vaughan, *J. Chem. Phys.* **33**, 194 (1960).
[69] K. A. Jensen, *Zeit. anorg. allgem. Chem.* **232**, 193 (1937).
[70] P. J. Fisher, N. E. Taylor, and M. M. Harding, *J. Chem. Soc.*, 2303 (1960).
[71] S. Ooi, T. Kawase, K. Nakatsu, and H. Kuroya, *Bull. Chem. Soc. Japan* **33**, 861 (1960).
[72] A. Turco, C. Panattoni, and E. Frasson, *Nature* **187**, 772 (1960).
[73] B. Meuthen and M. V. Stackelberg, *Zeit. anorg. allgem. Chem.* **305**, 279 (1960).
[74] G. J. Bullen, R. Mason, and P. Pauling, *Nature* **189**, 291 (1961).
[74a] J. L. Hoard, M. Lind, and J. V. Silverton, *J. Amer. Chem. Soc.* **83**, 2770 (1961).

OTHER METHODS FOR ESTABLISHING STRUCTURAL FEATURES OF COMPLEXES

There are a very large number of properties of complexes whose measurement may lead to very specific information on the structure of the complex. Many of these are capable of giving very detailed information in favorable cases, but none of the properties listed below can compare with the X-ray or neutron diffraction studies in generality or power. Some of the properties or measurements which have been used in structural studies are:

1. Infrared and Raman Spectra
2. Rotatory Dispersion

3. Dipole Moment Measurements
4. Magnetic Susceptibility
5. Electrical Conductivity Studies
6. Colligative Properties (Esp. Cryoscopy in solvents or molten salts)
7. Electron Diffraction Studies
8. Nuclear Magnetic Resonance
9. Electron Paramagnetic Resonance
10. Visible and Ultraviolet Spectra
11. Optical Birefringence
12. Microwave Spectroscopy
13. Molar Volume

INFRARED AND RAMAN SPECTRA. Neither of these measurements has achieved quite the popularity in inorganic chemistry which they have enjoyed in organic chemistry. The chief reason for this is the wide variation in types of bonds which are encountered and the general scarcity of homologous compounds. Spectra on a large number of simple compounds have been published and these may be used for qualitative analysis.[75]. The number of published infrared spectra is quite large, however, and only some of the uses can be outlined here. Excellent resumés of both techniques and applications have been given by Cotton[76] and Nakamoto.[76]

Both the infrared and Raman spectra are dependent upon the vibrational frequencies characteristic of the absorbing species. In general a non-linear molecule of n atoms possess $3n$—6 fundamental modes of vibration. In addition overtones and resonance coupling may produce further absorption frequencies. Fortunately, the fact that *nearly specific* group frequencies characterize most groups and that the additional complications introduced by resonance coupling are usually slight, simplify the interpretation of the infrared spectra. Frequencies characteristic of metal-ligand bonds are found in infrared spectra.[77] With the exception of very simple molecules, complete analyses of the structures of molecules using only infrared spectra are usually *not* possible so it is not a self-sufficient structural tool. For complexes such as $Ni(CO)_4$ such a treatment can be carried quite far but such instances are rare. In most cases it is used to examine a single aspect of the structure of complexes as the following examples show.

[75] F. A. Miller and C. H. Wilkins, *Anal. Chem.* **24**, 1263 (1952) list the spectra of 159 compounds. Infrared and Raman spectra of some coordination compounds may be found in Landolt-Bornstein Tabellen, I Band, 2 Teil, Molekeln I, pp. 150–171 (1960).

[76] F. A. Cotton, "The Infra-Red Spectra of Transitional Metal Complexes" in J. Lewis and R. G. Wilkins, *Modern Coordination Chemistry*, Interscience Publishers, Inc., New York (1960), pp. 301–399; K. Nakamoto *Infrared Spectra of Inorganic and Coordination Compounds*, J. Wiley & Sons, New York (1963).

[77] J. Lecomte, "Discussions of the Faraday Society", No. 9, 125 (1950); H. W. Morgan, *U.S.A.E.C.D.*, 12656 (1949).

1. *Specific Information on the conformation of ligands.* The conformation of NCS—CH$_2$—CH$_2$—SCN in [PtCl$_2$(NCS—CH$_2$—CH$_2$—SCN)] has been examined via the infrared spectra of the complex.[78] It was possible to show that the 1,2–dithiocyanoethane in the complex was in the gauche configuration (rather than the *cis-* or *trans*-configuration of the NCS groups with respect to each other). This would lead to the expectation of optical isomers as the complex with the chelating agent in the gauche conformation would not be superposable on its mirror image. The gauche conformation seems to be favored by ethylenediamine in its complexes also.[79]

2. *Determination of the number of groups of chelating agent which are coordinated.* Infrared spectra have been used to characterize the five- and six-coordinated complexes of EDTA.[80] The infrared spectra of Ba[Co(C$_{10}$H$_{13}$N$_2$O$_8$)Br]$_2$·9H$_2$O and Na[Co(C$_{10}$H$_{13}$N$_2$O$_8$)(NO$_2$)]·H$_2$O showed *two* carbonyl bands at 1635cm^{-1} (Br complex, NO$_2$ complex at 1628) and at 1740 (1723 for the NO$_2$ complex). The band at 1740 is associated with the free carboxyl group when the EDTA acts as a pentadentate ligand. When the bromo complex is triturated with silver oxide, Ba[Co(C$_{10}$H$_{12}$N$_2$O$_8$]$_2$·4H$_2$O was produced. The infrared absorption spectra of this complex showed only a single band at 1638cm^{-1}!

3. *Differentiation of cis- and trans-isomers.* Since selection rules have their basis in symmetry, a more symmetrical species will generally show fewer infrared absorption bands than an isomer of lower symmetry. Faust and Quagliano[81] studied the *cis-* and *trans*-isomers of dinitrotetramminecobalt-(III) chloride and found that the *trans*-isomer did have fewer absorption bands (this difference is noticeable in the region 6.8–8.0 microns). It is not known if this is a reliable method of distinguishing *cis-* and *trans*-isomers in other instances, though it would be expected to be suitable.

4. *Metal-ligand frequencies.* These may be calculated for many complexes by the use of simple electrostatic theory.[82] They are found to lie generally in the region 500–600 cm^{-1}. A study of PtXACl$_2$ complexes where A is an ammonia or amine molecule *trans* to X has used the variation of the Pt—N frequencies to study the variation in the Pt—N bond strength as X is varied.

[78] J. V. Quagliano and S. Mizushima, *J. Amer. Chem. Soc.* **75**, 6084 (1953); S. Mizushima, I. Ichishima, I. Nakagawa, and J. V. Quagliano, *J. Chem. Phys.* **59**, 293 (1955).

[79] A. Nakahara, Y. Saito, and H. Kuroya, *Bull. Chem. Soc. Japan* **25**, 331 (1952). In the gauche form the two NH$_2$ groups are centered in planes that make an angle of approximately 120° with each other.

[80] D. H. Busch and J. C. Bailar, Jr., *J. Amer. Chem. Soc.* **75**, 4574 (1953).

[81] J. P. Faust and J. V. Quagliano, *J. Amer. Chem. Soc.* **76**, 5346 (1954).

[82] G. M. Barrow, R. H. Kreuger, and F. Basolo, *J. Inorg. Nuclear Chem.* **2**, 340 (1956); D. B. Powell and N. Sheppard, *J. Chem. Soc.*, 3108 (1956).

For all but one of the complexes studied, there was a weakening of the Pt—N bond as the *trans*-effect of X increased.[83a,b] The relation between the observed frequency and the force constant of the bond is usually assumed to be adequately represented by:

$$\text{frequency} = \nu = \sqrt{\frac{k}{4\pi m^2}}$$

where m = reduced mass of the oscillating system and k is the force constant and decreases as the bond strength decreases. Thus knowing the characteristic stretching frequency of a bond allows the study of the variation of the strength of that bond as the other groups in the molecule are changed.

A large number of other studies have also been concerned with metal-ligand frequencies. These include: (a) the use of such data in the determination of the bond stretching force constants for hexafluorides MF_6[83c,d]; (b) estimation of the ionic character of the metal ligand bond in beryllium complexes [83e], in the detection of double bonds between metals and oxygen, [83f] and the determination of the effect of other bonded groups on the strength of the Pt—C bond in platinum complexes.[83g] It is also possible to follow variations in the strengths of metal-ligand bonds by observing variations in the infrared absorption due to other parts of the molecule,[83h] though such procedures are of necessity accompanied by some uncertainty.

5. *N—H frequencies in ammines.* The variation of the N—H frequency as the central metal atom is varied, has been used to estimate both the strength and the degree of covalency in metal-ligand bonds. Thus in ammines of the type $M(NH_3)_x$, the N—H stretching frequency decreases as the covalency of the M—N bond increases.[84] The order of decreasing N—H frequency in the complexes studied is:

$$[Ag(NH_3)_2]^+ > [Ni(NH_3)_6]^{+2} = [Co(NH_3)_6]^{+2} > [Cu(NH_3)_4]^{+2} >$$

$$[Cr(NH_3)_6]^{+3} > [Co(NH_3)_6]^{+3} > [Pt(NH_3)_4]^{+2}.$$

6. *Infrared spectra may be used in many cases to obtain information on*

[83a] J. Chatt, L. A. Duncanson, and L. Venanzi, *J. Chem. Soc.*, 4461 (1955); 2712 (1956).

[83b] D. B. Powell, *ibid.*, 4495 (1956).

[83c] H. H. Claassen, *J. Chem. Phys.* **30**, 968 (1959).

[83d] B. Weinstock, H. H. Claassen, and J. G. Malm, *J. Chem. Phys.* **32**, 181 (1960).

[83e] E. Funck, *Zeit. physik. Chem. N.F.* **23**, 297 (1960). The infrared absorption due to such bands is at a much higher wave-number than is commonly found for metal ligand bands, e.g., 750–825 cm⁻¹.

[83f] C. G. Barrachlough, J. Lewis, and R. S. Nyholm, *J. Chem. Soc.*, 3552 (1959). The presence of such linkages results in absorption in the region 900 to 1,100 cm⁻¹.

[83g] D. M. Adams, J. Chatt, and B. L. Shaw, *J. Chem. Soc.*, 2047 (1960). The Pt—C linkage leads to absorption in the 500–600 cm⁻¹ region.

[83h] D. W. Thomas and A. E. Martell, *J. Amer. Chem. Soc.* **81**, 5111 (1959).

[84] G. F. Svatos, C. Curran, and J. V. Quagliano, *J. Amer. Chem. Soc.* **77**, 6195 (1955).

the change of environment of a group upon chelation. Where transitions of a free ligand are forbidden by symmetry restrictions, the formation of a complex may remove these restrictions. This has been observed with both nitrate and sulfate ions. The reverse situation is also found. The strong absorption band at 1,100 cm^{-1} characteristic of the free sulfate ion is completely absent from the infrared spectrum of $[Co(NH_3)_5SO_4]Cl$.[85] In an examination of the infrared spectra of bis(glycinato)copper(II) monohydrate and bis(glycinato)-nickel(II) dihydrate it was found that the bands at 3,300 cm^{-1}, 3,250 cm^{-1}, and 3,150 cm^{-1} for the copper complex and at 3,300 cm^{-1}, 3,250 cm^{-1}, and 3,170 cm^{-1} for the nickel complex could be assigned to N—H stretching vibrations which occur at 3,330 cm^{-1} in potassium glycinate. This easily noted difference was accompanied by absorption due to an antisymmetric C—O stretching vibration in the carboxylate ion at 1,600 cm^{-1} which was essentially identical with that found for the potassium glycinate at the same frequency. The obvious inference is that the complexing of the carboxyl group is via electrostatic forces which do not affect the stretching vibration appreciably.[86]

7. *The Determination of Structures.* One of the most important possibilities of infrared absorption spectra lies in the determination of the structures of complexes.[76] For this it is generally necessary to use additional information furnished by the Raman spectra of the complex. The Raman absorption is found for those vibrations which occur with a change in polarizability; infrared absorption for those vibrations which occur with a change in the dipole moment. Since the selection rules for these two types of absorption are different, the presence or absence of given frequencies in the infrared and Raman spectra may be used to obtain information on the symmetry and other properties of the absorbing species.[87] Such structural studies are less numerous than those concerned with only a few characteristic absorptions. The limitations of using only a narrow region of the spectra combined with low absorption have been clearly pointed out.[88] Where the structures of compounds are known with some certainty, these same considerations can be used to obtain a detailed picture of the bonding.[89,90]

[85] S. Mizushima and J. V. Quagliano, *J. Amer. Chem. Soc.* **75**, 4870 (1953).

[86] D. Sen, S. Mizushima, C. Curran, and J. V. Quagliano, *J. Amer. Chem. Soc.* **77**, 211 (1955).

[87] L. A. Woodward, *Quarterly Reviews* **10**, 185 (1956).

[88] F. A. Cotton and R. R. Monchamp, *J. Chem. Soc.*, 1882 (1960).

[89] M. Bigorgne and A. Zelwer, *Bull. Soc. chim. France*, 1986 (1960) contains such an analysis on $Ni(CO)_xL_{4-x}$ where L is a phosphine derivative.

[90] R. L. McCullough, L. H. Jones, and G. A. Crosby, *Spectrochimica Acta* **16**, 929 (1960) contains an analysis of $Na_2[Ni(CN)_4] \cdot 3H_2O$ and $Ba[Ni(CN)_4] \cdot 4H_2O$. The other papers of L. H. Jones related to this may be followed back from the references cited here. T. Shimanouchi and I. Nakagawa, *Spectrochimica Acta* **18**, 89, 101 (1962) treat cyanides and ammines.

8. *The KBr disk method.* A very popular method of obtaining the infra-red spectra of solid complexes is by means of the so-called "KBr disk method."[91] In this procedure a sample of the complex is ground up with pure dry potassium bromide and the mixture is then compressed into disks in an evacuable die by means of a hydraulic press. The absorption spectra of the disk is then obtained by mounting it in a holder on a standard infrared spectrophotometer. Because of the insolubility of most complexes in the solvents commonly used for infrared spectroscopy, this method has become very popular. It possesses a few disadvantages, [76] the most common being the reactivity of the potassium bromide with the compound under study. A simple example may be seen in the reaction of solid lead nitrate and potassium chloride[92] which may be followed in time in a disk; a more complicated ex-ample is the isomerization of $[Co(NH_3)_5ONO]Cl_2$ in potassium chloride disks.[93] In this second case a complete kinetic evaluation of rates and equili-brium constants for the reaction:

$$[Co(NH_3)_5ONO]^{+2} \rightleftharpoons [Co(NH_3)_5(NO_2)]^{+2}$$

was carried out.

9. *Infrared Spectra of Aqueous Solutions.* Although water has intense absorption over most of the infrared spectral region it is possible to obtain infrared spectrum on aqueous solutions in the regions 3.5 to 5.8μ and 6.5 to 10.5μ.[94] The cells have a very short path length (*less* than 75μ) and are constructed of a material resistant to attack by water, e.g., CaF_2 or BaF_2. One of the interesting results is the observation that the in-plane deformation of the —OH group in the lactate ion, which occurs at 1,275 cm^{-1} in the free ion, is displaced to 1,390 cm^{-1} in the zinc chelate. It seems reasonable to believe that this technique will be more widely used in the future.

The brief description above certainly does *not* do justice to the scope and power of infrared methods in coordination chemistry. The interested reader is strongly urged to study the review by F. A. Cotton,[76] or the book of Nakamoto.[76]

RAMAN SPECTRA. Raman spectra of inorganic complexes have been studied with two goals in mind: (a) to determine the extent of complex forma-tion and (b) to gain information on the symmetry and structure of stable

[91] G. Duychaerts, *The Analyst* **84**, 201 (1959); a review.

[92] F. Vratny, *J. Inorg. Nuclear Chem.* **10**, 328 (1959).

[93] I. R. Beattie and D. P. N. Satchell, *Trans. Farad. Soc.* **52**, 1590 (1956).

[94] J. D. S. Goulden, *Spectrochimica Acta* **15**, 657 (1959) also contains a general review of previous work; J. D. S. Goulden, *Spectrochimica Acta* **16**, 715 (1960): aqueous solutions of lactates and the effects of chelation; S. Fronaeus and R. Larson, *Acta Chem. Scand.* **14**, 1364 (1960), *ibid.*, **16**, 1433, 1447 (1962); K. Nakamoto, Y. Morimoto, and A. E. Martell, *J. Amer. Chem. Soc.* **83**, 4528 (1961).

complexes.[87] In determining whether complexation occurs, it is generally possible to utilize the occurrence of additional lines in the Raman spectra close to the parent exciting line. In general the weaker the bond the closer the characteristic line of that bond will be to the parent exciting line. Alternatively, additional lines may occur in the Raman spectrum if the formation of the complex lowers the symmetry of the ligand species. Complex ions which absorb light strongly are very difficult to study using this method. In normal cases the ratio of scattered to incident light is very small and the presence of an absorbing species in solution will lower this sufficiently to prevent the proper functioning of the photographic plate or other sensing device used.

For species such as the volatile $Fe(CO)_5$, Raman spectra allow the symmetry to be established in an unambiguous manner.[95] Similarly the Raman spectra of $Ni(CO)_4$ is consistent only with a tetrahedral configuration[96] as is that of $Ni(PF_3)_4$.[97] That of $Pt(CN)_4^{-2}$ indicates a square planar configuration.[98] The information obtained on the Raman scattering which is used to establish the symmetry of a molecule includes: (a) the total number of Raman lines observed and (b) their degree of polarization. The use of these data with typical inorganic compounds is reviewed by L. A. Woodward.[87] A typical example of the use of Raman spectra to study both simple and mixed complexes in aqueous solution is that of the halide complexes of cadmium(II) and mercury(II).[99] Only the MX_4^{-2} contributed to the Raman spectra and these were tetrahedral. Mixed iodo-bromo complexes were also detected of the type $MI_xBr_{4-x}^{-2}$. Many of the types of information more commonly obtained from infrared spectra may also be obtained from Raman spectra.[100] Results of much of the earlier work on the Raman spectra of complexes are collected in some of standard reference works on Raman Specra.[101,102,103]

[95] H. Stammreich, O. Sala, and Y. Tavares, *J. Chem. Phys.* **30**, 856 (1959).

[96] B. Crawford and W. Horwitz, *J. Chem. Phys.* **16**, 147 (1948).

[97] L. A. Woodward and J. R. Hall, *Spectrochimica Acta* **16**, 654 (1960).

[98] J. Mathieu and S. Cornevin, *J. Chim. Phys.* **36**, 271, 308 (1939).

[99] J. A. Rolfe, D. E. Sheppard, and L. A. Woodward, *Trans. Faraday Soc.* **50**, 1275 (1954).

[100] An example may be seen in the correlation of force constants in XY_4 species with the charge on X reported by L. A. Woodward, *Trans. Farad. Soc.* **54**, 1271 (1958). In this case the required fundamental frequency is obtained directly from the Raman spectra. See also, G. W. Chantry and R. A. Plane, *J. Chem. Phys.* **34**, 1268 (1961); L. A. Woodward and J. A. Creighton, *Spectrochim. Acta* **17**, 594 (1961).

[101] K. W. F. Kohlrausch, *Ramenspektren*, Akademische Verlag., Leipzig, 1943, pp. 417–421.

[102] J. H. Hibben, *The Raman Effect and its Chemical Applications*, Reinhold Publishing Corp., New York (1939), Ch. 28.

[103] *Handbuch der Physik*, Band XXVI, "Licht und Materie II", Springer-Verlag, Berlin-Gottingen-Heidelberg (1958), has a long review article on Raman spectra by S. Mizushima, p. 171–243 and a much longer review on infrared spectra by J. Lecomte, pp. 244–937.

ROTATORY DISPERSION[104,105]

One of the measurements due to increase in importance as our knowledge of the absolute configuration of complexes increases is that of rotatory dispersion. For the $Co(en)_3^{+3}$ ions of D- and L-configuration it is now possible to obtain an unambiguous relationship between the rotatory dispersion curve and the absolute configuration. Previous work has been concerned primarily with the classification of pairs of enantiomorphs into groups of similar absolute configuration.[106]

Since many optically active complex ions absorb light in the visible region of the spectrum, they usually show a range of values for their specific rotatory power depending on the wavelength of light used. It can even happen that an optically active complex may show *no* rotation for light of a certain wave length (this is not uncommon). This is a general result of the fact that most optically active complex ions show anomalous dispersion in the visible region of the spectrum.

Additional uses of rotatory dispersion curves include the following:

1. Determination of whether a reaction involving an optically active complex proceeds with the retention, inversion, or loss of configuration.[107]

2. The determination of which compounds of the types $[Co(AA)_2a_2]^+$ and $[Co(AA)_2XY]^+$ are the *cis-* and which are the *trans-*isomers.[108] The characterization of the *cis-* and *trans-*isomers of the general formula $[Co(AA)_2XY]$ depends upon the probable occurrence of induced asymmetry in the *cis-*isomer when the ligand AA is optically active itself. Since the *trans-*isomer is not capable of exhibiting such induced activity, its rotatory dispersion curve will be characteristic of the ligands alone. The *cis-*isomer, however, will show a rotatory dispersion curve of a different type due to the fact that one of the possible configurations D*ll* and L*ll* will be preferentially formed if a ligand such as *l*-AA is used.

[104] C. Djerassi, *Optical Rotatory Dispersion—Applications to Organic Chemistry*, McGraw-Hill Book Company, New York (1960); J. P. Mathieu, "Activite optique Naturelle," pp. 333–432 in *Handbuch der Physik*, Vol. XXXVIII, Springer-Verlag, Berlin-Gottingen-Heidelberg (1957) is a very complete discussion of the principles and general instrumentation.

[105] W. Heller, "Polarimetry" in A. Weissberger, *Physical Methods of Organic Chemistry*, Interscience Publishers, Inc., New York, 2nd ed. (1949), Part 2, pp. 1493–1610 contains a thorough discussion of visual instruments and some of the older photoelectric spectropolarimeters.

[106] An example may be seen in W. R. Matoush and F. Basolo, *J. Amer. Chem. Soc.* **78**, 3972 (1956).

[107] J. P. Mathieu, *Compt. rend.* **119**, 278 (1934).

[108] T. D. O'Brien, J. P. McReynolds, and J. C. Bailar, Jr., *J. Amer. Chem. Soc.* **70**, 749 (1948).

3. The occurrence of an anomalous rotatory dispersion curve may be used to prove the existence of an asymmetric structure which is too labile to be isolated. Kirschner[109] showed that a mixture of *l*-quinine hydrobromide and potassium ethylenediaminetetraacetatocuprate(II) in water showed a maximum rotation (not found for the *l*-quinine hydrobromide itself) in the same spectral region at which an absorption maximum occurred for the copper complex. This indicates that the absorbing species, the copper complex, is contributing to the rotation and must be present in an asymmetric form. It can generally be assumed that the optical rotation of a solution is made up of contributions from the various asymmetric species present; ionization and complexation affect the contribution of a given species and the careful measurement of such changes can be used to calculate both ionization[110] and stability[111] constants. In spite of the regular behavior of optical rotatory power in such cases, it should be noted that ion-pair formation may also cause measureable changes in this property.[112]

In some instances the curve of α vs λ will show several maxima. In such cases the curves may be analyzed into the various contributions. When two absorption bands are very close and overlap, the rotatory dispersion curve will contain contributions from both which may be separated by such an analysis.[113]

With the introduction of an automatic recording spectropolarimeter on the market (O. C. Rudolph and Sons, 1959) the process of obtaining rotatory dispersion curves has become much less tedious and it may be expected to find much wider use in the immediate future.

DIPOLE MOMENT MEASUREMENTS[114,115,116]

Dipole measurements are rather rarely used in coordination chemistry for the simple reason that they generally do *not* furnish unambiguous struc-

[109] S. Kirschner, *J. Amer. Chem. Soc.* **78**, 2372 (1956).

[110] L. I. Katzin and E. Gulyas, *J. Phys. Chem.* **64**, 1739 (1960).

[111] D. A. L. Hope, R. J. Otter, and J. E. Price, *J. Chem. Soc.*, 5226 (1960).

[112] M. J. Albinak, D. C. Bhatnagar, S. Kirschner, and A. J. Sonnessa, in S. Kirschner, editor, *Advances in the Chemistry of the Coordination Compounds*, The Macmillan Company, New York (1961), p. 154 ff.

[113] J. Hidaka, Y. Shimura, and R. Tsuchida, *Bull. Chem. Soc. Japan* **33**, 847 (1960); Y. Shimura, *Bull. Chem. Soc. Japan* **31**, 315 (1958); J. Hidaka, S. Yamada, and R. Tsuchida, *Bull. Chem. Soc. Japan* **31**, 92 (1958); A. Moscowitz, *Rev. Mod. Phys.* **32**, 440 (1960). See also, reference 104; J. G. Bushmiller, E. L. Amma, and B. E. Douglas, *J. Amer. Chem. Soc.* **84**, 111 (1962).

[114] C. P. Smyth, *Dielectric Behavior and Structure*, McGraw-Hill Book Company, New York (1955).

[115] J. W. Smith, *Electric Dipole Moments*, Butterworth's Scientific Publications, London (1955), esp. pp. 276–279.

[116] J. H. Van Vleck, *The Theory of Electric and Magnetic Susceptibilities*, Oxford University Press (1932).

tural information. Where the presence or absence of a dipole moment in itself is sufficient to decide which of two possible structures is actually present,
it provides a useful tool. Jensen[117] determined the dipole moments of two
isomeric forms of $[(R_3P)_2PtX_2]$ complexes. For one form the dipole moment
was zero, a situation which would be expected for a *trans*-complex. The other
form had a dipole moment of about 10 Debyes and was presumably the
cis-isomer. In some related platinum complexes the equilibrium constants
for the *cis-trans*-reaction were obtained from measurements of this same
general type.[118]

In the determination of the dipole moment the basic measurement carried
out is that of capacitance. This is related to the polarization of the species
present in solution between the condenser plates by the equation:

$$P = \frac{D-1}{D+2} \frac{M}{\rho}$$

where P is the total electric polarization, D is the dielectric constant measured,
M is the molecular weight of the species and ρ is its density. The relation
between the dielectric constant and the capacitance measured is

$$\frac{C_0}{C_x} = \frac{D_0}{D_x}$$

where C_0 is the capacitance measured for air of dielectric constant D_0
(1.0000 approx.) and C_x and D_x are the capacitance and the dielectric
constant when the condenser contains the compound x. When a solution in
a non-polar solvent is used the first equation takes the form:

$$P = \frac{D-1}{D+1} v \sum_i M_i f_i$$

where v is the volume of solution which contains a mole of particles, M_i is the
molecular weight of the i-th species and f_i is the mole fraction of the i-th
species in the mixture. For a mixture:

$$P = \sum_i P_i f_i$$

or for two components:

$$P = P_1 f_1 + P_2 f_2$$

where no interaction
occurs between components
(such as hydrogen bonding)

In solution work it is customary to determine the polarization of the solute
P_1 by extrapolation to $f_1 = 0$ of a plot of P_1 vs. f_1. There are a number of
alternative ways of carrying out this extrapolation which may be found in the
references cited.

P_1 is a composite term made up of contributions from the orientation

[117] K. A. Jensen, *Zeit. anorg. allgem. Chem.* **225**, 97 (1935); *idem, ibid.*, **229**, 225 (1936).
[118] J. Chatt and F. A. Hart, *J. Chem. Soc.*, 2807 (1960).

polarization due to the orientation of the molecule in the electric field, and of contributions due to the distortion of the atoms and the electronic paths in the molecule due to the field:

$$P_1 = P_0 + P_e + P_a$$

where P_0 is the orientation polarization, P_e is the electronic polarization, and P_a is the atomic polarization. Of these components, only P_0 is temperature dependent. The variation of the total polarization with temperature can be written as

$$P_1 = A + \frac{B}{T}$$

and Debye has shown that the form of the temperature dependent part is:

$$B = \frac{4}{3}\pi N\left(\frac{\mu^2}{3k}\right) = P_0 T$$

where N is Avogadro's number, μ is the dipole moment of the molecule, and k is Boltzmann's constant. For a solution of a polar molecule in a non-polar solvent the polarization will vary with temperature as shown in Figure 39.

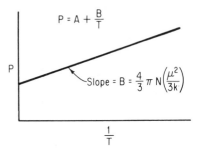

Fig. 39 Determination of the dipole moment from the temperature variation of the electric polarization.

Since the slope involves the square of the dipole moment, its magnitude but *not* its direction can be obtained from such measurements. At present there is only one molecule for which both the magnitude and direction of the dipole moment are known from *direct measurement* (many others have been inferred): CO whose moment is 0.11 Debye[119] with the polarity: $\overset{-\;\;+}{C\,O}$. Some of the difficulties which arise in the derivation of dipole moments from the experimental data on complexes have been discussed.[120] These include the presence of hydrolysis products and small amounts of water. In many cases the inner complex salts under study are prepared from aqueous systems so that these are frequent and real difficulties.

In certain cases it is possible to determine the dipole moment of a complex *ion*[121] but this has been done only rarely.

Some illustrative values of dipole moments of coordination compounds are listed in Table 7.2.

Note that the interpretation of the high moments of the acetylacetonates of Al(III), Cr(III), Fe(III), and Co(III) favors very large atomic polarization values, rather than the presence of permanent dipole moments in the molecule

[119] R. Rosenblum, A. H. Nethercat, and C. H. Townes, *Phys. Review* **109**, 400 (1958).
[120] P. Podleschka, L. Westland, and G. F. Wright, *Canadian J. Chem.* **36**, 574 (1958).
[121] A. B. Lamb and K. J. Mysels, *J. Amer. Chem. Soc.* **67**, 468 (1945).

TABLE 7.2

DIPOLE MOMENTS OF SOME COORDINATION COMPOUNDS

Compound	μ (Debyes)	Reference
$\alpha[PtCl_2(P(C_2H_5)_3)_2]$	0	117
$\beta[PtCl_2(P(C_2H_5)_3)_2]$	10.7	117
$Be(C_5H_7O_2)_2$	0	122
$Th(C_5H_7O_2)_4$	1.61(30°)	120
Bis(N-methylsalicylaldimine)nickel(II)	0	123
Bis(acetylacetone-ethylenediamine)copper(II)	4.53	124
$[Fe(NO)_2SC_2H_5]_2$	1.88	125
$[Co(NO_2)_2Cl]_2$	1.04	125
$[Co(NO_2)_2Br]_2$	1.02	125
Bis(dibenzoylmethano)oxovanadium(IV)	3.61	126
Bis(trifluoroacetylacetonato)beryllium(II)	4.42	127
Bis(trifluoroacetylacetonato)copper(II)	3.67	127
Bis(trifluoroacetylacetonato)cobalt(II)	3.42	127
Bis(N-ethylsalicylaldimine)palladium(II)	0	128
$Al(C_5H_7O_2)_3$	7.5	129, 122
$Fe(C_5H_7O_2)_3$	7.5	129, 122
$Cr(C_5H_7O_2)_3$	7.5	129, 122
$Co(C_5H_7O_2)_3$	7.5	129, 122

[122] I. E. Coop and L. E. Sutton, *J. Chem. Soc.*, 1269 (1938); A. E. Finn, G. C. Hampson, and L. E. Sutton, *J. Chem. Soc.*, 1254 (1938).

[123] L. Sacconi, P. Paoletti, and G. Del Re, *J. Amer. Chem.* Soc. 79, 4062 (1957).

[124] P. J. McCarty and A. E. Martell, *J. Amer. Chem. Soc.* 78, 2106 (1956).

[125] W. Hieber and W. Beck, *Zeit. anorg. allgem. Chem.* 305, 274 (1960).

[126] R. J. Hovey and A. E. Martell, *J. Amer. Chem. Soc.* 82, 2697 (1960).

[127] R. H. Holm and F. A. Cotton, *J. Inorg. Nuclear Chem.* 15, 63 (1960).

[128] L. Sacconi, M. Ciampolini, F. Maggio, and G. Del Re, *J. Amer. Chem. Soc.* 82, 815 (1960).

[129] J. Macqueen and J. W. Smith, *J. Chem. Soc.*, 1821 (1956).

as a whole.[129,122] In some calculations,[127] P_a is taken as 50% of P_e, in analogous treatments of organic compounds P_a is generally taken as 10% of P_e. The electronic polarization is set equal to R, the molecular refraction of the substance:

$$P_e = R = \frac{n^2 - 1}{n^2 + 2} \frac{M}{\rho}$$

R may then be obtained either from measurement of n, the refractive index, or from tables which contain the contributions of the various parts of the molecule to the total molar refraction. For measurements at a single temperature, P_e is calculated in this fashion and P_a is estimated to be a certain fraction of this. P_0 is then the difference between the measured polarization P, and $P_e + P_a$. The value of P_0 derived from measurements taken over a wide range of temperature is much more reliable but also much more difficult to obtain. Unfortunately, until this is done, there will be no dependable way of estimating P_a.[129a]

MAGNETIC SUSCEPTIBILITY MEASUREMENTS [130,131,132]

At present the use of magnetic susceptibility measurements in structural studies is less common than it was a decade ago. To a large extent this is due to a greater appreciation of the difficulties associated with the method. For many years the "magnetic criterion" was used to distinguish between ionic and covalent bonding in complexes but this *general* criterion has been abandoned by its originator[133] and no longer seems tenable. The most obvious value of this method is in the four-coordinate complexes of nickel(II). Unfortunately, the magnetic behavior of ions is as characteristic as their spectra and hence must be interpreted on an individual basis. In many studies it has been typical to measure the magnetic susceptibility at a single temperature and then assume that the following relations held between the measured magnetic susceptibility, χ, the magnetic moment, μ, and the number of unpaired electrons, n:

$$\chi = \frac{3k\mu^2}{N\beta^2 T} = \frac{\mu^2}{(2.84)^2 T}$$

$$\mu = \sqrt{n(n+2)} \quad \text{B.M}$$

here k is Boltzmann's constant, N is Avogadro's number, T is the absolute temperature, n is the number of unpaired electrons and β is the Bohr magneton, the commonly used unit for the magnetic moment. In general a diamagnetic correction is made for the contribution of other parts of the molecule to the magnetic susceptibility.[132] The interpretation really requires that data be available over a range of temperatures to insure that the inverse relationship between χ and T is actually found. In many cases the following relation holds where Δ is a constant:

$$\chi = \frac{C}{T + \Delta}$$

A further complication may arise if there is an appreciable contribution of the orbital angular momentum (L) to the magnetic moment. In such a case:

$$\mu = \sqrt{n(n+2)} = \sqrt{4S(S+1)}$$

[129a] O. A. Osipov and V. M. Artemova, *Doklady Akad. Nauk S.S.S.R.* **133**, 166 (1960), C.A. 55: 20557 contains a discussion of the relation between P_a and P_e which differs considerably from that customarily given. Measurements on acetylacetonates are also reported.

[130] P. W. Selwood, *Magnetochemistry*, Interscience Publishers, Inc., New York, 2nd ed. (1956).

[131] R. S. Nyholm, *Record of Chemical Progress* **19**, 45 (1958).

[132] B. N. Figgis and J. Lewis, "The Magnetochemistry of Complex Compounds" in J. Lewis and R. G. Wilkins, editors, *Modern Coordination Chemistry*, Interscience Publishers, Inc., New York (1960), Ch. 6.

[133] L. Pauling, *J. Chem. Soc.*, 1461 (1948).

must be replaced by a more complicated relationship; one of the commonly used ones is:

$$\mu = \sqrt{L(L+1) + 4S(S+1)}$$

Fortunately for most of the first row transition elements the simplest relationship is generally a reasonable approximation and the magnetic susceptibility may then be used to determine n in the complexes. For the second and third row transition elements the simple relationship is *not* generally useful.

In more recent years it has become customary to utilize compounds whose structures are known from X-ray studies to check the results of magnetic susceptibility measurements.[134,135] For complexes of the second and third row transition elements the behavior is much more complicated, though a theoretical treatment of such cases is available.[136]

ELECTRICAL CONDUCTIVITY MEASUREMENTS[137,138,139,140]

For the most part, electrical conductivity measurements have been used to determine the charge type of complexes in solution. While most of this work has been done in aqueous solutions, there is no necessary restriction of this method to the solvent water. In most cases, the *molar* conductance, not the equivalent conductance,[141] of the given type of complex electrolyte at a given concentration, will fall into a predictable range[142] and any species whose molar conductance falls in this range may be concluded to be an electrolyte of that charge type. The most serious difficulty connected with the use of this method with aqueous solutions is the very considerable changes which occur in the conductance of some solutions as they stand. These changes indicate that a reaction is occurring. In such a case an estimate of the correct conduc-

[134] B. N. Figgis and C. M. Harris, *J. Chem. Soc.*, 855 (1959), contains such a comparative study of Cu(II) complexes; J. Lewis, *Science Progress*, Vol. L, 419 (1962) reviews the theory for first row transition elements.

[135] F. A. Cotton and R. H. Holm, *J. Amer. Chem. Soc.* **82**, 2983 (1960) — cobalt(II) complexes.

[136] H. Kamimura, S. Koide, H. Sekiyama, and S. Sugano, *J. Phys. Soc. Japan* **15**, 1264 (1960).

[137] R. A. Robinson and R. A. Stokes, *Electrolyte Solutions*, Butterworth's Scientific Publications, London (1955).

[138] T. Shedlovsky, "Conductometry" in A. Weissberger, *Physical Methods of Organic Chemistry*, Interscience Publishers, Inc., New York, 2nd ed., Vol. I, Part II, 1651.

[139] H. S. Harned and B. B. Owen, *The Physical Chemistry of Electrolytic Solutions*, Reinhold Publishing Corp., New York, 3rd ed. (1958); C. B. Monk, *Electrolytic Dissociation*, Academic Press, Inc., New York (1961).

[140] I. L. Jenkins and C. B. Monk, *J. Chem. Soc.*, 68 (1951); G. S. Hartley and G. W. Donaldson, *Trans. Faraday Soc.* **33**, 457 (1937).

[141] C. P. Piriz-MacColl, *J. Chem. Education* **36**, 303 (1959).

[142] A. Werner and A. Miolati, *Zeit. phys. Chem.* **12**, 35 (1893); **14**, 506 (1894); **21**, 225 (1896).

tivity is obtained by extrapolation of the conductivity back to zero time. For water the ranges of molecular conductivities are generally given as:

Charge Type	Concentration	Molar Conductance Range
1:1 (two ions)	0.001 M	96–115 ohm^{-1}
2:1 (three ions)	0.001 M	225–270 ohm^{-1}
3:1 (four ions)	0.001 M	380–432 ohm^{-1}
4:1 (five ions)	0.001 M	about 520 ohm^{-1}

These characteristic values will be different in other solvents. It should be realized that for the most unambiguous data only one multiple charged species should be furnished by the complex. There is a certain dependence of the molar conductance on the size of the complex ion also. The molar conductance of a salt M_xA_y at infinite dilution will be:

$$\Lambda^\circ = x\Lambda^\circ_{M^{+y}} + y\Lambda^\circ_{A^{-x}}$$

and at other concentrations one may write:

$$\Lambda = x\Lambda_{M^{+y}} + y\Lambda_{A^{-x}}$$

The individual values of Λ° for different ions of the same charge type are generally inversely proportional to the radius of the ion (which may include solvent molecules). Some variation in the mobilities is found even for geometrical isomers; for *cis-* and *trans-*[Co(NH$_3$)$_4$(NO$_2$)$_2$]Cl at 1°C, the *cis*-isomer has a slightly lower conductance than the *trans*-isomer.[143] Some typical values from the literature are given in Table 7.3. It can be seen from the first two entries that the presence of an acidic hydrogen ion may result in a molar conductance much greater than would be predicted on the basis of the ranges characteristic for *salts*. This is due to the very high conductivity of the hydrogen ion. The tabulated values are for 25° C; at other temperatures they are different. Werner and Herty[148] found that 1,2- and 1,6-[Co(en)$_2$Cl$_2$]Cl underwent a rapid hydrolysis in water at 25° so they determined the conductance at 0° to determine the charge type. At 0° the molar conductance of of the 1,2-compound is about 50 which is a typical value for an electrolyte of this type at this temperature. The effect of gradually increasing the *size* of the complex ion while keeping the charge type constant may be seen in the downward trend of values in the series [Co(NH$_3$)$_6$]Cl$_3$, [Co(en)$_2$(NH$_3$)$_2$]Cl$_3$, and [Co(en)$_3$]Cl$_3$. When a complex is a neutral species such as [Pt(NH$_3$)$_2$Cl$_2$] it will usually possess a very small conductivity, presumably due to either impurities or hydrolysis products. When such products do show an appreciable conductivity, this arises as a result of hydrolysis and in many cases the change in the conductivity can be used to obtain data on the kinetics of the hydrolytic process.

There are available many sets of highly precise sets of data on the concen-

[143] V. Carassiti and M. G. Vittori, *Ann. chim.* (Rome) **45**, 644 (1955), C.A. 50:6879.

TABLE 7.3

MOLAR CONDUCTANCE OF SOME COMPLEXES IN WATER

Complex	Concentration	Λ	Ref.
$H[Ir(DH)_2(NO_2)_2]$	0.0005	344.56	144
$[Ir(DH)_2(NH_3)_2]I \cdot \frac{1}{2}H_2O$	0.001	96.22	145
$K[Rh(NH_3)_2(NO_2)_4] \cdot \frac{1}{2}H_2O$	0.001	110.4	146
$[Pt(NH_3)_3Cl]Cl$	$0.001(v = 1024)$	116.2	147
$[Pt(NH_3)_3Cl]NO_3$	$0.001(v = 1024)$	117.8	147
$[Pt(NH_3)_3Br]Br$	$0.001(v = 1024)$	118.2	147
$[Pt(NH_3)_3(NO_2)]NO_3$	$0.001(v = 1024)$	120.1	147
$1,2\text{-}[Co(en)_2Cl_2]Cl$	$0.008(v = 125)$	97.28	148
$1,6\text{-}[Co(en)_2Cl_2]Cl$	$0.008(v = 125)$	96.08	148
$[Co(NH_3)_6]Cl_3$	0.001	431.6	148
$[Co(en)_2(NH_3)_2]Cl_3$	0.001	365.61	148
$[Co(en)_3]Cl_3$	0.001	351.64	148
$cis\text{-}[Pt(NH_3)_2Cl_2]$	0.001	2.93	148
$trans\text{-}[Pt(NH_3)_2Cl_2]$	0.001	42.63	148
$cis\text{-}[PtCl_4(NH_3)_2]$	0.001	4.96	148
$trans\text{-}[PtCl_4(NH_3)_2]$	0.001	0.24	148
$[Pt(NH_3)_4](NO_3)_2$	$0.001(v = 1024)$	283.9	149
$K_3[Fe(CN)_6]$	0.001	486	150
$K_4[Fe(CN)_6]$	0.001	668	150
$K_3[Cr(CN)_6]$	0.001	513	150
$K_3[W(CN)_8]$	0.001	270	150

[144] V. V. Lebedinskii and I. A. Fedorov, *Ann. secteur platine, Inst. chim. gen.* (U.S.S.R.) **18**, 23 (1945), C.A. 41: 5045. D represents the dimethylglyoximate ion.

[145] V. V. Lebedinskii and I. A. Fedorov, *Ann. secteur platine, Inst. chim. gen.* (U.S.S.R.) **18**, 31 (1945), C.A. 41: 5045.

[146] V. V. Lebedinskii and E. V. Shenderetskaya, *Ann. secteur platine, Inst. chim. gen.* (U.S.S.R.) **18**, 19 (1945), C.A. 41: 5044.

[147] H. J. S. King, *J. Chem. Soc.*, 1912 (1948).

[148] A. Werner and C. Herty, *Zeit. phys. Chem.* **38**, 341–342 (1901). These values change with time. The values given are for a 2 min interval from the time of solution.

[149] H. J. S. King, *J. Chem. Soc.*, 1338, 1344 (1938).

[150] *International Critical Tables*, Vol. VI, 241–256.

tration dependence of the electrical conductivity of complex salts. Recent studies which may be consulted for further details, include examinations of the hexafluoroarsenate(V) salts[151] and the hexafluocomplexes of the Group IV elements.[152]

Electrical conductance of complex salts in non-aqueous solvents may also be used in the determination of charge type. Sutton[153] used the conductivity in nitrobenzene to characterize some Ti(III) and Ti(IV) complexes. In general

[151] G. Atkinson and C. J. Hallada, *J. Phys. Chem.* **64**, 1487 (1960).

[152] R. H. Schmitt, E. L. Grove, and R. D. Brown, *J. Amer. Chem. Soc.* **82**, 5292 (1960).

[153] G. J. Sutton, *Australian J. Chem.* **12**, 122 (1959).

complexes of a given charge type will have molar conductivities in the same range if measurements are carried out at approximately the same concentration. Sutton's data illustrate the use of these ideas:

Substance	Molar Conc.	Molar Conductance	Conclusions
$NH_4[Ti(SCN)_4(H_2O)_2]$	0.010	18.3 $(ohm)^{-1}$	1–1 electrolyte
$(NH_4)[Ti(SCN)_4]$	0.003	18.9	1–1 electrolyte
$(NH_4)[Ti(SCN)_4(OH)(H_2O)]$	0.003	21.4	1–1 electrolyte
$TiCl_3 \cdot D \cdot H_2O*$	0.006	0.53	non-electrolyte
$TiBr_3D \cdot H_2O$	0.011	0.31	non-electrolyte
$TiCl_4 \cdot D$	0.007	0.90	non-electrolyte
$TiBr_4 \cdot D$	0.006	1.30	non-electrolyte

*D is ortho-phenylenebisdimethylarsine:

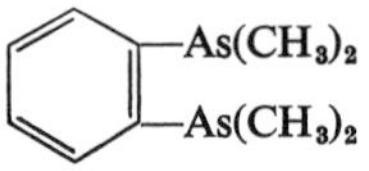

When complexes are easily dissociated they will give solutions which have conductivities which are *not* characteristic of the charge type. This may occur even in non-aqueous solvents such as nitrobenzene or nitromethane.[154]

COLLIGATIVE PROPERTIES

There are four colligative properties which may give information on the nature of coordination compounds:

1. freezing point depression measurements

2. boiling point elevation measurements

3. vapor-pressure lowering determinations

4. osmotic pressure measurements

Each of these properties, under suitable conditions, allows us to count the number of particles furnished by a given weight of sample and hence to determine the molecular weight of non-electrolytes. The presence of interionic attractions complicates the use of these properties with electrolytes. A solution to this problem is the use of solvents with very high dielectric constants or fused salts.

The use of freezing point depression measurements to determine the molecular weights of non-electrolytes has been very common practice. The techniques required are essentially those used for organic compounds. These are outlined in detail in standard reference works.[155]

[154] C. M. Harris and E. D. McKenzie, *J. Inorg. Nuclear Chem.* **19**, 373 (1961).

[155] The most comprehensive coverage in English is A. Weissberger, *Technique of Organic Chemistry*, Interscience Publishers, Inc., New York, 2nd ed. (1949), Vol. 1., Part I.

For ionic complexes, measurements in common organic solvents are usually not easily interpreted because of incomplete dissociation. For a solvent with a high dielectric constant such as sulfuric acid, the advantages of the high dielectric constant are offset by the great tendency of this solvent to solvolyze dissociated species. Parissakis and Schwarzenbach,[156] have carefully reexamined the use of $Na_2SO_4 \cdot 10H_2O$ as a cryoscopic medium. This melts at 32.384° to a suspension containing 63.4% of the Na_2SO_4 in solution and 36.6% of the solid anhydride in suspension. In such a medium the species Na^+, $SO_4^=$, and H_2O are cryoscopically inactive. The theoretical value of the cryoscopic constant, K_0, is 3.16°:

$$K_0 = \frac{\Delta T}{iC}$$

ΔT is the observed depression of the transition temperature, i is the number of foreign particles produced per formula weight of added substance and C is the concentration of added material per Kg of medium.

One of the results of this work was the confirmation of the double formula, $[Ag_2(en)_2]^{+2}$ for the ethylenediamine-silver(I) complex. One additional factor which must be taken into account is the variation which occurs as the concentration of the solute is changed. Thus a measurement at a single concentration is not reliable. An extrapolation of $\Delta T/C$ to $C = 0$ is required to accurately determine i. Unfortunately, the method seems to give peculiar results when polynuclear anionic complexes are present or when there is opportunity for the occurrence of hydrolysis. For stable complex ions such as $Fe(CN)_6^{-4}$, $Co(en)_3^{+3}$, etc., however, the method seems to work quite satisfactorily.[156a]

A thorough analysis of the problems which arise in the use of this method with polynuclear complexes has been presented by Tobias.[157] The chief source of difficulty is the need for precise data in very dilute solutions.

The other colligative properties are subject to similar limitations. The use of boiling point elevations is attended by the additional difficulty that the boiling point elevation constant is smaller than the freezing point depression constant and the requirement that the external pressure on the system must remain constant. Both vapor pressure depressions and osmotic pressure measurements are more promising, especially for more dilute solutions. Both are more difficult experimentally but certainly not prohibitively so. The availability of differential manometers of great sensitivity, precision osmotic balances and commercial osmometers (which provide an indirect measurement of osmotic pressure through determination of the temperature differences which arise as a result of different rates of evaporation of a solution and solvent) should make such measurements much easier.

[156] G. Parissakis and G. Schwarzenbach, *Helv. chim. Acta* **41**, 2042, 2425 (1958).
[156a] G. Jander and B. Fiedler, *Zeit. anorg. allgem. Chem.* **308**, 155 (1961).
[157] R. S. Tobias, *J. Inorg. Nuclear Chem.* **19**, 348 (1961).

ELECTRON DIFFRACTION[158,159,160]

Electron diffraction studies can be used for the determination of the structures of coordination compounds when they are sufficiently volatile and are also stable in the gas phase. As with X-rays, an observed diffraction pattern is matched with a computed one until a satisfactory fit is obtained. An example of an experimental set-up is shown in Figure 40.

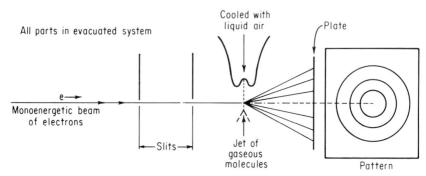

Fig. 40 Diagrammatic sketch of the apparatus used to obtain electron diffraction patterns of gaseous molecules.

The variation in the radial intensity of the diffraction pattern is recorded on a photographic plate. The analysis of this pattern is then carried out with the goal of obtaining a model of the compound whose theoretical diffraction pattern agrees with that found experimentally.

The requirement of volatility seriously restricts the number of molecules which may be studied by this method. Nickel carbonyl, $Ni(CO)_4$, was shown to be tetrahedral with Ni—C distances of 1.82 ± 0.03 A and C—O distances of 1.15 ± 0.02 A in an early study.[161] The C—O bond distance here corresponds to a triple bond and indicates that this bond is relatively unaffected by the coordination process.

This method has been used to study the gaseous forms of bis(acetylacetonato)copper(II)[162] and bis(acetylacetonato)nickel(II).[163] Both of these are found to be square planar *in this state*, with Ni—O = 1.90 A and Cu—O = 1.95 A. The results obtained for the copper complex were in good agreement

[158] R. Beeching, *Electron Diffraction*, Methuen & Co., Ltd., London, 3rd ed. (1950).

[159] M. H. Pirenne, *The Diffraction of X-rays and Electrons by Free Molecules*, Cambridge University Press, London (1946).

[160] L. O. Brockway, *Reviews Mod. Phys.* **8**, 231 (1936).

[161] L. O. Brockway and P. C. Cross, *J. Chem. Phys.* **3**, 828 (1935).

[162] S. Shibata and K. Sone, *Bull. Chem. Soc. Japan* **29**, 852 (1956).

[163] S. Shibata, *Bull. Chem. Soc. Japan* **30**, 753 (1957); S. Shibata, M. Kishita, and M. Kubo, *Nature* **179**, 320 (1957).

with the results of X-ray studies on this compound.[164] The distances between the central metal atoms and the oxygens indicated covalent bonding. The nickel complex apparently undergoes a structural change on vaporization as the solid is trimeric.[74]

Another example of a different sort may be seen in the results for $Cu(NO_3)_2$.[165] This compound is volatile and the gas is monomeric. In the vapor one of the NO_3 groups is bonded to the copper through an oxygen while the other is bonded directly through the nitrogen. These two nitrate groups differ in their chemical reactivity.

NUCLEAR MAGNETIC RESONANCE[166-173]

It has been known for some time that many nuclei have magnetic moments (i.e., "spin"). For such a nucleus whose maximum measurable component of angular momentum is I, there will be $2I + 1$ degenerate energy states in the absence of a magnetic field. For these states the measureable component will vary from $-I$ to $+I$. If an external magnetic field is applied this degeneracy is removed, however, and these are split into $2I + 1$ separate states. For a stationary magnetic field of strength H_0 these energy levels will have the values:

$$-\mu H_0, \quad -\mu\left(\frac{I-1}{I}\right)H_0, \quad \ldots \quad + \left(\frac{I-1}{I}\right)\mu H_0, \quad + \mu H_0$$

where

$$\mu = g\frac{eh}{2M_pc}$$

I = the magnetic moment of the nucleus. For a transition from one energy level to the next:

$$h\nu = \frac{\mu H_0}{I}$$

or $\nu = \gamma H_0/2\pi$ where $\gamma = \mu/I$h for $H_0 = 10,000$ gauss and for protons

[164] E. A. Shugam, *Doklady Akad. Nauk S.S.S.R.* **81**, 853 (1951), C.A. 46: 3894.

[165] S. H. Bauer and C. C. Addison, *Proc. Chem. Soc.*, 251 (1960).

[166] J. D. Roberts, *J. Chem. Ed.* **37**, 581 (1961).

[167] J. A. Pople, W. G. Schneider, and H. J. Bernstein, *High Resolution Nuclear Magnetic Resonance*, McGraw-Hill Book Company, New York (1959).

[168] J. D. Roberts, *Nuclear Magnetic Resonance*, McGraw-Hill Book Company, New York (1958).

[169] E. R. Andrew, *Nuclear Magnetic Resonance*, Cambridge University Press, London (1955).

[170] A. Losche, *Kerninduktion*, VEB, Deutscher Verlag der Wissenschaften, Berlin (1957).

[171] J. E. Wertz, *Chem. Revs.* **55**, 829 (1955).

[172] H. S. Gutowsky, "Analytical Applications of Nuclear Magnetic Resonance" in W. G. Berl, *Physical Methods in Chemical Analysis*, Academic Press, Inc., New York (1956), Vol. III, 303–381.

[173] A. K. Saha and T. P. Das *Nuclear Induction*, Saha Institute of Nuclear Physics, Calcutta (1957).

($\mu = 1.42 \times 10^{-23}$ erg/gauss) the required frequency is 42.6 Mc/sec, a radio frequency. The chemical usefulness of NMR is based on the effect of the electronic environment on the behavior of the nuclear magnetic moments in a magnetic field. In general the field at the nucleus will be less than the external field. This reduction will be determined by the electronic environment and proportional to the applied field:

$$H_{local} = H_0(1-\sigma)$$

σ is called the screening constant. This effect has been exploited in studying hydrogen compounds as each kind of hydrogen atom present will show resonance at a different part of the NMR spectrum. Thus for ethyl alcohol, the low resolution NMR spectrum has three maxima in the typical plot of energy absorption versus H, the magnetic field strength.

As yet, this method has not been exploited to a great extent compared with its full potentialities in the examination of coordination compounds. For some cobalt complexes the variation of σ with ligand type has been correlated with the spectra.[174] For the cobalt nucleus, the screening constant may be written as:

$$\sigma = A + \frac{B}{\Delta E}$$

where A and B are nearly constant for various ligands and ΔE is the electronic excitation energy characteristic of the ligand (i.e., the lowest energy for optical absorption). The variation of the Co^{59} resonance frequency (ν) with ligand type is of the sort $\nu \propto \lambda$ where λ is the wave length of the maximum in the visible absorption band of lowest frequency. A number of recent NMR studies are summarized in Table 7.4. These indicate some of the uses to which this method has already been put in the field of coordination chemistry.

TABLE 7.4

NMR STUDIES ON COORDINATION COMPOUNDS

Species Studied	Results	Reference
Co(III) complexes	Confirmed results of ref. 174	175
Cr(III) complexes and paramagnetic ions in methanol and ethanol	N—H exchange rates were determined as well as the line broadening due to paramagnetic ions	176
M(en)$_x$ complexes	Attempt to determine conformation of coordinated ethylenediamine	177
[PdCl$_2$(C$_2$H$_4$)]$_2$	C—H distances intermediate between those of C$_2$H$_4$ and C$_2$H$_6$, ethylene does not rotate about bond	178

[174] J. S. Owen and L. E. Orgel, *Trans. Faraday Soc.* **53**, 601 (1957).

Species Studied	Results	Reference
"$K_3[Rh(C_2O_4)_3] \cdot 4\frac{1}{2}H_2O$"	This compound consists of a mixture of complex rhodium anions, half are $[Rh(C_2O_4)_3]^{-3}$ and half are $[Rh(C_2O_4)_2(HC_2O_4)(OH)]^{-3}$	179
Allyl and crotyl palladium chloride complexes	Nonclassical structure suggested for Pd—organic bonding	180
π-$C_5H_5(C_5H_6)M$	Structure proposed based upon number and types of H present	181
$(C_5H_5)_2ReH$	Re—H linkage indicated	182
Co^{+2}—Cl^-—H_2O system	Effects of added salts on position of Cl^{35} chemical shift determined	183
$[M(NH_3)_6]Cl_x$ where $M = Co(III), Ni(II), Co(II), Mn(II)$ and $Fe(II)$	Hydrogens are rotating about M—N axis, metal to H distances estimated	184
Tl_2Cl_3 and $TlCl_3 \cdot xH_2O$	Species present in Tl_2Cl_3 is $Tl_3(TlCl_6)$; in $TlCl_3 \cdot xH_2O$ there are $Tl(H_2O)_x^{+3}$, $TlCl_4^-$, and $TlCl_6^{-3}$ ions	185
$CrCl_3$ solns, in H_2O	NMR spectra of protons depends on history of solution	186
Cis- and *trans*- $[M(benzoylacetonate)_3]$	These can be differentiated via their NMR spectra	186ᵃ

[175] S. S. Dharmatti and C. R. Kanekar, *J. Chem. Phys.* **31**, 1436 (1959).

[176] R. G. Pearson, J. Palmer, M. M. Anderson, and A. L. Allred, *Zeit. Elektrochemie* **64**, 110 (1960).

[177] D. B. Powell and N. Sheppard, *J. Chem. Soc.*, 791 (1959).

[178] L. W. Reeves, *Can. J. Chem.* **38**, 736 (1960).

[179] A. L. Porte, H. S. Gutowsky, and G. M. Harris, *J. Chem. Phys.* **34**, 66 (1961).

[180] H. C. Dehm and J. C. W. Chien, *J. Amer. Chem. Soc.* **82**, 4429 (1960).

[181] M. L. H. Green, L. Pratt, and G. Wilkinson, *J. Chem. Soc.*, 3753 (1959).

[182] M. L. H. Green, L. Pratt, and G. Wilkinson, *J. Chem. Soc.*, 3916 (1958).

[183] D. B. Chesnut, *J. Chem. Physics* **33**, 1234 (1960).

[184] P. H. Kim, *J. Phys. Soc. Japan* **15**, 445 (1960).

[185] R. Freeman, R. P. H. Gasser, and R. E. Richards, *Molecular Physics* **2**, 301 (1959).

[186] T. H. Brown, R. A. Bernheim, and H. S. Gutowsky, *J. Chem. Phys.* **33**, 1593 (1960).

[186a] R. C. Fay and T. S. Piper, *J. Amer. Chem. Soc.* **84**, 2303 (1962).

ELECTRON PARAMAGNETIC RESONANCE[187,188,189]

Electron paramagnetic resonance is a special kind of energy absorption found in systems where there are *electronic* magnetic moments which are not

[187] B. Bleaney and K. W. H. Stevens, *Reports on Progress in Physics*, Vol. XVI, 108 (1953).

[188] K. D. Bowers and J. Owen, *Reports on Progress in Physics*, Vol. XVIII, 304 (1955).

[189] S. A. Altshuler and B. M. Kozyrev, *Advances in Physical Sciences* **63**, 721 (1957) (English Translation).

strongly coupled to each other. Such systems are spoken of as being magnetically dilute and contain paramagnetic ions separated from each other by intervening diamagnetic species. Whenever an atom or an ion contains a partially filled shell it *may* give rise to a magnetic moment. The angular momentum of such a system is due in part to the orbital motion and in part to the intrinsic spin of the electrons. The method has its basis in the fact that an ion with a permanent magnetic moment and a resultant angular momentum parallel to this exhibits a special type of behavior when placed in a magnetic field, H. The angular momentum vector precesses about the axis of H with the frequency:

$$\omega = g\left(\frac{e}{2mc}\right)H$$

where g is the spectroscopic splitting factor, e is the charge on an electron, m is its mass and c is the velocity of light.

If a circularly polarized magnetic field is used, then the atoms will absorb radiation from the field when the following condition is met:

$$h\nu = g\beta H = g\left(\frac{eh}{4\pi mc}\right)H.$$

Here $h\nu$ is the separation of energy levels in the atom. The resonance condition can thus be used to measure the separation of energy levels in the systems. Since this splitting is dependent upon both H and the symmetry of the surroundings of the atom in the solid, such studies may be used to determine this symmetry. For most cases each kind of ion in a salt gives its own spectrum. Where such is not the case, appreciable interactions may be assumed to occur. The lowest energy levels are determined by the symmetry of the surroundings of the ion and thus we can get direct information on this as well as on the bonding type and strength involved between the paramagnetic ion and its surrounding diamagnetic ions. For example, investigation of Cs_3CoCl_5 reveals that the tetrahedron of Cl atoms around the Co atom is distorted.

A more sophisticated application may be seen in the study of the complexes $IrCl_6^=$ and $IrBr_6^=$.[190] This study revealed that pi bonding was present and that the electron responsible for the electron paramagnetic resonance moved partly in d orbitals around the central ion and partly in p_π orbitals around the outer halogen atoms of the complex.

The paramagnetic resonance absorption of solutions of $Cu(H_2O)_4^{+2}$ and $Cu(NH_3)_4^{+2}$ in glycerol has been used to show that the water is bound ionically while the ammonia is covalently bound.[191] This method has also been used to demonstrate that the single unpaired electron in

[190] J. H. E. Griffiths and J. Owen, *Proc. Roy. Soc.* **A226**, 96 (1954).
[191] E. Lutze and D. Bosnecker, *Zeit. Naturforschung* **14a**, 755 (1959).

$[(NH_3)_5Co—O—O—Co(NH_3)_5]^{+5}$ has an equal probability of being on either of the cobalt atoms.[192]

The g factor used above varies with the degree of covalency and is derived from the experimental data. For a free electron, g is 2.0023 but has a larger value in a paramagnetic complex. A study of some copper(II) chelates[193] used the approximate relation,

$$g = 2.0023 - \alpha^2 \frac{8\lambda}{\Delta}$$

to estimate α^2, the degree of mixing of metal and ligand orbitals in the composite molecular orbital. α ranges from 1 for a pure ionic bond to 0.5 for a pure covalent bond. λ was taken as $-828.7\ cm^{-1}$ in this particular study and Δ is the difference in energy of the two lowest states (i.e., $d_\epsilon - d_\gamma$ splitting). Some typical g values for copper complexes are:

bis(8-hydroxyquinolinato)copper(II)	$g = 2.145$
Cu(II) EDTA	$g = 2.144$
bis(salicylaldoximato)copper(II)	$g = 2.095$
copper(II) nitrilotriacetate	$g = 2.064$
bis(acetylacetonato)copper(II)	$g = 2.100$
bis(5,7-dibromo 8-hydroxyquinolinato) copper(II)	$g = 2.049$

As can be checked by calculations, the range of α values obtained from this equation do not appear to be very reasonable. For a complete analysis of complexes it is necessary to examine single crystals and in such cases the g value varies with the orientation of the crystal. Such a study may be seen in the work of McGarvey on single crystals of bis(acetylacetonato)copper(II).[194] From such a detailed study it was possible to estimate the relative importance of sigma and pi bonding in the compound. Unfortunately the detailed analysis of the data is a theoretical problem of some complexity. In Table 7.5 are to be found some recent examples of the use of this method in the study of coordination compounds. The chemical theory has been given by Owen[195] in an important paper.

VISIBLE AND ULTRAVIOLET SPECTRA

The use of the visible and ultraviolet absorption spectra of complexes is important from both a practical and a theoretical point of view. Aside from the very obvious use of this data in providing an analytical method for the determination of the concentrations of complex species in solution, it can

[192] I. Bernal, E. A. V. Ebsworth and J. A. Weil, *Proc. Chem. Soc.*, 57 (1959); E. A. V. Ebsworth and J. A. Weil, *J. Phys. Chem.* **63**, 1890 (1959).

[193] G. Schoffa, R. Ristau, and B. E. Wahler, *Zeit. phys. Chem.* **215**, 203 (1960).

[194] B. R. McGarvey, *J. Phys. Chem.* **60**, 71 (1956).

[195] J. Owen, *Proc. Roy. Soc.* (London) **A227**, 183 (1955). A review of this subject may also be found in: A. Carrington, *Endeavour* **21**, 51 (1962).

TABLE 7.5

SOME EXAMPLES OF EPR STUDIES ON COORDINATION COMPOUNDS

Species	Results	Reference
copper(II)phthalocyanine	electron delocalization in pi system demonstrated	196, 197
FeF_6^{-3}	distribution of unpaired electrons in molecular orbitals computed	198, 199
$K_3[Cr(CN)_5NO]H_2O$	unpaired electron spends most of its time on Cr. NO^+ present	200
copper Etioporphyrin II	odd electron spends 74% of its time in copper $d_{x^2-y^2}$ orbital	201
silver(II)deuteroporphyrin-IX dimethylester	Ag(II) compound more covalent than corresponding Cu(II) compound	202
copper(II)phthalocyanine	$\alpha = 0.81$	203
MnF_6^{-4}	g value is constant, interaction varies with distance as the environment is changed	204
$Ni(NH_3)_6Cl_2$	epr resonance *vanishes* below 74° C	205
$Cr(H_2O)_6^{+3}$	$\alpha = 0.61$	206
Cu(II) salts of carboxylic acids	Cu—Cu interaction considerable in *n*-butyrate salt; weak in trichloroacetate	207
Vanadyl porphyrins		207a

[196] D. J. E. Ingram and J. E. Bennett, "Discussions of the Faraday Society", No. 19, 140 (1955).

[197] D. J. E. Ingram and J. E. Bennett, *J. Chem. Phys.* **22**, 1136 (1954).

[198] L. Helmholz, *J. Chem. Phys.* **31**, 172 (1959).

[199] L. Helmholz and A. V. Guzzo, *J. Chem. Phys.* **32**, 302 (1960).

[200] I. Bernal and S. E. Harrison, *J. Chem. Phys.* **34**, 102 (1961).

[201] E. M. Roberts and W. S. Koski, *J. Amer. Chem. Soc.* **82**, 3006 (1960).

[202] F. Kneubuhl, W. S. Koski, and W. S. Caughey, *J. Amer. Chem. Soc.* **83**, 1607 (1961).

[203] E. M. Roberts and W. S. Koski, *J. Amer. Chem. Soc.* **83**, 1865 (1961).

[204] S. Ogawa, *J. Phys. Soc. Japan* **15**, 1475 (1960).

[205] M. Date, *J. Phys. Soc. Japan* **15**, 2115 (1960).

[206] G. Emch and R. Lacroix, *Helv. Phys. Acta* **33**, 1021 (1960).

[207] H. Abe and H. Shirai, *J. Phys. Soc. Japan* **16**, 118 (1961).

[207a] E. M. Roberts, W. S. Koski, and W. S. Caughey, *J. Chem. Phys.* **34**, 591–593 (1961).

furnish information on the structure and stability of complexes. Much of the primary data used in crystal field theory calculations is obtained from the visible and ultraviolet absorption spectra of complexes in solution. For convenience the subject will be divided into the following parts which are, however, closely related.

1. General empirical principles

2. *Cis-trans*-isomerism

3. Charge-transfer spectra

4. The spectrochemical and the nephelauxetic series of ligands

5. Crystal-field theory applications of spectra

6. Solvent effects

1. *General Empirical Principles.* Long before any comprehensive theoretical attack was made on the problem of the spectra of complexes, many studies were carried out on the absorption spectra of aqueous solutions of stable complexes. Luther and Nikalopulos[208] examined a number of cobalt(III) ammine complexes and reached the following conclusions:

1. The absorption spectrum is dependent only on the structure of the complex. (Valid where the anion does not absorb.)

2. Replacement of NH_3 in the complex by NO_3^-, H_2O, Cl^-, or Br^- causes a displacement of the absorption maximum toward the red. Replacement by NO_2^- causes a displacement toward the violet.

3. The greater the displacement of the absorption band toward the violet, the greater the stability of the complex. The steeper the curve (i.e., absorption curve), the greater the photochemical sensitivity.

Shibata and Urbain[209] confirmed the general results of this work. They found that the NO_2^- group was hypsochromic (displaced the absorption maximum toward the violet) and hyperchromic (increased the extinction coefficient). The groups Cl^-, OH^-, $C_2O_4^-$, were bathochromic (displaced the absorption maximum toward the red) and were hypochromic (decreased the extinction coefficient). Except for NO_2^-, negative substituents were found to be hypochromic. This represents the initial work of Shibata on this subject and in subsequent years he explored the field more fully as did R. Tsuchida. In the first of a series of papers on this subject, Shibata[210] showed that most complexes have maximum absorption bands at about 2,000 A, about 3,000 A, and *trans*-isomers showed an additional band at about 4,000 A. The band at 2,000 A is little affected by the type of ligand, but the other two are. Shibata also found that complexes of similar chemical composition have similar absorption spectra, e.g., a coordinated N from an ammonia molecule or an ethylenediamine has about the same effect on the absorption spectra but $-NO_2$ or $-ONO$ give different spectra from this and from each other. The sign of the charge on the complex ion was found not to have a great effect on the absorption spectra. The absorption spectra of optical isomers and racemates were found to be identical but geometrical isomers showed different absorption spectra. Finally, the anion was found to have no effect on the

[208] R. Luther and A. Nikalopulos, *Zeit. phys. Chem.* **82**, 361 (1913).

[209] Y. Shibata and G. Urbain, *Compt. rend.* **157**, 593 (1913).

[210] Y. Shibata, *J. Coll. Sci. Imp. Univ. Tokyo* **37**, Art. 2, 1–2–8 (1915), C.A. 10: 431.

gross absorption spectra. (It does have an effect on the extinction coefficient, however, as a result of variations in ion-pair formation tendencies.)[211] These qualitative generalizations have been extended and put on a more secure theoretical basis by later work.

2. *Absorption Spectra of Geometrical Isomers.* Following Shibata's observation of the differences in the spectra of geometrical isomers, Kuroya and Tsuchida[212] found that a third absorption band (at about 2,500 A) occurred only in those *trans*-isomers where the two *trans*-positions were occupied by negative substituents. In addition the absorption maxima in the ultraviolet occur at shorter wave lengths for *cis*-isomers. This feature of the absorption spectra of geometrical isomers has been subject to some scrutiny. Basolo[213] examined the spectra of numerous pairs of geometrical isomers and found that the presence of such third bands occurred with some *cis*-isomers as well as *trans*-isomers. Subsequently, Shimura[214] showed that the resolution of the spectra into the Gaussian components in these conflicting cases allowed the presence of the third band in the *trans*-isomers and its absence in the *cis*-isomers of some complexes to be established. Anyone interested in using this criterion should consult the original papers to appreciate the difficulties which arise in the interpretation of such spectra.

Linhard and his collaborators have examined the absorption spectra of a large number of related complexes and found that the number of bands is *not* as obvious a difference in these spectra as their appearance. In a plot of log ϵ (extinction coefficient) vs. frequency (in cm^{-1}) the *cis*-bands are invariably broader than the *trans* bands. In an examination of several examples of geometrically isomeric Co(III) complexes it was necessary to resolve the spectra into components.[215] In this same paper it was found that the splitting of the short wave length ("third" band of Tsuchida) was quite different for the *cis*- and *trans*-isomers. Linhard's analysis seems to be equivalent in method to that of Shimura although stated in different terms. It should be recalled that absorption may arise for any of the following reasons:

1. Transitions involving electronic transitions of the central metal ions. These will be intense if allowed and weak if partially forbidden by selection rules.

2. Transitions involving ligand electrons.

3. Charge transfer transitions of electrons from the ligand to metal or vice versa.

[211] E. J. King, J. H. Espenson, and R. E. Visco, *J. Phys. Chem.* **63**, 755 (1959); M. G. Evans and G. H. Nancollas, *Trans. Faraday Soc.* **49**, 363 (1953).

[212] H. Kuroya and R. Tsuchida, *Bull. Chem. Soc. Japan* **15**, 429 (1940).

[213] F. Basolo, *J. Amer. Chem. Soc.* **72**, 4393 (1950).

[214] Y. Shimura, *J. Amer. Chem. Soc.* **73**, 5079 (1951); J. J. A. Hartmann and G. P. van der Kelen, *Bull. soc. chim. Belges.* **68**, 568 (1959).

[215] M. Linhard and M. Weigel, *Zeit. anorg. allgem. Chem.* **271**, 101 (1952).

Normally the most direct and obvious differences in the spectra of geometrical isomers arise from transitions of the first type. Linhard has investigated the absorption spectra of a large number of complexes in which these various processes occur.[216]

The application of crystal field theory to some of the problems involved in the interpretation of the absorption spectra of Co(III) complexes may be seen in a study of the types of splitting to be found for complexes of the types $Co(A)_6$, cis-CoA_4B_2, and trans-CoA_4B_2.[217] It was predicted that of the two absorption bands found for CoA_6 complexes, the one of longer wave length should be split into two bands for both the cis- and trans-complexes. The splitting predicted for the trans-isomer is appreciably greater than that predicted for the cis-isomer. These investigators were unable to offer a crystal field theory explanation of the third band of Tsuchida. The results were found to be consistent with a large number of experimental curves and also to be a reliable guide to the interpretation of spectra of this type of geometrical isomer.

3. *Charge-transfer Spectra.*[218,219,216] In many cases the irradiation of a complex with light of appropriate wave length will result in the transfer of an electron from a ligand to the cation:

$$Fe^{+3} + CNS^- \xrightarrow{h\nu} Fe^{+2} + CNS$$

$$Co(NH_3)_6^{+3} + I^- \xrightarrow{h\nu} Co(NH_3)_6^{+2} + I$$

In complexes, the ultraviolet absorption is frequently ascribed to a charge transfer process involving the transfer of an electron from a central metal ion to a ligand or vice versa. Such processes are much more readily studied in complexes containing anions where the transfer of the electron to the cation occurs. In general the shifting of the absorption bands with wave length is predictable as it varies with the ease with which an electron can be removed from the anion. In some cases the electron may be transferred from the metal to the ligand, e.g.:

$$Fe(H_2O)_6^{+2} \xrightarrow{h\nu} [Fe(H_2O)_5(OH)]^{+2} + H\cdot$$

The charge transfer spectra are of importance in understanding the nature of photochemical reactions of coordination compounds. Many processes of this type have been substantiated for a wide variety of complexes.

4. *The Spectrochemical and the Nephelauxetic Series of Ligands.* The

[216] An extensive bibliography of earlier work is given in M. Linhard, *Zeit. Elektrochem.* **50**, 224 (1944). Later theoretical and experimental work is ably summarized by T. M. Dunn in J. Lewis and R. G. Wilkins, editors, *Modern Coordination Chemistry*, Interscience Publishers, Inc., New York (1960), pp. 229–300.

[217] F. Basolo, C. J. Ballhausen, and J. Bjerrum, *Acta Chem. Scand.* **9**, 810 (1955).

[218] L. E. Orgel, Quarterly Reviews **8**, 422 (1954).

[219] E. Rabinowitch, *Rev. Mod. Phys.* **14**, 112 (1942).

variation of the absorption spectra of complexes of the type $[Co(NH_3)_5X]$ allows the ordering of the group X in a series which gives the order of its ability to shift the absorption toward the ultraviolet part of the spectrum. This series seems to be a general one for most cations. Starting with the group which exerts the greatest effect (or crystal field) on the central ion we have:

  CN^- > *o*-phenanthroline > NO_2^- > ethylenediamine > NH_3 > NCS^- > H_2O >
  F^- > RCO_2^- > OH^- > Cl^- > Br^- > I^-.

This is called the Fajans-Tsuchida series.[220]

As might be imagined, developments in crystal field theory ultimately must face the problems of the degree of covalency in complexes and of the interactions of the electrons in the *d* orbitals. These problems are related. Schaffer and Jorgensen[221] devised a method for estimating the expansion of the *d* orbitals of the central atom under the influence of the ligands. These calculations are based on the smaller term values for the complexed ions as compared with the free ions. This varies from ligand to ligand in what is called the *nephelauxetic series* in the following manner: (in order of increasing covalency)

  F^- < H_2O < urea < NH_3 < en < oxalate < SCN^- < Cl^- < CN^- < Br^-

This additional series indicates that the expansion of the *d* orbitals should be used in accounting for the variation in term values as well as the $10Dq$ or Δ values. This expansion in the radial wave function goes hand in hand with an increasing covalency.

 5. *Crystal Field Theory Applications of Spectra.* In addition to the value of spectra in checking or revising ideas on the symmetry of complexes, they furnish the primary data for the estimation of the term values in complexes. Many specific examples of this have been cited in previous chapters. The general area is covered in the review of Dunn[216] and in symposia.[222]

 6. *Solvent Effects.* The solvent may exert an effect on the spectra of complexes but this is often hard to predict or eliminate. Its possible presence in affecting the spectra of aqueous solutions leads to many uncertainties in interpretation. Even in "organic" solvents such effects may be found but they can often be ordered in a systematic fashion if no solvolysis occurs. O. Popovych and L. B. Rogers[223] studied the effect of the solvent on the position of the absorption maxima for both 8-hydroxyquinoline and its zinc chelate. In those cases where the solvent did not react chemically, the shifts in frequency could be calculated using an equation due to McRae:[224]

[220] R. Tsuchida, *Bull. Chem. Soc. Japan* **13**, 388, 436, 471 (1938).
[221] C. A. Schaffer and C. K. Jorgensen, *J. Inorg. Nuclear Chem.* **8**, 143 (1958); C. K. Jorgensen, *Advances in Inorg. Chem.* **4**, 73 (1962).
[222] "Discussions of the Faraday Society", No. 26.
[223] O. Popovych and L. B. Rogers, *J. Amer. Chem. Soc.* **81**, 4469 (1959).
[224] E. G. McRae, *J. Phys. Chem.* **61**, 562 (1957).

$$\Delta \tilde{\nu} = (AL_0 + B) \left(\frac{n^2 - 1}{2n^2 + 1} \right) + C \left[\frac{D - 1}{D + 2} - \frac{n^2 - 1}{n^2 + 2} \right]$$

Here A, B, and C are constants; n and D are the refractive index and dielectric constant of the solvent respectively, and L_0 is a function of the solvent absorption spectrum but is generally taken as a constant for a given class of solvent. The first term in this equation takes into account the dispersion forces and the second the effects of permanent dipoles. For non-polar solvents only the first term is required. For solutions where solvolysis did not occur, the agreement between experimental and calculated solvent shifts was quite satisfactory.

Since a variation in the dielectric constant of the solvent will also cause variations in the extent of ion-pair formation, changes in the spectra of ionic complexes may occur as a result. In most instances this will change extinction coefficients to a detectable extent, though it would not be expected to have an important effect on the position of the absorption maxima.

OPTICAL BIREFRINGENCE AND RELATED PROPERTIES[225]

The optical properties of crystals can often give information on the structural units of which the crystal is composed. This arises from the fact that the optical properties of the crystal such as refractive index, polarization of light, and the absorption spectra depend upon the direction as this in turn is determined by the types of structure through which the light must pass. Planar components such as NO_3^- or $CO_3^=$ have different properties for light in the plane and light passing perpendicular to the plane of the ion. This includes the refractive index for polarized light and related properties. If the plane of polarization and the plane of the ion coincide, the refractive index will be high. If the plane of polarization is perpendicular to the plane of the group, the refractive index will be much lower. Thus the anisotropic nature of the structure will result in an anisotropy of absorption. Unfortunately the final optical properties of the crystal depend upon both the structure of the composite units and their relative orientation with respect to each other. The method requires expert microscopy if reliable results are to be obtained, and even then the theory and experimental results may differ.[226] The calculation of molar refractivities and refractive indices may be carried out with considerable success if the crystal structure of the solid is known.[227] The reverse process is less easily carried out. Some other examples, Co(III) complexes, have been examined by Ballhausen and Moffitt.[228]

A somewhat different approach to such work is seen in the work of Tsuchida and Yamada on the spectra of crystals. These investigators have

[225] N. H. Hartshorne and A. Stuart, *Crystals and the Polarizing Microscope*, Edward Arnold, Ltd., London, 3rd ed. (1960), esp. pp. 145–172.

[226] D. S. Flikkema, *Acta Cryst.* **6**, 37 (1953).

[227] W. L. Bragg, *Proc. Royal Soc.* (London) **A105**, 370 (1924).

[228] C. J. Ballhausen and W. Moffitt, *J. Inorg. Nuclear Chem.* **3**, 178 (1956).

studied numerous instances of dichroism in the crystals formed by coordination compounds. *Dichroism* is the term used to designate the variation of the absorption spectra, with direction, of uniaxial crystals since such crystals have two principal absorption axes (the general term is *pleochroism*). The absorption bands of planar complexes at the longer wave lengths are closely related to the linkages in the complex and the absorption of incident light is greater along the directions parallel to these linkages than in a direction perpendicular to them. The application of such measurements can best be appreciated from the original literature.[229]

The results of studies of crystal spectra have been used to: (a) determine the energy levels involved in the transitions[230a] in the Co(III)acetylacetonate,[230a] trisoxalatometallates,[230b] and Cr(III)acetylacetonate,[230c] (b) to detect the presence of appreciable interaction between the central metal atoms of adjacent complex ions,[231] and (c) to obtain characteristic vibrational frequencies for in plane and out of plane vibrations.[232]

MICROWAVE SPECTROSCOPY[233-237]

Microwave spectroscopy is concerned with the absorption of radiation of

[229] S. Yamada, A. Nakahara, Y. Shimura, and R. Tsuchida, *Bull. Chem. Soc. Japan* 28, 222 (1955): *trans*-[Co(en)$_2$X$_2$]; S. Yamada and R. Tsuchida, *Bull. Chem. Soc. Japan* 31, 813 (1959): Magnus Green Salt; S. Yamada, H. Nakamura and R. Tsuchida, *Bull. Chem. Soc. Japan* 30, 647 (1957): Cr(C$_6$H$_6$)$_2$I; S. Yamada and R. Tsuchida, *Bull. Chem. Soc. Japan* 30, 715 (1957): bis(dimethylglyoximato)gold(III)dichloroaurate(I); S. Yamada, H. Nakamura, and R. Tsuchida, *Bull. Chem. Soc. Japan* 30, 953 (1957): Cu(II)formate, acetate, and propionate; S. Yamada and R. Tsuchida, *Bull. Chem. Soc. Japan* 33, 98 (1960): Cr(en)$_3^{+3}$ and Co(en)$_3^{+3}$ salts; S. Yamada, H. Nishikawa, and R. Tsuchida, *Bull. Chem. Soc. Japan* 33, 1278 (1960): Cu(II)mono-, di-, and tri-chloroacetates. The greatest activity in this work has been by R. Tsuchida and his students at Osaka. Much of the earlier work is collected in a book in Japanese: R. Tsuchida and M. Kobayashi, *The Color and the Structure of Metallic Compounds*, Zoshindo, Osaka (1944).

[230] (a) T. S. Piper, *J. Chem. Phys.* 35, 1240 (1961); (b) T. S. Piper and R. S. Carlin, *J. Chem. Physics* 35, 1809 (1961); (c) A. Chakravorty and S. Basu, *J. Chem. Phys.* 33, 1266 (1960).

[231] S. Yamada, *J. Amer. Chem. Soc.* 73, 1579 (1951); J. R. Miller, *Proc. Chem. Soc.*, 318 (1960).

[232] C. Moncuitt, *Compt. rend.* 249, 2526 (1959).

[233] D. J. E. Ingraham, *Spectroscopy at Radiofrequency and Microwave Frequencies*, Butterworth's Scientific Publications, London (1955); also contains material on NMR and EPR.

[234] W. Gordy, "Microwave Spectroscopy", *Handbuch der Physik, Spectroscopy II*, Springer-Verlag, Berlin (1957), Vol. XXVIII, 1–78.

[235] E. B. Wilson, Jr., *Annual Reviews of Physical Chemistry* 2, 151–176 (1951).

[236] M. K. Wilson and V. A. Crawford, *Ann. Revs. of Phys. Chem.* 9, 341–343 (1958) contains a tabulation of some results.

[237] W. Gordy, W. V. Smith, and R. F. Trambarulo, *Microwave Spectroscopy*, John Wiley & Sons, Inc., New York (1953).

microwave frequencies (10^{12} to 10^{18} cps) by molecules and atoms. The microwave frequency range thus joins on to the infrared spectrum but measures changes which require even smaller quanta of energy. The wavelengths used are from 1 mm to 1 m. The information which can be obtained consists of: (a) pure rotational spectra for molecules which possess dipole moments, (b) inversion spectra such as that found for NH_3 and ND_3, (c) microwave atomic spectra, and (d) related information such as dipole moments. Since microwave spectroscopy deals with polar gases at relatively low pressures, 0.001 to 0.1 mm of mercury, it is not capable of giving information on most coordination compounds. The spectra studied so far include only two volatile complexes.[237a] The techniques used are analogous to those used with visible, ultraviolet, or infrared spectroscopy in that isotopic substitution is employed to obtain spectra on molecules with different moments of inertia but identical internuclear distances. The precision of the method in establishing internuclear distances, bond angles, and dipole moments is very high. Some illustrative information from the compilation of Wilson is summarized in the following tables.

COMPOUND	PARAMETERS
BrF	Br—F distance is 1.759 A
NF_3	N—F distance is 1.371 A; < FNF is 102°9′
$AsCl_3$	As—Cl distance is 2.161 A; < ClAsCl is 98° 25′
HN_3	distances are $H(1.021 A)N_1 (1.240A)N_2 (1.134 A)N_3$ < HN_1N_2 is 112°39′
H_3BCO	B—H distance is 1.194 A, B—C distance is 1.540 A, C—O distance is 1.131 A; < HBH is 113° 52′

COMPOUND	DIPOLE MOMENT IN DEBYES
BrF	1.29
N_2O	0.166
AsF_3	2.815
HCN	2.957
H_3BCO	1.795
CH_3SiH_3	0.73

MOLAR VOLUME[238]

In 1927, W. Biltz[239] suggested that the molecular volume (molecular weight/density) could be used to detect stronger (and hence shorter) bonds in complexes such as Co(III) when these were compared with the complexes of Co(II). Although such a suggestion might seem reasonable at first glance, the factors which determine the structures of solid complexes (and hence their molar volumes) include the relative sizes and charges of all the constitu-

[237a] A. M. Prokhorov and G. P. Shipulo, *Optika i Spektroskopiya* **8**, 419 (1960).
[238] R. W. Parry, *Chem. Revs.* **46**, 507 (1950).
[239] W. Biltz, *Zeit. anorg. Chem.* **164**, 245 (1927).

ent ions as well as the types of bonds which may be present. The molecular volume criterion is thus generally unsatisfactory, though the Co—N distances should be suitable for this purpose when they are available from X-ray studies. Unfortunately, this latter type of data is much more difficult to obtain than other data which can yield the same information.

NEUTRON DIFFRACTION[240]

In neutron diffraction, a beam of neutrons of nearly constant energy (and hence wave length) is used to determine atomic parameters of a solid in much the same manner as a beam of X-rays. The differences in behavior are based upon the fact that neutron scattering is done primarily by the nuclei of the sample (rather than the extranuclear electrons as is the case for X-rays) and that within a factor of three, the scattering power of nuclei is equal, regardless of nuclear mass. This means that neutron diffraction is especially useful in locating hydrogen atoms (whose power to diffract X-rays is too small to be generally useful) and in detecting other light atoms and differentiating between them (e.g., C and N). This method has been used in a number of such cases with success. The neutrons used for this work are those "thermal neutrons" obtained from atomic piles with wave lengths of the order 1.5 A. The structure of the F—H—F⁻ ion was shown to be linear using this method[241] with the H atom occupying a central position. Other examples are collected in standard references.[240,242]

OTHER PROPERTIES

There are a large number of other properties which may provide structural information of some sort and which may become of greater importance in the future. These include: (a) measurements of nuclear quadrupole moments which can be used to determine the relative importance of various possible hybridizations,[243,244] (b) various classical magneto-optic effects such as the Faraday effect,[245] (c) ultrasonic relaxation techniques,[246] (d) electron micros-

[240] G. E. Bacon, *Neutron Diffraction*, Oxford University Press, Oxford (1955).

[241] S. W. Peterson and H. A. Levy, *J. Chem. Phys.* **20**, 704 (1952).

[242] G. R. Ringo, "Neutron Diffraction and Interference" in *Handbuch der Physik*, Springer-Verlag, Berlin (1957), Vol. XXXII, 552 ff.

[243] H. Kopfermann, *Nuclear Moments*, Academic Press, Inc., New York (1958).

[244] C. H. Townes "Determination of Nuclear Quadrupole Moments" in *Handbuch der Physik*, Springer-Verlag, Berlin (1958), Vol. XXXVIII, part 1, 377 ff.; K. Ito, D. Nakamura, Y. Kurita, K. Ito, and M. Kubo, *J. Amer. Chem. Soc.* **83**, 4526 (1961) contains such a study of K_2PtCl_6, K_2PdBr_6, K_2PdBr_4, and K_2PtBr_4.

[245] W. Schutz, "Magnetooptik" in W. Wien and F. Harms, editors, *Handbuch der Experimental Physik*, Akademische Verlags, Leipzig, (1936), Vol. 16, Part 1.

[246] M. Eigen, *Zeit. Elektrochem* **64**, 115 (1960) and the literature cited therein as well as the other papers in this symposium on pp. 124–142.

copy, (e) field emission,[247,248] (f) molecular refraction,[249] and (g) molecular polarizability.[250]

Such methods are often capable of furnishing detailed information about certain aspects of the structure if suitable standards are available. Their lack of popularity in many cases arises from a general lack of familiarity with their use or the limited availability of the apparatus required; it has no necessary relation to their potential utility.

[247] E. W. Muller, *Ergebnissee der Exakten Naturwissenschaften* **27**, 290 (1953).

[248] R. Gomer, *Field Emission and Field Ionization*, Harvard University Press, Cambridge, Mass. (1961).

[249] S. S. Batsanov, *Refractometry and Chemical Structure*, Consultants Bureau, New York (English translation of Russian edition of 1959).

[250] R. J. W. LeFevre, *J. Proc. Roy. Soc.*, New South Wales **95**, 1 (1961).

EXERCISES

1. What would you expect the dipole moment of gaseous $Ni(CO)_4$ to be? Explain your answer.

2. The following values were obtained for the electric polarization (P) of beryllium acetylacetonate [I. E. Copp and L. E. Sutton, *J. Chem. Soc.*, 1269 (1938)]. What is the dipole moment of beryllium acetylacetonate from this data? Explain.

T° C	200.1	211.3	220.2	254.7
P	86.0	86.2	86.1	86.0

3. Find, in the literature, the structural parameters for the ion $Co(NH_3)_6^{+3}$. Do these structural parameters indicate that this ion is a regular or a distorted octahedron?

4. Describe two methods, not involving a diffraction process, that you might use in deciding which of the two possible structures is the correct one for the given compound. You may use a chemical method where it leads to unambiguous results.
   (a) $[Co(NH_3)_3(H_2O)_3](NO_2)_3$ or $[Co(NH_3)_3(NO_2)_3] \cdot 3H_2O$
   (b) *cis*- or *trans*-isomers of $[Co(NH_3)_4Cl_2]Cl$
   (c) Whether two optically active compounds of the type [PtABCDEF] are enantiomorphs or geometrical isomers
   (d) Whether a complex $[Pt(PH_3)_2Br_2]$ was the *cis*- or the *trans*-isomer.
   (e) Whether $[Cu(en)]^+$ or $[Cu_2(en)_2]^{+2}$ is present in the complex $[Cu(en)]_2SO_4$
   (f) Whether $[Pt(en)_2(NH_3)_2]^{+4}$ lost a hydrogen from the en or the NH_3 group when it acted as a weak acid.

5. Explain what the Cotton effect is and how it can be used in the study of coordination compounds.

6. Explain how the term "Walden Inversion" is used in inorganic chemistry. How does this differ from its usage in organic chemistry?

7. Would you expect the Al^{+3}—SCN^- system in water to exhibit a charge transfer spectrum of the type found in the Fe^{+3}—SCN^- system? Explain the reasons for your answer.

8. When one gram of a complex is dissolved in 100 grams of benzene the temperature at which solid benzene just began to separate out is 4.99°. The same solution, however, was found to boil at 80.7°. What reasonable explanation can you offer for such observations? You may assume the experimental data to be correct. If you prepared this complex from aqueous solution would you attempt to dry it at 100°? If not, why?

9. Hydrogen is a very common constituent of coordination compounds. Suggest how you could get the following information on hydrogen in such compounds:
   (a) tendency to ionize
   (b) change in strength of bond between the hydrogen and the rest of the ligand as a result of coordination
   (c) its position
   (d) ability to exchange with D_2O
   (e) ligand field strength of an H directly bonded to a central metal
   (f) its rate of exchange with H_2O in aqueous solution

10. Tell how you would proceed to establish the absolute configuration of the dextro and levo forms of $[Rh(en)_3]^{+3}$. What kind of data would you obtain to get information on the conformation of the ligand in the complex?

CHAPTER

8

The Determination of Stability Constants[1-6]

INTRODUCTION

There are many physical and chemical properties which may, in principle, be used to detect the formation of complexes in solution and to measure the stability constants of these complexes. The detection of the complexes and the determination of the stability constants are very closely related problems and most of the methods which can be used to detect complexes can conceivably also be used to obtain stability constants. In practice, however, many of these methods are so troublesome to use that a much smaller number of methods suffices to examine most of the complexes found in solution. Any physical property may be used for this purpose if variations in it can be attributed unambiguously to specific chemical interactions. This restriction has the result that very small changes in a property can usually *not* be interpreted in terms

[1] A. Jacques, *Complex Ions in Aqueous Solutions*, Longmans, Green & Company, Ltd., London (1914), primarily of historical interest at present.

[2] G. Charlot and R. Gauguin, *Les Methodes D'Analyse Des Reactions En Solution*, Masson et Cie, Paris (1951).

[3] A. E. Martell and M. Calvin, *Chemistry of the Metal Chelate Compounds*, Prentice-Hall, Inc., Englewood Cliffs, N. J. (1952), Ch. 2.

[4] K. B. Yatsimirskii and V. P. Vasil'ev, *Instability Constants of Complex Compounds*, Consultants Bureau, New York (1960).

[5] F. J. C. Rossotti and H. Rossotti, *The Determination of Stability Constants*, McGraw-Hill Book Company, New York (1961). This is the standard work in the English language on the subject and represents the most complete treatment available.

[6] H. L. Schlafer, *Komplexbildung in Lösung*, Springer-Verlag, Berlin (1961). Similar to ref. 5 in many respects, but is more oriented toward the practical aspects.

275

of complex formation. Thus many non-reactive systems show variations in such properties as electrical conductivity, electrical polarization, refractive index, viscosity, surface tension, and heat of mixing which cannot be attributed to any specific chemical interactions of the type required for the formation of coordination compounds.

Historically, the first method of studying complexes in aqueous solution was by the determination of the transference number. This method was used by Hittorf in 1853–1859. For example, Hittorf established that iron accumulated in the anode compartment during the electrolysis of potassium ferrocyanide and he also determined the transport numbers of the species involved. If one Faraday of electricity passes through a solution it must be carried by the migration of ions. If x is the fraction of the current carried by the anions and $1 - x$ the fraction carried by the cations, then after one Faraday flows the difference in the amount of the two species in the two halves of the cell must be one equivalent. The electrode processes must be taken into account in such a calculation. The following example from Hittorf's work illustrates how such data can be used.

A solution of potassium ferrocyanide was subjected to electrolysis in a compartment cell. Analysis of 13.7207 g of the original solution gave 2.0505 g of K_2SO_4 and 0.4769 g of Fe_2O_3. During the electrolysis, 0.5625 g of silver was deposited in a silver coulometer in series with the cell. After electrolysis, 23.3087 g of solution from the anode compartment gave 3.2445 g of K_2SO_4 and 0.8586 g of Fe_2O_3; the anode solution then contained 1.4585 g of potassium and 0.60096 g of iron. From Hittorf's data 1.4585 g of potassium is equivalent to 0.52810 g of iron. There is an *excess* of iron in the anode chamber. This proves that the iron is a constituent of an anion and has migrated to the anode during the electrolysis. From this data it is possible to calculate the transport numbers, knowing that cyanogen was discharged at the anode. The anode chamber solution contained 23.3087 g of solution of which 2.4282 g was KCN, 1.1591 g was $Fe(CN)_2$, and 0.1353 g was cyanogen. This means that 19.5861 g of water are present. Before electrolysis, this amount of water would have contained 1.5641 g of potassium so the net loss is 0.1056 g. The number of equivalents passed corresponded to 0.204 g of potassium so the transference number of potassium in this solution is 0.1056/0.204 or 0.518.

When a system containing several complexes is considered (e.g., the $Zn^{+2} - Cl^-$ system in water) the definition of transport number and its relation to the experimentally measured quantities becomes more complex.[7] The moving boundary method for determining the mobilities of ions (and hence transference number) has been applied to a quantitative determination of equilibrium constants in $Cd^{+2} - I^-$ system[8] but this is perhaps the only such study. The transference numbers of more stable complex ions have been

[7] M. Spiro, *J. Chem. Ed.* **33**, 464 (1956).

[8] R. A. Alberty and E. L. King, *J. Amer. Chem. Soc.* **73**, 517 (1951).

determined in several instances.[9] A simple process, much used with colored complexes, is to determine the sign of the charge on the complex by observation of the direction of motion of the complex in solution in the presence of a high electrical field.

In the years following Hittorf's work other methods came into use for examining the constitution of complexes in solution and by 1913 a wide range of procedures was available. A few of these are worth describing briefly.

An obvious change in the absorption spectrum accompanies the formation of many complexes. Where this occurs the absorption spectrum may be used to study both the composition and the stability of the complexes.

The potential of a reversible electrode immersed in a solution of the ion to which it is reversible varies with the concentration of that ion. If the addition of a ligand species to this solution changes the potential of the electrode, this change may be used to determine the type and the stability of the complexes in solution.

A method in use for sixty years or more is that of measuring the distribution ratio of either ligand or (more recently) of the metal between two immiscible phases. In 1901, Dawson and McCrae[10] studied the distribution of ammonia between water and chloroform and the way in which this altered when the aqueous solution contained cupric salts. They were able to show that each cupric ion tied up about four ammonia molecules by this method. More recently, the use of chelates has allowed the distribution of the metal between immiscible phases to be used in the determination of successive stability constants.

Another method which has been used for many years is the effect of a ligand species on the solubility of a slightly soluble salt. In some cases, such as the AgCN—KCN system, the behavior is quite simple. Here the addition of one mole of KCN raises the amount of AgCN in solution by one mole so the complex formed is obviously, $KAg(CN)_2$. In other instances, the law of mass action may be used to calculate the equilibrium constants. This latter treatment is required for weaker complexes.

Before passing on to a more detailed explanation of the quantitative interpretation of such data, it should be noted that almost any property of the solution which is affected by the complexation reaction is a conceivable tool for the investigation of such processes. A limitation which must be satisfied, however, is the *predictability* of that property for mixed solutions where no complexation occurs. There are a number of properties which are not strictly additive or predictable with certainty in solutions containing two

[9] R. Lorenz and J. Posen, *Zeit. anorg. allgem. Chem.* **95**, 340 (1916); **96**, 81, 217 (1916); G. S. Hartley and G. W. Donaldson, *Trans. Faraday Soc.* **33**, 457 (1937); F. Holzl and W. Stockmair, *Monatsh.* **58**, 289 (1931).

[10] H. M. Dawson and J. McCrae, *J. Chem. Soc.* **79**, 493, 1072 (1901).

or more salts. These include electrical conductivity, surface tension, and viscosity among others. The difficulties which may arise can be illustrated by a consideration of electrical conductivity. This property is *very* useful in examining reactions which are stoichiometric, or nearly so, and proceed with a large change of electrical conductivity. Where these conditions are met, a procedure such as conductometric titration can be used to establish the stoichiometry, and, in rarer instances, the equilibrium constants for such a reaction.[11]

As the reaction departs more and more from a stoichiometric one (as the stability constants of the products formed decrease), a point is reached where the changes in conductivity due to complexation are comparable to those due to the failure of the law of additivity of the conductances of the individual ions in the mixture. In this region the interpretation of the conductivity changes in terms of complexation reactions will probably be inaccurate at least. Furthermore, it is possible to find systems for which complexation reactions in the usual sense are excluded which will exhibit behavior similar to that found with the complex-containing system. Under *such conditions* the method is not suitable for the study of complexation reactions.

METHODS FOR ESTABLISHING THE COMPOSITION AND STABILITY CONSTANTS OF COMPLEXES IN SOLUTION

As knowledge of aqueous solutions containing complex ions has grown, increasingly sophisticated methods for examining complexation reactions have been evolved and used. The development has not been even, however, and until recently it has progressed at several different levels simultaneously. Formerly, it was generally considered sufficient to be concerned about only a single one of the several complexation equilibria which were or could be present. It is now apparent that the use of the methods developed to treat such processes must be limited to systems where a single complex species is formed so predominantly that the other complex species never exceed a very small and very negligible proportion of the total concentration of complexed metal present.

The step-wise formation of complexes in solution has a considerable history, dating back to work before the turn of the century. It was developed by Bodlander, Morse, N. Bjerrum, and others, chiefly physical chemists. Jacques' book published in 1914 contains the information required to determine the successive stability constants of a complex from potential measurements on cells. The important work of Bodlander was terminated by his early and unexpected death in 1904.[12] Bodlander's associate in much of this work,

[11] H. T. S. Britton, *Conductometric Titrations*, Chapman & Hall, Ltd., London (1931); C. W. Davies, *The Conductivity of Solutions*, Chapman & Hall, Ltd., London (1932); C. B. Monk, *Electrolytic Dissociation*, Academic Press, Inc., New York (1961).

[12] This work is reviewed in G. Biedermann and L. G. Sillen, *Arkiv for Kemi* **45**, 425 (1953).

the great German inorganic-physical chemist, Richard Abegg, was killed in a balloon accident in 1907. Jacques' book in 1914 represents apparently his last published work in this field also. His removal from this field represented a considerable loss as his published work indicates that he had obtained workable solutions to many of the problems in the field. The First World War interrupted the development of this area quite effectively and the amount of interest in these problems was at a low ebb in the years 1914–1938.

One permanent contribution of this early work is the notion of the stepwise formation of complexes. The assumption of the step-wise formation of complexes merely states that in the formation of say $Cu(NH_3)_4^{+2}$ from $Cu(H_2O)_4^{+2}$, there are four equilibria involved, each characterized by its own equilibrium constant, viz.:

1. $$Cu(H_2O)_4^{+2} + NH_3 \rightleftharpoons [Cu(H_2O)_3(NH_3)]^{+2} + H_2O$$

$$K_1 = [Cu(H_2O)_3(NH_3)^{+2}][H_2O] / [Cu(H_2O)_4^{+2}][NH_3]$$

usually written as the stability constant:

$$k_1 = \frac{[Cu(NH_3)^{+2}]}{[Cu^{+2}][NH_3]}$$

2. $$[Cu(H_2O)_3(NH_3)]^{+2} + NH_3 \rightleftharpoons [Cu(H_2O)_2(NH_3)_2]^{+2} + H_2O$$

with a stability constant:

$$k_2 = \frac{[Cu(NH_3)_2^{+2}]}{[Cu(NH_3)^{+2}][NH_3]}$$

3. $$[Cu(H_2O)_2(NH_3)_2]^{+2} + NH_3 \rightleftharpoons [Cu(H_2O)(NH_3)_3]^{+2} + H_2O$$

whose stability constant is:

$$k_3 = \frac{[Cu(NH_3)_3^{+2}]}{[Cu(NH_3)_2^{+2}][NH_3]}$$

4. $$[Cu(H_2O)(NH_3)_3]^{+2} + NH_3 \rightleftharpoons [Cu(NH_3)_4]^{+2} + H_2O$$

with a stability constant of:

$$k_4 = \frac{[Cu(NH_3)_4^{+2}]}{[Cu(NH_3)_3^{+2}][NH_3]}$$

In addition to this assumption, information is required on the activity coefficients of the various species. There are two ways of approaching this activity coefficient problem. The first is to carry out a series of measurements at various ionic strengths and then extrapolate the results to zero ionic strength. The second method is to use a procedure originally suggested by Bodlander, namely to work in a medium of constant high ionic strength, maintaining this constant high ionic strength by the addition of an inert electrolyte such as sodium nitrate or sodium perchlorate. Under these conditions the activity coefficients of all charged species will remain constant and concentrations rather than activities may be used with the law of mass action to get a set of relative stability constants. This method has been widely used for a very simple reason: it often offers the *only* direct experimental approach to the determination of complexation equilibrium constants. Whether it is completely justified or not, it does lead to reproducible equilibrium constants. In the usual method of using this procedure to derive equilibrium constants, additional, generally hidden, assumptions are made about the relative magnitudes of the activity coefficient terms. When charged ligands are involved these assumptions are of the type $\gamma_N/\gamma_{N-1}\cdot\gamma_- =$ constant for any N. Once these assumptions are made it is possible to set up (for mononuclear complexes) linear algebraic equations involving the concentrations of the ligand species and the successive stability constants. These equations can then be solved by a large number of numerical, graphical, or strictly algebraic methods.

The solution of these equations generally involves the use of the average number of ligands bound per metal ion, which is defined as:

$$\bar{n} = \frac{C_A - A}{C_M}$$

where C_A and C_M are the *total* concentrations of ligand A and metal ion M in solution and $[A]$ is the concentration of *free* ligand in solution. The average number of ligands per metal ion is also given as:

$$\bar{n} = \frac{[MA] + 2[MA_2] + 3[MA_3] + \cdots}{[M] + [MA] + [MA_2] + [MA_3] + \cdots}$$

Since

$$k_1 = \frac{[MA]}{[M][A]}; \quad k_2 = \frac{[MA_2]}{[MA][A]}; \quad k_3 = \frac{[MA_3]}{[MA_2][A]};$$

and

$$[MA] = k_1[M][A]; \quad [MA_2] = k_2[MA][A] = k_2k_1[M][A]^2$$

$$[MA_3] = k_3[MA_2][A] = k_3k_2k_1[M][A]^3, \text{ etc.}$$

we can replace the terms $[MA]$, $[MA_2]$, $[MA_3]$, etc., and factor out $[M]$ to get:

$$\bar{n} = \frac{k_1[A] + 2k_1k_2[A]^2 + 3k_3k_2k_1[A]^3 + \cdots}{1 + k_1[A] + k_2k_1[A]^2 + k_3k_2k_1[A]^3 + \cdots}$$

This interesting result shows that the average number of ligand molecules bound per metal ion depends only on the stability constants and the concentration of free ligand in solution. If we know N different values of $\bar{n}$ at N values of $[A]$ we can determine N constants $k_1, k_2, \ldots, k_N$. For the calculation of these constants graphical or numerical methods are widely used[5] though the use of computers is replacing these methods to a large extent.

The methods to be considered in detail consist of two types: (a) those methods useful only or primarily where one complex is present at a time. This condition can be satisfied by working in a narrow pH range in some cases. (b) Those methods designed to take step-wise formation of the complexes into consideration without worrying about whether all of the possible complexes are present or not. With such methods it generally happens that any extra complexes present in the equations which are not present in solution end up with equilibrium (stability) constants very close to or actually zero.

METHODS USEFUL WHEN ONE COMPLEX IS PRESENT

1. *The Slope-Ratio Method.*[13] This method was originally used with spectrophotometric measurements and is restricted to cases where a single complex is formed at a time. The reaction:

$$mA + nB \rightleftharpoons A_mB_n$$

is taken as the only one which needs to be considered. By making the concentration of B large and constant, the equilibrium concentration of the complex A_mB_n will be proportional to the analytical concentration of A added:

$$[A_mB_n] = C_A/m$$

If the absorption spectra of the various species do not overlap seriously one may write for the optical density at a suitable wave length:

$$A_s = ab[A_mB_n]$$

where a is the extinction coefficient of A_mB_n and b is the length of the absorption cell. Here and throughout the remainder of this chapter, Beer's Law will be used in the form $A_s = abc$, where A_s is the optical density, a the extinction coefficient, b the length of the absorption cell path, and c the concentration of the species under consideration. The wave length is selected so that absorption is due only to the complex and the absorption follows Beer's Law. Substituting for $[A_mB_n]$ one gets:

$$A_s = \frac{abC_A}{m}$$

Since a, b, and C_A are known, a plot of A_s vs. C_A will be a straight line of slope ab/m from which m may be established. In a similar manner the concentration of A may be kept at a large constant value and the concentration of B varied. In this case we have a similar set of equations:

$$A_s = ab[A_mB_n]; \quad [A_mB_n] = \frac{C_B}{n}$$

$$A_s = \frac{abC_B}{n}$$

So a plot of A_s vs. C_B under these conditions will be a straight line of slope ab/n. Since a can be established by such a swamping procedure, both m and n can be established in this manner. Once the a of the complex has been established, the equilibrium constant can be determined (if it is not too large)

[13] A. E. Harvey and D. L. Manning, *J. Amer. Chem. Soc.* **72**, 4488 (1950); A. S. Meyer, Jr., and G. H. Ayres, *J. Amer. Chem. Soc.* **79**, 49 (1957).

by measurements on solutions in which the concentration of A and B are roughly equal.

2. *Job's Method* (also called *Method of Continuous Variations* or *Method of Isomolar Solutions*). This method differs from several others in the same category in that it can be extended to more complicated systems. Unfortunately, the correct usage of the method with these more complicated systems is extremely tedious and the same results can generally be obtained more readily using another method such as Bjerrum's method of corresponding solutions (q.v.). Because of the apparent experimental simplicity of the method it has been, and continues to be, widely used. In general it is most suitable for systems where one complex predominates. It is especially suitable for use with spectrophotometric measurements and is generally used with them.

The old problem of how to treat deviations from additivity in mixtures is essentially the problem attacked by the formulators of this method. Since this was studied by many workers it is not surprising that the method of continuous variations has been developed independently by several investigators. Many of the earlier presentations were based only on assumptions as to how the data should behave. The probable reason for its being called *Job's method* is that Vosburgh, who finally popularized it, based his work on the very extensive studies (theoretical and experimental) of Paul Job.[14] Since that time the method has enjoyed considerable popularity in spite of the serious restrictions on its general use.[15] In the Russian literature this is called the *Ostromisslensky method*.

The following treatment shows how this method is developed for a simple case. If we consider that only a single complex can form and that this process is unaffected by pH (or is studied in a buffer system) the complexation reaction may be written:

$$A + nB \rightleftharpoons AB_n$$

This system is then studied using solutions in which the sum of the number of moles of A and B present is a constant, M. These are prepared by making solutions which contain $(1-x)M$ moles of A per liter and xM moles of B per liter. The concentrations of A, B, and AB_n will be designated C_1, C_2, and C_3, respectively and these are related by the equations:

$$C_1 = M(1-x) - C_3$$
$$C_2 = Mx - nC_3$$

While these solutions are commonly made up by mixing $(1-x)V$ ml of an M

[14] P. Job, *Compt. rend.* **180**, 928 (1925); *Annales de Chimie* (10), **9**, 113 (1928); (11), **6**, 97 (1936).

[15] F. Woldbye, *Acta Chem. Scand.* **9**, 299 (1955); M. M. Jones and K. K. Innes, *J. Phys. Chem.* **62**, 1003(1958); M. M. Jones, *J. Amer. Chem. Soc.* **81**, 4495 (1959); K. O. Watkins and M. M. Jones, *J. Inorg. Nuclear Chem.* **24**, 809 (1962); idem, ibid., **24**, 1235, 1607 (1962).

molar solution of A with xV ml of an M molar solution of B to give a final volume of solution V, the occurrence of any volume change does not invalidate the use of the method of continuous variations. It merely makes this particular method of preparing the isomolar solutions unsuitable for that system. If we assume that activities can be replaced by concentrations, we may write the equilibrium constant for the complexation reactions as:

$$K = \frac{C_3}{C_1 \cdot C_2^n}$$

or

$$KC_1C_2^n = C_3$$

Differentiating this expression with respect to x allows the determination of the relationship between the maximum value of C_3 and x:

$$K \left\{ \frac{dC_1}{dx} \cdot C_2^n + nC_2^{n-1} C_1 \frac{dC_2}{dx} \right\} = \frac{dC_3}{dx}$$

For a maximum value of C_3, dC_3/dx must equal zero so

$$C_2^n \frac{dC_1}{dx} + nC_1C_2^{n-1} \frac{dC_2}{dx} = 0$$

now when dC_3/dx is zero,

$$\frac{dC_1}{dx} = -M \text{ and } \frac{dC_2}{dx} = M$$

or

$$(-M)C_2^n + nC_1C_2^{n-1}(M) = 0$$

$$nC_1 = C_2$$

so

$$n[M(1-x) - C_3] = Mx - nC_3$$

$$n = \frac{x}{1-x}$$

So by determining at what value of x a maximum in C_3 occurs allows the establishment of n. The concentration of the complex is usually determined spectrophotometrically. If the extinction coefficients of A, B, and AB_n are a_1, a_2, and a_3, respectively, the difference (Y) between the measured absorption and that predicted upon the assumption of no reaction is:

$$Y = b[C_1a_1 + C_2a_2 + C_3a_3 - M(1-x)a_1 - Mxa_2]$$

where b is the length of the light path. The variation of Y with x can be examined by differentiation as

$$\frac{dY}{dx} = b \left(a_1 \frac{dC_1}{dx} + a_2 \frac{dC_2}{dx} + a_3 \frac{dC_3}{dx} + a_1M - a_2M \right)$$

Since

$$\frac{dC_1}{dx} = -M \text{ and } \frac{dC_2}{dx} = M,$$

and when C_3 is a maximum, dC_3/dx is zero so

$$\frac{dY}{dx} = b(-Ma_1 + Ma_2 + a_3 \frac{dC_3}{dx} + a_1M - a_2M) = 0$$

Thus Y will pass through an extremum when C_3 is a maximum. Whether this extremum will be a maximum, minimum, or inflection point cannot be determined by evaluating d^2Y/dx^2 as this is found to be zero, as are all succeeding derivatives. This means that Y, of necessity, will be either a maximum or minimum when dC_3/dx is zero and C_3 at a maximum. This will depend on whether $a_3 \gtrless a_1 + a_2$. If $a_3 > a_1 + a_2$ a maximum will be found; if $a_3 < a_1 + a_2$, a minimum occurs. These plots have very sharp maxima when a single very stable complex is the preponderant species. When a single complex of only moderate or slight stability is present, the maxima are broadened and usually of smaller magnitude. When other complexes are present the maxima are displaced from the stoichiometric point and x is *not* the ratio of two small whole numbers.

For more complicated sets of equilibria the point of maximum deviation of Y is related to x, but not in the simple manner as given above. Vosburgh and Cooper[16] examined the case where two complexes are formed:

$$A + nB \rightleftharpoons AB_n$$
$$AB_n + qB \rightleftharpoons AB_{n+q}$$

The pertinent equations for this system are:

$$C_1 = M(1-x) - C_3 - C_4$$
$$C_2 = Mx - nC_3 - (n+q)C_4$$
$$C_1 C_2^n = K C_3$$
$$C_3 C_2^q = K' C_4$$

The condition for a maximum in C_3 is such that n is related to x by:

$$n = \frac{x}{1-x} + \frac{q(q+n)C_4}{M(1-x)}$$

In such a case an extremum in Y will generally not coincide with an extremum in C_3 or C_4 unless very special conditions hold. These involve adjusting conditions so that $C_3 \gg C_4$ or vice versa and using wave lengths of light for which certain conditions are met.

A more general case, that where three complexes are present, has been treated by Katzin and Gebert.[17] Their results may be summarized qualitatively as follows. When a single complex is formed, its maximum concentration occurs at its formal composition ratio, n. When two complexes are formed, the first reaches its maximum concentration at a reagent ratio below the formal value, n, for this complex, and the concentration of the second complex is a maximum at a reagent ratio somewhat above the formal ratio $(n + p)$ for the complex AB_{n+p}. When three complexes are involved, the lowest is a maximum below its formal ratio n; the highest is a maximum above its formal composition ratio $n + p + q$ for AB_{n+p+q}, and the inter-

[16] W. C. Vosburgh and G. R. Cooper, *J. Amer. Chem. Soc.* **63**, 437 (1941).
[17] L. I. Katzin and E. L. Gebert, *J. Amer. Chem. Soc.* **72**, 5455 (1950).

mediate complex is a maximum approximately at its ratio $(n+p)$, the exact location depending on the formulas and the dissociation constants of the complexes in the given system.

It should be noted that the use of Job's method with physical properties other than light absorption is likely to lead to difficulty in relating the variation of that property to the variation in the concentrations of the different species present.

3. *Solubility Methods.* There are several methods for using solubility data to study complexation reactions in solution and some of these are capable of being used to determine successive stability constants. The following example is one of the procedures useful where solubility changes are due to a single new complex. Vosburgh and Beckmann[18] studied the solubility of cadmium oxalate in cadmium perchlorate solutions. It was suspected that the complex $[CdC_2O_4Cd]^{+2}$ formed in aqueous solution by the reaction:

$$CdC_2O_4 + Cd^{+2} \rightleftharpoons [CdC_2O_4Cd]^{+2}$$

with an instability constant of:

$$K_1 = \frac{[Cd^{+2}][CdC_2O_4]}{[CdC_2O_4Cd^{+2}]}$$

The activity of the undissociated CdC_2O_4 in solution was found to be $1.44 \times 10^{-4}M$. Cadmium oxalate is more soluble in solutions of cadmium perchlorate than it is in pure water. The test of the assumption of the presence of the ion $[CdC_2O_4Cd]^{+2}$ as the species responsible for this increase in solubility was carried out by determining the variation in the solubility of CdC_2O_4 in aqueous solutions of cadmium perchlorate of known strength. The following data were obtained:

$Cd(ClO_4)_2$ $M \times 10^3$	Total Oxalate $M \times 10^3$	$[CdC_2O_4]$ $M \times 10^3$	$[C_2O_4^{-2}]$ $M \times 10^3$	$[CdC_2O_4Cd^{+2}]$ $M \times 10^3$	K_1
5	0.173	0.144	0.008	0.021	0.034
10	0.191	0.144	0.005	0.042	0.034
20	0.234	0.144	0.004	0.086	0.034
30	0.272	0.144	0.003	0.125	0.035
40	0.323	0.144	0.003	0.176	0.033
50	0.353	0.144	0.003	0.206	0.035

The total oxalate was determined by titration with permanganate; the concentration of the complex $[CdC_2O_4Cd]^{+2}$ was given by:

$$[CdC_2O_4Cd^{+2}] = \text{total oxalate} - \underset{\text{(constant)}}{[CdC_2O_4]} - \underset{\text{(very small)}}{[C_2O_4^=]}$$

The ionization constant of CdC_2O_4 is 1×10^{-4} and can be used to estimate the free oxalate concentration. The use of solubility data to obtain successive stability constants in the system $PbI_2 - I^-$ is given by Lanford and Kiehl.[19] A

---

[18] W. C. Vosburgh and J. F. Beckmann, *J. Amer. Chem. Soc.* **62**, 1028 (1944).

[19] C. E. Lanford and S. J. Kiehl, *J. Amer. Chem. Soc.* **63**, 667 (1941). A method using solubility minima is given by J. E. Barney, C. A. Reynolds, and W. Argersinger, *J. Amer. Chem. Soc.* **73**, 3785 (1951).

somewhat more complicated instance where solubility studies were used to determine complexity constants is the case of the $Yb^{+3} - C_2O_4^{=}$ system which was studied by Crouthamel and Martin.[19a]

Yb^{139} which decays by K capture with a half-life of 33 days was used in conjunction with counting techniques to determine the concentration of ytterbium in oxalate solutions of known pH and oxalate ion concentration. In *this* case the complexing occurs to such an extent that it can be assumed that the concentration of complexed oxalate is negligible in comparison with the total oxalate present. The equations used to obtain the concentration of the various species derived from oxalic acid are:

$$M = M_{H_2C_2O_4} + M_{HC_2O_4^-} + M_{C_2O_4^=}$$

$$K_1 = 5.38 \times 10^{-2} = \frac{(\gamma_1)(M_{HC_2O_4^-})(a_{H^+})}{(M_{H_2C_2O_4})}$$

$$K_2 = 5.42 \times 10^{-5} = \frac{(\gamma_2)(M_{C_2O_4^=})(a_{H^+})}{(M_{HC_2O_4^-})}$$

where the a's represent activities and the M's molar concentration. γ_1 is the activity coefficient of $HC_2O_4^-$ and γ_2 that of $C_2O_4^=$; M is the total molar concentration of oxalate as determined from a permanganate titration. Since the $C_2O_4^=$ species is the one responsible for the complexing of the ytterbium it is necessary that its activity be known. This results from the simultaneous solutions of the three equations above and is:

$$a_{C_2O_4^=} = \frac{K_1K_2M}{(a_{H^+})^2 + \dfrac{a_{H^+}K_1}{\gamma_1} + \dfrac{K_1K_2}{\gamma_2}}$$

γ_1 was assumed to be equal to $\gamma_{\pm}$ for HCl in KCl solutions of the same ionic strengths. The other activity coefficients required were estimated from precise data on oxalic acid solutions.[19b]

The experimental results were plotted in a graph of log $[Yb]_{total}$ vs. log $a_{C_2O_4^=}$ which gave a curve with a broad minimum. From the slope of the curve in regions of high oxalate concentrations, n in $Yb(C_2O_4)_n^{+3-2n}$ could be estimated as 2. The presence of $Yb(C_2O_4)_3^{-3}$ was *not* required for explaining the experimental data. The equilibria considered were:

$$Yb(C_2O_4)_2^- \rightleftharpoons Yb(C_2O_4)^+ + C_2O_4^= \qquad\qquad\qquad I$$

$$Yb(C_2O_4)^+ \rightleftharpoons Yb^{+3} + C_2O_4^= \qquad\qquad\qquad II$$

$$Yb_2(C_2O_4)_3(solid) \rightleftharpoons Yb(C_2O_4)_2^- + Yb(C_2O_4)^+ \qquad\qquad\qquad III$$

The three equilibrium constants used were:

$$\frac{(M_{Yb(C_2O_4)^+})(a_{C_2O_4^=})}{(M_{Yb(C_2O_4)_2^-})} = K_I$$

[19a] C. E. Crouthamel and D. S. Martin, Jr., *J. Amer. Chem. Soc.* **72**, 1382 (1950).
[19b] G. D. Pinching and R. D. Bates, *J. Res. Natl. Bur. Stds.* **40**, 405 (1948).

$$\frac{(M_{\mathrm{Yb}^{+3}})(a_{\mathrm{C_2O_4}^=})\gamma_3}{(M_{\mathrm{Yb(C_2O_4)}^+})\gamma_1} = K_{\mathrm{II}}$$

$$\gamma_1^2 (M_{\mathrm{Yb(C_2O_4)}^+})(M_{\mathrm{Yb(C_2O_4)_2}^-}) = K_{sp}$$

When the total ytterbium concentration is given by:

$$[\mathrm{Yb}]_{\mathrm{total}} = M_{\mathrm{Yb}^{+3}} + M_{\mathrm{Yb(C_2O_4)}^+} + M_{\mathrm{Yb(C_2O_4)_2}^-}$$

the relation among $[\mathrm{Yb}]_{\mathrm{total}}$, the equilibrium constants, the activity coefficients, and the activity of oxalate is

$$[\mathrm{Yb}]_{\mathrm{total}} = \sqrt{\frac{K_{\mathrm{I}}K_{sp}}{\gamma_1^2}} \left[\frac{K_{\mathrm{II}}\gamma_1}{\gamma_3} (a_{\mathrm{C_2O_4}^=})^{-3/2} + (a_{\mathrm{C_2O_4}^=})^{-\frac{1}{2}} + \frac{(a_{\mathrm{C_2O_4}^=})^{+\frac{1}{2}}}{K_{\mathrm{I}}} \right]$$

This equation can be obtained by using the equations for K_{II} to obtain a value for $[\mathrm{Yb}^{+3}]$ in terms of $[\mathrm{Yb(C_2O_4)}^+]$; the equations for K_{I} to obtain a value for $[\mathrm{Yb(C_2O_4)_2^-}]$ in terms of $[\mathrm{Yb(C_2O_4)}^+]$ and then using the product $K_{\mathrm{I}}K_{sp}$ to obtain an expression for $[\mathrm{Yb(C_2O_4)}^+]$ which contains $K_{\mathrm{I}}K_{sp}$, γ_1 and $a_{\mathrm{C_2O_4}^=}$. This was found to represent the data satisfactorily when:

$$K_{\mathrm{I}} = 2.6 \times 10^{-5}$$
$$K_{\mathrm{II}} = 5.0 \times 10^{-8}$$
$$K_{sp} = 1.9 \times 10^{-10}$$

For more complicated systems containing several complexes solubility measurements may be used in conjunction with Leden's method (q.v.).

4. *The Logarithmic Method of Bent and French.*[20] The use of this method is well illustrated by the original work. Consider the complexation equilibrium:

$$mM + nN \rightleftharpoons M_mN_n$$

The instability constant for M_mN_n will then be:

$$K = \frac{[M]^m[N]^n}{[M_mN_n]}$$

Taking logarithms of both sides gives:

$$\log [M_mN_n] = m \log [M] + n \log [N] - \log K$$

If the complex is the only species which absorbs light at a given wave length, the optical density may be written as:

$$A = ab[M_mN_n]$$

or

$$\log A = \log ab + m \log [M] + n \log [N] - \log K$$

Under suitable circumstances the concentration of N can be kept constant while that of M is varied. In such a case a plot of $\log A$ vs. $\log [M]$ will be a straight line of slope m. Conversely, the concentration of M may be kept constant while that of N is varied. In this latter case a plot of $\log A$ vs. $\log$

[20] H. E. Bent and C. L. French, *J. Amer. Chem. Soc.* **63**, 568 (1941).

$[N]$ will be a straight line of slope n. The great shortcoming in such a method is that it is strictly impossible to keep $[N]$ constant while varying $[M]$. Another shortcoming is that an observed slope of unity may be meaningless.[21] Thus if the concentration of M is kept constant and much larger than N:

$$[M_mN_n] = (1-\alpha)\frac{[N]}{n}$$

where α is the degree of dissociation. A plot of $\log[M_mN_n]$ vs. $\log A$ or of $\log A$ vs. $\log [N]$ will be linear when $n = 1$, if α is zero or if α is a constant.

If α is zero:

$$\log [M_mN_n] = \log [N] - \log n$$

so the slope of the log-log plot is unity no matter what the value of n. If α is large, it will only assume a constant value if n is unity as may be seen from the following considerations. Using:

$$K = \frac{[M]^m[N]^n}{[M_mN_n]}\;;\; [M_mN_n] = \frac{[M]^m[N]^n}{K}$$

also

$$[M_mN_n] = \frac{[M]^m(\alpha[N])^n}{K}$$

or

$$\frac{(1-\alpha)[N]}{n} = \frac{[M]^m(\alpha[N])^n}{K}$$

for a constant degree of dissociation:

$$[N] = K'[N]^n$$

but this can hold only when K' and n are unity so,

$$\alpha = \frac{K}{([M]^m+K)}$$

5. *The Method of Edmonds and Birnbaum.*[22] This method was originally devised for use with the $Fe^{+3} - CNS^-$ system where it was set up as follows. From the complexation reaction:

$$Fe^{+3} + nCNS^- \rightleftharpoons Fe(CNS)_n^{3-n}$$
$$(C_a-x)\quad (C_b-nx)\qquad x$$

so

$$K = \frac{(C_a-x)(C_b-nx)^n}{x}$$

If conditions are adjusted so $C_b \gg C_a$ or x, K becomes

$$K = \frac{(C_a-x)C_b^n}{x}$$

For a fixed cell length and concentration of ferric ion, spectrophotometric measurements allow the solution of the two equations:

[21] J. B. Herniter, *Baskerville Chem. Journal* 3, No. 1, 13 (1952).
[22] S. M. Edmonds and N. Birnbaum, *J. Amer. Chem. Soc.* 63, 1471 (1941).

$$\frac{(C_a-x)C_{b_1}^n}{x} = \frac{(C_a-y)C_{b_2}^n}{y}$$

where C_{b_1} and C_{b_2} are two different concentrations of the ligand and x and y are the corresponding values for the complex; and,

$$y/x = \log I_y/\log I_x$$

where I_y and I_x are the relative intensities of a standard light intensity after passage through the solutions. Then

$$K = \frac{C_{b_1}^n C_{b_2}^n (\log I_y - \log I_x)}{C_{b_2}^n \log I_x - C_{b_1}^n \log I_y}$$

For the case studied, $n = 1$ and $K = 0.0079 \pm 0.0006$. For this method to be useful, $K \gg C_b^n$.

6. *Molar Ratio Method*.[23] This method was applied by Yoe and his students in spectrophotometric studies. It is applicable only to reactions which are stoichiometric or nearly so. By measuring the intensity of light (optical density) for a solution in which the reaction:

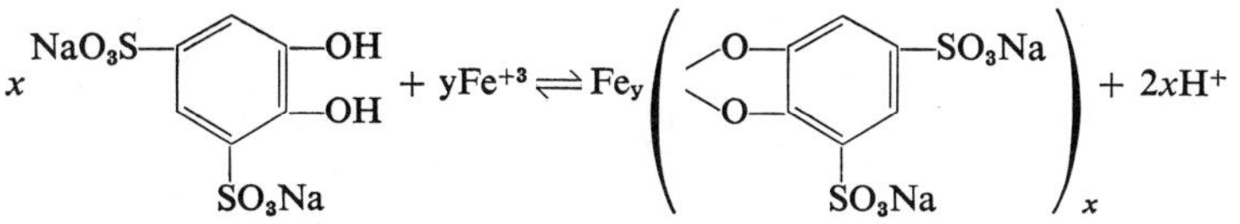

was occurring, it was found possible to determine the reacting ratio of the species. By adding various amounts of chelating agent to a solution containing ferric ion and measuring the optical density, a set of data is obtained from which a plot of optical density vs. the ratio [chelating agent]/[ferric ion] may be constructed. This increases to a large constant value at the ratio of [chelating agent]/[ferric ion] which represents the composition of the complex.

The relation of this method to the method of continuous variations has been developed by Siddhantha.[24]

7. *Babko's Method*.[25] If a complexation reaction occurs and the optical density of the solution at a given wave length is due to the complex, Babko's method may be used in the following form. First define a quantity

$$\Delta = \frac{a_1 - a_n}{a_1}$$

where a_1 is the original extinction coefficient and a_n the extinction coefficient

[23] J. H. Yoe and A. L. Jones, *Ind. Eng. Chem. Anal. Ed.* **16**, 111 (1944), J. H. Yoe and A. E. Harvey, Jr., *J. Amer. Chem. Soc.* **70**, 648 (1948).

[24] S. K. Siddhantha, *J. Indian Chem. Soc.* **25**, 584 (1948).

[25] A. K. Babko, *Zavodskaya Lab.* **13**, 9 (1947), C. A. **41**: 7175; *idem, Physico-Chemical Analysis of Complex Compounds in Solution*, Publishing House of the Academy of Sciences of the Ukranian S.S.R., Kiev (1955), p. 120 ff.

when the solution has been diluted n-fold. Then

$$a_1 = p(1-\alpha_1) \text{ and } a_n = p(1-\alpha_n)$$

where p is the coefficient of proportionality, then

$$\Delta = \frac{a_1 - a_n}{a_1} = \frac{(1-\alpha_1) - (1-\alpha_n)}{(1-\alpha_1)} = \frac{\alpha_n - \alpha_1}{1 - \alpha_1}$$

If $\alpha \ll 1$

$$\Delta = \alpha_n - \alpha_1$$

and for our reaction

$$MA \rightleftharpoons M^+ + A^-, \quad [MA] = (1-\alpha)C_1$$
$$[M] = [A] = \alpha C_1$$

$$K = \frac{[M^+][A^-]}{[MA]} = \frac{\alpha^2 C^2}{(1-\alpha)C} = \frac{\alpha^2 C}{1 - \alpha} = \alpha^2 C$$

and

$$C_n = C_1/n$$

so

$$\alpha_1^2 C_1 = \alpha_n^2 C_n = \alpha_n^2 C_1/n; \quad n\alpha_1^2 = \alpha_n^2$$

or

$$\alpha_n = \alpha_1 \sqrt{n}$$

$$\Delta = \alpha_1 \sqrt{n} - \alpha_1 = \alpha_1(\sqrt{n}-1)$$

or

$$\Delta = \frac{(K)^{\frac{1}{2}}}{C_1}(\sqrt{n}-1)$$

As written here, the equation is only valid where only one complex need be considered at a time. By varying the pH it is possible to select regions where the various complexes in a system are each present to a predominant extent *in some cases.* Thus where the successive dissociation constants are not too close, this method may be used "in a series of separate studies." Babko and N. P. Komar' have developed extensions of this treatment for other equilibria. In his papers Komar also discusses many aspects of the use of spectrophotometric data in determining stability constants.

GENERAL METHODS

The seven methods described above are restricted in their application to relatively simple systems where only one or two complexes may be present. If more complexes occur in a system, these methods may be extended to their study only at the expense of great labor both in the development of special equations and in the accumulation of the data. General solutions for multiple equilibria in solution are therefore very desirable and their development has very largely resulted in the obsolescence of the simpler and less exact procedures.

The first such general solution is apparently that presented by Jacques' in 1914. He had also presented a study of the lead(II)acetate system involving three complexes in 1909.[26] The subsequent development of this field has been largely due to the efforts of Scandinavian investigators: N. Bjerrum; his son, J. Bjerrum; I. Leden; S. Fronnaeus; and L. G. Sillen. Both experimental and theoretical studies have been carried on concurrently in their work and most modern studies are derived directly or indirectly from their methods. The amount of effort which has been expended in refining these methods can only be appreciated from a consideration of standard works on the subject.[5,6] The descriptions given below are intended to illustrate the general nature of the methods rather than their most sophisticated mathematical formulation.

1. *J. Bjerrum's Potentiometric Method.*[27] In this publication (Bjerrum's doctoral dissertation) is presented a very complete survey of the problems involved in the determination of successive stability constants of metal ammines and related complexes. In the earlier stages of his investigation he used the partial pressure of ammonia over these ammine solutions to establish the ammonia concentration. He also gave some brief consideration to spectrophotometric methods but finally settled on the glass electrode as the most convenient method for determining the concentration of ammonia in these solutions. This work on the use of the glass electrode in studying the complexation equilibria involved in the formation of the ammines is almost universally regarded as a classic. By using a medium which contained a large amount of an ammonium salt, such as ammonium nitrate, Bjerrum was able to generate the ammines by the addition of a strong base. For any solution:

$$[NH_3] = k_{NH_4^+}\left(\frac{[NH_4^+]}{[H^+]}\right)$$

where $k_{NH_4^+}$ is the acid dissociation constant of the NH_4^+ ion. The total ammonia concentration can be determined from the pH, and the total ammonium ion concentration is fixed by the experimental conditions. From these quantities, which we can follow using pH measurements, we can calculate $\bar{n}$ by either the exact expression:

$$\bar{n} = \frac{C_{NH_3} + [H^+] - [NH_3]}{C_{Me}}$$

or by the approximate (and commonly used expression)

$$\bar{n} = \frac{C_{NH_3} - [NH_3]}{C_{Me}}$$

For the various equilibria in which $Me(NH_3)_x$ are formed we can then determine the successive stability constants using:

$$\bar{n} = \frac{k_1[NH_3] + 2k_1k_2[NH_3]^2 + 3k_1k_2k_3[NH_3]^3 + \cdots}{1 + k_1[NH_3] + k_1k_2[NH_3]^2 + k_1k_2k_3[NH_3]^3 + \cdots}$$

[26] A. Jacques, *Trans. Farad. Soc.* 5, 225 (1909).

[27] J. Bjerrum, *Metal Ammine Formation in Aqueous Solution*, P. Haase and Son, Copenhagen (1941, 1957).

Bjerrum's thesis and Martell and Calvin[3] present a variety of approximate and graphical methods for obtaining solutions for these sets of equations. General solutions have *not* been published for an arbitrary number of complexes but they are available for cases where up to three ligands are coordinated. Block and McIntyre[28] have given exact algebraic solutions for the formation constants for $N = 1, 2,$ and 3 which are useful in the treatment of most complexation reactions involving polydentate ligands. Starting with a generalized formation function:

$$\bar{n} = \frac{\sum\limits_{n=1}^{n=N} nK_n[A]^n}{1 + \sum\limits_{n=1}^{n=N} K_n[A]^n} = \sum_{n=1}^{n=N} (n-\bar{n})\,[A]^n\,K_n = \sum_{n=1}^{n=N} J_n K_n$$

solutions are obtained for cases up to $N = 3$ as follows:

N

1 $k_1 = \bar{n}/J_1$

2 $k_1 = (\bar{n}J_2' - \bar{n}'J_2)\,/\,(J_1 J_2 - J_1'J_2)$

   $k_2 = (\bar{n}'J_1 - \bar{n}J_1')\,/\,(\bar{n}J_2 - \bar{n}'J_2)$

3 $k_1 = (L_3^* M_{23}' - L_3' M_{23}^*)\,/\,(M_{13}^* M_{23}' - M_{13}' M_{23}^*)$

   $\quad = (L_3' M_{23}'^* - L_3'^* M_{23}')\,/\,(M_{13}' M_{23}'^* - M_{13}'^* M_{23}')$

   $\quad = (L_3^* M_{23}'^* - L_3'^* M_{23}^*)\,/\,(M_{13}^* M_{23}'^* - M_{13}'^* M_{23}^*)$

   $k_2 = (L_3^* M_{13}' - L_3' M_{13}^*)\,/\,(L_3' M_{23}^* - L_3^* M_{23}')$

   $\quad = (L_3' M_{13}^* - L_3'^* M_{13}')\,/\,(L_3'^* M_{23}' - L_3' M_{23}'^*)$

   $\quad = (L_3^* M_{13}'^* - L_3'^* M_{13}^*)\,/\,(L_3'^* M_{23}' - L_3^* M_{23}'^*)$

   $\quad = (L_1' L_3^* - L_1^* L_3')\,/\,(L_2^* L_3' - L_2' L_3^*)$

   $k_2 = (L_1'^* L_3' - L_1' L_3'^*)\,/\,(L_2' L_3'^* - L_2'^* L_3')$

   $\quad = (L_1'^* L_3^* - L_1^* L_3'^*)\,/\,(L_2^* L_3'^* - L_2'^* L_3^*)$

   $k_3 = (L_1^* L_2' - L_1' L_2^*)\,/\,(L_1' L_3^* - L_1^* L_3')$

   $\quad = (L_1' L_2'^* - L_1'^* L_2')\,/\,(L_1'^* L_3' - L_1' L_3'^*)$

   $\quad = (L_1^* L_2'^* - L_1'^* L_2^*)\,/\,(L_1'^* L_3^* - L_1^* L_3'^*)$

where the following terms are used:

$M =$ the general symbol for a metallic ion

$A =$ the general symbol for a ligand

$[\ ] =$ molar concentration of the species in brackets

$n =$ the actual number of ligands bound to a single given metallic ion

$\bar{n} =$ the average number of ligands bound per metallic ion in a given solution

[28] B. P. Block and G. H. McIntyre, Jr., *J. Amer. Chem. Soc.* **75**, 5667 (1953).

N = the maximum coordination number of the metallic ion for the ligand in question

$k_n = [MA_n] / [MA_{n-1}] [A]$, the step-wise formation constant

K_n = the product $k_1 k_2 k_3 \cdots k_n$

$J_n = (n - \bar{n}) [A]^n$

$J_n' = (n - \bar{n}') ([A]')^n$

$J_n^* = (n - \bar{n}^*) ([A]^*)^n$

$L_n' = \bar{n} J_n' - \bar{n}' J_n$

$L_n^* = \bar{n} J_n^* - \bar{n}^* J_n$

$L_n'^* = \bar{n}' J_n^* - \bar{n}^* J_n'$

$M_{np}' = J_n J_p' - J_n' J_p$

$M_{np}^* = J_n J_p^* - J_n^* J_p$

$M_{np}'^* = J_n' J_p^* - J_n^* J_p'$

A sample of the use of these equations on the $Ag^+ - NH_3$ system involves the use of two $\bar{n}$ values to determine the two constants k_1 and k_2. In $2N$ NH_4NO_3 at $30°$, $\bar{n} = 0.495$ at $[NH_3] = 1.53 \times 10^{-4}$ and $\bar{n} = 1.477$ at $[NH_3] = 5.86 \times 10^{-4}$. From these, J_1 and J_2 values are calculated for each value of n:

$\bar{n}$	$[NH_3]$	J_1	J_2	$\log k_1$	$\log k_2$
0.495	1.53×10^{-4}	7.72×10^{-5}	3.52×10^{-8}	3.19	3.83
1.477	5.86×10^{-4}	-2.80×10^{-4}	1.79×10^{-7}		

Some experimental examples should make both the general procedure and some of the calculations somewhat clearer. The method of calculation given above is not generally used but has some advantages over many of the methods in the literature. Graphical methods are widely used, especially, when the accuracy of the data is not extremely high.

Calvin and Wilson[29] studied complexation equilibria for a number of chelating agents by the use of Bjerrum's technique. Their method consisted of determining the hydrogen ion concentration (using a pH meter) of a solution containing known amounts of cupric ion, chelating agent, acid, and base. Knowing the acid dissociation constants of the chelating agents it was possible to determine the stability constants from titration curves. The curves obtained were of the type shown in Figure 41.

The first flat portion of the curve represents the formation of the copper chelate, the sharp rise indicates that chelate formation is complete. The last flat portion represents the titration of the excess diketone. The hydrogen ion concentration calculated at the midpoint of the final flat portion was used to calculate the acid dissociation constant of the diketone (pH = pK_a here). The copper chelate forms in steps, the equilibria being:

$$Cu^{+2} + Ke^- \rightleftharpoons CuKe^+$$

[29] M. Calvin and K. W. Wilson, *J. Amer. Chem. Soc.* **67**, 2003 (1945).

$$CuKe^+ + Ke^- \rightleftharpoons CuKe_2$$

$$k_1 = \frac{[CuKe^+]}{[Cu^{+2}][Ke^-]}, \quad k_2 = \frac{[CuKe_2]}{[CuKe^+][Ke^-]}$$

The equations used in the calculations are:

$$T_{Cu}{}^{+2} = [Cu^{+2}] + [CuKe^+] + [CuKe_2] = \text{Total copper in solution}$$

$$T_{HKe} = [HKe] + [Ke^-] + [CuKe^+] + 2[CuKe_2] = \text{Total chelating agent}$$

$$[CuKe^+] + 2[Cu^{++}] + [Na^+] + [H^+] = [ClO_4{}^-] + [OH^-] + [Ke^-]$$

$$K_d = \frac{[H^+][Ke^-]}{[HKe]}$$

$$[ClO_4^-] = [A] + 2T_{Cu}{}^{+2}, \text{ where } [A] = \text{original } [HClO_4] \text{ added.}$$

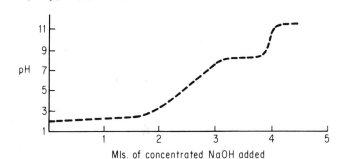

Fig. 41 Schematic titration curve for the complexation reaction of HA with M^{+2}. Total volume = 100 ml initially. The concentration of the ligand is about ten times that of the metal which is approximately $1 \times 10^{-3} M$. A known excess of a strong acid such as perchloric acid is initially present. The concentration of the added sodium hydroxide is approximately $1 M$. (Reproduced by permission of the American Chemical Society.)

Solving these equations gives:

Total Bound Ketone (TBK) = $[CuKe^+] + [CuKe_2]$

$$= [Na^+] + [H^+] - [A] - \frac{10^{-14}}{[H^+]} - \frac{K_d}{[H^+]}\left(T_{HKe} + [A] - [Na^+] - [H^+] + \frac{10^{-14}}{[H^+]}\right)$$

$$\text{then } \bar{n} = \frac{TBK}{T_{Cu}}$$

By plotting $\bar{n}$ vs. pKe^- the formation constants may be determined from the curve as:

$$\left(\frac{1}{[Ke^-]}\right)_{\bar{n}=0.5} = K_1; \quad \left(\frac{1}{[Ke^-]}\right)_{\bar{n}=1.5} = K_2$$

Some typical data are listed below. The solvent is 50/50 v/v/dioxane/water. Total cupric ion concentration is $2.5 \times 10^{-3} M$, $[HKe]$ is $0.02M$, and $[HClO_4]$ is $0.02M$. Titration carried out with $1.025M$ NaOH.

3,*n*-Propyl-Salicylaldehyde, $pK_d = 9.6$

ml	NaOH	2.034	2.118	2.157	2.198	2.283
pH		4.40	4.93	5.22	5.52	6.12
$\bar{n}$		0.52	0.86	1.01	1.17	1.51

2-Hydroxy-1-Naphthaldehyde, $pK_d = 8.4$

ml	NaOH	1.976	2.073	2.126	2.180	2.283
pH		2.97	3.35	3.59	3.88	4.57
$\bar{n}$		0.56	0.76	0.90	1.07	1.44

Trifluoroacetylacetone $pK_d = 6.7$. This was done by titrating the diketone ($T_{Hke} = 0.01M$) with aqueous $Cu(ClO_4)_2$ (0.125M).

ml	$Cu(ClO_4)_2$	5.000	3.010	2.001	1.602	0.859
pH		2.42	2.52	2.60	2.65	2.89
$\bar{n}$		0.58	0.78	0.99	1.10	1.50

Another example of the use of this method is the determination of stability constants for a number of amine complexes including those of ethylenediamine and propylenediamine by Carlson, McReynolds, and Verhoek.[30] Here the chelating agent was added to a solution containing a known amount of inert electrolyte (e.g., KCl or KNO_3), strong acid (HCl or HNO_3), and metal salt. The pH was determined on a series of mixtures and used to determine the formation constants (a titration procedure is more typical). The ionization constants for the amines were determined by titrations in which a non-complex forming ion was substituted for the metal salt. For bidentate chelating agents it is unnecessary to consider complexes higher than MA_3 so the following equations contain this as the upper member. The average number of ligands bound per metal atom is given by:

$$\bar{n} = \frac{[MA] + 2[MA_2] + 3[MA_3]}{[M] + [MA] + [MA_2] + [MA_3]}$$

or

$$\bar{n} = \frac{k_1[A] + 2k_1k_2[A]^2 + 3k_1k_2k_3[A]^3}{1 + k_1[A] + k_1k_2[A]^2 + k_1k_2k_3[A]^3}$$

Since the ligand used is basic, allowance must be made for its reaction with hydrogen ion. For a ligand which is a monoamine, the total amine concentration is:

$$C_A = [A] + [AH^+] + \bar{n}C_M$$

If we use α to designate the fraction of uncomplexed amine which is free and $\bar{n}_A$ as the mean number of hydrogen ions bound to uncomplexed amine, we have:

$$\alpha = \frac{[A]}{[A] + [AH^+]} = \frac{k_{AH}}{k_{AH} + [H^+]}$$

$$\bar{n}_A = \frac{[AH^+]}{[A] + [AH^+]} = \frac{[H^+]}{k_{AH} + [H^+]}$$

[30] G. A. Carlson, J. P. McReynolds, and F. H. Verhoek, *J. Amer. Chem. Soc.* **67**, 1334 (1945).

where k_{AH} is the acid dissociation constant of the corresponding proto-nated amine. By eliminating $[A] + [AH^+]$ one obtains:

$$\bar{n} = \frac{C_A - \left(\frac{[AH^+]}{\bar{n}_A}\right)}{C_M} = \frac{C_A - \frac{C_{H^+} - [H^+]}{\bar{n}_A}}{C_M}$$

and

$$[A] = \frac{\alpha[AH^+]}{\bar{n}_A} = \frac{\alpha}{\bar{n}_A}(C_{H^+} - [H^+])$$

where C_{H^+} represents the total concentration of added strong acid. This gives the required equations as $\bar{n}$ and $[A]$ can be determined from the measured values of the total concentration of metal ion, amine, and acid, the pH and previously determined values of k_{AH}.

For a ligand which is a diamine, the corresponding equations are:

$$C_A = [A] + [AH^+] + [AH_2^{+}] + \bar{n} C_M$$

$$k_{AH} = \frac{[A][H^+]}{[AH^+]}; \; k_{AH_2} = \frac{[AH^+][H^+]}{[AH_2^{+}]}$$

$$\alpha = \frac{k_{AH}k_{AH_2}}{k_{AH}k_{AH_2} + k_{AH_2}[H^+] + [H^+]^2}$$

and

$$\bar{n}_A = \frac{[AH^+] + 2[AH_2^{+}]}{[A] + [AH^+] + [AH_2^{+}]}$$

or

$$\bar{n}_A = \frac{k_{AH_2}[H^+] + 2[H^+]^2}{k_{AH}k_{AH_2} + k_{AH_2}[H^+] + [H^+]^2}$$

Each set of experimental values of $\bar{n}$ and $[A]$ give an equation for the forma-tion function in terms of the stability constants and it is only necessary to have one such equation for each stability constant that is to be determined.

The solutions for the individual k's were given by Carlson *et al.* as:

$$k_1 = \frac{1}{[A]}\left(\frac{\bar{n}}{(1-\bar{n}) + (2-\bar{n})[A]k_2 + (3-\bar{n})[A]^2 k_2 k_3}\right)$$

$$k_2 = \frac{1}{[A]}\left(\frac{(n-1) + \frac{\bar{n}}{[A]k_1}}{(2-\bar{n}) + (3-\bar{n})[A]k_3}\right)$$

$$k_3 = \frac{1}{[A]}\left(\frac{(\bar{n}-2) + \frac{\bar{n}-1}{[A]k_2} + \frac{\bar{n}}{[A]^2 k_1 k_2}}{(3-\bar{n})}\right)$$

A rough formula for estimating the k's is given as:

$$k_n = \left(\frac{1}{[A]}\right)_{\bar{n} \, = \, n-\frac{1}{2}}$$

This same article has a method of carrying out the calculations by a converg-ence procedure. The equations of Block and McIntyre are also applicable here and provide a more rapid answer. A typical determination requires first that the dissociation constants of the amine be determined in a solution whose ionic strength is the same as that used to study complexation. When there are several constants for the ligand which are close together a method given by Monnier and Kapetanidis[31] may be used. For simple amines, the amine may be used as a titrant and the pH followed. The second step is to carry out a titration in which the metal ion is present. From this data the $\bar{n}$ and $[A]$ values may be obtained as indicated above, and then the k's determined from these. Typical data are given in the following table. These determinations were not run as titrations, though such procedure is customary. The conditions of the initial solutions were: concentration of $NiCl_2$: about $0.04725M$, concentration of HCl: $0.1009M$, concentration of KCl: $0.5M$, "titrant" used: propylenediamine.

ml ligand	0.598	0.995	1.624	2.000	2.295
C_Hm/l	0.0997	0.0990	0.0978	0.0971	0.0965
C_{N_1}m/l	0.04669	0.04633	0.04577	0.04544	0.04518
C_Am/l	0.05677	0.0937	0.1511	0.1848	0.2108
pH	5.00	5.61	6.56	7.14	7.56
$\alpha \times 10^5$	0.0132	0.213	13.7	115.00	427.00
$\bar{n}_A$	2.000	1.965	1.763	1.458	1.233
$\bar{n}$	0.148	0.937	2.091	2.601	2.933
pA	8.18	6.97	5.12	4.11	3.48

In many cases the chelating agents are too insoluble in water to make this a convenient solvent for such studies. In such cases dioxane-water mixtures are often convenient as well as alcohols. For information on such work see the papers of L. G. van Uitert, W. C. Fernelius, and their collaborators.[32]

2. *J. Bjerrum's Method of Corresponding Solutions.*[33] Corresponding solutions are defined by Bjerrum as solutions which have the same percentage distribution of the complexes. For two such solutions $\bar{n}$ and $[A]$ are also the same:

$$\bar{n} = \frac{C_A^\circ - [A]}{C_M^\circ} = \frac{C_A - [A]}{C_M}$$

The procedure used can be either a titrimetric one using a colorimeter or as a spectrophotometric method. Since the quantities required in the calculation of the k's are $\bar{n}$ and $[A]$, one may use a spectrophotometer to find two different solutions with the same distributions of complexes but different metal ion concentrations. This is done by determining the molar extinction coefficient

[31] D. Monnier and I. Kapetanidis, *Helv. Chim. Acta* **61**, 1652 (1959).

[32] L. Van Uitert, and C. G. Haas, *J. Amer. Chem. Soc.* **75**, 451 (1953); L. Van Uitert, C. G. Haas, W. C. Fernelius, and B. E. Douglas *ibid.*, **75**, 455 (1953); L. Van Uitert, W. C. Fernelius, and B. E. Douglas, *ibid.*, **75**, 457 (1953); *idem, ibid.*, **75**, 2736 (1953); *idem, ibid.*, **75**, 2739 (1953); *idem, ibid.*, **75**, 3577 (1953); L. G. Van Uitert and W. C. Fernelius, *ibid.*, **76**, 375, 379, 5887 (1954). These papers contain a discussion of both theory and methods involving the use of the glass electrode in non-aqueous solvents as well as numerous specific examples.

[33] J. Bjerrum, *Det. Klg. Dansk Videnskabernes Selskab, Mat-fys. Medd.* XXI, No. 4 (1944).

at all wavelengths and selecting solutions for which these curves match. In *practice* it is usually sufficient to use a single wave length where neither the metal ion nor the ligand absorb. For two such solutions the $\bar{n}$'s are identical and we can obtain $\bar{n}$ and $[A]$ as:

$$\bar{n} = \frac{C_A^\circ - C_A}{C_M^\circ - C_M}; \quad [A] = \frac{C_M^\circ C_A - C_M C_A^\circ}{C_M^\circ - C_M}$$

It is convenient in such work to construct an adjustment curve, a plot of ϵ vs. C_A at a given wave length and with C_M held constant. Thus if the curve is constructed for a constant total metal ion concentration and a measurement is carried out on a solution containing a known but arbitrary total metal ion concentration, the measured ϵ value can be used with the graph to obtain directly the C_A of the corresponding solution. Once the adjustment curve is constructed, the process of obtaining sets of corresponding solutions is relatively simple. The chief restrictions on the method are: (a) both the free metal ion and the ligands should not absorb light in the spectral region used, (b) the complexes should not be too weak or too strong, and (c) polynuclear species should be absent.

3. *N. Bjerrum's Isolation and Analysis Procedure.*[34] The reaction of thiocyanate ion with chromium(III) ion in aqueous solution is very slow at room temperature, but speeds up considerably as the temperature is raised. At 50° the equilibria are attained in a few days and the subsequent quenching of the mixtures allows the composition to be determined. The properties of the successive complexes differ considerably. The concentrations of the first two must be obtained indirectly but the higher complexes can be isolated separately. This represents an unusual case and there have been very few comparable studies on other systems. The complexes formed here have stability constants which were determined from this analytical data on the solutions to be:

$$K_{Cr(CNS)_n} = \frac{[Cr(CNS)_n(H_2O)_{6-n}]}{[Cr(CNS)_{n-1}(H_2O)_{5-n}][SCN^-]}$$

$$K_1 = 328, \quad K_2 = 17.5, \quad K_3 = 4.56, \quad K_4 = 1.93, \quad K_5 = 0.81, \quad K_6 = 0.41$$

Bjerrum subsequently[35] determined these constants in media of varying ionic strength and corrected the constants to zero ionic strengths.

4. *Leden's Method.*[36] This method utilizes a reversible electrode to determine the concentration of free metal ion in solution. It is thus used mostly with complexes of cadmium, mercury, lead, silver, tin, and more active metals which can form amalgam electrodes with mercury which form reversible electrodes. It can be used to study the complexes of other ions if the effect of the other complexes on the reversible electrode behavior is sufficiently well

[34] N. Bjerrum, *Zeit. anorg. allgem. Chem.* **119**, 179 (1921).
[35] N. Bjerrum, *Ergebnisse der exakten Naturwissenschaften* **5**, 125, (1925).
[36] I. Leden, *Zeit. phys. Chem.* **188**, 160 (1941).

defined. This method is especially suitable for the study of complexes which are not too stable. One reason for the success of this method is the use of a solvent medium of high ionic strength. Leden[36] showed that in such a medium, the Nernst equation for the variation of electrode potential with metal ion concentration is followed within the limits of experimental error.

In the original work, cadmium complexes were studied with various anions using a cell which was set up as follows:

| Au | quinhydrone(solid) 2.99 M in $NaClO_4$ 0.01 M in $HClO_4$ | 3 M $NaClO_4$ | xM in $Cd(ClO_4)_2$ $(3-3x-y)M$ in $NaClO_4$ y M in NaA | Cd(Hg) |

When the concentration of the salt furnishing the ligand (NaA) is changed, the amount of cadmium ion in solution changes and thus the measured potential of the cell changes as well. The variation of this potential, in a medium of high ionic strength, is adequately described by the Nernst equation:

$$\Delta E = \frac{RT}{2F} \ln \frac{x}{[Cd^{+2}]}$$

where x is the original concentration of free cadmium ion and $[Cd^{+2}]$ is the concentration after the coordinating species has been added. The validity of this procedure was established by setting up a similar cell which did *not* contain any complexing agent. When the concentration of cadmium ion was varied by the addition of cadmium perchlorate solution to the electrode compartment containing the cadmium amalgam electrode, the measured potentials of the cell was found to follow the equation:

$$\Delta E = \frac{RT}{2F} \ln \left(\frac{x_1}{x_2}\right)$$

as predicted. Thus the potential can be used as a direct measure of the concentration of free cadmium ion in such cells.

In order to use these cadmium ion determinations to determine the stability constants, the following procedure was given by Leden. First the law of mass action (for a system containing up to four ligands per cadmium ion) allows four equations to be written:

$$\frac{[CdA_i]}{[Cd^{+2}][A^-]^i} = \beta_i, \quad i = 1,2,3,4$$

If the total cadmium ion concentration is designated by x and the total ligand concentration by y, these are related to the concentration of the species actually present in the system by:

$$x = [Cd^{+2}] + \sum_i [CdA_i]$$

$$y = [A^-] + \sum_i i[CdA_i]$$

It is also possible to show that:

$$\frac{x - [Cd^{+2}]}{[Cd^{+2}][A^-]} = \sum_i \beta_i [A^-]^{(i-1)} = \beta_1 + \beta_2[A^-] + \beta_3[A^-]^2 + \beta_4[A^-]^3$$

If an auxiliary function, $F(A)$ is introduced which is defined as:

$$F(A) = \frac{x - [Cd^{+2}]}{[Cd^{+2}][A^-]}$$

and the average number of ligands bound per *complexed* cadmium ion is denoted by N:

$$N = \frac{\sum_i i\,[CdA_i]}{\sum_i [CdA_i]}$$

the concentration of free ligand is then given by:

$$[A^-] = y - N(x - [Cd^{+2}])$$

So, if N is known, $[A^-]$ can be obtained. This information is obtained by the method of successive approximations in the original paper. The starting point is the manner in which E varies with y. For a given solution or for two solutions close together in composition, it is possible to write as an approximation:

$$\frac{[CdA_n]}{[Cd^{+2}][A^-]^N} = \text{constant}$$

Since

$$E = \frac{-RT}{2F}\ln[Cd^{+2}] + \text{constant},$$

a substitution can be made for $[Cd^{+2}]$ to obtain:

$$E = \frac{RT}{2F} N \ln[A^-] + \text{constant},$$

again using the restriction to solutions of similar composition. For two such solutions, the difference in potential will be:

$$E_I - E_{II} = \frac{RT}{2F} N(\ln[A^-]_I - \ln[A^-]_{II})$$

$$\approx \frac{RT}{2F} N(\ln y_I - \ln y_{II})$$

since, for the weak complexes studied $[A^-] \approx y$. The emf measurements can now be used directly to get N and then $[A^-]$ values. From these, $F(A^-)$ can be obtained at various values of $[A^-]$. $F(A)$ is then plotted against $[A^-]$ and the graph extrapolated to $[A^-] = 0$, at which point the intercept is β_1. The function $\dfrac{F(A) - \beta_1}{[A^-]}$ is then plotted against $[A^-]$ and the extrapolation to

$[A^-] = 0$ gives β_2. To obtain β_3 and β_4 one plots the function: $(F(A^-) - \beta_1 - \beta_2[A^-]) / [A^-]$ vs. $[A^-]$ and the extrapolation to $[A^-] = 0$ gives β_3 as the intercept, and the limiting slope is β_4. This yields approximate values for β_1, β_2, β_3 and β_4. These are then used to determine new N values using:

$$N = \frac{\displaystyle\sum_i i\beta_i[A^-]^{(i-1)}}{\displaystyle\sum_i \beta_i[A^-]^{(i-1)}}$$

and these in turn are used to obtain new values for $[A^-]$ from:

$$[A^-] = y - N(x - [Cd^{+2}])$$

The process of using the $F(A)$ values to obtain the β's is repeated using these new $F(A)$ values. The process is then repeated until the β's do not change. Typical data obtained from such a procedure are given below. This data is for the $Cd^{+2} - Cl^-$ system. The cell used was described above.

x	9.52	9.52	9.52	9.52	9.52
y	0	20	40	100	128
ΔE in mv	0	6.5	11.8	22.8	27.1
$[Cd^{+2}] \times 10^3$	9.52	5.74	3.80	1.64	1.15
N	1	1.07	1.15	1.35	1.43
$[Cl^-] \times 10^3$	0	16.0	33.5	89.4	116
$F(Cl^-)$	X	41.2	44.9	53.8	62.8

For this system the approximate constants are: $\beta_1 = 38.5$, $\beta_2 = 170$, $\beta_3 = 260$, and $\beta_4 = 0$. Leden has applied this method to the study of a number of other systems.[37] This general graphical computational procedure can also be used to derive stability constants from the variation of the solubility of a salt, MA_x, in solutions of B^- of varying concentration. Some of the systems which have been studied by this method or slight variants thereof are the $Cd^{+2} - Cl^-$ [38] and the $Ag^+ - SCN^-$ [39] systems. In this latter system the variation of activity coefficients was incorporated into the treatment. This method, when used with solubility measurements, is, of course, not restricted to central ions which can participate in reversible electrode reactions.

This method has also been used by Watters and Mason[40] to study complexes of mercury(II); these workers also showed how this method, and the closely related polarographic method, can be used with complexes containing two different types of ligands. A considerable increase in the precision of the

[37] I. Leden, *Svensk Kemisk Tid.* **56**, 31 (1944): $Cd^{+2} - CN^-$; *ibid.*, **58**, 129 (1946): $Cd^{+2} -$ Ac^- and $Ag^+ - Ac$; *Acta Chem. Scand.* **3**, 1318 (1949): $Ag^+ -$ benzoate; *ibid.*, **6**, 971 (1952): $Cd^{+2} - SO_4^=$ and $Ag^+ - SO_4^=$; *ibid.*, **6**, 1152 (1952): $Ag^+ - F^-$.

[38] E. L. King, *J. Amer. Chem. Soc.* **71**, 319 (1949).

[39] G. C. B. Cave and D. N. Hume, *J. Amer. Chem. Soc.* **75**, 2893 (1953).

[40] J. I. Watters and J. G. Mason, *J. Amer. Chem. Soc.* **78**, 285 (1956).

data may be effected by the use of concentration cells of the sort introduced by Vanderzee and his students[41] as well as others.[42] These are set up so that the initial concentration in both sides of the cell are the same; the ligand solution is then added to one side. The resulting change in emf is due to dilution and complexation only and can be measured with a high degree of precision. When a reference electrode, such as the quinhydrone electrode, is used this small change in emf is superimposed on a larger constant emf and must be obtained from the difference of relatively larger numbers.

The reduction of the data obtained with Leden's method is usually somewhat tedious and alternative methods have been presented. The problem can be simply stated as follows: given $[M] = f_1(C_A)$, what is $\bar{n} = f_2[A]$? One method of treating this data is that of Hindman and Sullivan.[43] For a cell which is constructed so the measured potential is determined by the concentration of free metal through the Nernst equation, the following equation is valid:

$$\frac{dE}{d\ln[A^-]} = -\bar{n}\frac{(RT)}{nF} \text{ where } \bar{n} = \frac{C_A - [A^-]}{C_M}$$

When C_M is not much greater than $[M]$, the N defined by Leden can *not* be approximated successively as:

$$\bar{n} = N\frac{C_M - [M]}{C_M}$$

In this case the $[A^-]$ values can be obtained using:

$$[A^-] = C_A - \bar{n}C_M$$

When the assumption that $[A^-] \approx C_a$ falls down, $[A^-]$ can be estimated from:

$$[A^-] = C_A - N(C_M - [M]).$$

Another method for avoiding these tedious iterative calculations is by the extension of the ideas used in Bjerrum's method of corresponding solutions to concentration cells.[44]

Leden's method may be used for any system in which $[M]$ and N can be determined. Although originally designed for emf measurements, the general

[41] C. E. Vanderzee and D. E. Rhodes, *J. Amer. Chem. Soc.* **74**, 3552 (1953): $Sn^{+2} - Cl^-$ system; C. E. Vanderzee, *ibid.*, **74**, 4806 (1953): $Sn^{+2} - Br^-$ system; C. E. Vanderzee and H. J. Dawson, Jr., *ibid.*, **75**, 5659 (1954): $Cd^{+2} - Cl^-$ system.

[42] J. F. Tate and M. M. Jones, *J. Amer. Chem. Soc.* **83**, 3024 (1961): Cd^{+2} — aromatic sulfonates; *ibid., J. Phys. Chem.* **65**, 1661 (1961): $Cd^{+2} - NO_3^-$ system.

[43] J. C. Hindman and J. C. Sullivan, *J. Amer. Chem. Soc.* **74**, 609 (1952). This article also gives a detailed comparison of methods of Bjerrum, Leden, and Fronnaeus for the computation of stability constants; J. Z. Hearon and J. B. Gilbert, *J. Amer. Chem. Soc.* **77**, 2594 (1955).

[44] J. C. Tomkinson and R. J. P. Williams, *J. Chem. Soc.*, 2010 (1958); J. W. Gryder, *Proc. Natl. Acad. Sci. U.S.* **46**, 952 (1960).

procedure, like that of Bjerrum, may be adapted to other experimental techniques capable of giving the required information.

5. *Ion-Exchange Methods.*[45] The technique of studying complexes in solution via ion-exchange equilibria has been used for systems containing both a single complex as well as systems in which several complexes are present. The fundamental point which must be established is the relationship which exists between the amount of metal adsorbed on the ion exchange resin and the concentration of free metal ion in solution. Where only a single neutral or negatively charged complex is present in the system the use of a *cation* exchange resin eliminates the possible adsorption of any species other than the metallic ion. In such a case the amount of metal adsorbed on the cation exchange resin is directly proportional to the concentration of free metal ion in solution. The amounts of resin, the ionic strength, the pH, and the temperature must all be held constant in the experiments.

Kruger and Schubert (*loc. cit.*) describe the application of this method in determining the stability constant of the complex formed between strontium and citrate ions in aqueous solutions of pH 7.25. The equilibrium between the ion-exchange resin and the strontium ion is:

$$Sr^{+2} + 2NaR \rightleftharpoons SrR_2 + 2Na^+$$

Since only tracer amounts of Sr^{+2} are used, no appreciable change in the Na^+ concentration occurs in either phase. The equilibrium constant for the reaction will be:

$$K_q = \frac{[SrR_2][Na^+]^2}{[Sr^{+2}][NaR]^2}$$

In the presence of citrate ion the strontium is partially complexed by the anion as:

$$Sr^{+2} + n\ cit^{-3} \rightleftharpoons Sr(cit)_n^{2-3n}$$

which complex has a formation constant of:

$$K_f = \frac{[Sr(cit)_n^{2-3n}]}{[Sr^{+2}][cit^{-3}]^n}$$

The distribution coefficient of the strontium between the aqueous solution and the solid resin is:

$$K_d = \left(\frac{\%\ Sr^{+2}\ in\ exchanger}{\%\ Sr^{+2}\ in\ solution}\right) \cdot \left(\frac{vol.\ of\ soln.\ (ml)}{mass\ of\ exchanger\ (mg)}\right)$$

When no citrate ion is present in solution, the distribution coefficient will be

[45] J. E. Salmon, *Reviews of Pure and Applied Chem.* **6**, No. 1, 24 (1956); P. Kruger and J. Schubert, *J. Chem. Ed.* **30**, 196 (1953); J. Schubert, *Ann. Reviews Phys. Chem.* **5**, 413 (1954); K. A. Kraus and G. E. Moore, *J. Amer. Chem. Soc.* **73**, 9 (1951); F. Helfferich, *Ion Exchange*, McGraw-Hill, Inc., New York (1962), pp. 202–206. An example, a study of the $Ag^+ - S_2O_3^=$ system may be seen in Y. Marcus, *Acta Chem. Scand.* **11**, 619 (1957).

designated K_d°. This is equal to $[SrR_2]/[Sr^{+2}]$ because $[Na^+]^2/[NaR]^2$ is held constant. Thus,

$$K_d^\circ = \frac{[SrR_2]}{[Sr^{+2}]} \quad \text{or} \quad [Sr^{+2}] = \frac{[SrR_2]}{K_d^\circ}$$

$$K_d = \frac{[SrR_2]}{[Sr^{+2}] + [Sr(cit)_n^{2-3n}]}$$

so

$$[Sr(cit)_n^{2-3n}] = \frac{[SrR_2]}{K_d} - [Sr^{+2}] = \frac{[SrR_2]}{K_d} - \frac{[SrR_2]}{K_d^\circ}$$

When the expressions for $[Sr^{+2}]$ and $[Sr(cit)_n^{2-3n}]$ obtained here are substituted into the formation constant the result is:

$$K_f = \frac{(K_d^\circ/K_d) - 1}{[cit^{-3}]^n}$$

If $[cit^{-3}]$ is known and K_d° and K_d are determined by measuring the fraction of the radioactive strontium which is in the solution at equilibrium, both K_f and n can be determined. This is most readily done by using the logarithmic form of the last equation:

$$\log\left(\frac{K_d^\circ}{K_d} - 1\right) = \log [cit^{-3}] + \log K_f$$

or alternatively, the last equation may be rearranged to give:

$$1/K_d = \frac{1}{K_d^\circ} + [cit^{-3}]^n \frac{K_f}{K_d^\circ}$$

Using this last equation, a plot of $1/K_d$ vs. $[cit^{-3}]^n$ for the proper n value will be a straight line which extrapolates to $1/K_d^\circ$ when $[cit^{-3}] = 0$.

Ion exchange techniques have been applied to the determination of successive stability constants by several authors.[45] Fronnaeus[46] has studied a number of systems using a technique which does not necessitate the use of radioactive tracers. He has given an indirect method for determining the amounts of simple cation and adsorbed cationic complexes on the resin.

Fronnaeus' procedure may be illustrated by his study of the cupric-acetate system. He started, as usual, with the sodium form of the resin and worked in a medium kept at unit ionic strength by the addition of sodium perchlorate. His equations are developed as follows: C_M' and C_A' are the total concentrations of M and A in solution before the ion exchanger is added. C_M and C_A are the total concentrations of M and A at equilibrium with the ion-exchanger. (MR_2), (MAR), and (NaR) are the moles of M^{+2}, MA^+, and Na^+ contained in unit weight of the exchanger at equilibrium. Then

$$C_{MR} = (MR_2) + (MAR)$$

$$\phi = \frac{C_{MR}}{C_M}; \quad \phi_1 = \left(\frac{1}{\phi} - \frac{1}{l_0}\right)\frac{1}{[A^-]}; \quad l_0 = \text{a constant}$$

[46] S. Fronnaeus, *Acta Chem. Scand.* **5**, 859 (1951); **6**, 1200 (1952); **7**, 21 (1953).

$$\beta_j = \text{the complexity constant of } MA_j^{2-j} \ (j \leqslant N)$$

$$X = 1 + \sum_{j=1}^{N} \beta_j [A^-]^j; \qquad X_j = \frac{(X_{j-1} - \beta_{j-1})}{[A^-]}$$

$$X_0 = X, \qquad \beta_0 = 1$$

$$\bar{n} = \frac{C_A - [A^-]}{C_M}; \qquad \bar{n}_R = \frac{(MAR)}{C_{MR}}$$

The equilibria involved with the exchanger are:

$$M^{+2} + 2NaR \rightleftharpoons MR_2 + 2Na^+$$

$$MA^+ + NaR \rightleftharpoons MAR + Na^+$$

and the corresponding mass action expressions are:

$$\frac{(MR)}{[M^+]} = k_0 \frac{(NaR)^2}{[Na^+]}; \qquad \frac{(MAR)}{[MA^+]} = k_1 \frac{(NaR)}{[Na^+]}$$

k_0 and k_1 are assumed to be constants at a fixed value of C_{MR}. Then

$$l_0 = k_0 \frac{(NaR)^2}{[Na^+]^2}; \qquad l_1 = k_1 \frac{(NaR)}{[Na^+]}$$

If $C_M \ll$ ionic strength, $[Na^+]$ is constant. For (NaR) we have:

$$(NaR) = a - 2(MR_2) - (MAR)$$

$$(NaR) = a - (2 - \bar{n}_R) \cdot C_{MR}$$

where a is the exchange capacity which is presumably a constant at constant pH. For C_{MR} we have:

$$C_{MR} = l_0 [M^{+2}] + l_1 [MA^+]$$

This is combined with

$$[MA^+] = \beta_1 [M^{+2}][A^-], \quad C_M = [M^{+2}] \cdot X$$

and

$$\frac{l_1 \beta_1}{l_0} = l$$

to get

$$\phi = l_0 \left(\frac{1 + l \cdot [A^-]}{X} \right)$$

For constant a and a small value of C_{MR}, the term $(2 - \bar{n}_R) C_{MR}$ can be neglected so,

$$\bar{n}_R = \frac{l \cdot [A^-]}{1 + l[A^-]}$$

To determine C_{MR} and ϕ we can use:

$$C_{MR} = \frac{v}{M} (C_M' - C_M \delta)$$

where

$$v = \text{the initial volume of the solution}$$

$$v\delta = \text{the volume of the solution at equilibrium}$$

and

$$m = \text{the weight of the ion exchange resin}$$

In practice, ϕ values are obtained at different C_A values but C_{MR} is constant. For a rough approximation one may use:

$$\bar{n} \approx -\frac{C_A}{\phi}\left(\frac{\partial\phi}{\partial C_A}\right)_{C_{MR}}$$

then $[A^-]$ values may be calculated from

$$[A^-] = C_A - \bar{n}\cdot C_M$$

To obtain the β_j, the product $\phi\cdot X$ is differentiated twice with respect to $[A^-]$ and using the equation for ϕ we get:

$$\phi''\cdot X + 2\phi'\cdot X' + \phi\cdot X'' = 0$$

$$\phi' = \frac{d\phi}{d[A^-]} \; ; \qquad \phi'' = \frac{d^2\phi}{d[A^-]^2}, \text{ etc.}$$

Substitution of the expressions for X, X', and X'' leads to:

$$\phi'' + \sum_{j=1}^{N}([A^-]^j\cdot\phi'' + 2j[A^-]^{j-1}\cdot\phi' + j(j-1)[A^-]^2\cdot\phi)\beta_j = 0$$

or

$$\phi'' + \sum_{j=1}^{N}a_j\beta_j = 0$$

A graph of ϕ vs. $[A^-]$ allows ϕ' to be evaluated and a graph of ϕ' vs. $[A^-]$ allows ϕ'' to be obtained. When ϕ'' and the a_j terms are known at N values of $[A^-]$ the complexity constants β_j can be computed.

For the cupric acetate system, only β_1 could be accurately evaluated in this manner. The remaining constants were obtained by a procedure reminiscent of that used by Leden:

$$\text{as } [A^-]\to 0 \text{ } \lim\frac{1}{\phi} = \frac{1}{l_0}$$

then

$$\left(\frac{\beta_1 - l}{l_0}\right)_{[A^-]\to 0} = \lim\phi_1 \text{ where } \phi_1 = \left(\frac{1}{\phi} - \frac{1}{l_0}\right) / [A^-]$$

When l_0 and l are determined in this way, X can be calculated and the complexity constants determined from equations of the type:

$$X = 1 + \sum_{j=1}^{N}\beta_j[A^-]^j$$

When the only complexes present in solution are neutral or have negative charges, the calculations are considerably simplified.

Anion exchangers may also be used to study complexation processes.[47]

---

[47] A review of recent work in this field may be found in an article by K. A. Kraus and F. Nelson in W. J. Hamer, editor, *The Structure of Electrolytic Solutions*, Ch. 23. This article describes the interpretation of the data when activity coefficients are not ignored.

6. *Solvent Extraction Methods.*[48-56] When a solution in a given solvent is mixed with another immiscible solvent, the solute species distributes itself between both solvents. For a *simple* species the resultant equilibrium reaction may be written as:

$$B(a) \rightleftharpoons B(o)$$

where $B(a)$ designates the solute species present in the aqueous phase and $B(o)$ that present in the immiscible organic phase. For this equilibrium, the equilibrium constant is:

$$K_d = \frac{[B]_o}{[B]_a}$$

As a result, the concentration of B measured in one phase can be used to determine the concentration of B present in the other phase. If B is a species capable of acting as a coordinating agent it is found that only the free (uncomplexed) B is distributed between the two phases in many cases. If we have a system where only one or two components out of several are appreciably soluble in the two immiscible solvents, solvent extraction procedures can conveniently be used to study any simple complexation reactions which occur. By a suitable choice of conditions and chelating agent, these conditions may be approximated very readily.

The earliest studies using solvent extraction methods to investigate complexation were on systems such as the polyhalide ions I_3^-, I_5^-, etc.[57,58] and the cupric amines.[59] In these systems only one of the constituent species needs to be considered as soluble in the organic phases and the equilibria used in the interpretation of the data are:

$$
\left.
\begin{aligned}
I_2(w) &\rightleftharpoons I_2(o) \\
I_2(w) + I^-(w) &\rightleftharpoons I_3^-(w) \\
I_3^-(w) + I_2(w) &\rightleftharpoons I_5^-(w)
\end{aligned}
\right\} \text{ Polyiodide system}
$$

[48] G. H. Morrison and H. Freiser, *Solvent Extraction in Analytical Chemistry*, John Wiley & Sons, Inc., New York (1957).

[49] A. Krishen and H. Freiser, *Anal. Chem.* **31**, 923 (1959).

[50] J. Rydberg, *Acta Chem. Scand.* **4**, 1503 (1950); *Arkiv for Kemi* **8**, 101, 113 (1955); *Rec. trav. chim.* **75**, 737 (1956); *Acta Chem. Scand.* **14**, 157 (1960) contains references to much of the earlier work.

[51] D. Dyrssen and L. G. Sillen, *Acta Chem. Scand.* **7**, 663 (1953).

[52] B. Hok-Bernstrom, *Acta Chem. Scand.* **10**, 163, 174 (1956).

[53] M. Costing, *Anal. Chim. Acta* **21**, 301 (1959).

[54] R. E. Connick and W. H. McVey, *J. Amer. Chem. Soc.* **71**, 3182 (1949).

[55] D. Dyrssen, *Svensk Kem. Tid.* **63**, 43 (1953).

[56] R. A. Day and R. W. Stoughton, AECD–2756 (1949).

[57] M. Roloff, *Zeit. phys. Chem.* **13**, 341 (1894).

[58] A. A. Jakowkin, *Zeit. phys. Chem.* **13**, 539 (1894); **18**, 585 (1895), **20**, 19 (1896).

[59] H. M. Dawson and J. McCrae, *J. Chem. Soc.* **77**, 1239 (1900); **78**, 496, 1072 (1901).

$$NH_3(w) \rightleftharpoons NH_3(o)$$

$$Cu^{+2}(w) + 4NH_3(w) \rightleftharpoons Cu(NH_3)_4^{+2}(w)$$ } Cupric ammine system

In both systems the concentration of the one component in the water can be established directly by the determination of its concentration in the organic phase and the use of the equilibrium constants:

$$K_{DI_2} = \frac{[I_2]_o}{[I_2]_w} ; \qquad K_{DNH_3} = \frac{[NH_3]_o}{[NH_3]_w}$$

The method by which the complexation equilibrium constants are derived from these results is quite simple: the scheme for which a constant equilibrium constant is obtained is assumed to be the correct one. The *excess* concentration of the distributed solute in the aqueous solution is assumed to be present in a complex. The following data of Dawson and McCrae illustrate this method as well as its limitations. The distribution coefficient of ammonia between water and chloroform was determined by direct measurement and found to be:

$$\frac{[NH_3]_w}{[NH_3]_o} = 26.3$$

When cupric sulfate is present in the aqueous solution containing a known initial amount of ammonia, and this is equilibrated with chloroform, it is found that a larger fraction of the ammonia in the system is present in the aqueous phase than would be predicted from the distribution coefficient given above. The excess ammonia in the aqueous phase was assumed to be present as a cupric ammine complex and the mole ratio of the constituents in the complex was determined in this way. The following data are illustrative:

M of NH$_3$ initially	$([Cu^{+2}] / [NH_3]_{total})$	$\left(\dfrac{[Cu^{+2}]_w}{[NH_3]_{bound}}\right)$
0.15	1:6	1:3.16
0.20	1:8	1:3.64
0.25	1:10	1:3.68
0.40	1:16	1:3.96
0.45	1:18	1:4.04

In the region in which Dawson and McCrae worked the predominating complex was thus $Cu(NH_3)_4^{+2}$. Their results show that the complex dissociated considerably and also that higher complexes might be present in smaller amounts.

While solvent extraction can be used with simple ligands or with polydentate uncharged ligands to get $\bar{n}$ vs. $[A]$ data, especially with neutral ligands, it is not commonly used in this manner. Because of the analytical and industrial importance of chelates of the type where one neutral and one negatively charged coordination group are present, the vast majority of the work in the literature is on chelates of this type. Thus ligands such as oxine, acetylacetone, dithizone, etc., have been studied in great detail. Treatments of the equilibria involved, of greater or lesser generality, have been given by Rydberg, Connick and McVey, Krishen and Freiser, and in the book of Freiser. The form of the equations used will depend on the experimental conditions and the manner in which the data has been obtained. The usual data obtained is the ratio of the total metal present in the organic layer to the total metal present in the aqueous layer, regardless of the form in which it is present. In a very general treatment given by Rydberg (*loc. cit.*) all possible complexes of the type:

$$[M_mA_n(OH)_p(HA)_r(Org)_s(H_2O)_t]$$

are considered. The formation constant of such a complex is:

$$\beta_{m,n,p,r,s,t} = \frac{[M_mA_n(OH)_p(HA)_r(Org)_s(H_2O)_t]}{[M]^m[A]^n[OH]^p[HA]^r[Org]^s[H_2O]^t}$$

The variables in this equation are not all independent. Additional relationships among them include:

$$[HA] \cdot k_a = [H^+][A^-]$$
$$[H_2O] \cdot k'_w = [H^+][OH^-]$$

so

$$[M]^m[A]^n[OH]^p[HA]^n[Org]^s[H_2O]^t = [M]^m[HA]^{n+r}[H^+]^{-n-p}[Org]^s k_a^n \cdot k_w^p$$

If we use $n + r = x$; $n + p = y$; and $p + t = z$, the formula of the general complex may be written:

$$M_m(HA)_x(H)_{-y}(H_2O)_z(Org)_s$$

The chief importance of this result is that it is *not possible* to distinguish between *isomeric* complexes of these types by our distribution measurements. Also, for a species whose coordination number is fixed, z can be determined by difference if the other subscripts are known. We can thus consider the complexes present to be of the type $M_m(HA)_x(H)_{-y}(Org)_s$ with complexity constants:

$$\beta_{m,x,y,s} = \frac{[M_m(HA)_x(H)_{-y}(Org)_s]}{[M]^n[HA]^x[H]^{-y}[Org]^s}$$

so

$$\beta_{m,n,p,r,s,t} \cdot k_a \cdot k_w = \beta_{m,x,y,s}$$

The charge of the complex will be $mN - y$ where N is the charge on the central ion. If only uncharged species are extracted into the organic phase, these will satisfy the restriction $mN = y$. The distribution of the metal between the aqueous and the organic phase will then be described by:

$$q = \frac{\sum\limits_{1}^{m}\sum\limits_{0}^{x}\sum\limits_{0}^{s} m\beta_{m,x,mN,s}\, \Lambda_{m,x,mN,s}[M]^m[HA]^x[H^+]^{-mn}[Org]^s}{\sum\limits_{1}^{m}\sum\limits_{0}^{x}\sum\limits_{0}^{y}\sum\limits_{0}^{s} m\beta_{m,x,y,s}[M]^m[HA]^x[H^+]^{-y}[Org]^s}$$

where

$$\Lambda_{m,x,mN,s} = \frac{[M_m(HA)_x(H)_{-mN}(Org)_s]_{\text{organic phase}}}{[M_m(HA)_x(H)_{-mN}(Org)_s]_{\text{aqueous phase}}}$$

Thus while polynuclear complexes can be studied using distribution coefficients, such studies are rather difficult to carry out. For mononuclear complexes the equations are simpler and if it is assumed that the organic solvent molecules do not enter the coordination spheres the distribution ratio becomes:

$$q = \frac{\displaystyle\sum^x \beta_{x,n}\,\Lambda_{x,n}\,[HA]^x[H^+]^{-N}}{\displaystyle\sum^x\sum^y \beta_{x,y}[HA]^x[H^+]^{-y}}$$

This illustrates a general rule for situations where the equilibrium do not involve hydrolysis, polymerization in the organic phase, etc.; the distribution ratio depends only on [HA] and [H]. Where special conditions are encountered, these relationships may simplify even further. Where only one complex is soluble in the organic phase one obtains:

$$q = \frac{\beta_{NN}\,\Lambda_{NN}\,[HA]^x[H]^{-N}}{\displaystyle\sum^x \beta_{xx}[HA]^x[H^+]^{-x}}$$

When only A and H_2O are bound to the central atom and only MA_N dissolves in the organic solvent this reduces to:

$$q = \frac{\beta_N \lambda_N\,[A^-]^N}{\displaystyle\sum_{n=0}^{n=N} \beta_n[A]^n}, \qquad \lambda_N = \frac{[MA_N]_{\text{org.}}}{[MA_N]_{\text{aq.}}}, \qquad \beta_0 = 1$$

In this final form, it is easy to see the relationship of the data obtained in this manner with that obtained using Bjerrum's or Leden's method. For N values of q at N values of $[A^-]$ the N β_i values may be calculated. The calculations are frequently simplified to this point in the evaluation of the β's.

The treatment of Rydberg's is the most general and most rigorous one presently available. The most commonly used simplification is that the uncharged chelate complex is present only in the organic phase. When the working conditions are adjusted so that no hydrolysis occurs and when no complexing anions other than that of the chelating agent are present the distribution coefficient may be written as:

$$q = \frac{[MR_n]_o}{[M^n]_w + [MR_1]_w + [MR_2]_w + [MR_3]_w + \cdots + [MR_n]_w}$$

using the equilibrium constants:

$$k_i = [R^-][H^+]\,/\,[HR]_w \quad \text{for} \quad RH \rightleftharpoons R^- + H^+$$

and the step-wise stability constants:

$$M^{+n} + R^- \rightleftharpoons MR^{n-1}, \quad k_1 = [MR^{n-1}] / [M^{+n}][R^-]$$

$$MR^{n-1} + R^- \rightleftharpoons MR_2^{n-2}, \quad k_2 = [MR_2^{n-2}] / [MR^{n-1}][R^-]$$

$$MR_{n-1}^+ + R^- \rightleftharpoons MR_n, \quad k_n = [MR_n] / [MR_{n-1}^+][R^-]$$

and also using $K_f = k_1 k_2 k_3 \cdots k_n$

$$K_{DR} = \frac{[HR]_o}{[HR]_w} \quad \text{and} \quad K_D = \frac{[MR_n]_o}{[MR_n]_w}$$

q becomes:

$$q = \frac{K_f K_D [R^-]^n}{1 + k_1[R^-] + k_1 k_2 [R^-]^2 + \cdots + K_f[R^-]^n}$$

We can transform this into an equation more directly useful by using equations of the type:

$$[MR_n]_w = k_n[MR_{n-1}^+][R^-]$$

$$= K_f[R^-]^n = K_f\left(\frac{(k_i)}{[H^+]}\right)^n = [HR]_w^n$$

$$= K_f\left(\frac{(k_i)}{[H^+]}\right)^n \left(\frac{[HR]_o}{K_{DR}}\right)^n$$

The equation for the distribution ratio then becomes:

$$q = \frac{k_i^n K_f K_D}{K_{DR}^n} \left\{ \frac{1}{\dfrac{[H^+]}{[HR]_o} + \dfrac{k_i k_1}{K_{DR}}\left(\dfrac{[H^+]}{[HR]_o}\right)^{n-1} + \cdots + \dfrac{k_1 k_2 k_n k_i^n}{K_{DR}^n}} \right\}$$

There are now $n + 1$ constants which must be determined, i.e., K_D and $k_1, k_2, \cdots k_N$, so $n + 1$ values of q are required under conditions where $[H^+]$ and $[HR]_o$ are known. K_{DR} can be independently determined as can k_i. It is usually possible to determine K_D more accurately from independent measurements also.

In practice it is often possible to use somewhat simpler expressions for the distribution ratio. Krishen and Freiser (*loc. cit.*) use the expression:

$$q = \frac{(K_D - q) K_f[HR]_o^n k_i^n}{[H^+]^n + k_1[HR]_w k_i[H^+]^{n-1} + \cdots + k_1 k_2 \cdots k_{n-1}[HR]_w^{n-1} k_i^{n-1}[H^+]}$$

to study the extraction of acetylacetone complexes and to determine their successive formation constants. From n and q values the n constants can be determined if $[H^+]$ and $[HR]_w$ are known. The experimental procedure used was quite straightforward. Pure metal acetylacetonates such as $Cu(acac)_2$ were dissolved in acetylacetone which had been saturated with water. The aqueous phase was prepared by adjusting the pH with sodium hydroxide and perchloric acid and then saturating it with acetylacetone. Ten ml of each phase were added to a 50 ml volumetric flask and this was placed in a constant temperature bath and shaken for two hours. At the end of this period the pH of the aqueous phase was determined with a pH meter and an aliquot of each phase was removed and analyzed for the total metal content.

J. Rydberg[50] examined the Th^{+4}-acetylacetone complexes using tracer amounts of Th^{234}. He found that the pH could be adjusted to eliminate hydrolysis completely and that no polynuclear complexes were formed. This paper gives rather complete experimental details as well as fairly complete information on the reduction of the data. Since acetylacetone is a weak acid, its distribution between water and an organic solvent like benzene varies with pH and this can be used to vary the concentration of the chelating anion.

7. Janssen's Spectrophotometric Method.[60] This is a spectrophotometric method designed for systems containing one ligand, two complexes and the central ion, all of which may absorb light in the same spectral region. The definitions and equations used are:

$[M]$ = concentration of metal not complexed
C_L = concentration of ligand not bound in complex
$[L]$ = concentration of free coordinating anion derived from LH

These terms must be differentiated in cases where the ligand is a species such as 8-hydroxyquinoline-5 sulfonic acid.

$[ML_n]$ = concentration of ML_n
T_M, T_L = the stoichiometric concentrations of M and L
E_1, E_2, E_3, and E_M = the molar extinction coefficients of L, ML, ML_2, and M, respectively
D = the optical density = $\log(I_0/I_D)$
$K_n = [ML_n] / [ML_{n-1}] [L]$
$\beta_2 = [ML_2] / [M] [L]^2 = K_1 K_2$
$K_j^H = [LH_j] / [LH_{j-1}] [H]$
$\beta_j^H = [LH_j] / [L] [H]^j = K_1^H K_2^H \cdots K_j^H$
$$A = \sum_{j=0}^{j=j} \beta_j^H [H]^j, \qquad (\beta_0 = 1)$$
B = the pH meter reading
U_H = Antilog $(B) / [H^+]$; conversion factor for obtaining $[H^+]$ from B

Then

$$T_L = C_L + [ML] + 2[ML_2]$$

$$T_M = [M] + [ML] + [ML_2]$$

$$D = E_m[M] + E_1 C_L + E_2[ML] + E_2[ML_2]$$

$$K_1 = \frac{[ML] \cdot A}{[M] \cdot C_L}, \qquad K_2 = \frac{[ML_2] \cdot A}{[ML] \cdot C_L}$$

When only the first step needs to be considered:

$$K_1 = \frac{(D - E_M T_M - E_1 T_L)(E_2 - E_M - E_1)A}{[(E_2 - E_1)T_M + E_1 T_L - D][(E_2 - E_M)T_L + E_M T_M - D]}$$

[60] M. J. Janssen, *Rec. trav. chim.* **75**, 1397 (1956).

and when only the second step needs to be considered:

$$K_2 = \frac{[(E_2-E_1)T_M + E_1T_L - D][E_1 + E_2 - E_3] \cdot A}{[(E_3-E_2)T_L - (E_3-2E_2)T_M - D][(E_3-2E_1)T_M + E_1T_L - D]}$$

TABLE 8.1

SOME SPECTROPHOTOMETRIC METHODS FOR OBTAINING STABILITY CONSTANTS

System	Example studied	Reference
Simple and mixed complexes, successive complexes should show considerable differences in their absorption spectra	$Bi^{+3} - Cl^-$	61
Precision determination of a stability constant for first complex in series	$Cu^{+2} - SO_4^=$	62
Method for first and second stability constants	$Cu^{+2} - Cl^-$	63
Successive stability constants of a set of several complexes	$Cu^{+2} - NO_2$	64
Two complexes	$CrO_4^= - H_2PO_4^-$	65
Three complexes, two at a time	Fe^{+3} – sulfosalicylate	66
Three complexes, two at a time, uses isobestic points which must be obtained	Fe^{+3} – sulfosalicylate	67
Single complex, two absorbing species present	I_2 – aromatic hydrocarbon	68
Competition between colored and colorless complexes	$Fe^{+3} - Cu^{+2}$ 8-hydroxyquinoline-5-sulfonic acid	69
1:1 complexes in the presence of hydrolytic products of the metal ion		70
1:1 complex	Fe^{+3} – glycine	71
1:1 complexes, one component associated	ethanol + acetic anhydride	72
Successive complexes, two predominant	Fe^{+3} – salicylate and Fe^{+3} – sulfosalicylate	73
Successive complexes, more generalized version of above	Fe^{+3} – salicylate and Fe^{+3} – sulfosalicylic	74
1:1 complexes	Fe^{+3} – phenols	75

[61] L. Newman and D. N. Hume, *J. Amer. Chem. Soc.* **79**, 4571, 4576, 4581 (1957).
[62] R. Nasanen, *Acta Chem. Scand.* **3**, 179 (1949); **4**, 140 (1950).
[63] H. McConnel and N. Davidson, *J. Amer. Chem. Soc.* **72**, 3164 (1950).
[64] S. Fronnaeus, *Acta Chem. Scand.* **5**, 149 (1951).
[65] F. Holloway, *J. Amer. Chem. Soc.* **74**, 224 (1952).
[66] A. Agren, *Acta Chem. Scand.* **8**, 270 (1954).
[67] L. Vareille, *Bull. Soc. Chim. France*, 870 (1955).
[68] N. J. Rose and R. S. Drago, *J. Amer. Chem. Soc.* **81**, 6138, 6141 (1959).
[69] J. Molland, *J. Amer. Chem. Soc.* **62**, 541 (1940).
[70] M. Arden, *J. Phys. Chem.* **61**, 1674 (1957).
[71] C. R. Maxwell, D. C. Peterson, and P. M. Watlington, *J. Phys. Chem.* **62**, 92 (1958).
[72] E. Grunwald and W. C. Coburn, Jr., *J. Amer. Chem. Soc.* **80**, 1322 (1958).
[73] J. C. Colleter and P. Romain, *Bull. Soc. Chim. France*, 858, 867 (1958).
[74] J. C. Colleter, *Ann. Chimie* [13], **5**, 415 (1960).
[75] R. M. Milburn, *J. Amer. Chem. Soc.* **77**, 2064 (1955).

These conditions can usually be attained by wide variations in the metal/ligand ratio. The requirement that all of the molar extinction coefficients be known effectively limits the use of this method to reactions which exhibit only two steps, as the swamping conditions used to obtain these can usually be driven to two extremes only. Only when the separation of the successive stability constants is very large and changes in pH can be used reliably for this same purpose can methods such as this be used on more complicated systems. Because the absorption of the ligand is considered as well as that of the uncomplexed metal, this method is *not interchangeable* with the method of corresponding solutions. Janssen also describes an experimental set-up for carrying out these determinations as spectrophotometric titrations in a Beckman DU spectrophotometer. The systems studied by Janssen were those involving Cu^{+2} and ligands such as oxine derivatives where the method is adequate to treat the equilibria occurring in detail.

8. *Some Other Spectrophotometric Methods.* There are perhaps more spectrophotometric methods available than methods of any other type. Almost all of these seem not to be capable of general *practical* application. The chief reason for this is that most of the methods require that the molar extinction coefficients of the complexes involved be evaluated. This is not always possible, especially if the successive constants are rather close together. The most general method published is that of Newman and Hume mentioned below. It has this same drawback, however, and this restricts its use. It seems reasonable to state that spectrophotometric methods are often of very considerable use in particular instances but do not have the same broad region of applicability as the potentiometric methods. Table 8.1 contains a listing of some of the spectrophotometric methods available in the literature and some of the systems upon which they have been used.

9. *Polarographic Study of Complexes in Solution.*[76,77] A dropping mercury electrode may be used to advantage in certain instances to determine the stability constants of complexes. The measurements of its applied potential vs. a standard calomel electrode is carried out with the simultaneous measurement of the current that potential causes to flow in the system. The current which flows is composed of two parts: (a) a residual current and (b) a current due to the electrode reaction. It is the limiting value of this second current and the characteristic potential at which one-half of this limiting current is obtained which are of most direct value in the polarographic study of complexes. It is possible to use the polarograph to obtain successive stability constants or to use it to determine overall constants for systems in which one or two complexes predominate. Both types of use are outlined below. It should

[76] J. J. Lingane, *Chem. Reviews* **29**, 1 (1941).

[77] I. M. Kolthoff and J. J. Lingane, *Polarography*, Interscience Publishers, Inc., New York, 2nd ed. (1952), pp. 211–234.

also be noted that the reaction at the dropping mercury electrode (d.m.e.) may involve the reduction of either the free metal ion or the complex ion or both. The literature contains many polarographic methods which have been developed for special types of complexes in special environments. In the matter of adaptability the polarographic method is far better than its relatively limited usage might suggest. In the precision of results, however, the polarograph is generally inferior to the more commonly used methods of Bjerrum or Leden. This is due primarily to the fact that the voltage measurements are rarely accurate to better than ± 1 mv and the recording instruments (whose convenience makes the polarographic method attractive) usually have an accuracy not exceeding ± 5 mv in measurements of the half-wave potential.

The analysis is based upon the fact that the characteristic potential at which the current reaches one-half of its limiting value (the half-wave potential, $E_{\frac{1}{2}}$) varies with the concentrations of the species present in a manner given by the Nernst equation.

Case (a).

The free ion is reduced reversibly to the metal which forms an amalgam with the dropping mercury electrode.[76,78]

From the Nernst equation one writes:

$$E = E^{\circ} + \frac{0.059}{n} \log \frac{[Ox]}{[Red]} \tag{1}$$

for the equation occurring as:

$$Ox + ne \rightleftharpoons Red \tag{2}$$

If a complexing agent is present, this equation is not the only chemical reaction occurring in solution; the additional complexing reaction is:

$$Ox + pA \rightleftharpoons OxA_p \tag{3}$$

For this complex the stability constant is:

$$K = \frac{[OxA_p]}{[Ox][A]^p} \tag{4}$$

and the concentration of the oxidized form of the metal will be:

$$[Ox] = \frac{[OxA_p]}{K[A]^p} \tag{5}$$

When this is substituted back into equation (1) the result is:

$$E = E^{\circ} + \frac{0.059}{n} \log \frac{[OxA_p]}{K[A]^p[Red]} \tag{6}$$

The half-wave potential, $E_{\frac{1}{2}}$, which is derived from the polarogram, is defined as the potential at which half of the oxidized form which reaches the d.m.e. is reduced. If the complex is reasonably stable and if the concentration of A

[78] K. H. Gayer, A. Demmler, and M. J. Elking, *J. Chem. Educ.* **30**, 557 (1953).

is sufficiently great then when $E = E_{\frac{1}{2}}$, $[Red] = [OxA_p]$ and equation (6) becomes:

$$E_{\frac{1}{2}} = E^\circ + \frac{0.059}{n} \log \frac{1}{K[A]^p} \tag{7}$$

or

$$E_{\frac{1}{2}} = E^\circ - \frac{0.059}{n} \log K - \frac{0.059p}{n} \log [A] \tag{8}$$

Since n will be known from the charge on the ion used, K may be determined from a polarogram obtained on a solution for which $[A] = 1$ and log $[A]$ is hence zero. The value of p may be obtained from a plot of $E_{\frac{1}{2}}$ vs. log $[A]$ which should be a straight line of slope $-0.059p/n$.

   Case (b).

   The complex is reduced to another complex containing the central ion in a lower oxidation state.

   In this case the equation for the reaction at the d.m.e. is:

$$OxA_p + ne \rightleftharpoons RedA_q + (p-q) A \tag{9}$$

There are now two stability constants:

$$K_0 = \frac{[OxA_p]}{[Ox][A]^p} \text{ and } K_r = \frac{[Red A_q]}{[Red][A]^q} \tag{10}$$

When the expressions:

$$[Ox] = \frac{[OxA_p]}{K_0[A]^p} \tag{11}$$

and

$$[Red] = \frac{[RedA_q]}{K_r[A]^q} \tag{12}$$

are substituted into the Nernst equation one obtains:

$$E = E^\circ + \frac{0.059}{n} \log \frac{[OxA_p]K_r[A]^q}{K_0[A]^p[RedA_q]} \tag{13}$$

Once again we introduce the identification of $E_{\frac{1}{2}}$ with E when $[O_xA_p] = [RedA_q]$ and obtain the expression:

$$E_{\frac{1}{2}} = E^\circ + \frac{0.059}{n} \log \frac{K_r[A]^{q-p}}{K_0} \tag{14}$$

This is usually rearranged to a form more useful for the graphical treatment of the data, namely:

$$E_{\frac{1}{2}} = E^\circ + \frac{0.059}{n} \log \frac{K_r}{K_0} - \frac{0.059}{n} (p-q) \log [A] \tag{15}$$

Differentiation of this shows that:

$$\frac{d E_{\frac{1}{2}}}{d \log [A]} = \frac{0.059}{n} (p-q) \tag{16}$$

So a plot of $E_{\frac{1}{2}}$ vs. log $[A]$ will be a straight line of a slope $(-0.059/n)(p-q)$ if only one complex of each oxidation state is present and if the electrode reaction is reversible. The *ratio* K_r/K_0 can be obtained from the $E_{\frac{1}{2}}$ value at $[A] = 1$. To determine the actual numerical values of K_r and K_0 in such a case it is customary to obtain one of them from some other type of measurement.

A very useful modification of this procedure which is suitable for use with systems where the complexing agent is a weak acid has been presented by Gayer, Demmler, and Elkind.[78] For such a ligand an additional equilibrium must be considered, namely the ionization reaction:

$$HA \rightleftharpoons H^+ + A^- \tag{17}$$

for which

$$K_a = \frac{[H^+][A^-]}{[HA]} \tag{18}$$

so

$$[A] = \frac{K_a[HA]}{[H^+]} \tag{19}$$

when this is substituted into equation (15), one obtains:

$$E_{\frac{1}{2}} = E° + \frac{0.059}{n} \log \frac{K_r}{K_0} - \frac{0.059}{n} (p-q) \log \frac{K_a[HA]}{[H^+]} \tag{20}$$

or on rearrangement:

$$E_{\frac{1}{2}} = E° + \frac{0.059}{n} \log \frac{K_r}{K_0} - \frac{0.059}{n} (p-q)(\text{pH}-pK_a) - \frac{0.059}{n} (p-q) \log [HA] \tag{21}$$

For a pH range in which the concentration of free acid remains essentially constant, $E_{\frac{1}{2}}$ will be a linear function of the pH. Furthermore

$$\frac{dE_{\frac{1}{2}}}{d\text{pH}} = \frac{0.059}{n} (p-q)$$

Thus, if n is known, $p-q$ can be obtained from such data. Keefer[79] studied the copper(II) complex with glycine. For this system $q = 0$ and p was found to be 2. Since $n = 2$ and the reduction occurs to give a copper amalgam, rather than a copper(I) complex, it was also possible to determine the stability constant here. It was found to be 1.27×10^{15} in very good agreement with the value of 1.35×10^{15} obtained via Bjerrum's potentiometric method.

LIMITATIONS OF THE POLAROGRAPHIC METHOD. Underlying the equations given above are several assumptions common to most of the polarographic methods for studying complexes. These include, first the assumption that the electrode reaction is reversible. This can be tested by a graph of $\log i/(i_d - i)$ vs. $E_{\text{d.m.e.}}$ where i is the measured current, i_d is the diffusion current due to the reduction process, when it has reached a limiting value. In addition to this restriction, there are others (apparently commonly satisfied) involving the interrelation of the diffusion current, the concentrations of the reduced species in the main body of the solution and in the region surrounding the dropping mercury electrode, and the concentration of the ligand species. It is usually

[79] R. M. Keefer, *J. Amer. Chem.* **68**, 2329 (1946).

sufficient to work with an excess of ligand in order to insure that slight variations in its concentration around the d.m.e. do not seriously affect the results. These restrictions are discussed at length by Lingane (*loc. cit.*).

POLAROGRAPHIC DETERMINATION OF STEP-WISE FORMATION CONSTANTS.

There are two methods for obtaining step-wise formation constants of complexes from polarographic data. Both of them are patterned after Leden's method.

(a) The Polarographic Method of DeFord and Hume.[80,81] This method is useful in studying complex ions which are reversibly reduced at the dropping mercury electrode. By an analysis of the shift of half-wave potential with ligand concentration, the successive complex ions which are formed can be identified and this then permits the evaluation of the formation constants.

If the electrode reactions are reversible, the potential of the dropping mercury electrode is given by:

$$E_{d.m.e} = E_a^\circ - \frac{RT}{nF} \ln \frac{C_a^\circ f_a}{C_M^\circ f_M} \tag{22}$$

where C_a° is the concentration of the amalgam at the electrode surface, C_M° is the concentration of the simple metal ions at the electrode surface, and the f's are the corresponding activity coefficients. Since the amalgam formed at the electrode surface is very dilute, f_a is considered to be unity.

If the formation of the complex ion is rapid and reversible, a formation constant may be written for each individual complex:

$$C_{MX_j} f_{MX_j} = K_j C_M f_M (C_X)^j (f_X)^j$$

Here, C_{MX_j} is the concentration of the complex $MX_j^{+(n-jd)}$ in the body of the solution, K_j is the formation constant of the complex, C_M and C_X are the concentrations of the simple metal ion and ligand species, respectively, in the body of the solution. The f's are the corresponding activity coefficients.

By addition of equations of the type (23) one may obtain:

$$C_M^\circ f_M = \frac{\sum_j C_{MX_j}^\circ}{\sum_j \left\{ \frac{K_j (C_X)^j (f_X)^j}{f_{MX_j}} \right\}} \tag{24}$$

and by combining equations (22) and (24) one obtains:

$$E_{d.m.e.} = E_a^\circ - \frac{RT}{nF} \ln C_a^\circ \frac{\sum_j \left\{ \frac{K_j (C_X)^j (f_X)^j}{f_{MX_j}} \right\}}{\sum_j C_{MX_j}^\circ} \tag{25}$$

[80] D. D. DeFord and D. N. Hume, *J. Amer. Chem. Soc.* **73**, 5321 (1951).
[81] D. D. DeFord, D. N. Hume, and G. C. B. Cave, *J. Amer. Chem. Soc.* **73**, 5323 (1951).

By assuming the presence of excess supporting electrolyte to eliminate the migration current, it is possible to show that the half-wave potential of the reducible ion in the presence of the complex forming substance can be given by:

$$(E_{\frac{1}{2}})_c = E_a^\circ - \frac{RT}{nF} \ln \frac{I_c}{I_M} \sum_j \left\{ \frac{K_j (C_X)^j f_x^j}{f_{MX_j}} \right\} \tag{26}$$

where I_c represents the measurable diffusion current constant and I_M the diffusion current constant of the metal atoms in mercury.

In an analogous manner the half-wave potential of the simple ion can be shown to be:

$$(E_{\frac{1}{2}})_s = E_a^\circ - \frac{RT}{nF} \ln \frac{I_s}{f_s I_M} \tag{27}$$

When the activity coefficient of the ion is unity the half-wave potential is given by:

$$(E_{\frac{1}{2}}^\circ)_s = (E_{\frac{1}{2}})_s - \frac{RT}{nF} \ln f_s = E_a^\circ - \frac{RT}{nF} \ln (I_s/I_M) \tag{28}$$

Combination of equations (26) and (28) gives, on rearrangement

$$F_0(X) = \sum_j \left\{ \frac{K_j C_X^j f_X^j}{f_{MX_j}} \right\} = \text{antilog} \left\{ 0.435 \frac{nF}{RT} (E_{\frac{1}{2}})_s - (E_{\frac{1}{2}})_c + \log (I_s/I_c) \right\} \tag{29}$$

$F_0(X)$ is the experimentally measured quantity, K_j is the formation constant of the complex $MX_j^{+(n-jb)}$, and C_X is the concentration of the free ligand species. If the activity coefficients are assumed to be unity, equation (29) reduces to:

$$F_0(X) = \sum_{j=0}^{j=X} K_j C_X^j \tag{30}$$

The function $F_1(X)$ is introduced and defined by the equation:

$$F_1(X) = [F_0(X) - K_0]/C_X \tag{31}$$

and $F_2(X)$ defined by:

$$F_2(X) = [F_1(X) - K_1]/C_X, \text{ etc.} \tag{32}$$

in a manner similar to that used by Leden. The solution of these equations may then be obtained by graphical or numerical methods.[80,81,82]

(b) The Polarographic Method of Eriksson and Ringbom.[83,84] This procedure was devised for the polarographic determination of consecutive complexity constants. If suitable indicator ions are present, the method may be used even though the central metal ion is not reduced. The complexity con-

[82] K. O. Watkins and M. M. Jones, *J. Inorg. Nuclear Chem.* **16**, 187 (1961).
[83] L. Eriksson and A. Ringbom, *Acta Chem. Scand.* **7**, 1105 (1953).
[84] L. Eriksson, *Acta Chem. Scand.* **7**, 1146 (1953).

stants are obtained by the solution of linear equations of the same type as are encountered in Leden's method:

$$F_1 = \beta_1 + \beta_2 A_0 + \beta_3 A_0^2 + \beta_4 A_0^3 \tag{33}$$

where the A_0 values, the concentration of free ligand, are obtained in the following manner:

1. The average ligand number of the system, $\bar{n}$, is expressed as

$$\bar{n} = \frac{\text{total number of bound ligands}}{\text{total number of metal atoms}} \tag{34}$$

where $\bar{n}$ can be calculated from Bodlander's equation:

$$\bar{n} = \frac{-dE}{d \ln A} \cdot \left(\frac{mF}{RT} \right) \tag{35}$$

Here, m is the change in the charge of the metal ion, A represents the concentration of free ligand, and E is the potential.

For a metal ion system at 25° C which undergoes two electron changes, equation (35) becomes:

$$\bar{n}_0 = \frac{-d\Delta E}{d \log A_0} \cdot \frac{1}{29.58} \tag{36}$$

where the subscript 0 refers to concentrations at the electrode surface.

2. Values of ΔE, the difference between the potential of a metal perchlorate solution with ligand present and without any ligand present at a specified current, can be obtained from polarograms taken at various ligand concentrations. The potentials are expressed as a fraction of the diffusion current, i_d, e.g., i/i_d.

3. Since A_0 is not known, the total concentration of A in the system, C_A, is used as a first approximation to obtain $\bar{n}_0$ values. For a system such as $Cd^{+2} - Br^-$ or $Cd^{+2} - Cl^-$, the differences between C_A and A_0 are small. The approximate $\bar{n}_0$ values obtained from (36) are used to compute new values of A_0 from the equation:

$$A_0 = C_A - \bar{n}_0 \cdot \left(\frac{i_d - i}{i_d} \right) C_M \tag{37}$$

With these new A_0 values, new values of $\bar{n}_0$ are computed using the Bodlander equation.

4. The concentration of the metal ion at the electrode surface, M_0, is calculated from the equation:

$$\Delta E = -29.58 \log \frac{C_{0M}}{M_0} \tag{38}$$

where C_{0M} represents the total metal ion concentration at the drop surface,

$$\left(\frac{i_d - i}{i_d} \right) C_M$$

5. To calculate the β's, functions F_n are introduced and defined as:

$$F_n = \frac{F_1}{A_0^{(n-1)}} = \frac{C_{OM} - M_0}{M_0 \cdot A_0^n} = \frac{\left(\frac{C_{OM}}{M_0} - 1\right)}{A_0^n}$$

Values of F_n corresponding to various values of A_0 can then be determined. These values can then be used to obtain the successive β's by a graphical procedure. The extrapolation of the F's to $A_0 \to 0$ will give various combinations of the coefficients of equation (33). Thus F_1 in the limit of $A_0 \to 0$ goes to β_1 and the limiting slope of this curve is β_2. A plot of F_4 against $1/A_0$ can be used to obtain β_4 and β_3 in an analogous manner.

The polarographic methods are generally of less precision than the potentiometric method of Leden or its modification by Vanderzee and they are also less convenient from the point of experimental manipulations.

10. *The "Core Plus Links" Method of Sillén for the Study of Hydrolytic Equilibria.*[85] The general problem of giving a quantitative treatment for hydrolytic equilibria is a very old and a very difficult one. One of the most interesting recent developments in this area is that of Sillen. The assumptions used are the same as those used in the treatment of equilibria involving mononuclear complexes in such treatments as those of J. Bjerrum or I. Leden plus some special ones required to provide an experimentally useful method (i.e., to allow the data to be treated in as simple and systematic a manner as is possible under the circumstances).

Sillén considers polynuclear complex formation in a very general manner. Two reacting species, in solution, designated as A and B form complexes of the type A_pB_q. The total concentrations of A and B in solution are then given by:

$$A = a + \sum_p p[A_pB_q], \qquad B = b + \sum_q q[A_pB_q] ;$$

where a and b are the concentrations of free A and B.

The usual activity assumptions are made, viz., that concentrations may be substituted for activities in all relevant mass action expressions. Thus for

$$pA + qB \rightleftharpoons A_pB_q , \qquad A_pB_q = \kappa_{pq}a^pb^q$$

where κ_{pq} is the equilibrium constant for the reaction. Another term is now introduced which is defined as the complexity sum, S:

$$S = \sum[A_pB_q] = \sum \kappa_{pq}a^pb^q$$

From these equations it is possible to find $A-a$, the amount of A bound in complexes:

$$A - a = \sum p[A_pB_q] = \sum p\kappa_{pq}a^pb^q = a\left(\frac{\partial S}{\partial a}\right)_b = \left(\frac{\partial S}{\partial \ln a}\right)_b$$

[85] L. G. Sillen, *Acta Chem. Scand.* **8**, 299, 318 (1954).

Likewise the amount of B bound in complexes is:

$$B - b = \sum q\kappa_{pq} a^p b^q = b\left(\frac{\partial S}{\partial b}\right)_a = \left(\frac{\partial S}{\partial \ln b}\right)_a$$

The average number of A bound per B is designated Z:

$$Z = \frac{A - a}{B}$$

From the previous equations:

$$Z = \frac{a\left(\frac{\partial S}{\partial a}\right)_b}{b\left[1 + \left(\frac{\partial S}{\partial b}\right)_a\right]} = \frac{\left(\frac{\partial(S+b)}{\partial \ln a}\right)_b}{\left(\frac{\partial(S+b)}{\partial \ln b}\right)_a}$$

These equations are somewhat too general for use in their original form and an additional assumption was introduced to make them more tractable, the core plus links hypothesis. This can be most readily appreciated from a $p-q$ diagram. All positive values of either variable are possible so the intersection of the lines of constant integral q with those of constant integral p give the points representative of all possible polynuclear complexes as shown in Figure 42(a). A knowledge of the (p, q) values of the various complexes can thus simplify our problem considerably. Thus the same diagram for a system where only monouclear complexes A_nB are formed with n values of 1, 2, 3, and 4 will look like Figure 42(b).

When the core plus links hypothesis is introduced it allows a considerable systematization of these polynuclear complexes. This hypothesis is that all polynuclear complexes can be represented by points on a few (generally *one*) lines in such a diagram. This means that these polynuclear complexes consist of a core, such as A_2B_2, and successive links which are added to this in the course of polymerization, such as A_2B units. The p, q diagram for such a situation is shown in Figure 42(c). The slope of this line will be $1/t$ where $r = -ts$ and the equation for the line will be:

$$p = tq + r = t(q-s)$$

These polynuclear complexes may be written as $A_r(A_tB)_n$ or $B_s(A_tB)_n$, where r, s, and t are constants and n is any number that will result in integral values for p and q. This hypothesis does not require that all of the possible polynuclear complexes be present, but only that those present be of the designated core plus links type. The relationship between the core plus links hypothesis and the more general equations can now be developed to yield experimentally useful forms. All possible polynuclear complexes need not be considered but only those of the form $A_r(A_tB)_n$ and we shall designate the equilibrium constant for this as κ_n:

$$(r+nt)\, A + nB \rightleftharpoons A_r(A_tB)_n$$

$$[A_r(A_tB)_n] = \kappa_n a^{r+nt} b^n = \kappa_n a^r(a^t b)^n = \kappa_n a^r u^n$$

$$u = a^t b$$

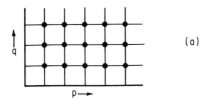

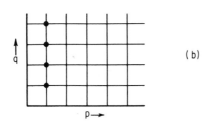

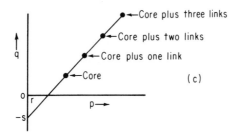

Fig. 42 q-p diagrams for polynuclear complexes (after Sillén). (a) All possible polynuclear complexes present. (b) Only mononuclear complexes present. (c) All complexes present are formed in accord with the core plus links hypothesis. (Reproduced by permission of the Editor, *Acta Chemica Scandinavica*.)

Using these in our previous expressions for S, $A-a$ and $B-b$:

$$S = a^r \sum \kappa_n u^n = a^r \phi(u)$$

$$A - a = a\left(\frac{\partial S}{\partial a}\right)_b = a^r[r\phi(u) + t\,u\,\phi'(u)] = BZ$$

$$B - b = b\left(\frac{\partial S}{\partial b}\right)_a = a^r\,u\,\phi'(u)$$

The expressions for u, $A-a$, and $B-b$ form the basis of the methods of extracting r and t from the experimental data.

Of fundamental importance in this theory are the $Z(\log a)_B$ curves. The experimental data is summarized by plotting

$$Z = \left.\frac{A - a}{B}\right\} \quad \text{as a function of log } a \text{ for various constant values of } B.$$

For most of the systems studied, the $Z(\log a)_B$ curves are either parallel with a spacing ($\Delta \log a$) proportional to $\Delta \log B$ or else coincident. Both types of curves are readily interpreted on the basis of the core plus links mechanism for condensation. These types may be treated separately for purposes of showing the manner in which the reduction of the data is carried out.

Parallel Curves of $Z(\log a)_B$. For parallel curves

$$\frac{\Delta \log B}{\Delta \log a} = R = \frac{\partial \log B}{\partial \log a} = \text{constant}; \quad Z(a^{-R}B)$$

so Z must be a function of $a^{-R}B$. Then

$$Z = \frac{A - a}{B} = \frac{\sum p \kappa_{pq} a^p b^{q-1}}{1 + \sum q \kappa_{pq} a^p b^{q-1}}$$

$$a^{-R}B = a^{-R}(b + \sum q \kappa_{pq} a^p b^q) = a^{-R}b(1 + \sum q \kappa_{pq} a^p b^{q-1})$$

If Z is to be a function of $a^{-R}B$ only, then the conditions required depend upon whether b is negligible or not.

b Not Negligible. Here all the terms $a^p b^{q-1}$ in the expressions above must be powers of $a^{-R}b$, which will appear as a separate term in the last equation. So, $p = R(q-1)$ and the core plus links complexes have $R = r = -t$; $s = 1$, i.e., $B(A_t B)_n$ or $A_{-t}(A_t B)_n$ and the spacing of the curves gives r and t.

b Is Negligible. When this is the case we may write

$$Z = \frac{A - b}{B} = \frac{\sum p \kappa_{pq} a^p b^{q-1}}{\sum q \kappa_{pq} a^p b^{q-1}}$$

and

$$a^{-R}B \approx a^{-R}b \left(\sum q \kappa_{pq} a^p b^{q-1}\right)$$

When both of these expressions are multiplied by $a^{-R}b$ the sums will contain the same terms $a^{p-R}b^q$. The condition for Z to be a function of $a^{-R}B$ is then that all of these terms are powers of the same variable which may be written as a^{tb}, where t is an undetermined constant.

From the parallel curves one may deduce that:

$$p - R = tq$$

There are now core plus links complexes present of the general formula $A_r(A_t B)_n$ where $r = R$. To determine t one may use the limiting values of Z:

$$Z = \frac{A - a}{B} \begin{cases} t + \dfrac{r}{n_{\max}} \ \text{for decreasing log } a & \text{if } r > a \text{ and} \\[2ex] t + \dfrac{r}{n_{\min}} \ \text{for increasing log } a & \text{always } b \ll B \end{cases}$$

Several special cases of this behavior are treated in greater detail by Sillén (loc. cit.).

Coinciding Z(log a)$_B$ Curves. Coinciding Z (log a)$_B$ curves mean that Z is a function of a only. Here:

$$\left(\frac{\partial \log B}{\partial \log a}\right)_z = \infty$$

so the equations developed in terms of R become indefinite. Returning to the general equation:

$$Z = \frac{A-a}{B} = \frac{\sum p\kappa_{pq}a^p b^q}{b + \sum q\kappa_{pq}a^p b^q}$$

the conditions for Z to be a function of a only are found to be:

(1) for b not negligible, it is necessary that the sums are of the first order with respect to b so it can be eliminated. In this case $q = 1$ and the complexes are of the type A_nB.

(2) for b negligible, b can be eliminated from the equation above if only one value of q is used. The complexes are therefore homonuclear ones, A_nB, or A_nB_2, etc., (if p/q is constant so is Z).

The application of these ideas to specific cases shows how the core plus links hypothesis succeeds in explaining many hydrolytic equilibria. In this case B represents the metal and A is OH^-. The hydrolysis reaction is:

$$pH_2O + qB \rightleftharpoons B_q(OH)_p + pH^+$$

$$[B_q(OH)_p] = *\beta_{pq}[H^+]^{-p}[B]^q = *\beta_{pq}h^{-p}b^q$$

then

$$B = [B] + \sum q[B_q(OH)_p] = b + \sum q *\beta_{pq}h^{-p}b^q$$

$$BZ = \sum p[B_q(OH)_p] = \sum p *\beta_{pq}h^{-p}b^{-q}$$

$$\eta = \log \frac{(B)}{(b)} = \log \left(1 + \sum q *\beta_{pq}h^p b^{q-1}\right)$$

To obtain numerical values for p, q, and the $*\beta$'s requires measurements of B, Z, b, and h over as wide a range of values as is possible. B is known from the total amount of metal ion admitted to the system, $h = [H^+]$ is generally measured with a glass or quinhydrone electrode. Z is obtained from h and the assumption that the number of protons in the solution is the same as that originally added. The experiments are carried out as titrations in a medium of constant high ionic strength. The type of hydrolysis product present may be established more readily than the hydrolysis constants. These latter may be obtained by methods analogous to those used for mononuclear complexes.

The use of this method to establish the composition of the hydrolytic products in the case of gallium(III) may be seen in the work of Ruff and Tyree.[86] They prepared solutions of gallium(III) perchlorate in $1M$ $NaClO_4$

[86] J. K. Ruff and S. Y. Tyree, *J. Amer. Chem. Soc.* **80**, 5654 (1958).

and adjusted the OH/Ga ratio by the addition of sodium carbonate (sodium bicarbonate may also be used). A series of solutions was prepared with the same OH/Ga ratio and varying total concentrations of Ga, and this process was repeated for several OH/Ga values. After three weeks the pH values were determined. Z values were then calculated using the equation:

$$Z = \frac{h + H}{m}$$

where $h = [H^+]$, $H = OH/Ga$, and m is the total gallium concentration. When Z was plotted against pH, a set of parallel curves was obtained. This indicated that the core plus links hypothesis could be used to describe hydrolysis in these solutions and that the complexes present were of the type $Ga[Ga(OH)_t]_n$. A plot of pH vs. m at constant Z should then give a straight line of slope t. The graphical value of t was 2.1 so the complexes were of the type $Ga[Ga(OH)_2]_n$. If this is a correct interpretation, a plot of $\log m - t \log h$ vs. Z should give a single curve for all of the experimental points and this was found to be approximately true. From this t value and the data, $\bar{n}$ can be calculated for the various solutions.

A more complete discussion of this method as it is applied to the hydrolysis of stannous ion has been given by Tobias.[87] Tobias measured the hydrogen ion concentration h, with a glass electrode, and the concentration of stannous ion was determined with a tin amalgam electrode. The glass electrode allowed values of:

$$Z = \frac{h - H}{B}$$

to be determined. H is the analytical excess of the hydrogen ion assuming no hydrolysis (all tin in the form of Sn^{+2}). It can be negative in the latter part of a titration after much base has been added. This data gives the $Z(\log h)_B$ curves. In other titrations the concentration of stannous ion was also measured to determine values of

$$\eta = \log \frac{B}{b}$$

This data is summarized in $\eta(\log h)_B$ curves. The $Z(\log h)_B$ and $\eta(\log h)_B$ curves show that Z and η are functions of both B and h in this system and thus indicate polynuclear complexes. If only mononuclear complexes were formed, neither Z nor η would depend on B. First the equations:

$$\left(\frac{\partial \log B}{\partial \log h} \right)_z = \left(\frac{\partial \log B}{\partial \log h} \right)_n = t$$

were used to evaluate t which was found to be 2. This value may be tested by plotting Z and η vs. $\log B - t \log h$. All of the Z data and all of the η data should fall on two lines, one for Z and one for η (which they did). The

[87] R. S. Tobias, *Acta Chem. Scand.* **12**, 198 (1958).

core plus links hypothesis requires that Z and η be functions of the single variable $u = (bh^{-t})$ and since $Bh^{-t} = f(u)$, then Z and η are functions of Bh^{-t}. The data were then plotted as:

$$y(= Z/2) \text{ vs. } x(= \log Bh^{-t})$$

and

$$\eta \text{ vs. } x$$

The equilibrium constants for the hydrolytic reactions can then be calculated from the $y(x)$ and $\eta(x)$ curves. The method used for this can be illustrated using one of the three methods given by Tobias.

For the reaction:

$$(n+1) \text{ Sn}^{+2} + 2n \text{ H}_2\text{O} \rightleftharpoons \text{Sn}[\text{Sn(OH)}_2]_n^{+2} + 2n \text{ H}^+$$

the equilibrium constant designated k_n is related to B by:

$$B = b + \sum (n+1)[\text{Sn}[\text{Sn(OH)}_2]_n^{+2}] = b + \sum (n+1)k_n \, h^{-2n}b^{n+1}$$

substituting $u = h^{-2}b$ gives:

$$B = b(1 + \sum (n+1)k_n \, u^n)$$

Setting:

$$g = \sum k_n u^n; \qquad \frac{dg}{du} = g'$$

so

$$B = b\left(\frac{d}{du}\right)(u+gu) = b(1+g+ug')$$

From this equation:

$$(1+g) = u^{-1} \int_0^u Bb^{-1} \, du = u^{-1} \int_0^u 10^\eta \, du$$

and from the definitions of x and u,

$$\log u = x - \eta$$

Thus, $g(u)$ can be obtained from these last two equations using $\eta(x)$ data obtained with the amalgam electrode. The average number of links in the complexes is given by:

$$\bar{n} = \frac{\sum n \, C_n}{\sum C_n} = \frac{ug'}{g}$$

or

$$\bar{n} = \frac{Bb^{-1} - g^{-1}}{g}$$

Sillén previously derived the relation:

$$\log (1+g) = \eta + \log (1-y)$$

which can be used to get:

$$\bar{n} = \frac{y}{1 - y - bB^{-1}}.$$

We can obtain η from the glass electrode data using equations due to Sillén:

$$\eta = y \log e + \int_{-\infty}^{y} y \, dx$$

with $\log u = x - \eta$

The $g(u)$ and $\eta(x)$ can be obtained from either the glass electrode data or the amalgam data. To evaluate the polynuclear complexity constants:

$$gu^{-1} = k_1 + k_2 u + \cdots$$

can be used and solved in a variety of ways. For the stannous system, $BZ(B-b)^{-1}$, the average number of hydroxyl groups bound per metal atom was 1.30 ± 0.03, indicating the complex $Sn_3(OH)_4^{+2}$ over a wide range of x values. The following equilibrium constants were obtained:

$$Sn^{+2} + H_2O \rightleftharpoons Sn(OH)^+ + H^+ \qquad \log K_{11} = -3.92 \pm 0.15$$

$$2Sn^{+2} + 2H_2O \rightleftharpoons Sn_2(OH)_2^{+2} + 2H^+ \qquad \log K_{22} = -4.45 \pm 0.15$$

$$3Sn^{+2} + 4H_2O \rightleftharpoons Sn_3(OH)_4^{+2} + 4H^+ \qquad \log K_{43} = -6.77 \pm 0.03$$

11. *The Bodlander-Brønsted Postulates.* Underlying much of the experimental data on successive complexity constants are certain assumptions involved in the elimination of activity coefficients from the mass action expressions. These assumptions are *necessary* if information on many successive stability constants for a single ion-ligand combination are to be calculated. It may well be asked: (a) what is the nature of these assumptions and (b) to what extent, if any, are they justified by available experimental information?

The historical background of this problem is discussed in some detail by Biedermann and Sillén.[88] Apparently the first use of the high ionic strength medium in studying successive complexity constants is found in the work of H. Grossmann[89] who used it at the suggestion of Bodlander (who died at the end of 1904). Grossmann used potassium nitrate solutions to keep the ionic strength constant in studies of the thiocyanate complexes of mercury. Subsequently, N. Bjerrum used potassium chloride solutions $0.1M$ in KCl to obtain "constant" hydrolysis constants in a study of the hydrolysis of chromic chloride (1908). The definite formulation of this idea and its application to a number of types of equilibria is usually credited to J. N. Brønsted.[90] In 1927 Brønsted summarized his conclusions as follows "It has been shown that the

[88] G. Biedermann and L. G. Sillén, *Arkiv for Kemi* 5, 426 (1953). This is the source of much of the information in this section.

[89] H. Grossmann, *Zeit. anorg. Chem.* 43, 356 (1905).

[90] J. N. Brønsted, *Det Kgl. Danske Videnskab, Selskab, Skrifter Natur. math. Afdel* (17), 12, p. 252 ff., No. 6 (1914–15); *Medd. Vetensk. Nobel Inst.* 5, No. 25 (1919); *Kgl. Danske Vid. S.M.f.M.* 3, No. 9 (1920); *Trans. Farad. Soc.* 23, 429 (1927); *Zeit. phys. Chem.* 98, 239 (1921); J. N. Brønsted and K. Pedersen, *Zeit. phys. Chem.* 103, 307 (1923); some supporting data is found in G. N. Lewis and L. W. Sargent, *J. Amer. Chem. Soc.* 31, 355 (1909).

Nernst formula for electromotive force, the solubility product, and mass action law in the case of a complicated ion equilibrium are applicable in their classical form to such concentrated salt solutions, the reason for this simplicity being the practical constancy of the activity coefficients in the practically constant medium. Utilization of these results would mean in many cases a great simplification in problems pertaining to electrolytic solutions." J. Bjerrum in 1931 used the ionic medium method in the study of the cupric ammine complexes,[91] and after the publication of his thesis in 1941 and that of Leden in 1943 the method gained considerable popularity.

The nature of these assumptions may be seen more exactly by considering some of the implications of replacing activities by concentrations. In the reduction of the data for the calculation of the successive stability constants we ultimately use a term such as the $\bar{n}$ of Bjerrum, the N of Leden, or an analogous expression. This is then manipulated to give linear algebraic equations in which these stability constants are the only unknowns. Such equations can then be solved by a variety of standard methods. By examining the steps in this reduction we can see that it is *not* sufficient to have constant activity coefficients, they must also be interrelated in a very specific way. For $\bar{n}$ we may write as a *defining* equation:

$$\bar{n} = \frac{[MA] + 2[MA_2] + 3[MA_3] + \cdots + N[MA_N]}{[M] + [MA_2] + [MA_3] + \cdots + [MA_N]}$$

The equilibrium constants for the steps:

$$M + A \rightleftharpoons MA$$
$$MA + A \rightleftharpoons MA_2$$
$$MA_{N-1} + A \rightleftharpoons MA_N$$

will be:

$$k_1 = \frac{a_{MA}}{a_M \cdot a_A}, \qquad k_2 = \frac{a_{MA_2}}{a_{MA} \cdot a_A}, \qquad k_3 = \frac{a_{MA_3}}{a_{MA_2} \cdot a_A}$$

$$k_N = \frac{a_{MA_N}}{a_{MA_{N-1}} \cdot a_A}$$

In terms of activity coefficients and concentrations, these become:

$$k_1 = \frac{\gamma_{MA}[MA]}{\gamma_M[M]\gamma_A[A]}, \qquad k_2 = \frac{\gamma_{MA_2}[MA_2]}{\gamma_{MA}[MA]\gamma_A[A]}, \qquad k_3 = \frac{\gamma_{MA_3}[MA_3]}{\gamma_{MA_2}[MA_2]\gamma_A[A]}$$

$$k_N = \frac{\gamma_{MA_N}[MA_N]}{\gamma_{MA_{N-1}}[MA_{N-1}]\gamma_A[A]}$$

When we solve these equations for substitution in the $\bar{n}$ definition all terms involving the *concentrations* of the complexes are to be separated:

$$[MA] = k_1[M][A]\frac{\gamma_M \gamma_A}{\gamma_{MA}}$$

[91] J. Bjerrum, *Det Kgl. Danske Vid. Selskab Mat. fys. Medd.* **11**, No. 5 (1931).

$$[MA_2] = k_2[MA][A] \frac{\gamma_{MA}\gamma_A}{\gamma_{MA_2}} = k_1 k_2 [M][A]^2 \frac{\gamma_M \gamma_A^2}{\gamma_{MA_2}}$$

$$[MA_3] = k_3[MA_2][A] \frac{\gamma_{MA_2}\gamma_A}{\gamma_{MA_3}} = k_1 k_2 k_3 [M][A]^3 \frac{\gamma_M \gamma_A^2}{\gamma_{MA_3}}$$

etc. . . . . Substitution of these expressions into the definition of $\bar{n}$ will yield:

$$\bar{n} = \frac{k_1[A]\frac{\gamma_M \gamma_A}{\gamma_{MA}} + 2k_1 k_2 [A]\frac{\gamma_M \gamma_A^2}{\gamma_{MA_2}} + 3k_1 k_2 k_3 [A]^3 \frac{\gamma_M \gamma_A}{\gamma_{MA_3}} + \cdots}{1 + k_1[A]\frac{\gamma_M \gamma_A}{\gamma_{MA}} + k_1 k_2 [A]^2 \frac{\gamma_M \gamma_A^2}{\gamma_{MA_2}} + k_1 k_2 k_3 [A]^3 \frac{\gamma_M \gamma_A^3}{\gamma_{MA_3}} + \cdots}$$

In order to reduce this equation to its usually encountered form it is necessary that:

$$\frac{\gamma_M \gamma_A}{\gamma_{MA}} = \frac{\gamma_M \gamma_A^2}{\gamma_{MA_2}} = \frac{\gamma_M \gamma_A^3}{\gamma_{MA_3}} = \cdots = \frac{\gamma_M \gamma_A^N}{\gamma_{MA_N}} = 1$$

or stated in an equivalent form:

$$\frac{\gamma_M \gamma_A}{\gamma_{MA}} = \frac{\gamma_{MA}\gamma_A}{\gamma_{MA_2}} = \frac{\gamma_{MA_2}\gamma_A}{\gamma_{MA_3}} = \cdots = \frac{\gamma_{MA_{N-1}}\gamma_A}{\gamma_{MA_N}} = 1$$

Thus the degree of validity of this assumption obviously depends on how many complexes are present in the system and what their charges are. In general, the more complexes present, the less satisfactory this assumption will be.

It is certainly worthwhile at this point to review the experimental evidence which led originally to the proposal that the concentrations may replace the activities in a medium of high ionic strength in both the law of mass action and the Nernst equation. In the article of Brønsted and Pedersen cited above the reaction subjected to study was:

$$2Fe^{+3} + 2I^- \rightleftharpoons 2Fe^{+2} + I_2$$

The iodine liberated was determined by titration with thiosulfate. The reaction was studied using various small concentrations of potassium iodide and ferric chloride in a solution $1.65M$ in KCl and $0.1M$ in HCl. The thermodynamic equilibrium constant for this system is

$$K_a = \frac{a_{Fe^{+2}}^2 \cdot a_{I_2}}{a_{Fe^{+3}}^2 \cdot a_{I^-}^2} = \frac{C_{Fe^{+2}}^2 \gamma_{Fe^{+2}}^2 \cdot C_{I_2} \gamma_{I_2}}{C_{Fe^{+3}}^2 \gamma_{Fe^{+3}}^2 \cdot C_{I^-}^2 \gamma_{I^-}^2}$$

If the ionic strength is kept constant the activity coefficients should remain constant and the equilibrium constant in terms of concentrations should be likewise, viz.:

$$K_C = \frac{C_{Fe^{+2}}^2 \cdot C_{I_2}}{C_{Fe^{+3}}^2 \cdot C_{I^-}^2} = K_a \frac{\gamma_{Fe^{+3}}^2 \cdot \gamma_{I^-}^2}{\gamma_{Fe^{+2}}^2 \cdot \gamma_{I_2}}$$

In this reaction it was found that K_C was indeed constant with a value of 21.1 and a range of values from 20.5 to 21.6 for the range of KCl and $FeCl_3$ concentrations used. In the calculations the iodide-iodine-triodide equilibrium was taken into account. This was studied independently and found also to exhibit a nearly constant "concentration" equilibrium constant under these same circumstances.

In another study, Brønsted[80e] determined solubility products for $[Co(NH_3)_5Cl]Cl_2$, $[Co(NH_3)_5Cl]Br_2$, $[Co(NH_3)_5Br]Cl_2$, and $[Co(NH_3)_5Br]Br_2$ in $0.5M$ solutions of potassium formate or sodium chlorate. The results are summarized in part in the following table:

SOLUBILITY PRODUCTS IN $0.5M$ POTASSIUM FORMATE ALL $\times$ 10^6

[Br⁻] or [Cl⁻] added	S.P.(A)Cl$_2$	S.P.(A)Br$_2$	S.P.(B)Cl$_2$	S.P.(B)Br$_2$
0	16.54	9.01	4.12	0.709
0.1	16.61	8.86	4.15	0.697
0.2	16.65	8.81	4.18	0.707

(A) is $[Co(NH_3)_5Cl]^{+2}$
(B) is $[Co(NH_3)_5Br]^{+2}$

It can be seen that the solubility products are much more constant than they are in aqueous solutions under similar conditions. The validity of the Nernst equation has been checked in a rather direct manner by I. Leden. This was done by the use of a cell of the type:

Au	Quinhydrone (solid) .01M HClO$_4$ 2.99M NaClO$_4$	3M NaClO$_4$	xMCd(ClO$_4$)$_2$ (3 − 3x)M NaClO$_4$	Cd(Hg)

and measure of the potential with varying amounts of Cd^{+2} present in a solution of constant ionic strength. He tested the measured values with the equation:

$$E = E_0 - \frac{10^3 RT}{2} \ln x$$

where E_0 is a constant (or should be) and the potentials are expressed in *millivolts*. The following table contains his results and the point by point values calculated for E_0. As can be seen, they exhibit good constancy.

$x \cdot 10^3$	E	E_0
1	1008.7	920.0
2	999.2	919.5
3.33	993.1	919.9
5	988.0	920.0
10	979.4	920.3
33.3	963.6	919.9
50.0	958.4	920.0
100	949.6	920.1

More stringent tests of the Nernst equation have been carried out with similar results.[91a]

J. N. Brønsted examined the solubility product of AgCl in $2M$ solutions

[91a] J. F. Tate and M. M. Jones, *J. Inorg. Nuclear Chem.* **24**, 1010 (1962); also gives previous literature.

of KNO_3, $NaNO_3$, and $MgSO_4$.[90] He found that the solution laws, expressed in terms of concentrations, gave a satisfactory interpretation of the data and summarized his results in the statement "the simple gas laws are valid for ions present in salt solutions, the concentration of which is large compared with the concentration of the ions concerned." He estimated that the range of concentrations for which this statement was valid was up to $0.2M$ or higher in mixtures of uni-univalent electolytes but only up to about $0.05M$ in mixtures of 2–1 or 2–2 electrolytes such as $MgCl_2$ and $MgSO_4$ under these circumstances.

As a result of these studies we can see that the ionic medium method is well established experimentally for certain types of *simple equilibria*. It is likewise equally uncertain that it can be applied in the customary manner in systems containing numbers of successive equilibria. Fortunately, most of these successive equilibrium constants are not required to be of the same high accuracy as the equilibrium constants mentioned above. In conclusion it seems reasonable to say that the stability constants obtained using this method are more nearly valid than the strict thermodynamicist would allow (especially for the first few) but considerably less valid than some of the work in the field might require.

12. *The Liquid Junction Potential Problem.* The measurement of the total potential of a cell is the experimentally determined quantity in many studies of complexation. Biedermann and Sillén,[88] made a very careful study of the liquid junction potentials and the related activity coefficient variations in cells of various types, for example with the cell:

Hg, Hg₂Cl₂	4M NaCl	3M NaClO₄	X⁻, H⁺ xM in HX (3−x)M in HClO₄	AgX, Ag

It was found that the liquid junction potential varied in a predictable manner if the measured potential E was divided into three portions: (a) a constant E_0 different for each combination of electrodes, (b) the Nernst term for the variation of E with the concentration of the ions, and (c) a term E_j which included the liquid junction potential E_j and terms for the variation of activity factors with $[H^+]$ as it replaced $[Na^+]$ in the solution. It was found that the liquid junction potential could be calculated quite readily using the Henderson equation. The variations in the activities of positive ions remain constant when part of the $[Na^+]$ is replaced by $[H^+]$. The activity factors of negative ions changed by noticeable amounts as the positive ions present were changed. Thus, when the reactants are of opposite charge, the changes in activities due to this may be difficult to distinguish from changes in activities due to complexation.

The ionic medium method is fortunately in harmony with a suggestion made by Nernst in 1897 that liquid junction potentials may be reduced almost to the vanishing point by using as a solvent, not water, *but a solution of a suitable indifferent electrolyte!*

THE CORRELATION OF STABILITY CONSTANTS WITH OTHER FACTORS

1. *The Statistical Effect.* Before it is possible to sort out the effect of structure of the ligand on the various stability constants of a series of complexes it is necessary to consider other factors which may vary in the system and the manner in which these may be sorted out. Following J. Bjerrum (thesis, p. 39) one may consider the various factors which tend to make successive stability constants different by defining the total effect $T_{n,n+1}$ as:

$$T_{n,n+1} = \log \left(\frac{k_n}{k_{n+1}} \right)$$

In turn the total effect is composed of a statistical effect and a ligand effect which is itself composed of an electrostatic effect and a rest effect:

$$T_{n,n+1} = S_{n,n+1} + L_{n,n+1}$$

$$L_{n,n+1} = E_{n,n+1} + R_{n,n+1}$$

where $S_{n,n+1}$ represents the statistical effect, $L_{n,n+1}$ is the ligand effect, $E_{n,n+1}$ is the electrostatic portion of the ligand effect, and $R_{n,n+1}$ is a term called *the rest effect* which includes any residual effects which cannot be explained on either a statistical or an electrostatic basis.

The statistical effect arises from the simple fact that the initial entering ligand has a better chance to give rise to a higher complex than successive entering ligands, while the tendency to reverse this process in the complex formed will depend on the total number of such ligands already present. If all the coordination positions are equivalent, the tendency of the complex $MA_n(H_2O)_{N-n}$ to split off an A will be proportional to n while its tendency to take on an A will be proportional to $N-n$. The ratios of the successive constants will, on a purely statistical basis, be expected to be:

$$\frac{N}{1}, \frac{N-1}{2} \dots \frac{N-n+1}{n}, \frac{N-n}{n+1}, \dots \frac{2}{N-1}, \frac{1}{N}$$

The ratio between any two successive constants will be:

$$\frac{k_n}{k_{n+1}} = \frac{(N-n+1)}{(N-n)} \frac{(n+1)}{(n)}$$

This can be seen by considering the reactions:

$$MA_{n-1} + A \rightleftharpoons MA_n$$

where

$$k_n \propto (N-n+1), \qquad k_n \propto \frac{1}{n}$$

$$MA_n + A \rightleftharpoons MA_{n+1}$$

and

where

$$k_{n+1} \propto (N - n), \qquad k_{n+1} \propto \frac{1}{n+1}$$

or

$$\frac{k_n}{k_{n+1}} = \frac{(N - n + 1)}{n} \frac{(n+1)}{N - n}$$

Where the positions are *not* all equivalent it is possible to derive analogous expressions involving q, the factor which tells how much more readily a ligand is split off from one position than from another (J. Bjerrum, thesis, pp. 39–80). It is possible to correct the successive stability constants for this statistical effect and this is generally done before attempting any explanation of electrostatic or specific ligand effects in a series of mononuclear complexes. The way in which this is done can be seen in the following example. We will assume that the coordination of successive ligands is not affected by the positions already coordinated in any manner except through the statistical effect. If this is true then we may assume that the successive stability constants corrected for this statistical effect will *all be equal*. These statistically corrected constants will be designated by K's:

$$K_1 = K_2 = K_3 = \cdots = K_N$$

For a case where N ligands may be coordinated, there will be $N-1$ relations between successive constants of the form:

$$\frac{k_n}{k_{n+1}} = \frac{(N - n + 1)}{(N - n)} \frac{(n+1)}{(n)}$$

and the additional equation required is based on the assumption that the mean stability constant will be the same whether it is calculated from the k's or the K's, viz.:

$$\bar{k}_N = \sqrt[N]{k_1 k_2 k_3 \cdots k_N} = \sqrt[N]{K_1 K_2 K_3 \cdots K_N}$$

For a system with four equivalent coordination positions, these conditions lead to the equations:

$$\frac{k_1}{k_2} = \left(\frac{4 \cdot 2}{3 \cdot 1}\right) = 8/3$$

$$\frac{k_2}{k_3} = \left(\frac{3 \cdot 3}{2 \cdot 2}\right) = 9/4$$

$$\frac{k_3}{k_4} = \left(\frac{2 \cdot 4}{1 \cdot 3}\right) = 8/3$$

and

$$\sqrt[4]{k_1 k_2 k_3 k_4} = K_1 = K_2 = K_3 = K_4$$

Since we wish to get the conversion factors for changing k_1 to K_1, k_2 to K_2, k_3 to K_3, and k_4 to K_4 we can eliminate all the k's but one from the final equation using the relationship established by the first three. This leads to:

$$\sqrt[4]{k_1 \cdot 3/8 \, k_1 \cdot 12/76 \, k_1 \cdot 3/48 \, k_1} = K_1 \text{ or } K_1 = \tfrac{1}{4} k_1$$

Similarly we can obtain the remaining relations which are:

$$K_2 = 2/3\,k_2, \qquad K_3 = 3/2\,k_3, \qquad K_4 = 4k_4$$

After calculation of the K's they will be found, in practice, to be equal *only* when the statistical effect is the *only effect* operative in making the k's different. For each value of N the correction factors for converting k's to K's will be different. These are tabulated for N values from 1 to 10 in the table below:

CONVERSION FACTORS FOR THE STATISTICAL EFFECT

N	K_1	K_2	K_3	K_4	K_5	K_6	K_7	K_8	K_9	K_{10}
1	k_1									
2	$\frac{1}{2}k_1$	$2k_2$								
3	$1/3k_1$	k_2	$3k_3$							
4	$1/4k_1$	$2/3k_2$	$3/2k_3$	$4k_4$						
5	$1/5k_1$	$\frac{1}{2}k_2$	k_3	$2k_4$	$5k_5$					
6	$1/6k_1$	$2/5k_2$	$3/4k_3$	$4/3k_4$	$5/2k_5$	$6k_6$				
7	$1/7k_1$	$1/3k_2$	$3/5k_3$	k_4	$5/3k_5$	$3k_6$	$7k_7$			
8	$1/8k_1$	$2/7k_2$	$\frac{1}{2}k_3$	$4/5k_4$	$5/4k_5$	$2k_6$	$7/2k_7$	$8k_8$		
9	$1/9k_1$	$\frac{1}{4}k_2$	$3/7k_3$	$2/3k_4$	k_5	$3/2k_6$	$7/3k_7$	$4k_8$	$9k_9$	
10	$1/10k_1$	$2/9k_2$	$3/8k_3$	$4/7k_4$	$5/6k_5$	$6/5k_6$	$7/4k_7$	$8/3k_8$	$9/2k_9$	$10k_{10}$

2. *The Electrostatic Effect.* When the complexation reaction involves the taking up of negatively charged ligands by a cation it is obvious that the electrostatic work involved in bringing the negatively charged ion up to the coordination center will vary considerably as the number of coordinated groups changes. N. Bjerrum[92] proposed that the electrostatic effect, $E_{n,n+1}$ be represented by:

$$E_{n,n+1} = 0.4343 \frac{\phi_{n,n+1}}{kT}$$

where

$$\phi_{n,n+1} = Z_1 Z_2 / Dr$$

is the electrostatic energy in bringing charges Z_1 and Z_2 up to a separation distance of r in a medium of dielectric constant D. More sophisticated electrostatic treatments have been proposed by other investigators (see, J. Bjerrum, Thesis, p. 52). N. Bjerrum found that the ratio of the successive stability constants in the chromic-thiocyanate system could be calculated using only the statistical and electrical effects when the latter were given by the equation:

$$E_{\text{average}} = \frac{3.3}{r} \text{ with } r = 5.5\ A^\circ$$

[92] N. Bjerrum, *Zeit. phys. Chem.* **106**, 238 (1932); Ya. D. Fridman, *Zhur. Neorg. Khim.* **6**, 1501 (1961), C.A. 57: 1840.

J. Bjerrum (Thesis, p. 61) considers that the rest effect $R_{n,n+1}$, which contains a variety of terms, should be used in cases such as this to get a more realistic estimate of r and hence of $E_{n,n+1}$. This lumping together of unknown effects would seem to be no less objectionable than the earlier treatment unless these miscellaneous effects can be specified more precisely and definitely.

3. *The Chelate Effect.* One of the characteristic features of chelation is the enhanced stability which is found for metal chelates when these are compared with simple complexes containing nearly identical donor groups. This is an experimental fact for which various theoretical explanations have been proposed. If a comparison is made between the logarithms of the formation constants for $M(NH_3)_2^{+x}$ and $M(en)^{+x}$, the greater stability of the chelated structures is immediately obvious:

STABILITY CONSTANTS FOR AMMINES AND ETHYLENEDIAMINE COMPLEXES[93]

	Co^{+2}	Ni^{+2}	Cu^{+2}	Zn^{+2}	Cd^{+2}
$\log \bar{K}_{M(NH_3)_2}$	3.68	4.99	7.68	4.69	4.69
$\log K_{M(en)}$	5.99	7.77	10.73	5.92	5.63

The generalization resulting from examination of this and related data is that chelation leads to more stable complexes and that the more numerous the chelate rings the greater the stability constant as long as specific stereochemical difficulties do not arise.[94]

The stereochemical aspects of the general problem have been examined in most detail by Schwarzenbach;[95] some cyclohexane, and cyclopentane derivatives have been studied by Kroll and Gordon.[96] These studies have shown that the relative conformations of the donor groups are of importance in determining the stabilities of chelates of isomeric molecules. One goal of these studies has been chelating agents of greater specificity. These have been found in a few instances, but complete specificity has yet to be attained by this method. One example[95] may be seen in a comparison of the coordinating tendencies of the Schiff bases derived from acetylacetone and 1,2-diamines. These are tetradentate chelating agents with two nitrogen and two oxygen donors. When the diamine is ethylenediamine, the resulting chelating agent is a general one for transition elements which favor a square planar arrangement of ligands. It forms complexes with Pt^{+2}, Pd^{+2}, Cu^{+2}, Ni^{+2}, and Co^{+2}. If *cis*-1,2-diaminocyclohexane is used as the amine, some steric hindrance is introduced and the formation of an undistorted square planar arrangement

[93] Data from G. Schwarzenbach, "The Specificity of Metal Complex Formation" in F. R. N. Gurd, editor, *Chemical Specificity in Biological Interactions*, Academic Press, Inc., New York (1954).

[94] G. Schwarzenbach, *Helv. Chim. Acta* **35**, 2344 (1952).

[95] G. Schwarzenbach, *Advances in Inorganic Chemistry and Radiochemistry* **3**, 273 (1961).

[96] H. Kroll and M. Gordon, *Federation Proceedings* **20**, No. 3, Part II, 51 (1961).

is no longer quite possible. As a result, Co^{+2} does not form a complex. When the *trans*-1,2-diaminocyclohexane is used, a chelating agent is obtained in which the attainment of a square planar arrangement is even more difficult. The Schiff base derived from this last amine complexes only with Pt^{+2} and Pd^{+2}.

While the chelate effect is well established experimentally, there is not a completely general agreement on its underlying theoretical basis or even on the types of chelate structure for which it is legitimate to claim a chelate effect. The two types of theory are based alternatively on: (a) entropy arguments and (b) enthalpy arguments. Both depend ultimately on the choice of standard states as $1M$ for all the reactants. Adamson[97] showed that a great portion of the chelate effect vanished for uncharged ligands when the standard states taken are those of reactants at unit mole fraction. Some structural specificity may remain but it is a much smaller effect than when the standard state taken is that of unit molality. Adamson restates the chelate effect as: $\Delta F°$ values tend to be negative and $\Delta S°$ values positive for processes of the type:

$$MX_p^a + \frac{p}{2}Y \rightleftharpoons MY_{\frac{p}{2}}^a + pX$$

where X and Y are neutral and Y is a bidentate group.

The general equation for the formation of a complex ion from a hydrated metal ion and a ligand is:

$$M(H_2O)_n^a + pX^b \rightleftharpoons [M(H_2O)_{n-p}X_p]^{(a+pb)} + p\,H_2O$$

The transformation of $\Delta F°$ and $\Delta S°$ data obtained using unit molality as the standard state to $\Delta F°'$ and $\Delta S°'$ using unit mole fraction as the standard state may be accomplished by the use of the equations:

$$\Delta S°' = \Delta S° - \Delta nR \ln 55.5 = \Delta S° - 7.9\Delta n \text{ (at } 25°)$$
$$\Delta F°' = \Delta F° + \Delta nRT \ln 55.5 = \Delta F° + 2360\Delta n \text{ (at } 25°)$$

The relative as well as the absolute values of a sequence of ΔF or ΔS values may change on changing the standard state. Comparable data for the reaction:

$$M(NH_3)_p + \frac{p}{2}\,en \rightleftharpoons M(en)_{p/2} + pNH_3$$

are given in the table below for several metal ions:

M	P	$\Delta F°$	$\Delta F°'$	$\Delta S°$	$\Delta S°'$
Co^{+2}	2	-3.2	-0.9	$\cdots$	$\cdots$
Cu^{+2}	2	-4.3	-2.0	5.7	-2.2
Zn^{+2}	2	-1.6	0.7	5.7	-2.2
Cd^{+2}	2	1.3	1.0	4.4	-3.5

[97] A. W. Adamson, *J. Amer. Chem. Soc.* **76**, 1578 (1954).

The argument of Adamson that a very large contribution to the translational entropy in the usual standard state produces large $\Delta S°$ values is supported by the much smaller $\Delta S°{}'$ values. The smaller $\Delta F°{}'$ values support the claim that the extra stability of chelates will generally vanish with this new choice of standard states.

The explanation of the chelate effect using unit molality standard state data which has been offered by Schwarzenbach is compatible with Adamson's work. In essence Schwarzenbach's basic idea is that dissociation of a simple ligand leads to its loss whereas dissociation of a single coordinated group of a chelating agent from the metal ion leads to a situation in which that coordination position of the chelating agent is still held in the neighborhood of the metal ion. This loose coordinating group produces a very much higher concentration of that group in the immediate neighborhood of the metal ion, and hence makes its recoordination extremely probable. If the concentration effect cannot enter in this manner because of the reduction of the data to a new standard state, it would appear that the new standard state would be decidedly less useful in practice, though certainly not wrong.

An alternative argument, due to Williams[98] suggests that large heat effects may be important as a basis for the chelate effect when combination occurs between ions of opposite charge. Williams argues that in the formation of such complexes from chelate molecules it is not necessary to bring the oppositely charged ligands together because the chelating molecules already holds them together at distances rather close to those required for coordination. Adamson's examples were mostly examples where the coordinated groups were uncharged, so the treatment of the chelate effect may be different for these two types of complexes. One of the reasons for the slow quantitative development in this direction is the paucity of experimental data of the required accuracy. $\Delta F°$ data are available in great numbers but the required $\Delta S°$ and $\Delta H°$ data are available in only a few cases.

CORRELATIONS OF STABILITY WITH OTHER FACTORS

The other factors with which correlations have been established are ones related to the acid-base character of the pair of atoms involved in the coordinate bond. For convenience, the metal ions (other than transition metal ions) may be divided into two groups following Schwarzenbach.[95] The first group consists of those cations with an inert gas electronic configuration and are designated *A*-cations. The second group consists of those cations containing an outer shell of 18 electrons and are designated *B*-cations.

The behavior of the *A*-cations is such that the stabilities of their complexes

[98] R. J. P. Williams, *J. Phys. Chem.* **58**, 121 (1954). More recent data suggest the problem may be more complicated; G. Atkinson and J. E. Bauman, *Inorganic Chem.* **2**, 64 (1963).

can be explained (quantitatively in some cases) in simple electrostatic terms. Thus the complexes become more stable as the cation size decreases and its charge increases and as the ligand size decreases and its charge increases. The *A*-cations form complexes preferentially with fluoride or oxygen donor species. Except for series where the coordination number changes, the stability sequence is generally regular.

The *B*-cations show behavior which is more complex as superimposed on this electrostatic behavior are covalency factors. As a result, the most stable complexes are found in those metal-ligand pairs where the metal electronegativity is highest and the ligand electronegativity is lowest. These metals show many specific interactions also.

The transition metal ions show a behavior which is best explained in terms of crystal field theory.[99]

When the complexes of a single metal ion with a large number of related coordination agents are examined it is frequently found that there is a correlation between stability of the complexes and the basic strength of the coordinating group. This correlation is generally dependent upon specific structural features in a manner which is difficult or impossible to predict. For example, for monodentate heterocyclic amines which coordinate with Ag^+ these plots take the form:

$$pK_{AgAm_2} = ApK_{H^+} + B$$

where *A* and *B* are constants.[100]

Unfortunately, when large numbers of different ligands are studied the correlation requires the use of a large number of different straight lines! In general there is a relation between the affinities of a ligand for a proton and its affinity for a metal ion which is complicated by the small size of the proton. Whenever there is steric hindrance in the formation of the metal chelate there will never or rarely be a corresponding difficulty in the formation of the protonated ligand. Unexpectedly the same trouble arises from various types of log-log plots involving different metals of combination plots of related equilibria. Several different straight lines are required to obtain the desired linear relationship between the different *pK* values.

A number of such correlations or correlation attempts are summarized in Table 8.2.

Of the various correlations between the stability of a complex and a *single property* of the central metal ion, the most satisfactory is that between the log *K* and the ionization potential corresponding to the last electron lost. This is reasonable in that this ionization potential should be a direct measure

---

[99] This statement is certainly an oversimplification. For a somewhat different view see, R. J. P. Williams, *Annual Reports on the Progress of Chemistry*, Vol. LVI, pp. 67–110 (1959).

[100] A. E. Martell and M. Calvin, *Chemistry of the Metal Chelate Compounds*, Prentice-Hall, Inc., Englewood Cliffs, N.J. (1952), p. 159.

TABLE 8.2

SOME STABILITY CORRELATIONS WITH LIGAND BASICITY

System	Result	Literature
Transition metal ions and substituted 1,10-phenanthrolines	$\log \beta_n = ApK + B$	101
Ag^+ and aromatic amines	$\log \beta_1 = ApK + B$	102
Pb^{+2} – carboxylates	$\log \beta_1 = ApK + B$	103
Fe^{+3} – phenols	$\log \beta_1 = ApK + B$	75
Co^{+2}, Ni^{+2}, Cu^{+2}, Zn^{+2}, Cd^{+2}, and anthranilic acid derivatives	steric factors and variations in ligand flexibility affect relative stability order	104
metal complexes of hydroxyquinones	$\log K_{stab}$ roughly proportional to pK but some irregularities	105
Ag^+ – amine systems	$\log \beta_1 = ApK + B$, but several lines needed for all types of amines	106
Fe^{+2} – substituted phenanthrolines	$\log \beta_1 = ApK + B$	107
Zn^{+2}, Cd^{+2}, complexes with substituted phenanthrolines and dipyridines	$\log \beta_1 = ApK + B$ but dipyridines on different line from orthophenanthrolines	108
Ag^+ and 3– and 4– substituted pyridines	weaker bases sometimes form stronger complexes	109
Alkylamines and diacetylbisbenzoylhydrazinonickel(II)	each class of amines gives a different correlation line	110
Cd^{+2} – aromatic sulfonates	no apparent correlation	42[a]
Cu^{+2} complexes with β-diketones, and hydroxynaphthaldehydes	correlations for each type, stability of complex increases with ligand base strength	111
Cu^{+2} complexes with substituted biguanides	no apparent relation between base strength and stability	112
Ag^+ complexes with aromatic and heterocyclic N bases	stability increases with π electron density on N	113

Literature Cited in Table 8.2:

[101] C. V. Banks and R. I. Bystroff, *J. Amer. Chem. Soc.* **81**, 6153 (1959).
[102] V. Armeanu and C. Luca, *Zeit. phys. Chem.* **214**, 81 (1960); **217**, 389 (1961).
[103] V. K. Klemencic and K. Filipovic, *Croat. Chem. Acta* **30**, 99 (1958).
[104] A. Young and T. R. Sweet, *J. Amer. Chem. Soc.* **80**, 800 (1958).
[105] H. Kido, W. C. Fernelius, and C. G. Haas, Jr., *Anal. Chim. Acta* **23**, 116 (1960).
[106] R. J. Bruehlman and F. H. Verhoek, *J. Amer. Chem. Soc.* **70**, 1401 (1948).
[107] W. W. Brandt and D. K. Gullstrom, *J. Amer. Chem. Soc.* **74**, 3532 (1952).
[108] M. Yasuda, K. Sone, and K. Yamasaki, *J. Phys. Chem.* **60**, 1667 (1956).
[109] R. K. Murmann and F. Basolo, *J. Amer. Chem. Soc.* **77**, 3484 (1955).
[110] L. Saconni and G. Lombardo, *J. Amer. Chem. Soc.* **82**, 6266 (1960).
[111] M. Calvin and K. W. Wilson, *J. Amer. Chem. Soc.* **67**, 2006 (1945).
[112] A. K. Ray, *Zeit. anorg. u. allgem. Chem.* **305**, 207 (1960).
[113] W. S. Fyfe, *Nature* **169**, 69 (1952); *J. Chem. Soc.*, 2018 (1952).

of the tendency of that species to pick up electrons whether free or combined to a ligand. This was originally suggested by H. Irving and R. Williams,[114] who proposed the now famous Irving-Williams order for the stability of complexes of divalent metal ions:

$$Mn^{+2} < Fe^{+2} < Co^{+2} < Ni^{+2} < Cu^{+2} > Zn^{+2}$$

In this series the second ionization potentials are found to rise in this same order, with a maximum at copper. In general log K vs. ionization potential plots are linear when complexes of a single ligand are examined for this sequence of metals.

Of the composite correlations, that of Van Uitert, Fernelius, and Douglas[115] is perhaps the most useful. This involves the product of the electronegativity of the metal and the bond strength of the hybrid orbitals used. This product is linearly related to the log K values i.e., $pK \propto X_m B_h$, where X_m is the electronegativity of the metal and B_h is the hybrid bond strength taken from Pauling's tables. While this correlation seems to be useful, its basis is not very clear. Both the X_m and B_h values used are numbers for which recent theoretical work seems to find no satisfactory basis.

This brief summary is only indicative of the work which has been done on correlations of complex stabilities. More complete details may be found in several reviews.[116-120b]

EXERCISES

1. The following data were obtained by H. Jahn and his co-workers [*Zeit. phys. Chem.* 37, 705 (1901)] for the transference numbers for cadmium in various solutions of cadmium iodide. How would you explain these results?

Concentration

CdI_2	0.1164	0.1751	0.2311	0.4500	0.686	0.882	1.357	2.597
$t_{Cd}{}^{+2}$	0.446	0.427	0.407	0.343	0.281	0.223	0.075	-0.003

[114] H. Irving and R. J. P. Williams, *Nature* 162, 746 (1948); *J. Chem. Soc.*, 3192 (1952).

[115] L. G. Van Uitert, W. C. Fernelius, and B. E. Douglas, *J. Amer. Chem. Soc.* 75, 2736 (1953).

[116] A. E. Martell, *Ann. Reviews of Phys. Chem.* 5, 239 (1955).

[117] A. R. Burkin, *Quarterly Reviews* 5, 1 (1951).

[118] S. Ahrland, J. Chatt, and N. R. Davies, *Quarterly Reviews* 12, 265 (1958).

[119] F. R. N. Gurd, *Chemical Specificity in Biological Interactions*, Academic Press, Inc., New York (1954).

[120] S. Chaberek and A. E. Martell, *Organic Sequestering Agents*, John Wiley & Sons, Inc., New York (1959).

[120a] R. J. P. Williams, *Ann. Report Progress Chem.* (1959), pp. 87–110.

[120b] Y. T. Chen, *Zeit. phys. Chem.* 220, 231 (1962).

2. Using the following data of H. M. Dawson and J. McCrae, *Trans. Chem. Soc.* **79**, 1072 (1901), estimate the number of ammonia molecules bound per cupric ion in the cupric sulfate-ammonia solutions. Temperature 30°; distribution coefficient for ammonia between water and chloroform = $(NH_3)_w/(NH_3)_c = k = 22.60$; concentration of $CuSO_4 = 0.10N$; concentration of NH_3 in the $0.10N$ $CuSO_4 = 10.310$ g/l; concentration of the ammonia in the chloroform layer in equilibrium with this solution is 0.3170 g/l.

3. Explain how a plot of Y vs. x would look, obtained using Job's method on a system in which M and Z react to give MZ if the system is studied spectrophotometrically at a wave length at which only Z absorbs.

4. The following data were obtained by I. Leden, *Zeit. Phys. Chem.* **A188**, 173(1941) on a cell of the type:

| Au | Quinhydrone (solid) 2.99M NaClO₄ 0.01M HClO₄ | 3M NaClO₄ | $10 \times 10^{-3}M$ Cd(ClO₄)₂ $(3M-3.10^{-2}M-Y)M$ NaClO₄ YM NaNO₃ | Cd(Hg) |

The voltage *differences* observed with varying concentration of sodium nitrate were:

ΔE in mv	0	1.6	4.1	7.2
YM	0	0.1	0.3	0.6

Show how the stability constant of the ion $[Cd(NO_3)]^+$ may be obtained from this data and calculate it. Indicate *all* of the work needed to reduce the data from a form such as that given above to the stability constant.

5. M. Calvin and K. W. Wilson[111] reported the following data in a study of the complex of 2-hydroxy-1-naphthaldehyde with cupric ion. A solution was used which had an original volume of 100 ml. The initial cupric ion concentration was 2.5×10^{-3} M. The solvent used was a 50/50, v/v mixture of dioxane and water. The pK of the ligand is 8.4 and its concentration is .01M. The initial concentration of the added perchloric acid was 0.02M.

ml. of 1.025 N NaOH added	1.976	2.073	2.126	2.180	2.283
pH		2.97	3.35	3.59	3.88	4.57

Show exactly how this data may be used to get the first and second stability constants of the chelates. Include *all* necessary calculations.

6. J. Schubert, *J. Phys. Chem.* **56**, 117 (1952), examined the complexation of Sr^{+2} with citric acid using an ion-exchange technique and tracer amounts of radioactive strontium. The distribution ratio of the strontium was found to vary with the citrate ion concentration in the following manner:

citrate conc. m/l	0	0.0016	0.0020	0.0030	0.0040
K_D		2.6630	1.2952	1.1796	0.8961	0.7483

From this data determine the stability constant for the strontium citrate complex present in these solutions.

9

Some Types of Coordination Compounds of Special Interest

THE CARBONYLS, CARBONYL-HYDRIDES, CARBONYL-NITROSYLS, AND RELATED COMPOUNDS[1-5]

The metal carbonyls and the compounds related to them form a class of unusual substances from the viewpoints of bonding, reactivity, and structure. The usual features of coordination compounds are apparently missing in these compounds and the metals exhibit only their "secondary" valences (as Werner said). A closer examination of these materials shows that they are closely related to the classical ammines and, in many cases, intermediate compounds with both carbon and nitrogen donors may be prepared. The chief feature governing the formation of the carbonyls seems to be the tendency of the metal to achieve the effective atomic number of an inert gas. This is accomplished by sharing of pairs of electrons with the carbon monoxide molecules and in the polynuclear carbonyls, by the formation of metal to

[1] H. J. Emeleus and J. S. Anderson, *Modern Aspects of Inorganic Chemistry*, D. Van Nostrand Co., Inc., New York, 2nd ed. (1952), Ch. XIV.

[2] J. W. Cable and R. K. Sheline, *Chem. Revs.* **56**, 1 (1956).

[3] J. A. Mattern and S. J. Gill, "Metal Carbonyls and Nitrosyls" in J. C. Bailar, Jr., *Chemistry of the Coordination Compounds*, Reinhold Publishing Corp., New York (1956), Ch. 16.

[4] J. S. Anderson, Quarterly Reviews **1**, 331–57 (1948).

[5] J. Chatt, P. L. Pauson, and L. Venanzi, "Metal Carbonyls and Related Compounds" in H. Zeiss, editor, *Organometallic Chemistry*, Reinhold Publishing Corp., New York (1960), p. 468 ff.

metal bonds. The only exception to this which is known presently[6-8] among the pure carbonyls are $V(CO)_6$ and $V_2(CO)_{12}$.

The carbonyls entered the chemical scene with the discovery of $Ni(CO)_4$ by Mond and his co-workers.[9] It was found that when a finely divided specimen of metallic nickel (such as that which is obtained by reducing nickel oxide with hydrogen at 400°) is held at 100° in a stream of carbon monoxide, a volatile compound is produced.

When the compound produced in this manner is heated to 150°, it decomposes to CO and Ni again, depositing the nickel on the surface of the vessel. By analyzing this gaseous compound they were able to show that it contained one nickel atom for every four carbon atoms and that the ratio of carbon to oxygen was one to one. They examined its physical properties and found its boiling point to be about 43° at 751 mm, its specific gravity to be 1.3185 at 17°, and that it solidified to colorless, needleshaped crystals at about −25°. The compound dissolves in alcohol, but is more soluble in chloroform and in benzene. It is inert toward dilute acids and alkalies as well as concentrated hydrochloric acid but is oxidized readily by concentrated nitric acid and by aqua regia. Mond found that cobalt did not readily undergo a similar reaction and developed a very successful commercial process for the separation of cobalt and nickel, making use of the reaction:

$$\left.\begin{array}{c} Ni \\ Co \end{array}\right\} \xrightarrow[100°]{CO} \begin{array}{c} Ni(CO)_4 \uparrow \\ + \\ Co \end{array} \quad , \quad Ni(CO)_4 \xrightarrow{150°} Ni + 4CO \uparrow$$

This allows a complete separation from cobalt, but the nickel produced is usually contaminated with a small amount of iron because of the concurrent formation and decomposition of the volatile iron pentacarbonyl.

Subsequently, a large number of other metal carbonyls have been prepared and characterized. The elements which form carbonyl complexes are limited to the transition elements and the elements of group Ib. Of these elements, not all form carbonyls which have been prepared, but in view of the recent preparation of the carbonyl of vanadium, it seems reasonable to expect that all of the metal carbonyls are not yet known.

The table on page 345 lists the carbonyl compounds which are known or reported.

In 1934, Sidgwick and Bailey[10] showed that for all the carbonyls known at that time, and for many of their simple derivatives, the compositions found were those required for the attainment of the effective atomic number of the

[6] R. L. Pruett and J. E. Wyman, *Chem. and Ind.*, 119 (1960): $V_2(CO)_{12}$.

[7] R. Ercoli, F. Calderazzo, and A. Alberola, *J. Amer. Chem. Soc.* **82**, 2966 (1960): $V(CO)_6$.

[8] G. Natta, R. Ercoli, F. Calderazzo, A. Alberola, P. Corradini, and G. Allegra, *Atti accad. Nazl. Lincel Rend. classe sci. fis. mat. e nat.* **27**, 107 (1959), C.A. 54: 16252: $V(CO)_6$.

[9] L. Mond, C. Langer, and F. Quincke, *J. Chem. Soc.* **57**, 749 (1890).

[10] N. V. Sidgwick and R. W. Bailey, *Proc. Roy. Soc.* **144**, 521 (1934).

Group V	Group VI	Group VII		Group VIII	
$V(CO)_6$ $V_2(CO)_{12}$	$Cr(CO)_6$	$[Mn(CO)_5]_2$	$Fe(CO)_5$ $Fe_2(CO)_9$ $Fe_3(CO)_{12}$	$[Co(CO)_4]_2$ $Co_4(CO)_{12}$	$Ni(CO)_4$
	$Mo(CO)_6$	$[Tc(CO)_5]_2$	$Ru(CO)_5$ $Ru_2(CO)_9$ $Ru_3(CO)_{12}$	$Rh_2(CO)_8$ $Rh_n(CO)_{3n}$	
	$W(CO)_6$	$[Re(CO)_5]_2$	$Os(CO)_5$ $Os_2(CO)_9$	$Ir_2(CO)_8$ $Ir_n(CO)_{3n}$	

next inert gas. For the polymeric carbonyls of the type $M_x(CO)_y$, they found that x and y were related to the atomic number of M (m), and G, the atomic number of the next inert gas by the equation

$$G - \frac{xm + 2y}{x} = x - 1$$

This implies that metal-metal bonds are present in polynuclear carbonyls, a proposal which is in accord with the magnetic properties of the polynuclear carbonyls. This rule is valid as a rough guide, but the existence of $V(CO)_6$ would certainly indicate its limitations. If this rule were valid no six-coordinate carbonyl of vanadium would exist. The atomic number of vanadium is 23, that of argon, the next inert gas, is 36. If vanadium is restricted to a coordination number of six with carbon monoxide it cannot attain the electron configuration of argon.

There are a number of methods by which metallic carbonyls may be prepared. Some of these are:

1. By the direct reaction of the finely powdered metal and carbon monoxide (which may or may not require pressure).

$$Ni + 4CO \rightarrow Ni(CO)_4$$

$$Fe + 5CO \rightarrow Fe(CO)_5$$

$$2Co + 8CO \xrightarrow[\Delta]{Pressure} Co_2(CO)_8$$

$$W + 6CO \xrightarrow[\Delta]{Pressure} W(CO)_6$$

$$Mo + 6CO \xrightarrow[\Delta]{Pressure} Mo(CO)_6$$

With the exception of the reactions with nickel and iron, which proceed rather readily, special conditions of temperature, catalysts, and pressure are usually critical if a satisfactory yield of carbonyl is to be obtained.

2. Reaction of carbon monoxide with an aqueous solution (or suspension) of a suitable compound or complex.

When a solution or a suspension of a suitable nickel(II) compound is treated with carbon monoxide, nickel carbonyl is often formed. Thus alkaline suspensions of the sulfide or cyanide are quite reactive toward carbon monoxide. The disproportionation reactions of some nickel complexes in the presence of CO leads to $Ni(CO)_4$ and a Ni(IV) complex. Examples of these types of reaction are:

$$Ni(CN)_2 \xrightarrow[CO]{NaOH \text{ soln.}} Ni(CO)_4$$

or

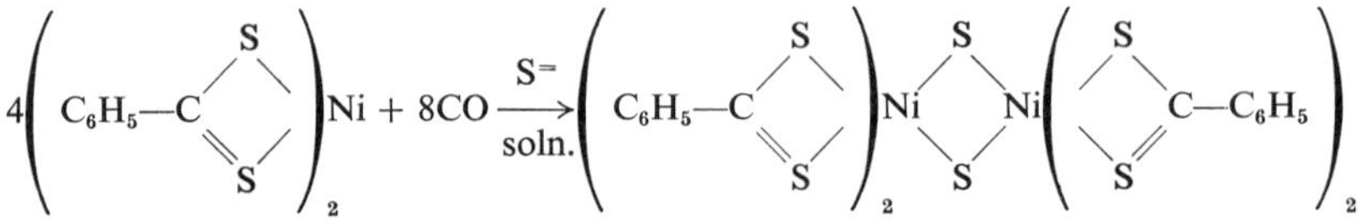

$$4\left(C_6H_5-C\underset{S}{\overset{S}{\diamondsuit}}\right)_2 Ni + 8CO \xrightarrow{S^=} \left(C_6H_5-C\overset{S}{\underset{S}{\diamondsuit}}\right)_2 Ni \underset{S}{\overset{S}{\diamondsuit}} Ni\left(\overset{S}{\underset{S}{\diamondsuit}}C-C_6H_5\right)_2$$

$$+ 2Ni(CO)_4 \quad [10a]$$

3. Reaction of anhydrous chlorides with carbon monoxide in the presence of a Grignard reagent.[11]

When a mixture of, for example, phenylmagnesium bromide in ether, and anhydrous chromium(III) chloride is treated with CO, and the resulting solution is hydrolyzed, $Cr(CO)_6$ is produced. Similar reactions may be used to produce the hexacarbonyls of molybdenum and tungsten.

4. Preparation of higher carbonyls by photochemical reaction.

Soon after the discovery of $Fe(CO)_5$, it was found that it was photosensitive and gave rise to polymeric carbonyls by a photochemical reaction:

$$Fe(CO)_5 \underset{h\nu}{\overset{h\nu}{\diagdown}} \begin{array}{l} Fe_2(CO)_9 + CO \\ \\ Fe_3(CO)_{12} + 3CO \end{array}$$

The structures of the carbonyls have been found to be quite closely related to the general run of coordination compounds. The simple carbonyls are found to be of three types: tetrahedral, such as $Ni(CO)_4$; trigonal bipyramidal, such as $Fe(CO)_5$, $Ru(CO)_5$, and $Os(CO)_5$; and octahedral, such as $Cr(CO)_6$, $Mo(CO)_6$, and $W(CO)_6$. The polynuclear carbonyls which have been investigated have structures in which bridging CO groups and/or metal to metal bonds serve to hold the metal atoms together. The evidence for these bridging groups also indicates that the carbonyl groups involved in them are

[10a] W. Hieber and R. Bruck, *Naturwissenschaften* **36**, 312 (1949).

[11] W. Hieber and E. Romberg, *Zeit. anorg. u. allgem. Chem.* **221**, 321 (1935). This contains references to the earlier work on this reaction which was discovered by A. Job and A. Cassal, *Compt. rend.* **183**, 58, 392 (1926).

different in some respects from the terminal carbonyl groups. In $Fe_2(CO)_9$ the structure is:

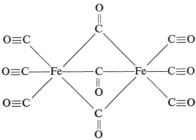

Although the carbon to oxygen bonds in these compounds are often written as triple bonds, present evidence seems to indicate that the preferred structure is one in which the bond is somewhere between a double and a triple bond but much closer to a double bond. In many of these compounds there is evidence that double bonds between the metal atom and the carbon form by the back donation of a pair of electrons from the metal atom.

The reactions of the carbonyls are quite varied in nature and allow the relationship of these compounds with several other types of compound to be demonstrated. In general, other pi bonding neutral coordinating groups may replace the carbon monoxide to a greater or lesser extent. In many cases the products which arise in this manner may be predicted on the assumption that the effective atomic number rule will be followed. Substitution reactions which have been studied include:

$$Cr(CO)_6 + 2C_5H_5N \rightarrow [Cr(CO)_4(C_5H_5N)_2] + 2CO$$
$$Ni(CO)_4 + 4PCl_3 \rightarrow Ni(PCl_3)_4 + 4CO$$
$$Co_2(CO)_8 + 2NO \rightarrow 2[Co(CO)_3 NO] + 2CO$$
$$Mo(CO)_6 + 3C_5H_5N \rightarrow [Mo(CO)_3 (C_5H_5N)_3] + 3CO$$
$$Co_2(CO)_8 + H_2 \rightarrow 2H[Co(CO)_4]$$
$$3Co_2 (CO)_8 + 4OH^- \rightarrow 4H[Co(CO)_4] + 2CO_3^= + 2[Co(CO)_3]_x$$

In cases which are sufficiently numerous to be a cause for concern, the effective atomic number rule appears to be a poor guide. Such is sometimes the case where mixed complexes are formed:

$$2Fe(CO)_5 + \text{Pyridine} \xrightarrow{80°C} [Fe_2(CO)_4(Pyr)_3] + 6CO$$
$$2Fe_3(CO)_{12} + 3 \text{ Pyridine} \rightarrow 3[Fe(CO)_3(Pyr)] + 3Fe(CO)_5$$

$$Mn_2(CO)_{10} + 2 \underset{(D)}{\left[\text{As(CH}_3)_2 \atop \text{As(CH}_3)_2}\right] \xrightarrow{160°} 2[Mn(CO)_3(D)] + 4CO \quad [12]$$

[12] R. S. Nyholm and D. V. Ramana Rao, *Proc. Chem. Soc.*, 130 (1959).

$$Mn_2(CO)_{10} + P(C_6H_5)_3 \rightarrow 2[Mn(CO)_4 \cdot P(C_6H_5)_3] + 2CO \quad [13]$$

In spite of these exceptions, the effective atomic number rule is a good rule of thumb in making a guess about the products of the reactions of the carbonyls.

Of the derivatives of the carbonyls, those discovered first were the carbonyl hydrides, the carbonyl halides, and the carbonyl nitrosyls.

The carbonyl hydrides are produced by the basic hydrolysis of some of the simple or polymeric carbonyls:

$$Fe(CO)_5 + 4OH^- \rightarrow Fe(CO)_4^= + CO_3^= + 2H_2O$$

when these solutions are acidified the carbonyl hydrides are produced:

$$Fe(CO)_4^= + 2H^+ \rightarrow H_2Fe(CO)_4$$

Iron carbonyl hydride is a weak dibasic acid in water:

$$H_2Fe(CO)_4 + H_2O \rightleftharpoons H_3O^+ + HFe(CO)_4^- \quad K_1 = 4 \times 10^{-5}$$
$$HFe(CO)_4^- + H_2O \rightleftharpoons H_3O^+ + Fe(CO)_4^= \quad K_2 = 4 \times 10^{-14} \quad [14]$$

It also forms a series of insoluble salts with the alkaline earth cations and cations of some heavy metals:

$$Hg^{+2} + H_2Fe(CO)_4 \rightarrow HgFe(CO)_4 \downarrow + 2H^+$$
$$Ca^{+2} + H_2Fe(CO)_4 \rightarrow CaFe(CO)_4 \downarrow + 2H^+$$

The other carbonyl hydrides such as $HCo(CO)_4$, $HRh(CO)_4$, $HIr(CO)_4$, and $H_2Os(CO)_4$ can be prepared by similar reactions. The effective atomic number rule is followed in these reactions. Some of the salts of these compounds are sufficiently stable that they may be handled in air, e.g., $Hg[Co(CO)_4]_2$.

The carbonyl halides can be made by allowing the carbonyl to react under very carefully controlled conditions with halogen, or by the reaction of carbon monoxide with the anhydrous metal halide. In some cases these compounds can even be formed in aqueous solution, though as a class they tend to be sensitive to the presence of water. A common example is the product formed when carbon monoxide is passed through an aqueous solution of a cuprous halide complex. For example, the gas is absorbed by solutions containing $CuCl_3^=$, and a solid material, $CuCl(CO)H_2O$, can be crystallized from solution. Cu(I), Ag(I), and Au(I) halides take up carbon monoxide to give compounds of the type MX(CO). Nickel, palladium, and platinum form complexes of this type when the anions present coordinate strongly with the metal, e.g., $K_2[Ni(CN)_3(CO)]$; $[Pd(CO)Cl_2]_2$; and $Pt(CO)_2Cl_2$. The reaction of iron pentacarbonyl with iodine passes through the sequence:

$$Fe(CO)_5 + I_2 \rightarrow Fe(CO)_5I_2 \rightarrow Fe(CO)_4I_2 + CO$$

[13] W. Hieber and G. Wagner, *Zeit. Naturforsch.* **12b**, 478 (1957).

[14] R. Krumholz and H. M. A. Stettiner, *J. Amer. Chem. Soc.* **71**, 3035 (1949); W. Heiber and W. Hubel, *Zeit. Naturforsch.* **7b**, 332 (1952).

Complexes of this type are known for the elements which form carbonyls (except for Cr, Mo, and W).

The carbonyl nitrosyls, for the most part, fit into the effective atomic number scheme if each NO is considered to donate three electrons to the central metal atom. One electron is lost in reducing the metal to a lower oxidation state and two are then shared to form the coordinate bond with the resulting NO^+. Examples of this class include $Co(CO)_3(NO)$, which is prepared by the reaction:

$$Co_2(CO)_8 + NO \rightarrow 2Co(CO)_3NO + 2CO$$

and $Fe(CO)_2(NO_2)_2$, prepared by the reaction:

$$Fe_2(CO)_9 + 4NO \rightarrow 2\,Fe(CO)_2(NO)_2 + 5CO$$

In addition to the variations in composition presented here, one may find mixtures of substituents on the central atoms which include those groups listed above as well as cyanide, thiols, amines of all sorts, phosphorus(III) halides, and other group III elements trihalides.

The uses of these compounds include: (a) the preparation of very pure metals, (b) the oxo process, (c) potential antiknock agents, and (d) catalysts in a very wide variety of industrial processes. Whenever the carbonyl is prepared with reasonable ease it can be used to prepare the pure metal in a very finely divided state by thermal decomposition. Carbonyl iron, for example, is a very pure iron produced by the thermal decomposition of $Fe(CO)_5$ in a hot chamber (not on a hot surface). It is made in large amounts for powder metallurgical applications. The *oxo* or *hydroformylation* reaction is one in which an unsaturated organic molecule or an alcohol is placed in a pressure reactor with a cobalt salt, hydrogen, and carbon monoxide under pressure and then heated. The reactions which occur include:

$$4C_2H_4 + 2H_2 + 4HCo(CO)_4 \rightarrow 4CH_3CH_2CHO + [Co(CO)_3]_4$$

$$C_2H_4 + H_2 \xrightarrow{Co_2(CO)_8} C_2H_6$$

$$R-CH_2OH + CO + H_2 \xrightarrow{Co_2(CO)_8} R-CH_2-CH_2-OH$$

$$R_2CH-OH + H_2 \xrightarrow{Co_2(CO)_8} R_2CH_3 + H_2O$$

The intermediate formation of cobalt carbonyl and cobalt carbonyl hydride in the processes is well established. In fact most of the reactions may be carried out using these compounds *per se*.

A large group of compounds of unusual interest is found in the hydrocarbon metal carbonyls.[15] These may be prepared from the carbonyls by replacement reactions, e.g.,

[15] P. L. Pauson, *Proc. Chem. Soc.*, 297–305 (1960), contains a summary of much of the work up to that time; H. D. Kaesz, *J. Chem. Ed.* **40**, 159 (1963) reviews compounds containing organic groups and various pi bonding ligands.

$$Fe(CO)_5 + CH_2{=}CH{-}CH{=}CH_2 \rightarrow (C_4H_6){-}Fe(CO)_3 + 2CO$$

$$Cr(CO)_6 + C_6H_6 \rightarrow (C_6H_6){-}Cr(CO)_3 + 3CO$$

In these products the unsaturated hydrocarbons are bonded to the metal atom by means of pi bonds formed by the donation of electrons from filled pi orbitals of the hydrocarbon to metal orbitals. The result is that the bond is formed in a direction perpendicular to the nodal plane of the orbitals.

The catalytic properties of cobalt carbonyl in the oxo process are related to the great reactivity of the hydrocarbon cobalt carbonyls which are formed as intermediates. Other transition metal carbonyls form similar complexes with similar reactivity. A well-characterized example of such a process is:

$$CH_3Mn(CO)_5 \underset{\Delta}{\overset{CO}{\rightleftharpoons}} H_3C{-}\underset{\underset{O}{\|}}{C}{-}Mn(CO)_5 \quad \text{[15a]}$$

In this reaction, only those carbonyl groups already attracted to the metal are transferred to the acetyl group! A very large number of complexes are formed with carbonyls and acetylene and in many cases these lead to synthetically useful reactions. Two of these are:

1. preparation of acrylic acids:

$$R{-}C{\equiv}C{-}R \xrightarrow{Ni(CO)_4} \text{Intermediate} \xrightarrow{H_2O} R{-}\underset{\underset{R}{|}}{C}{=}C{-}COOH$$

2. condensation of acetylene:

$$4HC{\equiv}CH + H_2Fe(CO)_4 + 2H_2O \rightarrow 2 \; \underset{OH}{\overset{OH}{\bigcirc}} + Fe(OH)_2 \quad \text{[16]}$$

The bonding in metal carbonyls has been the subject of much discussion.[17] The structural information on the simple carbonyls is reasonably complete and configurations and bond distances are known. The carbon-oxygen distance in these compounds provides a valuable clue to the bond order and to the probable charge distribution. In some of the carbonyls this distance is very close to 1.15 A; the value in carbon monoxide is 1.131 A. For BH_3CO, CO_2, CSO, and CH_2CO the distances are 1.131, 1.163, 1.164, and 1.16 A, respectively. In the metal carbonyls distances from 1.14 to 1.21 A are found.

[15a] F. Calderazzo and F. A. Cotton, *Inorganic Chemistry* **1**, 30 (1962).

[16] Numerous examples of related reactions are to be found in W. Reppe, *Ann.* **582**, 1–161 (1953).

[17] This is reviewed in J. W. Cable and R. K. Sheline, *Chem. Reviews* **56**, 1 (1956); J. W. Richardson, "Carbon-Metal Bonding" in H. Zeiss, editor, *Organometallic Chemistry*, Reinhold Publishing Corp., New York (1960).

This means that the bonds vary from nearly triple bonds to bonds intermediate in character between a single and a double bond. The carbon monoxide-metal bond consists of a σ component (arising from the donation of electrons from the carbon to the metal) and a π component (arising from the partial donation of electrons in the d orbitals of the metal to empty molecular orbitals of the ligand). The relative importance of these two forms is the subject of some controversy at present. In those polynuclear carbonyls with bridging carbonyl groups, the bridging groups are found to be quite different from the terminal carbonyls or the carbonyls in $Ni(CO)_4$. Infrared absorption spectra indicate that bridging carbonyls give rise to an intense band at about 1,850–1,800 cm^{-1} while the terminal carbonyls exhibit stretching frequencies in the region of 2,000 cm^{-1}, the number found being determined by the symmetry of the compound. This difference is generally used in estimating structures, though its limitations have been pointed out.[5]

FERROCENE, THE METAL CYCLOPENTADIENYLS AND THE ARENE COMPLEXES[18-24]

The recent discovery of ferrocene and the subsequent elucidation of the structures and properties of the metal cyclopentadienyls and the metal-aromatic complexes is a very forceful indication that there may be yet other types of compounds whose structures are unpredictable in terms of present-day theories and whose behavior is unthinkable in terms of present-day, orthodox chemical notions. The development of the chemistry of these compounds has proceeded at a very rapid rate and we now have a great deal of information on the preparation, properties, and reactions of these novel materials.

Ferrocene, $Fe(C_5H_5)_2$, was discovered accidentally and independently by two groups of workers, one in England and one in the United States. The former group[25] found that dicyclopentadienyl iron (ferrocene) was

[18] P. L. Pauson, *Quarterly Reviews* **9**, 391 (1955).

[19] E. G. Rochow, D. T. Hurd, and R. N. Lewis, *The Chemistry of Organometallic Compounds*, John Wiley & Sons, Inc., New York (1957).

[20] G. E. Coates, *Organo-Metallic Compounds*, Methuen & Co., Ltd., London, 2nd edition (1961).

[21] E. O. Fischer and H. P. Fritz, *Advances in Inorganic Chemistry and Radiochemistry* **1**, 56 (1959); *Angew. Chem.* **73**, 353 (1961).

[22] G. Wilkinson and F. A. Cotton, *Progress in Inorganic Chemistry*, **1**, 1 (1959).

[23] P. L. Pauson, "Cyclopentadienyl Metal Compounds" in H. Zeiss, editor, *Organometallic Chemistry*, Reinhold Publishing Corp., New York (1960), pp. 346–379.

[24] H. Zeiss, "Arene Complexes of the Transition Metals" in H. Zeiss, editor, *Organometallic Chemistry*, Reinhold Publishing Corp., New York (1960), pp. 380–425; M. D. Rausch, *J. Chem. Ed.* **37**, 568 (1960).

[25] S. A. Miller, J. A. Tebboth, and J. F. Tremaine, *J. Chem. Soc.*, 632 (1952). These investigators were the first to prepare the compound.

formed when cyclopentadiene was diluted with nitrogen, and passed over hot (300°) iron powder which contained oxides of aluminum, potassium, and molybdenum. The resultant compound was soluble in typical organic solvents and obviously was an organic compound of iron. This incidentally was the *first* organic compound of iron to be prepared. In the United States, Kealy and Pauson[26] prepared the same compound by the reaction of anhydrous ferric chloride with cyclopentadienylmagnesium bromide; if the Grignard reagent is present in excess it can reduce the ferrocinium ion produced initially to ferrocene:

$$FeCl_3 + 2 \, \begin{matrix} HC \!\!-\!\! CH \\ \| \quad \| \\ HC \quad CH \\ \diagdown \diagup \\ C \\ \diagup \diagdown \\ H \quad MgBr \end{matrix} \quad \rightarrow$$

Ferrocinium ion   Ferrocene

Subsequent studies established the "sandwich" structure of this compound which was first proposed by Wilkinson, Rosenblum, Whiting, and Woodward.[27] The pure compound is an orange-yellow crystalline solid which melts at 173° and sublimes readily. It is quite stable toward a variety of reagents, in contrast to the usual reactivity of organometallic compounds. It can be oxidized by concentrated nitric acid to the ferrocinium ion, $Fe(C_5H_5)_2^+$. It is also among the most thermally stable organometallic compounds. The bonding in this compound is usually considered to be based upon sd hybrid orbitals of the iron which are used to form two single bonds, one with each of the cyclopentadienide rings as a whole.[28] The $C_5H_5^-$ groups exhibit all those peculiarities which are summed up in the word *aromaticity*. They undergo electrophilic and nucleophilic reactions in much the same manner as benzene itself. The slightly higher acidity of the hydrogen atoms and some of the reactions indicate that the aromatic character of ferrocene may be actually greater than that of benzene itself. These reactions occur without disrupting the bond between the iron and the cyclopentadienide rings in most cases. Inasmuch as the chemical properties of ferrocene have been studied in great detail and can furnish a guide to the preparation and properties of related

[26] T. J. Kealy and P. L. Pauson, *Nature* **168**, 1639 (1951).

[27] G. Wilkinson, M. Rosenblum, M. C. Whiting, and R. B. Woodward, *J. Amer. Chem. Soc.* **74**, 2125 (1952).

[28] The interpretation of the bonding in this compound is still controversial. An excellent account of the theories up to 1959 is given in Ref. 22. More recent treatments are those of J. P. Dahl and C. J. Ballhausen, *Det Kgl. Danske Vendenskabernes Selskab, Mat.-fys. Medd.* **33**, No. 5 (1961) and E. M. Shustorovich and M. E. Dyatkina, *Zhur. Struk. Khim* **1**, 109 (1961), C.A. 57: 1747.

materials, this compound is well worth further discussion. The reactions given for ferrocene are indicative of the general reactions of the compounds in this class. Unfortunately, none of these other compounds appears to possess the unusual stability of ferrocene itself and for this reason, information on the corresponding compounds of other elements is much more limited.

The methods by which ferrocene may be prepared include the following:

1. The reaction of cyclopentadiene vapors with finely divided iron. This reaction is not very satisfactory for laboratory work, but may be suitable for the large scale preparation of the compound.

2. The reaction of an anhydrous ferrous or ferric halide with cyclopenta-dienylmagnesium bromide will produce ferrocene or the readily reduced ferrocinium ion. This method is one of general applicability for the preparation of the cyclopentadienyls of other elements from their anhydrous halides.

3. The reaction of cyclopentadienyl thallium and anhydrous ferrous or ferric halides. The cyclopentadienyl thallium is readily prepared from a solution of thallium acetate in potassium hydroxide in water by addition of cyclopentadiene. It can then be collected, dried and refluxed with the anhydrous halide:

$$C_5H_6 + KOH + Tl^+ \rightarrow K^+ + TlC_5H_5 + H_2O$$

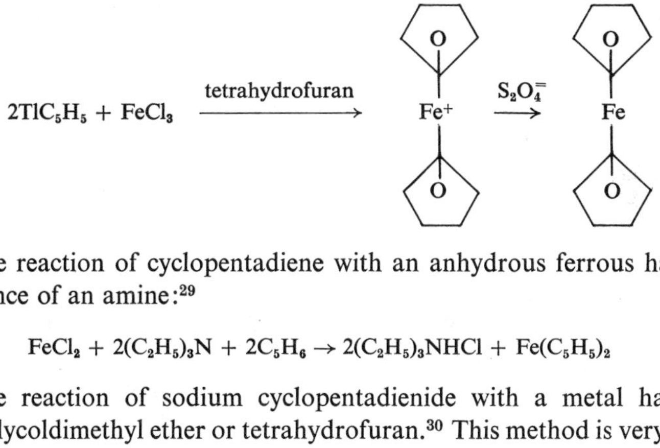

$$2TlC_5H_5 + FeCl_3 \xrightarrow{\text{tetrahydrofuran}} \quad \xrightarrow{S_2O_4^=}$$

4. The reaction of cyclopentadiene with an anhydrous ferrous halide in the presence of an amine:[29]

$$FeCl_2 + 2(C_2H_5)_3N + 2C_5H_6 \rightarrow 2(C_2H_5)_3NHCl + Fe(C_5H_5)_2$$

5. The reaction of sodium cyclopentadienide with a metal halide in ethyleneglycoldimethyl ether or tetrahydrofuran.[30] This method is very highly recommended and is of general utility.[22]

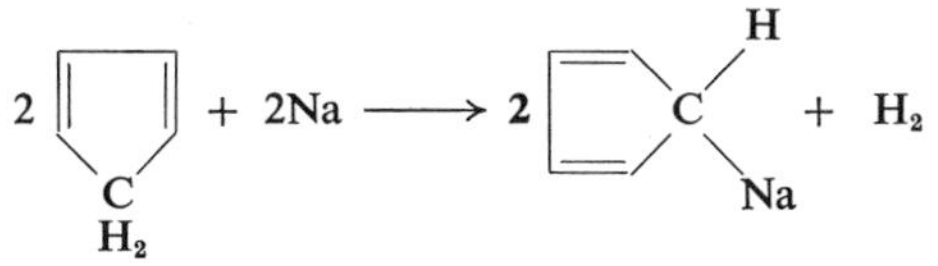

[29] J. M. Birmingham, D. Seyferth, and G. Wilkinson, *J. Amer. Chem. Soc.* **76**, 4179 (1954).
[30] G. Wilkinson and F. A. Cotton, *Chem. and Ind.*, 307 (1954).

6. The reaction of potassium cyclopentadienide with a metal ammine in liquid ammonia leads to the sandwich compound of the metal in several cases.[31]

7. The interaction of metal carbonyls with cyclopentadiene at elevated temperatures may lead to mixed derivatives in which both carbon monoxide and $C_5H_5^-$ are bound or to compounds in which all of the carbon monoxide has been replaced.[32]

In addition to the simple ferrocene, a large number of substituted ferrocene compounds have been prepared. Among these are numerous monosubstituted ferrocenes such as:

—R with R being [18,33,34]

—COCH$_3$	—NHCOOCH$_2$C$_6$H$_5$
—COOH	—NH$_2$
—COCl	—NHCOCH$_3$
—CONH$_2$	—C(CH$_3$)=NOH
—CH=CH$_2$	—C(CH$_3$)(OH)COCH$_3$
—CH$_2$—CH$_3$	—(CH$_2$)$_n$—COOH; n=1—5
—CON$_3$	—C(C$_6$H$_5$)$_3$
—C—(C$_5$H$_5$)$_2$	—C(CH$_3$)(H)(OH)
| OH	

The pronounced aromatic properties of ferrocene were shown in a very striking manner by Rosenblum, Whiting, and Woodward.[35] The behavior of the cyclopentadienyl groups provides every evidence for a complete delocalization of the pi electrons of the double bonds. Ferrocene will not undergo addition reactions with either maleic anhydride or with hydrogen in the presence of Adam's platinum oxide catalyst. The aromatic reactions which

[31] E. O. Fischer and R. Jira, *Zeit. Naturforsch.* **8b**, 217 (1953).

[32] G. Wilkinson, P. L. Pauson, and F. A. Cotton, *J. Amer. Chem. Soc.* **76**, 1970 (1954).

[33] F. S. Arimoto and A. C. Haven, *J. Amer. Chem. Soc.* **77**, 6295 (1955).

[34] R. J. Curley, Jr., K. L. Rinehart, and P. E. Sokol, *J. Amer. Chem. Soc.* **79**, 3420 (1957).

[35] M. Rosenblum, M. C. Whiting, and R. B. Woodward, *J. Amer. Chem. Soc.* **74**, 3458 (1952); the corresponding Os and Ru compounds also show such reactions: M. D. Rausch, E. O. Fischer, and H. Grubert, *J. Amer. Chem. Soc.* **82**, 76 (1960).

have been observed include: (a) sulfonation, (b) Friedel-Crafts acylation, (c) mercuration, (d) metalation, (e) arylation via reaction with diazonium salts, and (f) Claisen condensation and aldol condensation involving the alpha hydrogen of acetylferrocene. Electrophilic substitution reactions involving NO_2^+, Br^+, etc., usually result in oxidation rather than the expected products. Some of these reactions proceed as follows:

1. Sulfonation

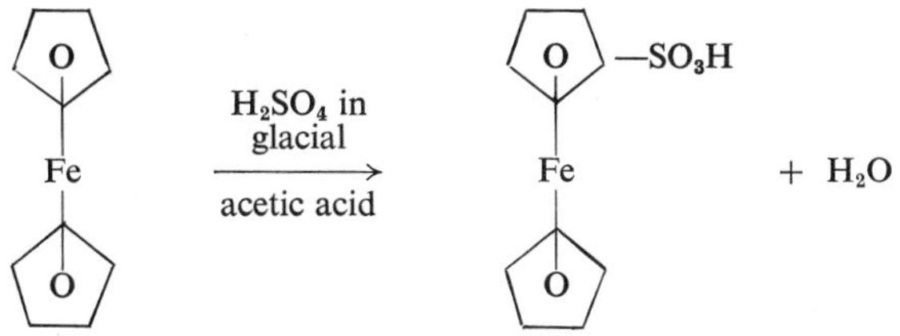

$$\text{(ferrocene)} \xrightarrow[\text{acetic acid}]{\substack{H_2SO_4 \text{ in} \\ \text{glacial}}} \text{(ferrocene--SO}_3\text{H)} + H_2O$$

2. Friedel-Crafts Acylation

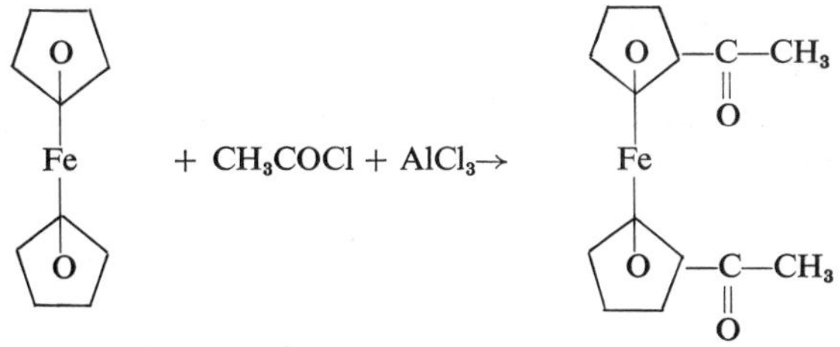

$$\text{(ferrocene)} + CH_3COCl + AlCl_3 \rightarrow \text{(diacetylferrocene)}$$

3. Mercuration

$$\text{(ferrocene)} + Hg(OAc)_2 \rightarrow \text{(ferrocene--HgOAc)} + HOAc$$

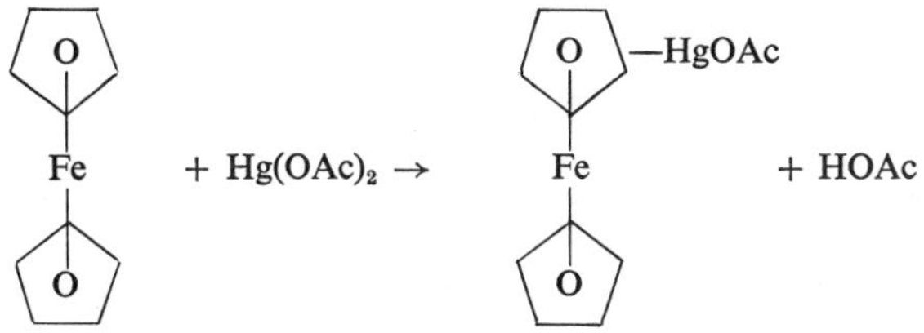

4. Metalation

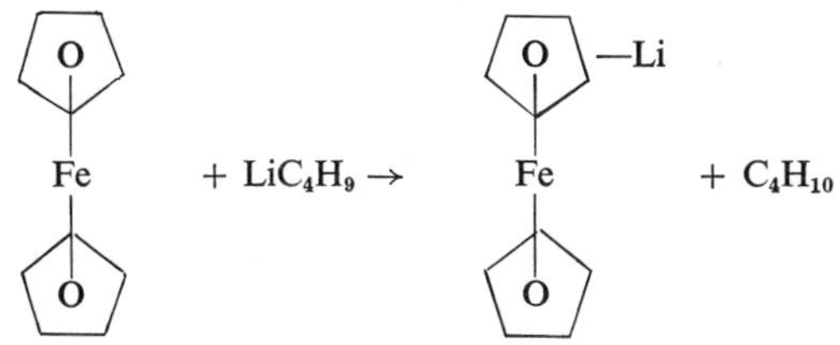

$$\text{(ferrocene)} + LiC_4H_9 \rightarrow \text{(ferrocene--Li)} + C_4H_{10}$$

5. Kosheshkov reaction of ferrocenyl lithium

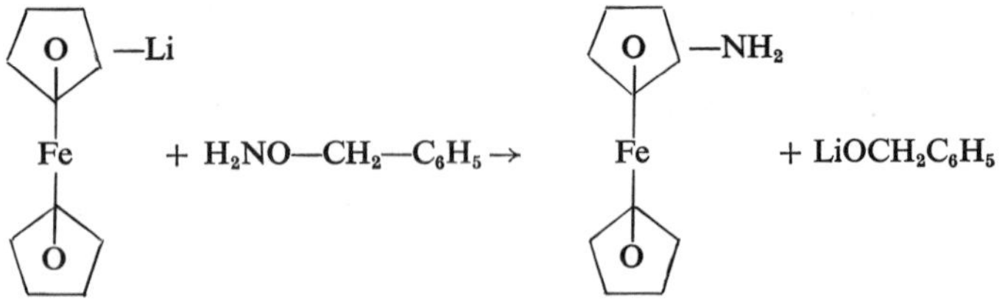

$$\text{Fe} \langle C_5H_4 \rangle{-}Li \quad + \; H_2NO{-}CH_2{-}C_6H_5 \rightarrow \quad \text{Fe} \langle C_5H_4 \rangle{-}NH_2 \quad + \; LiOCH_2C_6H_5$$

6. Indirect preparation of nitroferrocene[36]

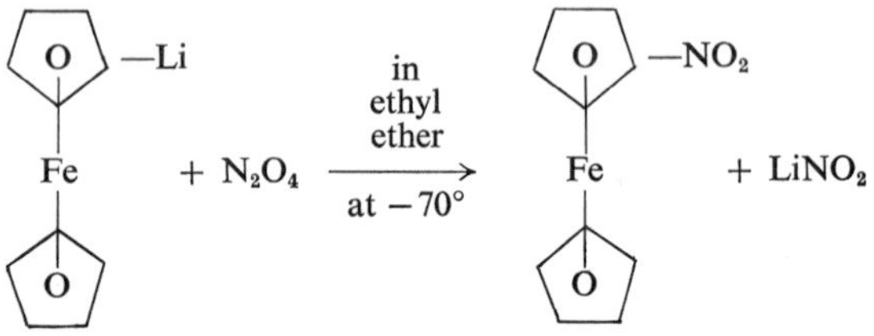

$$\text{Fe} \langle C_5H_4 \rangle{-}Li \quad + \; N_2O_4 \xrightarrow[\text{at } -70°]{\substack{\text{in} \\ \text{ethyl} \\ \text{ether}}} \quad \text{Fe} \langle C_5H_4 \rangle{-}NO_2 \quad + \; LiNO_2$$

The fact that only *one* isomer can be prepared for the diacetyl ferrocene (which has an acetyl group on each ring) is evidence for the free rotation of the cyclopentadienide groups about axes through the iron atom. The free rotation of the aromatic rings in this and similar materials seems to be a general phenomenon consistent with the physical and chemical properties of the compounds and with the numbers and types of isomers which can be characterized.

Other rings which can be used in the preparation of this type of compound include substituted cyclopentadienes of a wide variety, including indene. These compounds exhibit the same general features as ferrocene. Thus lithium indenyl and ferric chloride react to give bisindenyl iron. Hydrogenation of this compound gives rise to bistetrahydroindenyl iron hydrogenated in the benzene ring.

OTHER CYCLOPENTADIENYLS. Soon after the discovery of ferrocene, corresponding compounds of a number of other transition metals were prepared. In most cases these compounds were much less stable and much more reactive than ferrocene, many of them being rapidly attacked by atmospheric oxygen. Some of these are arranged in the following table. R represents the group C_5H_5.

One peculiar fact is that most of the *neutral* compounds of the type MR_2 melt at 172–173° C. It should be noted that because of the loss of a hydrogen ion from cyclopentadiene, C_5H_6, the group which is present in these compounds is the cyclopentadienide ion, $C_5H_5^-$. Thus ferrocene contains *ferrous* iron.

[36] J. F. Helling and H. Schechter, *Chem. and Ind.*, 1157 (1959).

Group IV	V	VI	VII	VIII		
TiR_2	VR_2	CrR_2	MnR_2	FeR_2	CoR_2	NiR_2
TiR_2^+	VR_2^+	CrR_2^+		FeR_2^+	CoR_2^+	NiR_2^+
	VR_2^{++}				Co_2R_5	
ZrR_2^+	NbR_2^{+3}	MoR_2Cl^+			RuR_2	RhR_2
		$MoR_2Cl_2^+$				
	TaR_2^{+3}	$WR_2Cl_2^+$	ReR_2H	OsR_2	IrR_2^+	

Before passing on to related materials it should be noted that one of the most prominent workers in this field, E. O. Fischer (University of Munich), considers these compounds to be a special type of penetration complex in which three pairs of pi electrons in each cyclopentadiene ring are shared with the central metal atom. Many of the properties of the complexes may be correlated with this kind of approach, though it is *not* generally accepted. One of the difficulties which arises is the isomer problem. If three-coordinate bonds were formed between the iron and each of the rings, substitution isomers would be expected for compounds in which one group was on each ring. No such isomers have been found *yet*. This picture does have the advantage that it would lead to the prediction that the electron pairs in the double bonds are definitely not available for any chemical reaction which does not disrupt the compound and this is certainly in accord with experimental evidence.

Thus Fischer considers the bonding in ferrocene to be based on the sharing of six pairs of pi electrons with the ferrous ion to give a nearly octahedral arrangement of bonds about the central metal atom. In molecular orbital notation, Fischer's scheme is:

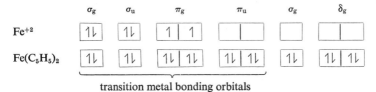

transition metal bonding orbitals

BISBENZENECHROMIUM(O) AND RELATED COMPOUNDS[21,22,24]

Arene complexes of chromium were first prepared by Hein in 1919. They were subsequently studied in some detail by him. The structures of these compounds were initially formulated as containing chromium to carbon bonds but the elucidation of their reactions did not occur until Onsager, Zeiss, and Tsutsui showed how these could also be formulated as sandwich complexes with the chromium atom located between two benzene rings oriented face to face. These compounds were independently reinvestigated by E. O. Fischer and his students. The synthesis of bisbenzenechromium developed by Fischer and Hafner is perhaps the most convenient and possesses two stages.[37]

The reaction was carried out in an autoclave or pressure vessel and involved heating chromic chloride, aluminum chloride, aluminum, and benzene to 180°. The initial product is a salt of the cation $[Cr(C_6H_6)_2]^+$:

$$3CrCl_3 + 2Al + AlCl_3 + 6C_6H_6 \rightarrow 3[Cr(C_6H_6)_2]AlCl_4$$

The cation can then be reduced to the brownish-black bisbenzenechromium(O) by dithionite in a basic solution:

$$2[Cr(C_6H_6)_2]^+ + S_2O_4^- + 4OH^- \rightarrow 2Cr(C_6H_6)_2 + 2H_2O + 2SO_3^-$$

Subsequent work on preparative methods has resulted in considerable improvement and in the extension of this reaction to other aromatic systems. In the presence of catalytic amounts of mesitylene, the reaction with benzene may be carried out under reflux conditions if provision is made to prevent the entry of air into the system. For chromium, it is possible to prepare materials of this type by a reaction such as that between phenylmagnesium bromide and chromic chloride followed by hydrolysis of the mixture to obtain solutions containing the cation $Cr(C_6H_6)_2^+$.[38,39] These species are rather readily oxidized by atmospheric oxygen. In addition to the benzene compound, compounds have been prepared with toluene, *o-*, *m-*, and *p-* xylene, mesitylene, pseudocumene, hexamethylbenzene, diphenyl, and tetralin. While dibenzoic acid chromium(O) is reported to be formed when CO_2 is added to the Grignard reagent-chromic chloride mixture in the synthesis of dibenzenechromium(O), the aromaticity of the rings in dibenzenechromium(O) seems to be absent or enormously reduced. No substitution reactions of the rings in this complex had been reported up to 1958 and the substituted derivatives which have been reported have all been prepared in an indirect manner. Its greater ease of oxidation is undoubtedly a deterrent to the further investigation of some of the more common electrophilic substitution reactions. Those compounds containing substituted aromatic rings which have been prepared may often be made by a direct method involving reaction of the substituted benzene with hexacarbonylchromium(O):

$$Cr(CO)_6 + C_6H_6 \rightarrow C_6H_6Cr(CO)_3 + 3CO$$
$$Cr(CO)_6 + C_6H_5Cl \rightarrow ClC_6H_5Cr(CO)_3 + 3CO$$
$$Cr(CO)_6 + C_6H_5NH_2 \rightarrow H_2NC_6H_5Cr(CO)_3 + 3CO$$
$$Cr(CO)_6 + C_6H_5OH \rightarrow HOC_6H_5Cr(CO)_3 + 3CO$$

[37] E. O. Fischer and W. Hafner, *Zeit. Naturforsch.* **10b**, 665 (1955); *idem, Zeit. anorg. u. allgem. Chem.* **286**, 146 (1956).

[38] F. Hein and H. Muller, *Ber.* **89**, 2722 (1956).

[39] H. H. Zeiss and W. Herwig, *Ann.* **606**, 209 (1957).

Tricarbonylbenzenechromium(O) is rather soluble in the usual run of organic solvents and is fairly stable in air.

The structure of bisbenzenechromium(O) has been determined.[40] In the solid, the chromium is nestled between two eclipsed benzene rings in a typical sandwich structure. The chromium to carbon distances are all identical, 2.19 A. The carbon-carbon distances are 1.38 A here, compared with 1.39 A in benzene.

Aromatic complexes of this type have since been made for the elements V, Mo, W, Re, Fe, Ru, Os, Co, Rh, and Ir so the complexing properties observed are general ones. This work has also resulted in a review and reorganization of the earlier work on the organochromium compounds of F. Hein. Starting in 1919, Hein prepared a large number of materials of this type by the interaction of chromic chloride and phenylmagnesium bromide. These have since been shown to be complexes of the same type as bisbenzenechromium(O) but with related aromatic groups. Thus the compound Hein reported as $Cr(C_6H_5)_3$ is $[Cr(C_6H_6)(C_6H_5C_6H_5)]$, viz.:

[41]

Further work on this class of compounds has shown that other ring systems with six pi electrons can also form sandwich compounds in which the metal sits between two aromatic rings. Such rings include both homo- and heterocyclic rings. The large numbers of such aromatic systems leads to the expectation that a very large number of such compounds may be prepared in the not too distant future. One of the recently reported complexes of this type involves the tropylium cation, $C_7H_7^+$, viz.: $C_7H_7Mo(CO)_3$. Tropylidene is made by expansion of the benzene ring with diazomethane and is:

tropylidene   tropylium ion

It is converted into the tropylium bromide by bromination followed by the removal of HBr.[42,43] The tropylium cation is less prone to form complexes than the cyclopentadienide anion.

[40] E. Weiss and E. O. Fischer, *Zeit. anorg. u. allgem. Chem.* **286**, 142 (1956).
[41] H. H. Zeiss and M. Tsutsui, *J. Amer. Chem. Soc.* **79**, 3062 (1957).
[42] W. von E. Doering and C. H. Depuy, *J. Amer. Chem. Soc.* **75**, 5955 (1953).
[43] W. von E. Doering and L. H. Knox, *J. Amer. Chem. Soc.* **76**, 3203 (1954).

COMPLEXES WITH UNSATURATED HYDROCARBONS[44,45,46]

In 1825, Zeise[47] reported the preparation of a compound containing platinum, chlorine, and ethylene as a potassium salt, which he made by refluxing $PtCl_4$ with alcohol and then adding potassium chloride to precipitate the solid. The reaction which occurs here was studied by Birnbaum[48] and is given by the equations:

$$2PtCl_4 + 4C_2H_5OH \rightarrow [PtCl_2 \cdot C_2H_4]_2 + 2CH_3CHO + 2H_2O + 4HCl$$

then

$$[PtCl_2 \cdot C_2H_4]_2 + 2KCl \rightarrow K[PtCl_3 \cdot C_2H_4]$$

Subsequently, a large number of analogous compounds have been prepared and characterized. Complexes involving olefins and metallic ions are known for the elements Pt, Pd, Ag, Cu, Ir, and many others. The compounds formed by mercury salts under similar conditions are organometallic compounds with Hg—C bonds, rather than complexes in which the double bond acts as a donor group.

Of the complexes of this type, those of platinum are most readily prepared. The methods of preparation which have been used include the following:

1. Reaction of a metal halide with an alcohol:[48,49]

$$PtCl_4 + C_3H_7OH \rightarrow [PtCl_2(CH_3CH=CH_2)]_2$$

$$IrCl_3 + C_2H_5OH \rightarrow [IrCl_2 \cdot C_2H_4]_{x=2?}$$

2. Reaction of a suspension of anhydrous Pt(IV) halide with the unsaturated hydrocarbon in an anhydrous solvent:[50]

$$+ \text{ other products}$$

This method was also used in the preparation of the corresponding complex with diazobenzene:

[44] B. E. Douglas, "Compounds of Metals with Olefins", in J. C. Bailar, Jr., editor, *The Chemistry of the Coordination Compounds*, Reinhold Publishing Corp., New York (1956), p. 487.

[45] G. E. Coates and F. Glockling, "Transition Metal Alkyls and Aryls" in H. Zeiss, editor, *Organometallic Chemistry*, Reinhold Publishing Corp., New York (1960), p. 426.

[46] A. Helman, *Complex Compounds of Platinum with Unsaturated Molecules*, Publishing House of the Academy of Science, U.S.S.R., Moscow (1945).

[46a] E. O. Fischer and H. Werner *Metall-π-Komplexe mit di-und oligoolefinische Liganden*, Verlag Chemie, Weinheim, (1963).

[47] W. C. Zeise, *Oversight Kgl. Danske Videns, Selskab. For.* (1825–1826), p. 13 cited in Poggendorff's Ann. **9**, 632 (1827).

[48] K. Birnbaum, Ann. **145**, 67 (1869).

[49] S. P. Sadtler, *Bull. Soc. chim. France* **17**, 54 (1872).

[50] M. S. Kharasch and T. A. Ashford, *J. Amer. Chem. Soc.* **58**, 1733 (1936).

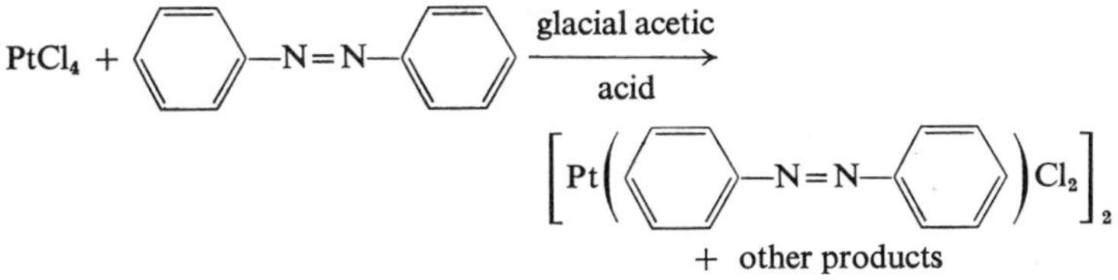
PtCl4 +
—N=N—
glacial acetic
acid
Pt
—N=N—
Cl2
2
+ other products

This latter compound is one of the few in which a double bond other than one between two carbon atoms is involved as a donor in compounds of this class. Usually the azo group exhibits coordination properties to a noticeable extent only when it is part of a chelate system. Kharash and Ashford found that *trans*-dichloroethylene forms a rather unstable compound of this type but *cis*-dichloroethylene formed no such compound at all. The presence of steric hindrance in this case seems questionable. This particular method does not work with unsaturated acids and their esters.

3. By the reaction of aqueous solutions of potassium tetrachloroplatinate(IV) with unsaturated alcohols or unsaturated esters.[51] The resulting complex species are rather soluble but may be precipitated by the addition of a salt of a large cation, e.g., salts of $Pt(NH_3)_4^{+2}$, or $[Co(en)_2Cl_2]^+$:

$$K_2PtCl_4 + R{-}CH{=}CHCH_2OH \rightarrow KCl + K[PtCl_3(R{-}CH{=}CH{-}CH_2OH)]$$

$$K[PtCl_3(R{-}CH{=}CH{-}CH_2OH)] + [Co(en)_2Cl_2]^+ \rightarrow [Co(en)_2Cl_2][PtCl_3(R{-}CH{=}CH{-}CH_2OH)] + K^+$$

4. The reaction of the gaseous olefin with acidic aqueous solutions of potassium tetrachloroplatinate(II):[52]

$$K_2PtCl_4 + C_2H_4 \xrightarrow[\text{15 days}]{\text{3–5\% HCl}} K[Pt(C_2H_4)Cl_3] + KCl$$

The reactions of $[Pt(C_2H_4)Cl_3]^-$ were studied in some detail by Chernyaev and Hel'man, *loc. cit.*:

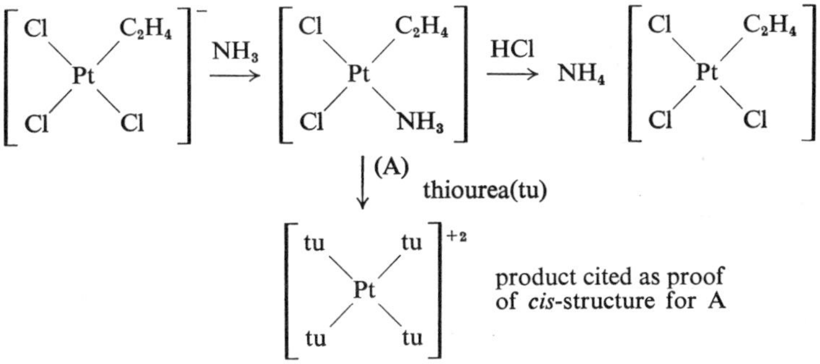
Cl
C2H4
Pt
Cl
Cl
NH3
Cl
C2H4
Pt
Cl
NH3
HCl
NH4
Cl
C2H4
Pt
Cl
Cl
(A)
thiourea(tu)
tu
tu
Pt
tu
tu
+2
product cited as proof
of cis-structure for A

[51] P. Pfieffer and H. Hoyer, *Zeit. anorg. u. allgem. Chem.* **211**, 241 (1933).

[52] I. I. Chernyaev and A. D. Hel'man, *Ann. secteur platine, Inst. Chem. gen.* (U.S.S.R.), No. 14, 77–121 (1937), C.A. 32: 445; E. Biilmann and A. Hoff, *Rec. trav. chim.* **36**, 306 (1916).

The configurations on these two compounds (A) with NH_3 or Py, are reported differently in the abstract of another paper.[53]

$$M[PtCl_3C_2H_4] + a \rightarrow trans\text{-}[PtCl_2(C_2H_4)a]$$
where a is NH_3 or pyridine

and

$$M[aPtCl_3] + C_2H_4 \rightarrow cis\text{-}[PtCl_2(C_2H_4)a] + MCl$$

It seems probable that the Kurnakov reaction is not sufficiently reliable to be used as the sole test of the configuration of the products. One point of interest is that both $[Pt(C_2H_4)NH_3Cl_2]$ and $[Pt(C_2H_4)pyCl_2]$ contain what Chernyaev calls "mobile halogen atoms." The further reactions of $[Pt(C_2H_4)NH_3Cl_2]$ prepared by the first reaction cited in this discussion(A) include the reaction with excess pyridine to give $trans\text{-}[Pt(py)_2Cl_2]$:

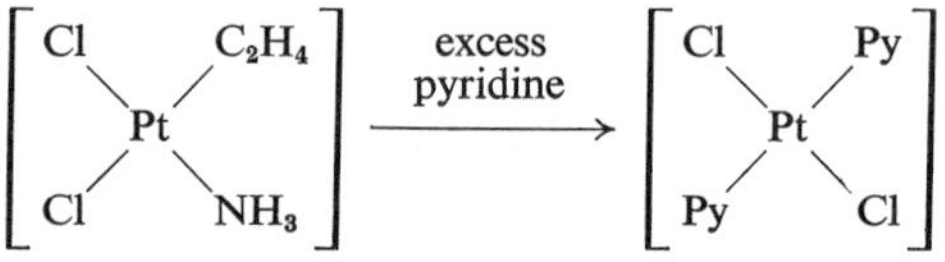

This is a rather unexpected reaction to say the least. Chernyaev and Hel'man reported that the stability of the ethylene complexes that contained a base decreased in the order thiourea > NH_3 > pyridine > quinoline and also that the corresponding complexes with anions other than chloride allows the sequence of stability for such complexes to be put in the order $Cl^- > Br^- > I^- > NO_2^- > NCS^- > CN^-$. Furthermore, the presence of an excess of *any* of these ions except Cl^- causes the replacement of the ethylene in the complex. Most of this information can be explained by the assumption that ethylene has a very high trans effect.

5. By the replacement of one olefin by another.[54]

$$K[PtCl_3C_2H_4] + PhCH=CH_2 \rightarrow K[PtCl_3(PhCH=CH_2)] + C_2H_4$$

The stabilities of olefin complexes have been investigated by the use of displacement reactions, vapor pressure measurements, distribution ratios, and spectrophotometric measurements.

Anderson[54] examined the complexes analogous to Zeise's salt which were formed by substituted ethylenes and found that *all* were less stable than the parent complex, but also more soluble in water. These compounds are also *very* readily reduced by hydrogen:

$$[PtCl_2(PhCH=CH_2)]_2 \xrightarrow{H_2} 2PhCH_2CH_3 + 2Pt + 4HCl$$

Anderson estimated the relative stabilities of some of these complexes by the

[53] I. I. Chernyaev and A. D. Hel'man, *Compt. rend. acad. sci. U.R.S.S.* (N.S.) 4, 181–4 (1936), C.A. 31: 2541.
[54] J. S. Anderson, *J. Chem. Soc.*, 1042 (1936).

ease with which the hydrocarbon reacted with the ethylene complex. The much greater volatility of ethylene allowed such reactions to proceed under reduced pressure even though the ethylene complexes are the most stable. This relative order of the vigor of the replacement reaction is given by Anderson as:

Hydrocarbon	Action on $[PtCl_2C_2H_4]_2$	Action on $K[PtCl_3C_2H_4]$
styrene	C_2H_4 liberated vigorously	C_2H_4 liberated vigorously
amylene	,, ,, ,,	,, ,, ,,
indene	C_2H_4 slowly displaced	no apparent action but C_5H_{10} displaced from $K[PtCl_3C_5H_{10}]$
other hydrocarbons	no action	no action

Other hydrocarbons included α,α-diphenylethylene, β phenylpropylene, tetraphenylethylene, etc.

In most cases steric factors seemed quite adequate to explain the factors which were acting to prevent the formation of stable complexes of this sort.

In a study of some complexes of Pt(II), complexes with substituted styrenes, Joy and Orchin[55] were able to determine the effect of substituents in the 3- and 4-positions of the aromatic ring on the stability of the complexes. The reaction examined was the competitive one between the styrene and the *l*-dodecene complex of the Zeiss's salt type:

$$X-C_6H_4-CH=CH_2 + [C_{12}H_{24}PtCl_3]^- \rightleftharpoons [X-C_6H_4CH=CH_2PtCl_3]^- + C_{12}H_{24}$$

The equilibrium constants obtained at $25.0 \pm 0.2°$ in approximately 0.1N HCl solution are:

X Substituent	H—	4-CH₃–	3-CH₃	4-CH₃O—	4-NO₂	3-Cl
K	0.027	0.037	0.030	0.052	0.048	0.031

The relatively great distance of the substituents from the coordinated ethylenic linkage would be expected to lead to a situation where any electronic effects could be separated from purely steric ones. When the logarithms of the equilibrium constants were plotted against the Hammett sigma constants for the substituents, a curve was obtained with a minimum at the unsubstituted styrene and higher values for both electron donating and electron withdrawing groups. The explanation given for this curious curve was that the overlap integral and the energy of the systems were related in a peculiar manner so that when the overlap integral increased the energy decreased for a certain range of values of the variables used to describe the system.

In a subsequent paper, Joy and Orchin[56] found that the ion of the type $[UnPtCl_3]^-$ formed from *cis*-4-methyl-2-pentene was more stable than the

[55] J. R. Joy and M. Orchin, *J. Amer. Chem. Soc.* **81**, 305 (1959).
[56] J. R. Joy and M. Orchin, *J. Amer. Chem. Soc.* **81**, 310 (1959).

corresponding ion formed from the *trans*-4-methyl-2-pentene. Equilibrium constants for the reaction:

$$PhCH=CH_2 + [UnPtCl_3]^- \rightleftharpoons Un + [PhCH=CH_2PtCl_3]^-$$

were 0.095 for the *cis*-isomer and 0.34 for the *trans*-isomer. These studies were carried out spectrophotometrically. Interestingly enough, the first unequivocal proof of the nonidentity of the platinum olefin complexes with *cis*- and *trans*-isomers was presented in 1957 by Jonassen and Kirsch[57] for the related complexes with *cis*- and *trans*-2-butene.

The use of distribution measurements has been most extensive in investigations of the weaker complexes which olefins form with the silver ion or the cuprous ion. An extensive series of studies on the olefin complexes of silver(I) was reported by H. J. Lucas and his co-workers.[58] In these studies the distribution of the olefin between carbon tetrachloride and aqueous solutions of silver salts was determined. In many cases, the aqueous solution was held at unit ionic strength by the addition of potassium nitrate. In some of the experiments there was evidence for a complex of the type BAg_2^{++}, where B represents the hydrocarbon. The equilibria which were considered in treating the data were:

$$B_w \rightleftharpoons B_c \qquad \text{(ionic strength unity)}$$

$$B \rightleftharpoons B_c \qquad \text{(variable ionic strength)}$$

$$B + Ag^+ \rightleftharpoons AgB^+$$

$$B_c + Ag^+ \rightleftharpoons AgB^+$$

$$BAg^+ + Ag^+ \rightleftharpoons BAg_2^{++}$$

$$K_w = \frac{(B_c)}{(B_w)} ; \qquad K_d = \frac{(B_c)}{(B)} ; \qquad K_1 = \frac{(BAg^+)}{(B)(Ag^+)} ; \qquad K_{01} = \frac{(BAg^+)}{(B_c)(Ag^+)}$$

$$K_2 = \frac{(BAg_2^{++})}{(B_c)(Ag^+)}$$

$$\left. \begin{aligned} K_E &= \frac{K_d[(Bt_w) - (B)]}{(B_c)[(Agt) - (Bt) - (B)]} \\ &= \frac{K_d[(Bt_w) - (B_c/K_d)]}{(B_c)[(Agt) - (Bt) + (B_c/K_d)]} \end{aligned} \right\}$$

evaluated constant, Ag_2B^{++} formation ignored $K_0 = \dfrac{K_i}{K_d}$

When only one reaction occurs in the aqueous phase between the silver ion and the unsaturated compound, K_E is equal to K_1. Thus by measuring the distribution ratio K_D, the determination of the total silver in the aqueous

[57] H. B. Jonassen and W. B. Kirsch, *J. Amer. Chem. Soc.* **79**, 1279 (1957).

[58] W. F. Eberz, H. J. Welge, D. M. Yost, and H. J. Lucas, *J. Amer. Chem. Soc.* **59**, 45 (1937); S. Winstein and H. J. Lucas, *ibid.*, **60**, 836 (1938); H. J. Lucas, F. Hepner, and S. Winstein, *ibid.*, **61**, 3102 (1939); H. J. Lucas, R. S. Moore, and D. Pressman, *ibid.*, **65**, 227 (1943); H. J. Lucas, F. W. Billmeyer, Jr., and D. Pressman, *ibid.*, **65**, 230 (1943); F. R. Hepner, K. N. Trueblood, and H. J. Lucas, *ibid.*, **74**, 1333 (1952); K. N. Trueblood and H. J. Lucas, *ibid.*, **74**, 1339 (1952). Rate studies of this kind of reaction may be found in P. Brandt, *Acta Chem. Scand.* **13**, 1639 (1959).

phase (Agt), and the total concentration of the unsaturated molecule in the aqueous phase (Bt_w) allows K_E to be obtained and hence K_1. For systems in which other equilibria occur in addition to the simplest, the relationship between K_E and the complexation constants is different.

For biallyl, a complex of the type $[(H_2C=CH(CH_2)_2CH=CH_2)Ag_2]^{++}$ was found and a similar complex was found with 2,3-dimethylbutadiene. For allyl alcohol and phenol, complexes of the type AgB_2^+ were found. The table below summarizes the first formation constants for the hydrocarbons studied by Winstein and Lucas, *loc. cit.*

Substance	K_1
$CH_2=CH(CH_2)_2CH=CH_2$	1850
n Bu—CH=CH$_2$	860
$(CH_3)_2CH=CH_2$	61.7
$(C_2H_5)CH=CH(CH_3)$	62.7
cyclohexene	79.3
$(CH_3)_2C=CH(CH_3)$	13.3
$H_2C=C(CH_3)—C(CH_3)=CH_2$	22.5

There was some evidence that replacing the KNO_3 by $AgNO_3$ in the aqueous phase had a definite effect in causing the ratio of the activity coefficients of Ag$^+$ and AgB^+ to vary. This was examined in further detail by Koenig[59] who found that the solubilities of cyclohexane and carbon tetrachloride in $1N$ KNO_3 were each about 6% less than in $1N$ $AgNO_3$. This indicates that the K^+ ion is a more effective salting out agent than the Ag$^+$ ion.

Studies on cuprous halide complexes with olefins have also been carried out in much the same manner. Keefer and Andrews,[60] examined the solubility of cuprous chloride in aqueous allyl alcohol solutions at 25° and an ionic strength of 0.1. They found that the reactions needed to account for their results were:

$$CuCl(s) + A \rightleftharpoons ACuCl \qquad K_1 = \frac{(ACuCl)}{(A)}$$

$$CuCl(s) + A \rightleftharpoons ACu^+ + Cl^- \qquad K_2 = \frac{(ACu^+)(Cl^-)}{(A)}$$

$$CuCl(s) \rightleftharpoons Cu^+ + Cl^- \qquad S.P. = 1.85 \times 10^{-7}$$

$$CuCl(s) + Cl^- \rightleftharpoons CuCl_2^- \qquad K_4 = \frac{[CuCl_2^-]}{[Cl^-]} = 0.065$$

From solubility measurements K_1 was found to be 0.41 and K_2 to be 0.97×10^{-2}. In a later paper, Keefer, Andrews, and Kepner[61] examined the effect of the structure of a number of unsaturated acids on the aqueous solubility of cuprous chloride and found that complexes of the type UnCuCl and UnCu$^+$ were formed, where Un represents the unsaturated species. Formation con-

[59] N. Koenig, "Ph.D. thesis", Calif. Inst. Technology (1950).
[60] R. M. Keefer and L. J. Andrews, *J. Amer. Chem. Soc.* **71**, 1723 (1949).
[61] R. M. Keefer, L. J. Andrews, and R. E. Kepner, *J. Amer. Chem. Soc.* **71**, 2381 (1949).

stants for both types of complexes were determined at 25° and are summarized in the following table:

Acid	Formula	$K_1 \times 10^2$	$K_2 \times 10^2$
Vinylacetic	$CH_2 = CH—CH_2COOH$	340	135
Fumaric	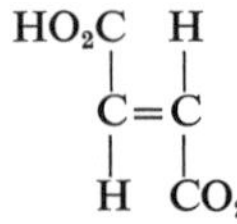 HO_2C H $\quad C=C$ H CO_2H	92	51
Itaconic	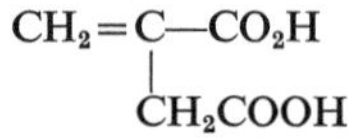 $CH_2=C—CO_2H$ $\quad CH_2COOH$	22	17
Maleic	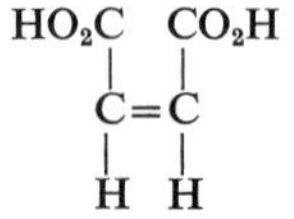 HO_2C CO_2H $\quad C=C$ H H	11.3	9.7
Crotonic	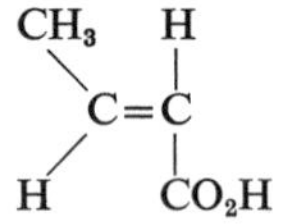 CH_3 H $\quad C=C$ H CO_2H	16	9.2
Tiglic	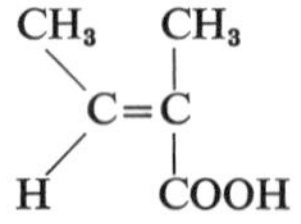 CH_3 CH_3 $\quad C=C$ H $COOH$	2.1	5.4
β,β-Dimethyl- acrylic	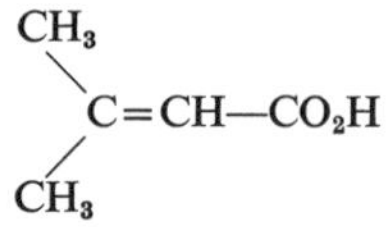 CH_3 $\quad C=CH—CO_2H$ CH_3	1.1	4.3
Mesaconic	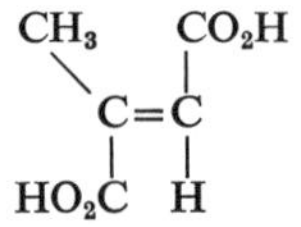 CH_3 CO_2H $\quad C=C$ HO_2C H	4.1	3.7
Citraconic	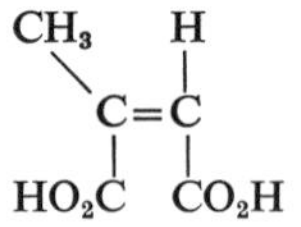 CH_3 H $\quad C=C$ HO_2C CO_2H	0.22	2.3

These data indicate that with these complexes, as with the corresponding complexes of platinum, steric effects predominate over electronic shifts to determine the relative stabilities of the complexes. Thus substitutions on the doubly bonded carbon atoms which increase the electronic density of the double bond usually introduce the greater concurrent disadvantage of steric hindrance.

The structure of the complexes of olefins with platinum and palladium have been determined by X-ray methods and found to be quite different from what had been predicted. The complex $K[PtCl_3C_2H_4]$ was examined by Wunderlich and Mellor.[62]

It was found that the internuclear axis of the double bond is approximately perpendicular to the square plane in which the other bonds of the platinum(II) are arranged. The structure of the related complex $[PdCl_2(C_2H_4)]_2$ was determined by Dempsey and Baenziger[63] who found it to be a bridged structure with two of the chlorides acting to bridge two square planar palladium(II) species. The ethylenes were in the *trans*-positions. Here the center of the double bond of the ethylene lies in the plane of the other bonds to palladium. The structure of the corresponding styrene complex, $[PdCl_2(C_6H_5CH{=}CH_2)]_2$, is similar if less symmetrical.[64] In this complex, the Pd—Cl bonds opposite the olefin were longer than the others, a feature which would be anticipated from a consideration of the large *trans*-effect of these olefinic groups.

The bonding in these olefin complexes is generally discussed on the basis of a suggestion by Dewar[65] which was developed by Chatt and Duncanson.[66] The platinum in a complex such as $K[PtCl_3C_2H_4]$ is divalent and uses $dsp^2(5d6s6p^2)$ hybrid orbitals for bonding to the ligand groups. The bonding electrons of the olefin are shared with an unoccupied dsp^2 orbital of platinum giving rise to a sigma bond. In addition the platinum shares a pair of electrons in a $dp(5d6p)$ hybrid orbital with the empty antibonding pi orbital of the olefin to give a pi bond.

THE PHTHALOCYANINE COMPLEXES[67-69]

There is a large and very important class of coordination compounds whose structure and properties are uniquely or primarily determined by the structure of the ligand. These generally are composed of a chelating agent with four donor nitrogens arranged in a square about a central area just large enough to comfortably accommodate a metal ion. The resultant complexes are ones in which the stereochemistry of the central ion is fixed by the chelating agent and we find such materials, many of which possess outstanding stab-

[62] J. A. Wunderlich and D. P. Mellor, *Acta Cryst.* **7**, 130 (1954); **8**, 57 (1955).

[63] J. N. Dempsey and N. C. Baenziger, *J. Amer. Chem. Soc.* **77**, 4984 (1955).

[64] N. C. Baenziger and J. R. Holden, *J. Amer. Chem. Soc.* **77**, 4987 (1955).

[65] M. J. S. Dewar, *Bull. Soc. chim. France* **18**, 71 (1951).

[66] J. Chatt and L. A. Duncanson, *J. Chem. Soc.*, 2939 (1953).

[67] H. A. Lubs, editor, *The Chemistry of Synthetic Dyes and Pigments*, Reinhold Publishing Corp., New York (1955), Chs. 9, 10.

[68] K. Venkataraman, *The Chemistry of Synthetic Dyes*, Academic Press, Inc., New York (1952), Vol. II, Ch. 37.

[69] O. Stallmann, *J. Chem. Ed.* **37**, 220 (1960); F. H. Moser and A. L. Thomas, *Phthalocyanine Compounds*, Reinhold Publishing Corp., New York (1963).

ility, even with ions which customarily form tetrahedral complexes. Important examples of this class include hemoglobin and related respiratory pigments containing copper, chlorophyll, and a host of similar naturally occurring materials of the utmost importance for the functioning of vital processes in both plants and animals. Another large group of examples is found in the phthalocyanine complexes and their derivatives. Though these materials are quite different in their applications, their similarities in structure and stability make it logical to emphasize these facts. One of the most important properties which many of them possess is a great reluctance to allow the metal ion to dissociate. An exceptional degree of thermal stability may also be found; as mentioned before, copper phthalocyanine may be heated to 850° in a vacuum without suffering decomposition. In an analogous manner, the iron in the human body (much of which is tied up in hemoglobin and related iron metalloporphyrins) is replaced only over a period of seven years. Most of the other molecules in the body suffer complete replacement in times of the order of weeks or months.

PHTHALOCYANINES. In 1928 the Scottish Dyes Corporation undertook the investigation of a blue-green solid which was formed when ammonia was passed into molten phthalic anhydride contained in iron vessels. This was found to be iron phthalocyanine. The characterization of this compound and related materials by R. P. Linstead and his co-workers led to the commercial development of one of the most unusual groups of coloring matters presently available, the phthalocyanines. These compounds may be prepared by:

1. Reaction of phthalonitriles with metals or metallic salts
2. Reaction of phthalic anhydrides or phthalimides with urea in the presence of metal salts
3. Reaction of ortho dihaloaromatics with metal cyanides
4. Reaction of free phthalocyanines with metal salts

The first reaction is:

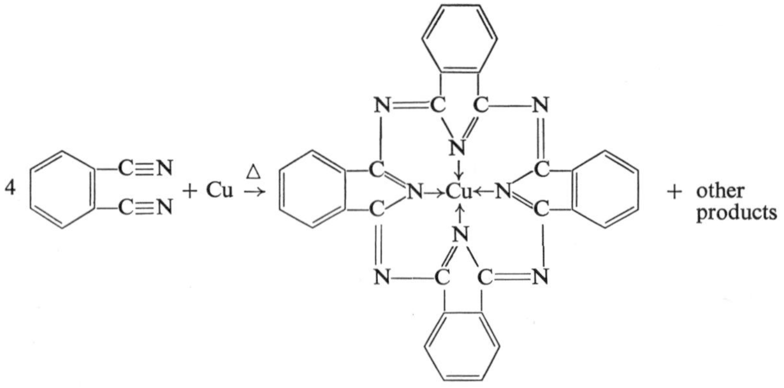

Copper(II) Phthalocyanine

The side reactions which occur are complex and are not yet completely understood. While many complexes of this type have been made, the copper complex(blue) is the one most commonly used as a pigment. Not all of the metal phthalocyanines are as stable chemically as the copper complex. The chemical reactivity is governed largely by the bonding requirements of the central ion. In those cases where a coordination number of four is quite unnatural for the central metal, further reaction may occur involving the addition of other ligands or the formation of polynuclear complexes.

Some of the chemical properties of the phthalocyanines are responsible for the interest shown in them. For the copper complexes their great chemical stability and special colors make them important as pigments. Derivatives of this molecule with functional groups such as sulfhydryl or sulfonate are useful as dyes. The chemical stability seems to be a result of the completely planar structure of these molecules with the resulting possibilities for electronic delocalization. At temperatures slightly above room temperature, phthalocyanine is an intrinsic semiconductor—the introduction of a metal atom to form a complex results in a compound with the same type of properties and there is even very little change in the activation energy of the conduction process.[70]

Berezin[71] studied the stabilities of some metal phthalocyanines by using their solubilities and absorption spectra, both in sulfuric acid. For the reaction:

$$MPhth(soln.) + 2H_3O^+ \rightleftharpoons H_2Phth + M^{++} + 2H_2O$$

he estimated equilibrium constants of the order of 10^{-6} for the complexes of the first series of transition elements. The nickel complex was estimated to be the most stable of the complexes involving metals in this part of the periodic table, but the Co^{+2}, Cu^{+2}, and Zn^{+2} complexes were not much less stable. In the second paper Berezin reported equilibrium constants for the reaction:

$$MPhth(solid) + H_2SO_4 \rightleftharpoons MPhthH^+ + HSO_4^-$$

for Zn^{+2}, Cu^{+2}, Co^{+2}, Ni^{+2}. He reported the following results: ($T=25°$)

cation	Cu^{+2}	Zn^{+2}	Co^{+2}	Ni^{+2}
pK	2.02	2.32	2.30	1.43
[H_2SO_4], m/l	14.52	14.52	14.52	14.52
soly., m/l	0.06520	0.000325	0.000338	0.000252

This data indicates that the zinc complex undergoes this reaction with the

[70] P. E. Fielding and F. Gutman, *J. Chem. Phys.* **26**, 411 (1957).

[71] B. D. Berezin, *Izvest. Vysshikh Ucheb. Zavedenni Khim. i Khim. Teknol.* **2**, 10–14, 165–72 (1959), C.A. 53: 16663, 18720.

least readiness but part of this is due to its low solubility in comparison with copper.

The use of metallic phthalocyanines as oxidation-reduction indicators has been reported in a series of papers by Rao and Sastri.[72] To obviate the problem of the insolubility of the parent phthalocyanines, sulfonated derivatives were used. The sodium salt of 4,4', 4'', 4'''-copper phthalocyaninetetrasulfonic acid was used. It was found to give a deep turquoise blue solution which passed through a transitory pink stage to a colorless product at the end point. This was found to function in a satisfactory manner as a redox indicator for the systems $Fe(II)–Fe(CN)_6^{-3}$, the cerimetric determination of U(IV), Mo(V), As(III), and some related cerimetric determinations of organic compounds.

A further reaction which emphasizes the relationship of these materials with the naturally occurring metalloporphyrins is the ability of manganese phthalocyanine to act as an oxygen carrier. Elvidge and Lever[73] found manganese(II) phthalocyanine to combine reversibly with oxygen, but in a different manner from that found for hemoglobin. A solution of this compound in pyridine is originally olive-green but on standing in air at room temperature it turns a dark blue. When this solution is boiled, the olive-green color returns. One molecule of oxygen is taken up for each two molecules of the manganese(II) phthalocyanine. The product isolated from the oxygenated solution has the composition PhthMnO·Py. This looses pyridine when heated at 180°/15mm to give a product PhthMnO. The reaction sequence proposed for these materials is:

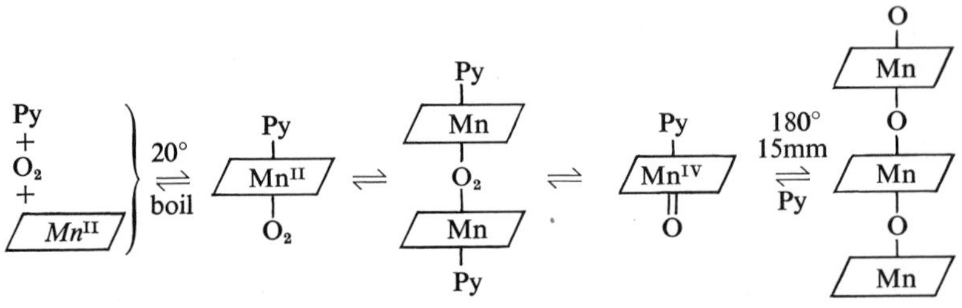

In these reactions, as well as some others,[74] it is found that the coordination positions of the central metal ion are not all occupied. For transition metals such as manganese and chromium an octahedral stereochemistry may be attained by the addition of various ligand species such as pyridine, hydroxide ion, water, and chloride ion.

[72] G. G. Rao and T. P. Sastri, *Zeit. anal. Chem.* **160**, 109 (1958); **163**, 1, 263, 266 (1958); **167**, 1 (1959).

[73] J. A. Elvidge and A. B. P. Lever, *Proc. Chem. Soc.*, 195 (1959).

[74] J. A. Elvidge and A. B. P. Lever, *Proc. Chem. Soc.*, 123 (1959); *J. Chem. Soc.*, 1257 (1961).

POLYMERIC COMPLEXES

Just as in organic chemistry, any molecule which possesses two or more reactive sites may form a polymer, so in coordination chemistry, central metal ions may enter into polymerization reactions. It is necessary that the coordinated species must also be capable of forming two or more coordinate bonds. Such materials have been known for many years and until recently have been treated as unworkable residues. In the last century Berzelius noted that vanadyl oxalate could not be obtained in crystalline form. When an attempt is made to prepare this substance by evaporation of an aqueous solution, a thick viscous liquid is obtained which can be drawn out into fibers by a stirring rod. It is, of course, dissolved by water.

In the years following 1950 an increased interest arose in the field of coordination polymers. This had its origin and inspiration in the enormous development in the field of organic polymers. It was hoped that materials might be developed for use under conditions where organic polymers are unsuitable, particularly at very elevated temperatures. The chief conclusion which may be drawn from these studies is that the coordinate bond furnishes a usually less satisfactory basis for polymers than simple carbon-carbon bonds. To a large extent this is due to the greater susceptibility of coordinate bonds to attack by acids, bases, water, oxidizing agents, and the like. There are a number of excellent reviews of the compounds which have been prepared.[75]

Some examples will show how these compounds are built up. One of the earliest reported polymers is that formed with quinizarin and stannic chloride. This is depicted by Pfeiffer[75a] as:

A large number of such chelate polymers have been reported; a few of these are listed in Table 9.1.

[75] D. W. Sowerby and L. F. Audrieth, *J. Chem. Ed.* **37**, 2, 134 (1960); A. A. Berlin and N. G. Matveeva, *Uspekhi Khim.* **29**, 277 (1959), C. A. 54: 16370; C. N. Kenney, *Chem. and Ind.* 880 (1960); I. Haiduc, *Uspekhi Khim*, **30**, 1124 (1961); V. V. Korshak, S. V. Vinogradova, V. A. Artemova, T. M. Babchinitser, and S. A. Pavlova, *Vysokomolekulyarnye Soedineniya* **3**, 1116 (1961), C.A. 56: 2562; B. P. Block, et al., *J. Inorg. Nuclear Chem.* **24**, 365, 371 (1962).

[75a] P. Pfeiffer, *Organische Molekulverbindungen*, F. Enke, Stuttgart, 2nd ed., p. 245.

TABLE 9.1

SOME COORDINATION POLYMERS BASED ON CHELATES

Ligand	Central Metals	Reference
1,6-dihydroxyphenazine	Cu(II)	76
2,5-dihydroxybenzoquinone	Cu(II)	76
Phthalocyanine	Cu(II)	77
Schiff bases of polymeric nature	Co(II), Cu(II)	78, 84a, 84d
Tetraacetylethane	Cu(II)	79, 81
1,4-dihydroxyanthraquinone	Cu(II)	79
Naphthazarin thiosemicarbazone	Cu(II), Zn(II), Ni(II)	80
Polymethacroylacetone	Ba^{+2}, Mg^{+2}, Mn(II), Ni(II), Cu(II)	82
Polyphthalocyanine	Cu(II)	83
Bis beta diketones	Cu(II)	84
p(1,3-butanedione)N-phenylglycine	various	84b
Bis 1,2-dioximes	Ni(II)	84c

There are two principle classes of compounds which have been studied: (a) those which possess a chain of carbon atoms as the basis for the polymer and this then chelates or coordinates metal atoms to groups to this chain and (b) those in which the polymerization occurs as a direct result of the formation of the coordinate linkage. Linear polymers may be built up in both ways and the gross behavior pattern for such polymers is the same for both classes.[81,85] The requirement of resistance to hydrolysis can be met by the preparation of materials of great insolubility in water or by the use of a central ion which undergoes ligand exchange reactions slowly. An example of this latter sort may be seen in some chromium complexes.[75a] Here the chromium through its ability to form coordinate bonds with both carboxyl groups and oxygen atoms of silicate groups, can serve to bond organic materials with carboxyl groups to a glass surface. Because of their comparatively greater stability and the availability of chromium salts and complexes, these are

[76] S. Kanda and Y. Saito, *Bull. Chem. Soc. Japan* **30**, 197 (1957).

[77] W. Drinkard and J. C. Bailar, Jr., *J. Amer. Chem. Soc.* **81**, 4795 (1959).

[78] C. S. Marvel and P. V. Bonsignore, *J. Amer. Chem. Soc.* **81**, 2668 (1959).

[79] F. W. Knobloch and W. H. Rauscher, *J. Polymer Science* **38**, 261 (1959).

[80] D. N. Chakravarty and W. C. Drinkard, *J. Indian Chem. Soc.* **37**, 517 (1960).

[81] R. G. Charles, *J. Phys. Chem.* **64**, 1747 (1960).

[82] M. T. Teyssie and P. Teyssie, *J. Polymer Sci.* **50**, 253 (1961).

[83] A. Epstein and B. S. Wildi, *J. Chem. Phys.* **32**, 324 (1960).

[84] W. C. Drinkard, D. Ross and J. Weisner, *J. Org. Chem.* **26**, 619 (1961).

[84a] H. A. Goodwin and J. C. Bailar, Jr., *J. Amer. Chem. Soc.* **83**, 2467 (1961); (b) L. E. Mattison, M. S. Phipps, J. Kazan, and L. Alfred, *J. Polymer Sci.* **54**, 117 (1961); (c) M. E. Jones, D. A. Thornton, and R. F. Webb, *Makromol. Chem.* **49**, 62, 69 (1961); (d) V. V. Zelentsov, W. M. Pei, I. A. Savich, and V. I. Spitsyn, *Vysokomolekulyarnye Soedineniya* **3**, 1535 (1961), C.A. 56: 10375.

[85] S. Kanda, *Nippon Kagaku Zasshi* **81**, 1347 (1960), C.A. 55: 22994. See also, ref. 89.

presently used in a variety of applications such as water proofing coatings[86] and tanning of leather[87] which are dependent upon the formation of high molecular weight coordination compounds *in situ*. A further example of this sort is the use of cuprous complexes of acrylonitrile fibers in their dyeing. These fibers are quite unreactive to most of the common dyes but formation of a mixed complex, in which the fiber and the dye molecule are both coordinated to copper, may be used to attach dyes to the fiber indirectly.[88] At present such applications of coordination compounds which are polymeric are much more important than the use of polymers of the type listed in Table 9.1 which are held together solely by coordinate bonds.

METAL HYDRIDE, ALKYL, AND ARYL COMPLEXES[89-91]

The continual discovery of new types of compounds which metals may form has dramatically demonstrated the continuity of the transition from pure coordination compounds to pure organometallic compounds. There are now known a large number of compounds which have metal to hydrogen and/or metal to carbon bonds as well as coordinate bonds, all to the same central metal. In general the coordinated groups are those with a very high "ligand field", such as CN^-, CO, PR_3, and the like. Some typical hydride preparative reactions are:[89]

$$Co_2(CO)_8 \xrightarrow[NH_3(1)]{Na} NaCo(CO)_4 \xrightarrow{H^+} HCo(CO)_4$$

$$[((C_6H_5)_3P)_2PtCl_2] \xrightarrow[\text{tetrahydrofuran}]{LiAlH_4} [((C_6H_5)_3P)_2PtHCl]$$

$$[((nC_3H_7)_3P)_2PtCl_2] + H_2 \xrightarrow[\text{pressure}]{} [((nC_3H_7)_3P)_2PtHCl] + HCl$$

$$Rh^{+3}(aq) + CN^- \xrightarrow[H_2O]{NaBH_4} [HRh(CN)_5]^{-3}$$

$$Fe(CO)_5 + NaOH(aq) \longrightarrow Na[HFe(CO)_4] \xrightarrow{H^+} H_2Fe(CO)_4$$

$$\pi\text{-}C_5H_5Fe(CO)_2Cl \xrightarrow[\text{tetrahydrofuran}]{NaBH_4} \pi\text{-}C_5H_5Fe(CO)_2H$$

[86] A. Suszer, A. Bader, J. Pilz, and E. Maurer, *Chem. Tech.* (Berlin) **12**, 412 (1960), C.A. 55: 4996.

[87] K. H. Gustavson, *Advances in Protein Chem.* 353 (1949).

[88] D. R. Graham and K. W. Statham, *J. Soc. Dyers Colourists* **75**, 452 (1959).

[89] M. L. H. Green, *Angew. Chem.* **72**, 719 (1960).

[90] H. Zeiss, *Organometallic Chemistry*, Reinhold Publishing Corp, New York (1960).

[91] G. E. Coates, *Organo-Metallic Compounds*, John Wiley & Sons, New York, 2nd ed. (1961).

The methods for the preparation of complexes which contain metal carbon bonds are mostly of relatively recent development. Many of these compounds are valuable synthetic intermediates or catalysts. Gold(III) and platinum(IV) compounds of this type have been known for many years:

$$4PtCl_4 + 12CH_3MgI \rightarrow [(CH_3)_3PtI]_4 + 6MgCl_2 + 6MgI_2 \quad [92]$$

$$2[(CH_3)_3PtI]_4 + 8Tl(C_5H_7O_2) \xrightarrow{\text{benzene}} [(CH_3)_3Pt(C_5H_7O_2)]_2 + 8TlI \quad [93]$$

$$2AuBr_3 + 4RMgBr \xrightarrow{\text{pyridine}} [Au_2Cl_2R_4] + 4MgBr_2 \quad [94]$$

The use of the Grignard reagent with other metal halides is not a generally applicable synthetic method unless the metal is coordinated to certain donor species. Even then the compounds must usually be prepared at a relatively low temperature. The attainment of the electronic structure of an inert gas is usually a condition of relative stability and this is generally achieved more readily in coordination compounds. The attainment of an electron configuration with two fewer electrons than the next inert gas is also a relatively stable arrangement. Some preparative reactions which have been used are:[90,91]

$$Na[Co(CO)_4] + CH_3I \rightarrow CH_3Co(CO)_4 + NaI$$

$$[((C_2H_5)_3P)_2NiBr_2] + 2C_6H_5MgBr \rightarrow [((C_2H_5)_3P)_2Ni(C_6H_5)_2] + 2MgBr_2$$

$$HMn(CO)_5 + CH_2N_2 \rightarrow CH_3Mn(CO)_5 + N_2$$

$$CH_3COCl + NaMn(CO)_5 \rightarrow CH_3COMn(CO)_5 + NaCl$$

$$[((C_2H_5)_3P)_2PdBr_2] + RMgBr \rightarrow [((C_2H_5)_3P)_2Pd(R)Br] + MgBr_2$$

The reactions of both the hydride and carbon bonded metal complexes are noteworthy as well as unusual in many respects. The following have been reported:

$$[(R_3P)_2PtHCl] + CCl_4 \rightarrow [(R_3P)_2PtCl_2] + \text{halomethanes} \quad [89]$$

$$CH_3COCH_3 + H_2 \xrightarrow{H_2Fe(CO)_4} CH_3CH(OH)CH_3 \quad [89]$$

$$[(C_2H_5)_2AuBr]_2 + 2NH_3 \rightarrow 2(C_2H_5)_2AuBr \cdot NH_3 \quad [90]$$

$$CH_3COMn(CO)_5 \underset{CO}{\rightleftharpoons} CH_3Mn(CO)_5 + CO \quad [90]$$

This type of compound requires stabilization of the sort that is furnished by ligands with high ligand fields and this fact has been exploited synthetically on a rather considerable scale. These compounds are a class which is rapidly growing in importance.

[92] W. J. Pope and S. J. Peachey, *J. Chem. Soc.* **95**, 571 (1909).

[93] R. C. Menzies and E. R. Wiltshire, *J. Chem. Soc.*, 21 (1933); R. C. Menzies, *J. Chem. Soc.*, 565 (1928).

[94] M. S. Kharasch and H. S. Isbell, *J. Amer. Chem. Soc.* **53**, 2701 (1931).

EXERCISES

1. Suggest a method of preparing each of the following compounds:

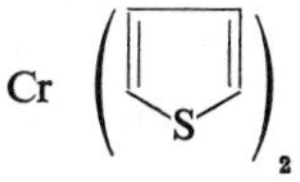

$$Cr\left(\text{[thiophene ring]}\right)_2$$

$$Co(CO)_3(NO) \quad ; \quad Fe \quad ; \quad Cr \quad ; \quad Fe$$

$$Ag_2Fe(CO)_4$$

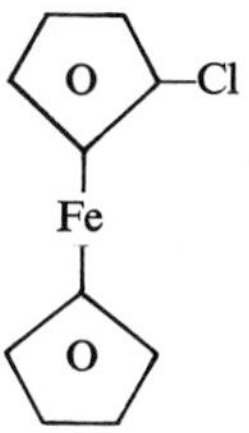

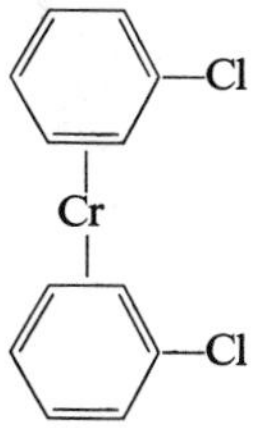

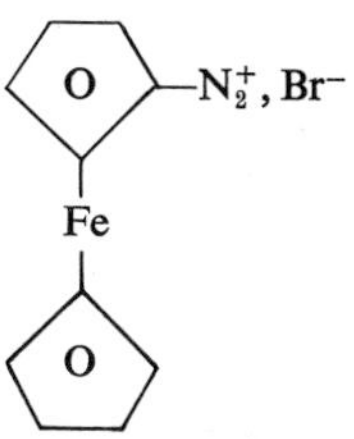

2. If $Cr(C_6H_6)_2$ has a fixed relative orientation of the aromatic rings, how many isomers would you expect to find for the compound $Cr(C_6H_5Cl)_2$? Enumerate them and give the structure of each. If there is free rotation of the aromatic rings about an axis passing through the chromium atom how many isomers would you expect to find for such a compound? Enumerate them and give the structure of each.

3. While it is conceivable that treatment of a complex such as $V(dipyr)_3$ with CO would lead to some substitution of carbon monoxide for dipyridyl, would you expect complete replacement to occur?

4. Suggest synthetic procedures for complexes of vanadium which contain vanadium to carbon bonds. Be careful to specify the ligands which you would use to assist in stabilizing the compounds.

10

Some Applications of Coordination Compounds

Catalytic Properties[1-8]

The number of instances where the coordination act is essential to catalytic activity is very large. Some of these, such as the oxo process and the Friedel-Crafts reaction, are of industrial importance. Others are concerned primarily with reactions which take place in living organisms while still further examples useful in laboratory preparative work may be found. No attempt at a complete listing will be made. Instead, illustrative examples of different sorts will be presented in the hope that the diversity of the catalytic possibilities of these materials may be appreciated.

The ultimate understanding and control of these processes must await a more thorough knowledge of the way in which coordination affects the

[1] G. Hesse "Katalyse durch Komplexbildung" in G. M. Schwab, *Handbuch der Katalyse*, Springer-Verlag, Vienna (1943), Vol. VI, p. 68.

[2] G. Hesse, "Katalyse über komplexe Kationen und Anionen" in E. Miller, editor, *Methoden der Organischen Chemie* (Houben-Weyl), G. Thieme Verlag, Stuttgart (1955), Band IV, Teil 2, p. 63–136.

[3] A. E. Martell, R. Gustafson and S. Chaberek, *Advances in Catalysis, IX*, 319 (1957).

[4] G. Thuillier, *Bull. chem. soc. France*, 1431 (1959).

[5] G. Natta and I. Pasquon, *Advances in Catalysis, XI*, 1 (1959).

[6] J. Halpern, *Advances in Catalysis, XI*, 301 (1959).

[7] S. Chaberek and A. E. Martell, *Organic Sequestering Agents*, John Wiley & Sons, Inc., New York (1959), p. 378 et. seq.

[8] E. T. Denisov and N. M. Emanuel, *Russian Chemical Reviews* **29**, 1409 (1960) (English translation).

[8a] "Reactions of Coordinated Ligands", *Advances in Chemistry Series* No. 37, American Chemical Society, Washington, D.C. (1963).

[8b] M. M. Jones and W. A. Connor, *Ind. Eng. Chem.* **55**, No. 9, 14 (1963).

electron density patterns and hence reactivity patterns of the ligand molecule. As might be suspected, coordination may aid, hinder, or have no effect on a given ligand reaction depending upon how it affects the ease with which the ligand may undergo the reaction. An example of this may be seen in the reaction of EDTA and its Cr^{+3} and Bi^{+3} complexes with permanganate.[9] The reaction of permanganate with EDTA is much faster than that of the complexes while other reactions can be prevented completely when coordination masks the functional groups. Coordination may accelerate a reaction if the complex furnishes an easier path for the process than is otherwise available. This occurs in the decarboxylation of aliphatic keto acids in which the same keto group is alpha to one carbonyl group and beta to another carboxyl group.[10] In this reaction the positive metal ion, upon coordination, promotes electron withdrawal from the carboxylate group which is to be split off.

The reactions of coordinated species may be classified in several ways. Martell, Gustafson, and Chaberek[3] center their attention on the central ion and divide the reactions into two groups: (a) those in which the central metal ion undergoes a permanent change and (b) those in which the central metal ion does not undergo a permanent change. It is also possible to classify these reactions on the basis of the way in which coordination affects the reactivity of the ligand, viz.:

1. instances where coordination allows the ligand and a third reactant to come together more easily by multiple coordination

2. instances where the polarization of the ligand by the central ion's positive charge is the essential function of coordination

3. instances where coordination stabilizes one form of the ligand which is more reactive than another form (e.g., the stabilization of enol forms of beta-diketones)

4. instances where coordination masks one or more of the reactive groups of a molecule so that the reaction occurs only at a limited number of sites

5. cases where coordination allows a chelate to be formed from two or more reactive species which do not readily react otherwise

6. instances where coordination allows a ligand to undergo an internal rearrangement which is otherwise very difficult or impossible

[9] M. T. Beck and O. Kling, *Acta Chem. Scand.* **15**, 453 (1961).

[10] K. Pedersen, *J. Amer. Chem. Soc.* **51**, 2098 (1929); H. A. Krebs, Biochem. J. **36**, 303 (1942); A. Kornberg, S. Ochoa, and A. L. Mellor, *J. Biol. Chem.* **174**, 159 (1948); R. Steinberger and F. H. Westheimer, *J. Amer. Chem. Soc.* **71**, 4158 (1949); idem, *ibid.*, **73**, 429 (1951); J. E. Prue, *J. Chem. Soc.*, 2331 (1952); K. J. Pedersen, *Acta Chem. Scand.* **6**, 285 (1952); R. J. P. Williams, *Nature* **171**, 304 (1953); E. Gelles and K. S. Pitzer, *J. Amer. Chem. Soc.* **77**, 1974 (1955); E. Gelles and J. P. Clayton, *Trans. Farad. Soc.* **52**, 353 (1956); E. Gelles and R. W. Hay, *J. Chem. Soc.*, 3673 (1958); E. Gelles and A. Salama, *J. Chem. Soc.*, 3683, 3689 (1958). A similar reaction occurs with other organic acids such as dihydroxymaleic acid: W. Francke and G. Brathuhn, Ann. **487**, 1 (1931).

7. cases where coordination is a prerequisite to the transfer of electrons.

It is very probable that this list will be expanded as studies of the reactions continue. This second listing will be used as the basis of the present discussion as it centers attention on the reactions of the ligand, the moiety of greater interest in these cases.

CLASS (1) LIGAND, METAL, AND THIRD REACTANT UNITED THROUGH COORDINATION

A good illustration of a rather simple coordination compound which exhibits catalytic properties falling into class (1) may be seen in the cuprous chloride-pyridine complex which functions as a catalyst for the autoxidation of aromatic amines by atmospheric oxygen. This reaction was discovered by A. P. Terentiev and studied by him and his students.[11] It was found that other cuprous or cupric compounds were ineffective as catalysts and also that pyridine, which was used as a solvent, could not be replaced by alcohols, dioxane, dichlorethane, or quinoline. A typical reaction is:

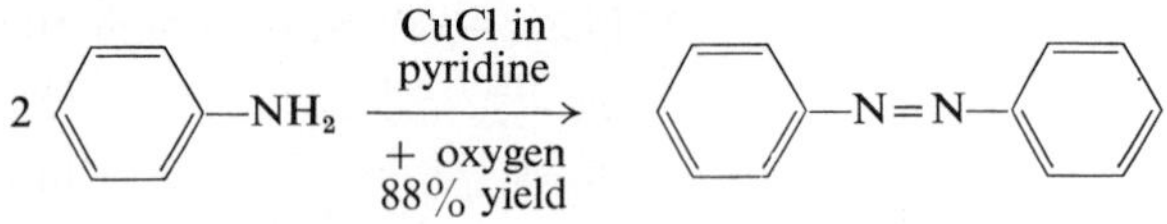

A solution of cuprous chloride in pyridine absorbs one g-mole of oxygen per cuprous chloride and this is presumably the route by which the oxygen is transformed into a species which is both selective and effective in the oxidations.

A similar set of reactions was studied by K. Kinoshita.[12] Here a solution of cuprous chloride in pyridine was used to catalyze the autoxidation of benzoin to benzil and then to benzoic acid. When cupric chloride was used as a catalyst, the autoxidation of the benzoin went only as far as benzil:

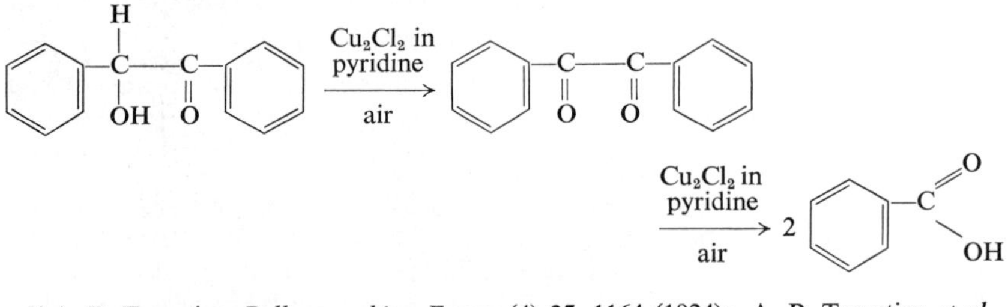

[11] A. P. Terentiev, *Bull. soc. chim. France* (4) **35**, 1164 (1924); A. P. Terentiev *et al.*, *Doklady Akad. Nauk U.S.S.R.*, 91 (1955), C. A. 50: 4807; A. P. Terentiev and Y. D. Mogilianski, *J. Gen. Chem.* **28**, 2002 (1958); **31**, 326 (1961) (English translations). See also, M. Paris and R. J. P. Williams, "Discussions Faraday Society", No. 29, 153 (1960).

[12] K. Kinoshita, *Bull. Chem. Soc. Japan* **32**, 777, 780, 783 (1959). These papers give further references to earlier work published in Japanese.

but also

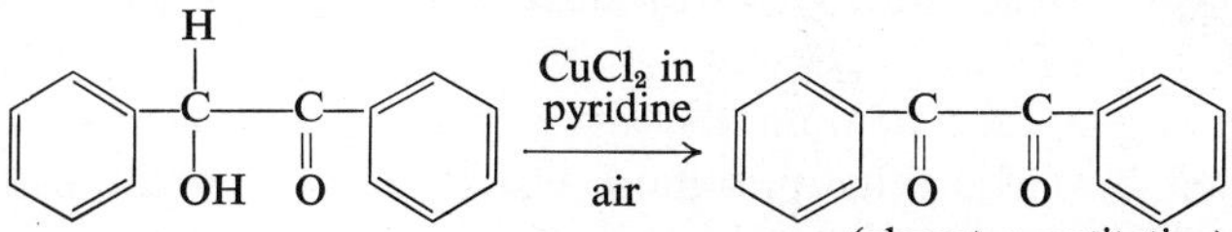

(almost quantitative)

The use of cupric chloride in this case gives an almost quantitative yield of benzil. For these oxidations, but not for the oxidations involving amines such as studied by Terentiev *et al.*, the cuprous acetate-pyridine complex was also found to be an effective catalyst. Kinoshita studied the amine oxidations and showed that an intermediate in this reaction was an oxidizing agent derived from the cuprous complex. The study of the oxidation of the aromatic amines led Kinoshita to propose the following reaction scheme for part of it:

$$Cu_2Cl_2 \xrightarrow[\text{pyridine}]{O_2} Cu^{II}\!-\!Cl \xrightarrow{C_6H_5NH_2} [C_6H_5NH_2Cu^{II}]^+Cl^- \rightarrow$$

$$\underset{+HCl}{[C_6H_5NH\!-\!Cu^{II}]} \rightarrow [C_6H_5NH\!-\!Cu^I] \rightarrow C_6H_5N\overset{H}{\underset{}{N}}NC_6H_5 + 2Cu(I)$$

No mechanism was suggested for the subsequent step:

$$C_6H_5\overset{H}{N}\!-\!\overset{H}{N}C_6H_5 \longrightarrow C_6H_5N\!=\!NC_6H_5$$

Copper(I) and copper(II) salts have been used widely as catalysts for a variety of oxidation reactions. C. W. Schwarz[13] found that cupric nitrate catalyzed the high temperature, high pressure oxidation of aliphatic substituents on the pyridine nucleus. A complex is presumably responsible for these reactions:

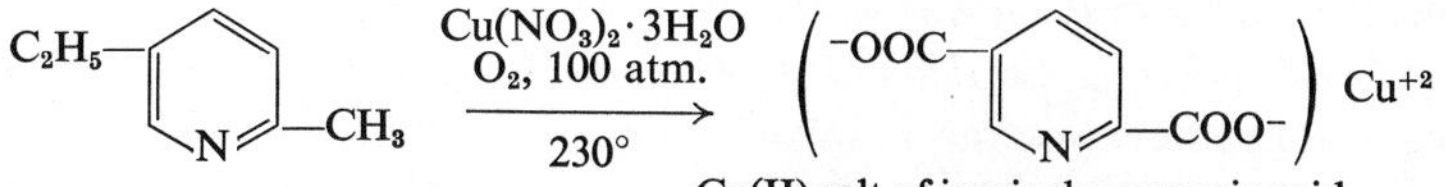

Cu(II) salt of isocinchomeronic acid

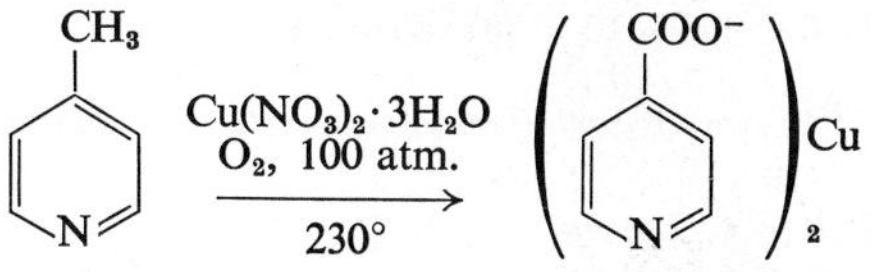

In addition to these reactions, several reactions using cuprous salts as catalysts are run at high temperatures in the absence of a solvent.

The study of metal ion catalysis of autoxidation reactions has been pursued for many years and the literature is quite extensive.[8] In many cases, trace amounts of metals are found to catalyze the autoxidation of industrial

[13] C. W. Schwarz, *Ger. Pat.* 1,010, 524, C.A. 53: 18970g.

and food products so the control of such reactions is often an economic necessity.

As an example, the oxidation of benzaldehyde in benzene-water mixtures is accelerated by ferric salts and, more effectively, by ferrous salts.[14] The principle product is benzoic acid. Other aldehydes undergo a similar reaction, e.g., butanol, 3, 5, 5-trimethyl-hexanal and related compounds.[15] These reactions are usually considered to be free radical reactions and the catalysts are instrumental in the initiation of the chain reaction.[16] In the catalysis of the autoxidation of benzaldehyde by cobaltous acetate, the initial step is the oxidation of the cobaltous to the cobaltic ion. This is followed by the reactions:

$$Co^{+3} + C_6H_5CHO \rightarrow Co^{+2} + C_6H_5CO\cdot + H^+$$

$$C_6H_5CO\cdot + O_2 \rightarrow C_6H_5COOO\cdot$$

$$C_6H_5COOO\cdot + C_6H_5CHO \rightarrow C_6H_5COOOH + C_6H_5CO\cdot$$

$$2C_6H_5COOO\cdot \rightarrow \text{inert products}$$

The second and third steps represent the propagation of the chain reaction. These steps are typical of many reactions of this type. A survey of recent work is available,[8] the older work has been surveyed by Schoberl.[17]

The effort to find differences in the behavior of enantiomorphs has led to the study of the oxidation of some racemic mixtures of amino acids in the presence of optically active complex salts.[18] It has been reported that one isomer of the racemic mixture was more rapidly oxidized by atmospheric oxygen in the presence of an optically active complex. The effect, if present, is apparently small as Pugh[19] obtained results which were not in agreement with the earlier work. Bailar[20] suggested that a possible mechanism for such a process might involve a complexation reaction in which one antipode of the mixture is preferentially coordinated. This type of coordination is known to occur in such a selective way with complexes of Co(III). Thus complexes of the type Co(*ddd*) or Co(*lll*) are formed between Co(III) and amino acids and never or rarely mixed types of the kind Co(*ldl*).

A series of instances in which complexes can catalyze hydrogenation reactions has been investigated in great detail by J. Halpern and his co-workers.[21]

[14] R. Kuhn and K. Meyer, *Naturwissenschaften* **16**, 1028 (1928); H. Wieland and D. Richter, *Ann.* **486**, 227 (1931).

[15] H. Hock and H. Kropf, *J. prakt. Chem.* (4), **14**, 71 (1961).

[16] C. E. H. Bawn and J. Jolley, *Proc. Roy. Soc.* **A237**, 297 (1956).

[17] A. Schoberl in G. H. Schwab, editor, *Handbuch der Katlayse*, Springer-Verlag, Vienna (1943), Vol. VII, Part 1, p. 494.

[18] Y. Shibata and R. Tsuchida, *Bull. Chem. Soc. Japan* **4**, 142 (1929); Y. Shibata, Y. Tanaka, and S. Goda, *Bull. Chem. Soc. Japan* **6**, 210 (1931).

[19] C. E. M. Pugh, *Biochem. J.* **27**, 480 (1933).

[20] J. C. Bailar, Jr., *Chem. Reviews* **19**, 82 (1936).

[21] Surveys are given in J. Halpern, *J. Phys. Chem.* **63**, 398 (1959); *idem, Advances in Catalysis XI*, 301 (1959).

Halpern has studied the homogeneous catalytic activation of molecular hydrogen by many simple and complex species. This kind of reaction was first discovered by M. Calvin,[22] who found that cupric acetate or benzoquinone dissolved in quinoline which contained cuprous acetate suffered reduction by molecular hydrogen at 100°, an unusually low temperature for such a homogeneous reaction. Subsequently, many instances of the activation of molecular hydrogen by such materials have been reported. Some of the ions which are capable of activating hydrogen in aqueous solution are Cu^{+2}, Ag^+, Hg^{+2}, Hg_2^{+2}, and MnO_4^-. This activation can be either by homolytic or heterolytic splitting of the hydrogen. Some of the reactions which are believed to be the rate determining ones in these systems are:

		activation
heterolytic splitting probable	$Cu^{+2} + H_2 \rightarrow CuH^+ + H^+$	energy $= 27$ Kcals/mole
	$Ag^+ + H_2 \rightarrow AgH + H^+$	„ 24 „ „
	$Hg^{++} + H_2 \rightarrow HgH^+ + H^+$	„ 18 „ „
	$MnO_4^- + H_2 \rightarrow HMnO_4^- + H^+$	„ 15 „ „
homolytic splitting probable	$2Ag^+ + H_2 \rightarrow 2AgH^+$	„ 15 „ „
	$Hg_2^{+2} + H_2 \rightarrow 2HgH^+$	„ 20 „ „
	$Ag^+ + MnO_4^- + H_2 \rightarrow AgH^+ + HMnO_4^-$	„ 9 „ „

Complex formation may either increase or decrease the activity of these metallic species as catalysts. Some of the data summarized by Halpern are given in Table 10.1.

TABLE 10.1

RELATIVE CATALYTIC ACTIVITIES

Species	Mean formation constant	Relative activity
$Cu(butyrate)_2$	—	150
$Cu(propionate)_2$	?	150
$Cu(acetate)_2$	30	120
$CuSO_4$	100	6.5
$CuCl_4^-$	1	2.5
Cu^{++}	—	1.0
$HgSO_4$	22	1.8
Hg^{++}	—	1
$Hg(Acetate)_2$	1.6×10^4	4×10^{-2}
$HgCl_4^-$	6×10^3	3.2×10^{-3}
$HgCl_2$	4×10^6	2.5×10^{-3}
$Hg(en)_2^{++}$	5.1×10^{11}	1×10^{-3}
Ag acetate	3	80
$Ag(en)_2^+$	7×10^3	25
Ag^+	—	1
$Ag(CN)_2^-$	2.4×10^9	inactive

[22] M. Calvin, *Trans. Farad. Soc.* **34**, 1181 (1938); *J. Amer. Chem. Soc.* **61**, 2230 (1938).

In some complexes, designated "bi-functional" by Halpern, very pronounced catalytic activity is found. This is found for molecules which possess both electron accepting and proton accepting sites. These groups must be disposed so that they can interact simultaneously with a hydrogen molecule but nevertheless be in a rigid framework which prevents them from reacting with each other. A model system such as this may be present in some enzymes.

CLASS (2) METAL ION POLARIZATION OF THE LIGAND PRODUCES CHANGES IN REACTIVITY

The most commonly utilized form of coordination catalysis is that involving the polarization of the ligand by the metal cation. This mode of action is generally considered to be present in the catalytic decarboxylations cited above,[10] catalytic hydrolyses of amino acid esters,[23] amino acid amides,[24] the hydrolysis of Schiff bases,[25] diisopropylphosphorofluoridate,[26] and phosphate esters.[27]

Although the examples cited above are recent, this general idea is of considerably greater age and was extensively developed by 1930, though for rather different examples. Much of this earlier work is to be found in the papers of Meerwein. He showed how coordination renders the ionization of hydrogen from the donor atom much easier. Thus:

$$
\begin{array}{c}
\text{O} \\
\parallel \\
\text{CH}_3\text{—C} \\
\diagdown \\
\text{O} \rightarrow \text{BF}_3 \\
| \\
\text{H}
\end{array}
$$

is an acid comparable in strength to sulfuric acid. This particular effect can be used for synthetic purposes and Meerwein[28] showed that alcoholic hydroxy groups which are normally unreactive toward diazomethane could be rendered reactive by coordination:

$$ \text{ROH} + \text{Al(OR)}_3 \rightleftharpoons \text{H[Al(OR)}_4] \xrightarrow{\text{CH}_2\text{N}_2} \text{Al(OR)}_3 + \text{ROCH}_3 $$

[23] H. Kroll, *J. Amer. Chem. Soc.* **74**, 2036 (1952).

[24] L. Meriwether and F. A. Westheimer, *J. Amer. Chem. Soc.* **78**, 5119 (1956).

[25] G. L. Eichhorn and J. C. Bailar, Jr., *J. Amer. Chem. Soc.* **75**, 2905 (1953); G. L, Eichhorn and I. M. Trachtenberg, *J. Amer. Chem. Soc.* **76**, 5183 (1954).

[26] T. Wagner-Jauregg, B. E. Hackley, Jr., T. A. Lies, O. O. Owens, and R. Proper, *J. Amer. Chem. Soc.* **77**, 922 (1955); R. C. Courtney, R. L. Gustafson, S. J. Westerback, H. Hyytiainen, S. Chaberek, and A. E. Martell, *J. Amer. Chem. Soc.* **79**, 3030 (1957).

[27] W. W. Butcher and F. H. Westheimer, *J. Amer. Chem. Soc.* **77**, 2420 (1955).

[28] H. Meerwein, *Ann.* **484**, 1 (1931).

The essential role of coordination in processes such as this is to provide an intermediate which can form an activated complex with a smaller requirement for activation energy.

The mechanism proposed by Kroll[23] for the catalytic hydrolysis of amino acid esters is typical in many respects of the way in which the ionic charge of the metal is considered to influence the course of the reaction. It provides for the attack of a coordination compound rather than the neutral molecule:

$$M^{+2} + H_2N-\underset{\underset{H}{|}}{\overset{\overset{R}{|}}{C}}-\overset{\overset{O}{\|}}{C}-OR'$$

This ligand polarization must be present in *all* complexes. It presumably is important for reactions such as the Friedel-Crafts reactions and many other examples treated below in other classes. It should be emphasized that while it is always present it need not always play a leading role in the process.

CLASS (3) COORDINATION STABILIZES ONE FORM OF LIGAND

There are a number of instances where only one tautomeric form of a ligand forms stable chelates. In these cases the reactions characteristic of this form may be made much more important than they are in the thermal equilibrium mixture of say a keto and an enol form. This is seen in the bromination of ethylacetoacetate[29] in which the first step is catalyzed by cupric ions as well as in several studies of the halogenation of chelates of beta-diketones. In these cases the observed reactions were essentially those of the enol form of the ligand.[30] The conscious use of this principle in the preparation of azo

[29] K. J. Pedersen, *Acta Chem. Scand.* 2, 252 (1948).

[30] H. Reihlen, R. Illig, and R. Wittig, *Ber.* 58, 12 (1925); R. W. Kluiber, *J. Amer. Chem. Soc.* 82, 4839 (1960); J. P. Collman, R. A. Moss, S. D. Goldby, and V. S. Trahanovsky, *Chem. and Ind.* (London) 122 (1959); J. P. Collman, R. A. Moss, H. Maltz, and C. C. Heindel, *J. Amer. Chem. Soc.* 83, 531 (1961); B. Schonbrodt, *Ann.* 253, 171 (1889); W. J. Barry, *J. Chem. Soc.* 670 (1960); W. S. Fyfe, *Anal. Chem.* 23, 174 (1951).

dyes may be traced back in the literature over sixty years. In this case the phenolate form of the ligand, which is more reactive toward diazonium salts, is desired and can be stabilized by chelate formation. After the ligand is coupled with the diazonium salt, the metal may be removed.[31]

CLASS (4) MASKING VIA COORDINATION

At least some of the reactions of a ligand will be modified by the steric and electronic changes which accompany coordination. In many cases, coordination will either prevent or enormously retard reactions which involve the atoms directly linked to the metal. This can often be put to use in the design of new preparative methods. One such case is the synthesis of citrulline from ornithine via the inner complex salt which copper forms with ornithine. This chelate formation removes one of the reactive amino groups of ornithine from the reaction and allows the desired reaction site to be the sole reaction site. This synthesis is:[32]

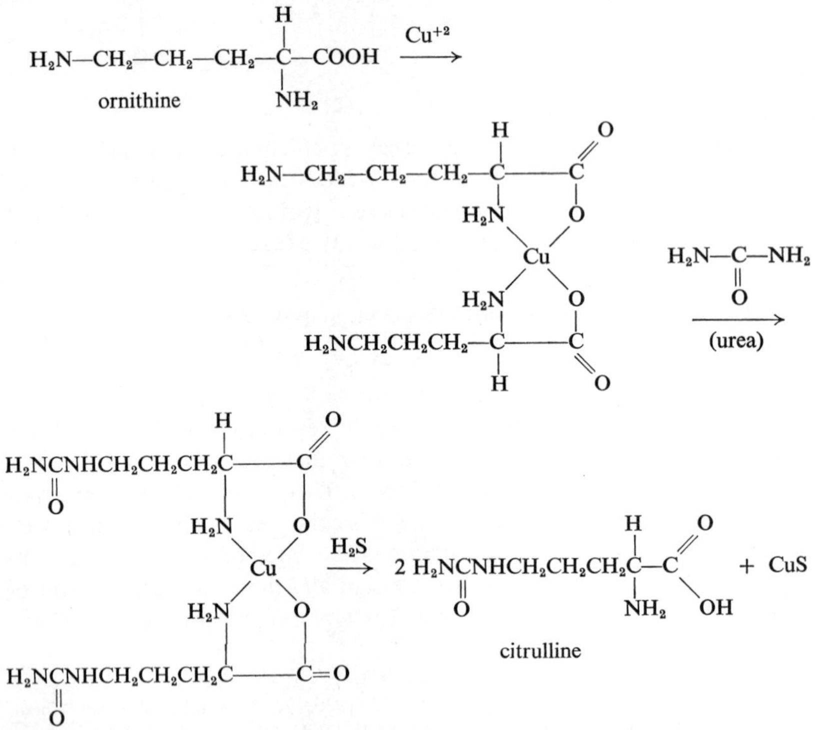

$$H_2N-CH_2-CH_2-CH_2-\overset{\overset{\displaystyle H}{|}}{\underset{\underset{\displaystyle NH_2}{|}}{C}}-COOH \xrightarrow{\quad Cu^{+2} \quad}$$

ornithine

$$\xrightarrow{\quad H_2S \quad} 2\ H_2N\overset{}{C}NHCH_2CH_2CH_2\overset{\overset{\displaystyle H}{|}}{\underset{\underset{\displaystyle NH_2}{|}}{C}}-\overset{\overset{\displaystyle O}{\parallel}}{C}{\diagdown}_{OH} + CuS$$

citrulline

---

[31] The literature is collected and newer work reported in V. I. Kuznetsov and A. A. Nemodruk, *J. Gen. Chem. U.S.S.R.* **26**, 3657 (1956).

[32] A. C. Kurtz, *Amer. J. Med. Sci.* **194**, 875 (1937); *J. Biol. Chem.* **122**, 447 (1938).

The same principle has been used in a number of other syntheses involving both aliphatic and aromatic ligands. The effectiveness of the masking is to a very considerable extent dependent upon the specific reaction as well as the stability of the complex. For example, the masking of the amino group of alpha amino acids by chelate formation with copper(II) is effective in preventing the acetylation of this group,[33] its reaction with fluorodinitrobenzene,[34] urea,[32] carbobenzoxyl chloride,[33] or *O*-methylisourea.[35] In these cases the masking may be utilized for syntheses which involve a reactive but unchelated group in the molecule. Similar studies of nickel dimethylglyoxime show that masking may be effective toward some reagents but not others. Thus this complex does not react with phenylisocyanide[36] but is disrupted by acetyl chloride.[37] In the case of nickel(II) complexes with substituted dithiooxamides, acetylation of a group not involved in the chelate ring can be effected. Thus half of the free hydroxy groups in N, N-bis(2-hydroxyethyl)-dithiooxamidonickel(II) could be acetylated by treatment with acetic anhydride in sulfuric acid.[38]

The proximity of the reactive center to the metal ion also has an effect which is somewhat difficult to predict. Thus the saponification of coordinated cyanide groups has long been known to be very much more difficult[39] than that of free cyanides or free isonitriles.

The reactions of coordinated amines indicate that the nitrogen, however, may not be so thoroughly inactivated. Kukushkin reports that the nitrogen-hydrogen bond in platinum(IV) ammines can be transformed into a nitrogen-chlorine bond by treatment with chlorine.[40]

With aromatic compounds the use of coordination to mask reactive groups has been used, perhaps unconsciously, for over sixty years. It is known that coordination of polyphenols allows them to be diazotized with a much smaller amount of concurrent oxidation. This has been utilized in the

[33] R. Klement, *Ber.* **66**, 1312 (1933); A. Neuberger and F. Sanger, *Biochem. J.* **37**, 515 (1943).

[34] T. Peters, *Biochem. Biophys. Acta* **39**, 546 (1960).

[35] F. Turba and K. H. Schuster, *Naturwissenschaften* **33**, 370 (1946); *Zeit. physiol. Chem.* **283**, 27 (1948).

[36] L. Tschugaev, *J. Chem. Soc.* **105**, 2192 (1914).

[37] R. A. Krause, D. C. Jicha, and D. H. Busch, *J. Amer. Chem. Soc.* **83**, 528 (1961).

[38] R. N. Hurd, G. DeLaMater, G. C. McElheny, and L. V. Pfeiffer, *J. Amer. Chem. Soc.* **82**, 4454 (1960).

[39] J. Meisenheimer, cited in *Ber.* **58**, 13 (1925); E. G. J. Hartley, *J. Chem. Soc.* **97**, 1066, 1725 (1910); **101**, 705; **103**, 1196 (1913); 101 (1933); *Proc. Chem. Soc.* **26**, 90 (1910); **28**, 101 (1912); **29**, 188 (1913); F. Holzl, Monatsh. **48**, 72 (1927); W. Heldt, in S. Kirschner, editor, *Advances in the Chemistry of the Coordination Compounds.* The Macmillan Company, New York (1961), p. 321.

[40] Y. N. Kukushkin, *Zhur. Neorg. Khim.* **2**, 2371–4 (1957); **4**, 2460 (1959); **5**, 1943 (1960), C.A. 52: 13509; 54: 18150; 55: 8142.

preparation of diazo compounds of many types.[41,42] As an example, the reaction of 4-diazodimethylaniline with chromotropic acid results in a 58% yield of the dye in which coupling has occurred at the 4 position of chromotropic acid (1, 8-dihydroxynaphthalene 3, 6-disulfonic acid). By using the calcium complex, the yield may be increased to 90%.[42] When the coordination is to a donor atom external to the aromatic system, there is no change in the orientation for such substitution reactions.[43]

The effectiveness of the masking process is dependent on the stability of the complex which is formed and the tenacity with which susceptible reaction sites are held in the complex.

CLASS (5) COORDINATION STABILIZES PRODUCT LIGAND

In at least some instances, the formation of a complex or of a chelate may result in the stabilization of a compound which would otherwise break down. In these instances, the additional coordinate bonds seem to furnish the required additional stabilization needed by the compound. The behavior of many Schiff bases is an excellent illustration, that formed between salicylaldehyde and ammonia furnishes one of the older examples.[44] Subsequently many other examples have been noted, e.g.[45] In this type of process the hydrolysis of the Schiff base occurs more readily for the free ligand and stabilization occurs via chelation and precipitation:

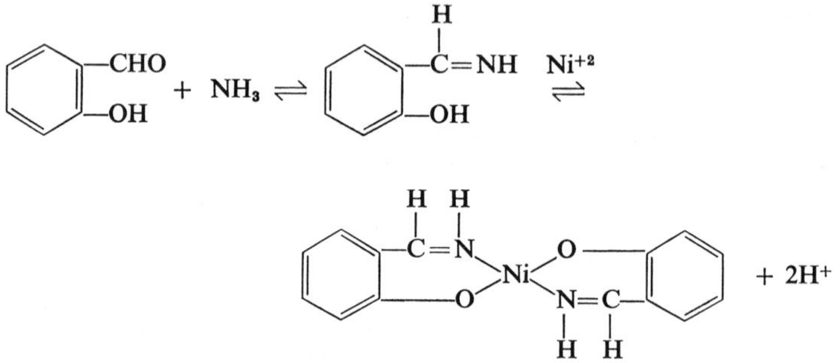

[41] German Patents 174, 905; 175, 827; 177, 624; 178, 304; 188, 819; cited in Friendlander, *Fortschritte der Teerfarbenfabriken und verwandte Industriezweige*, Vol. VIII, 612, 616, 619, 620 (1904).

[42] V. I. Kuznetsov, *J. Gen. Chem.* (U.S.S.R.) **26**, 3657 (1956); V. I. Kuznetsov and A. A. Nemodruk, *Sbornik Statei Obschei Khim.* **2**, 1378 (1953), C.A. 48: 10347; *idem*, **25**, 117 (1955), C.A. 50: 1698; A. A. Nemodruk, *ibid.*, **28**, 1051 (1958).

[43] J. C. Taft and M. M. Jones, *J. Amer. Chem. Soc.* **82**, 4196 (1960); R. L. Jetton and M. M. Jones, *Inorg. Chem.* **1**, 309 (1962); K. D. Maguire and M. M. Jones, *J. Amer. Chem. Soc.* **84**, 2316 (1962).

[44] P. Pfeiffer, E. Buchholz, and O. Bauer, *J. prakt. Chem.* **129**, 163 (1931).

[45] A. E. Martell, P. J. McCarthy, R. J. Hovey, and K. Ueno, *J. Amer. Chem. Soc.* **77**, 5820 (1955).

It must be noted that in many instances coordination has been found to accelerate the hydrolysis of Schiff's bases.[46]

In recent years several carboxylation reactions involving chelates have been examined by Stiles and his students.[47] An example is the carboxylation of ketones which possess enolizable methyl or methylene groups with magnesium methyl carbonate (MMC):

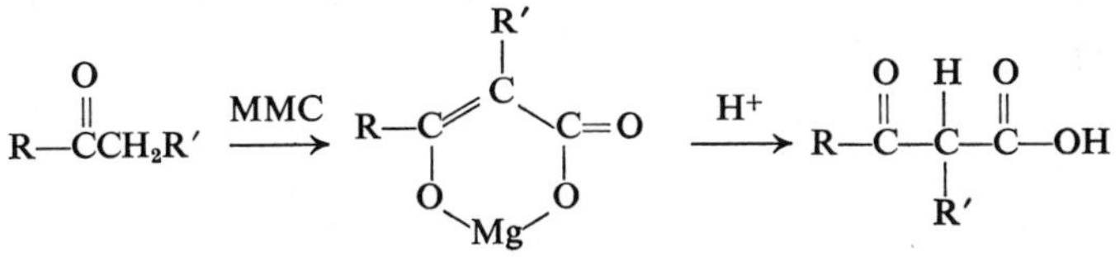

The same kind of reaction was used by Stiles to prepare nitroacetic acid:

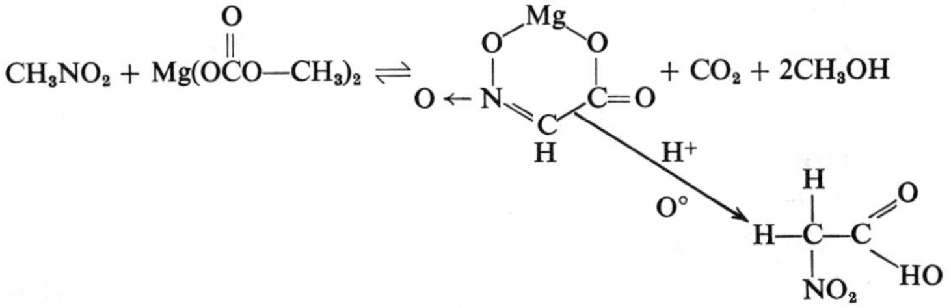

CLASS (6) COORDINATION FACILITATES AN INTERNAL REARRANGEMENT

Instances where coordination allows an internal rearrangement of the ligand are of considerable interest; the examples considered here involve Schiff bases.

If the copper chelate of a Schiff base derived from an optically active amino acid ester and salicylaldehyde is prepared, a rapid racemization occurs.[48] This is postulated to proceed through a tautomeric shift assisted by coordination:

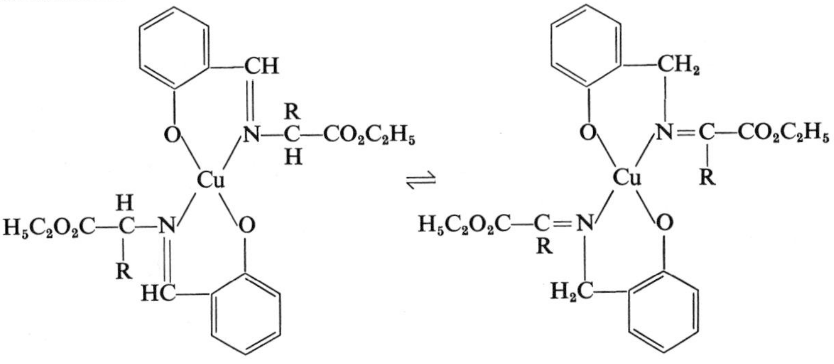

I   II

[46] R. L. Belford, A. E. Martell, and M. Calvin, *J. Inorg. Nuclear Chem.* **14**, 173 (1960) and the references cited therein.

[47] M. Stiles, *Ann. N.Y. Acad. Sci.* **88**, Art. 2, 332 (1960).

[48] P. Pfeiffer, W. Offerman, and H. Werner, *J. prakt. Chem.* **159**, 313 (1942).

The symmetry of the optically active carbon is lost in structure II and the regeneration of structure I would lead to equal amounts of both enantiomorphic forms.

The catalysis, by metals, of transamination and transesterification reactions may fall in this same category.[49] Thus transesterification reactions of compounds such as I above may be effected by merely refluxing in an alcohol, while transaminations may be effected by the same operation with an amine. The mechanism proposed by Verter and Frost is different from that suggested by earlier workers and is:

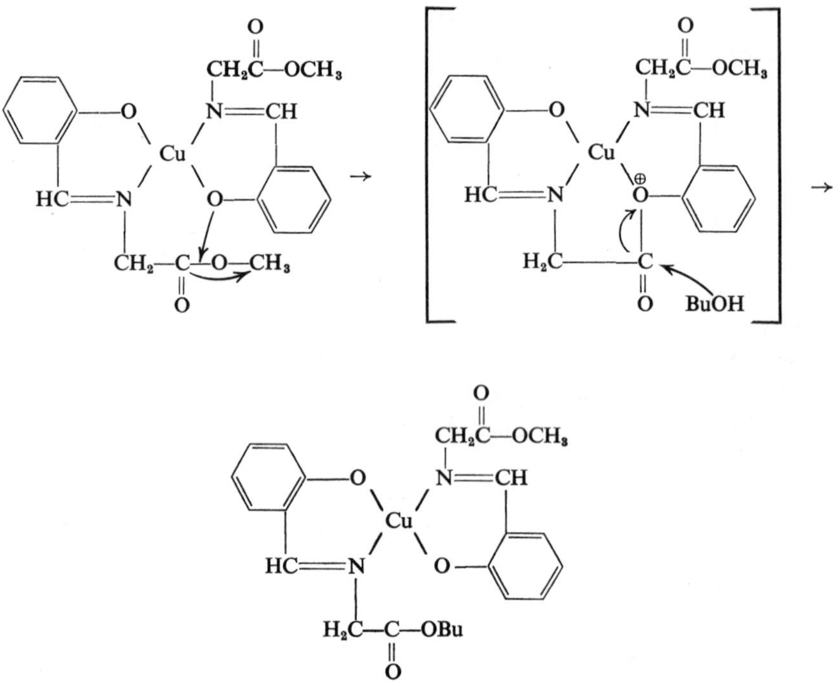

The second methyl group is then released in another process of this type. The transamination and deamination reactions involving an amino acid, pyridoxal, and a metal ion are related reactions which involve presumably an internal tautomeric shift, such as that proposed by Pfeiffer, followed by hydrolysis:[50,51]

[49] H. S. Verter and A. E. Frost, *J. Amer. Chem. Soc.* **82**, 851 (1960).

[50] E. E. Snell, *Physiological Reviews* **33**, 509 (1953) contains much of the literature.

[51] D. E. Metzler, M. Ikawa, and E. E. Snell, *J. Amer. Chem. Soc.* **76**, 648 (1954).

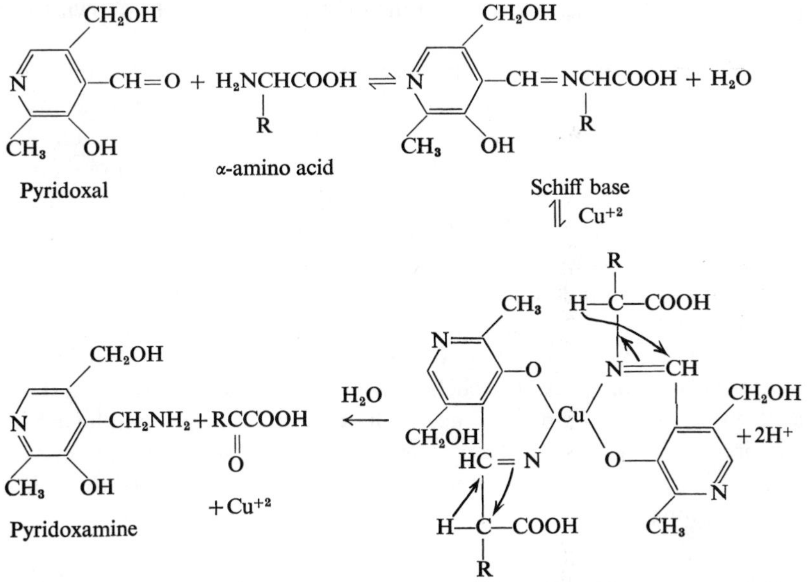

$$\text{Pyridoxal} \; (-CH=O) + H_2NCHCOOH \text{ (}\alpha\text{-amino acid)} \rightleftharpoons \text{(} -CH=NCHCOOH \text{) Schiff base} + H_2O$$

Pyridoxal [ring: CH_2OH, N, CH_3, OH] —CH=O + H_2NCHCOOH (R) (α-amino acid) ⇌ [ring: CH_2OH, N, CH_3, OH] —CH=NCHCOOH (R) Schiff base + H_2O

Schiff base ⇅ Cu^{+2}

Pyridoxamine [ring: CH_2OH, N, CH_3, OH] —CH_2NH_2 + RCCOOH (‖O) + Cu^{+2} ← (H_2O) [Cu complex intermediate] + 2H^+

If another alpha keto acid is present, $R'COCOOH$, it can enter similar intermediates and be transformed to $R'CH(NH_2)COOH$. The synthetic possibilities of these reactions are considerable even though the mechanisms are still the subject of some dispute.

CLASS (7) ELECTRON TRANSFER REACTIONS AIDED BY COORDINATION

Coordination opens up many mechanisms by which electrons may be transferred.[52] Unfortunately, most of the systems whose mechanisms have been elucidated in some detail are rather different from the typical catalytic processes. Nevertheless, the general conditions favoring the electron transfer process are known and are given in detail by Fraser.[52] One condition is that the reaction path should not require the close approach of two ions of similar charge. This is usually the condition which determines the mechanisms of electron transfer between complex ions. Most of the catalytically interesting reactions involve the oxidation of a neutral or negatively charged organic species by a metallic cation. In these reactions the cation usually extracts an electron from the ligand and it is then subsequently oxidized by oxygen to regenerate the oxidized form. There are an enormous number of reactions which *may* be of this type and many autoxidations catalyzed by

---

[52] The literature on this subject may be readily obtained through R. T. M. Fraser, *Reviews of Pure and Applied Chem.* **11**, 64 (1961).

copper(II), iron(II)-(III) and similar ions may subsequently be shown to be of this type.

A reaction of this kind which has been studied in detail is the cupric ion catalyzed autoxidation of ascorbic acid.[53,54] Here the mechanism seems to involve a complex between the ascorbate ion, HA⁻, and the cupric ion. The polarization of the ligand by the cupric ion occurs under conditions favorable to the complete transfer of the electron to the copper to produce copper(I) and HA·. This is the rate determining step. Subsequently these are both oxidized by molecular oxygen. The effect of added chelating agents indicates that at least two coordination sites must be available for the critical electron transfer step.[53] Thus EDTA can completely prevent the reaction from following its normal course by simply preventing the ascorbate from occupying two adjacent coordination sites. The chelates with dipyridyl and orthophenanthroline seem to exhibit some of the same peculiarities in this system that have been noted previously in simpler cases: electron transfer seems to be possible through the aromatic system of the chelate so chelation does not result in a complete stoppage of the reaction.

STEREOSPECIFIC POLYMERIZATION

A peculiar kind of coordinated catalyst has been discovered and developed to large scale industrial use in very recent times. This class of catalyst was discovered by K. Zeigler and developed by him and independently by G. Natta. These catalysts can be used to carry out stereospecific polymerizations.[55,56] These catalysts are active heterogeneously and are most active on the surface of a microcrystalline phase which is generally a transition metal halide in which the transition metal is in a low oxidation state. Zeigler first showed how a catalyst prepared from titanium tetrachloride and aluminum trialkyls allowed the low pressure polymerization of ethylene to be carried out in such a manner that very high molecular weight polymers were obtained. The production of isotactic and syndiotactic polymers has been especially studied by G. Natta and his co-workers in Milan. Isotactic polymers are polymers in which all of the units are arranged in a head-to-tail manner and each unit has the same orientation as any other. In syndiotactic polymers there is a regular head-to-tail arrangement also, but the arrangement of a substituent is alternatively above and below the plane of the polymer chain. Polymers produced by the more customary processes are atactic, i.e., they

[53] V. S. Butt and M. Hallaway, *Arch. Biochem. Biophys.* **92**, 24 (1961), contains much of the literature.

[54] A. E. Martell and M. Calvin, *Chemistry of the Metal Chelate Compounds*, Prentice-Hall, Inc., Englewood Cliffs, N.J. (1952), p. 389–392.

[55] G. Natta, *J. Inorg. Nuclear Chem.* **8**, 589 (1959).

[56] G. Natta and I. Pasquon, *Advances in Catalysis*, XI, 1–66 (1959).

have a random arrangement of the mers from which the polymer is built up. Isotactic and syndiotactic polymers of $R-CH=CH$ may be represented as: (after Natta)

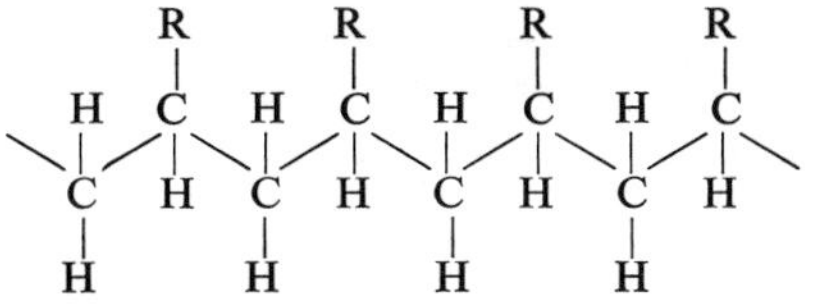

Isotactic

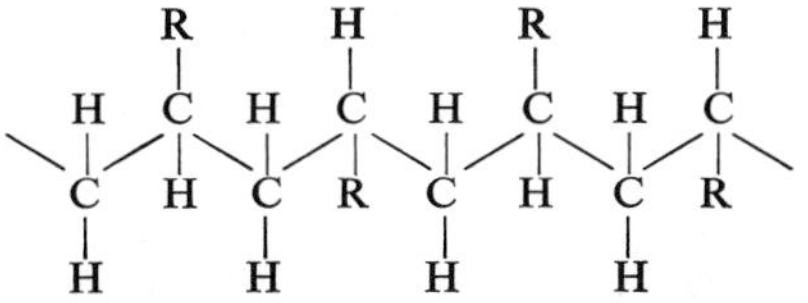

Syndiotactic

The types of complexes which have been isolated and subsequently shown to be active include:

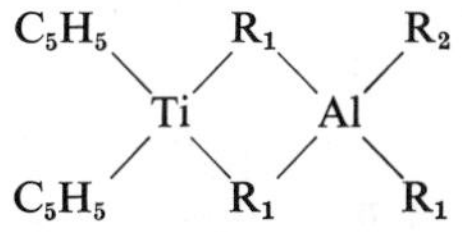

where R_1 is a halide or an alkyl group and R_2 is an alkyl group. These are made in practice by adding a beryllium or aluminum alkyl to a solid transition metal halide such as $TiCl_3$. The resulting heterogeneous catalyst is stereospecific and produces isotactic polymers which can be crystallized. The polymerization process starts at an active center, each of which catalyzes an asymmetric synthesis as it converts the monomer into polymer. In the polymer produced there will be the same number of each type of enantiomorphic polymer chain. The mechanism by which the chain grows is given by Natta and Pasquon (loc. cit.) as:

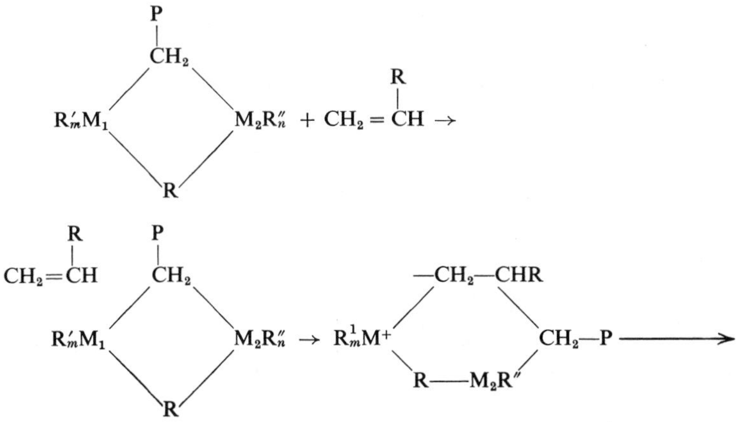

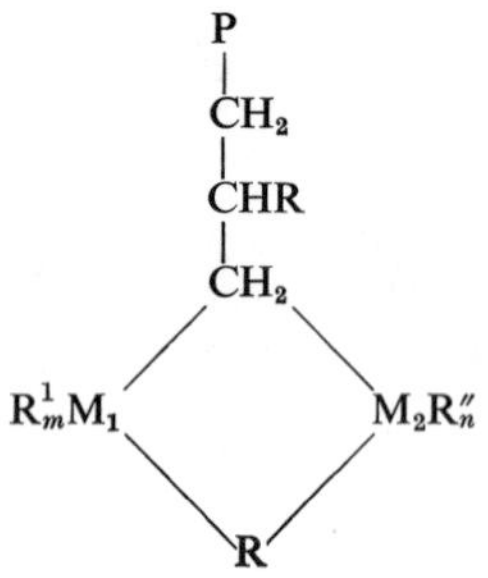

$$
\begin{array}{c}
\text{P} \\
| \\
\text{CH}_2 \\
| \\
\text{CHR} \\
| \\
\text{CH}_2
\end{array}
$$

R^1_mM$_1$ ⟨ ⟩ M$_2$R$''_n$

R

SPECIFIC REAGENTS FOR ANALYSIS AND THE ANALYTICAL USE OF CHELATES [57-63b]

It would be extremely convenient for many purposes if the addition of a single reagent to a solution produced an easily noted change which indicated the presence of a given ion in that solution. Such a reagent would have to be specific, in the strict sense of the word, and give the particular test only if that particular ion were present in the solution. There are few, if any, absolutely specific reagents for cations. When one limits the use of a reagent to certain conditions of pH and the concentrations of certain other reagents (e.g., NH$_3$) however, we find that many reagents are specific in a practical sense. Insofar as metallic cations in aqueous solutions are concerned, the vast majority of such reagents are chelating agents. The number of factors which may affect the interaction of a chelating agent and a metallic ion is so large that there is as yet no simple prescription for the preparation of a specific reagent. One of the most commonly used of these selective reagents is the chelating agent dimethylglyoxime. Under rigid conditions of pH, NH$_3$ concentrations, etc., this reagent gives a precipitate only with Ni(II) and Pd(II). Such a reagent is thus highly selective without being specific. The selectivity for Ni(II) and Pd(II) is found to be critically dependent upon the size of the ion *and* the structure of the solid precipitate. In the case of nickel and palla-

[57] F. Feigl, *Specific, Selective, Sensitive Reactions*, Academic Press, Inc., New York (1949).

[58] F. Feigl, *Spot Tests*, Elsevier Publishing Co., Amsterdam, (1954), 2 Vols.

[59] G. Schwarzenbach, *Complexometric Titrations*, Methuen & Co., Ltd., London (1957).

[60] H. Flaschka, *EDTA Titrations*, Pergamon Press, New York, (1959).

[61] F. J. Welcher, *Organic Analytical Reagents*, D. Van Nostrand Co., Inc., Princeton, N.J. (1947), 4 Vols.

[62] J. F. Flagg, *Organic Reagents*, Interscience Publishers, Inc., New York (1948).

[63] F. J. Welcher, *The Analytical Uses of Ethylenediaminetetraacetic Acid*, D. Van Nostrand Co., Princeton, N.J. (1958).

[63a] C. N. Reilley, R. W. Schmid and F. S. Sadek, *J. Chem. Ed.* **36**, 555, 619 (1959).

[63b] A. Ringbom, *Complexation in Analytical Chemistry*, John Wiley & Sons, Inc., New York (1963).

dium the packing of the molecules in the solid allows considerable interaction to occur between the nickel or palladium atoms of *adjacent* molecules. This is apparently responsible, to some extent, for the difference in the behavior of Ni(II) and some divalent ions of similar size in the same row of the periodic table.

A reagent which is apparently specific for copper(II) in ammoniacal media is found in benzoin oxime (cupron). Feigl[64] showed that the acyloin oximes are specific for copper. The reaction is probably:

This reaction is somewhat unusual in that the coordination number of copper is low. Feigl suggested that the aromatic rings were coordinated to the copper. A more reasonable coordination arrangement might be obtained if the packing of the solid were such that the copper completed its coordination sphere by sharing donor atoms of other molecules of the precipitate.

A reagent which is specific for zirconium (and presumably hafnium also) under suitable conditions is *n*-propylarsonic acid: $C_3H_7-AsO(OH)_2$. For the most part it is necessary to adjust the conditions of the solution quite carefully if a reaction is to be truly specific. It is sometimes possible to rely on catalytic properties of ions for tests and in many cases these kind of tests can be made very selective and sensitive.[57,58]

There are a number of other analytical applications of coordination compounds. For most of these applications chelates are used in preference to simple complexes because of their greater stability and because of the greater freedom available in the selection of the donor atoms. Some of these other uses are listed below:

1. *Quantitative Precipitants.* Many chelating agents which are not specific are useful in gravimetric analyses. The chief requirement of the analysis is that only one of the metallic ions present react and that one must be completely precipitated. The resultant precipitates can be either dried at a low temperature and weighed as the chelate or ignited to an oxide. The advantage of weighing the chelate is the high molecular weight of the precipitate and the low metal content. This makes possible the determination of small amounts of metal with great accuracy. In general, neutral metal chelates are not very soluble in water and are the species precipitated in such methods.

2. *Metal Indicators.* Metal indicators are dyes that are also chelating agents. They respond to the presence of some cations by changing color when

[64] F. Feigl, *Ber.* **56**, 2083 (1923); *Mikrochem.* **1**, 76 (1933).

the concentration of metal complex is sufficiently large. A commonly used example of this kind of dye is Eriochrome Black T:

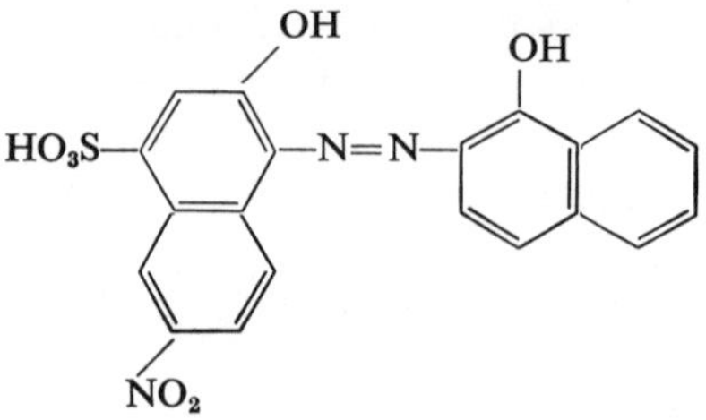

Between pH 7 and 11 the dye exists in a blue form, HD^{-2}. On reaction with many metals a red color appears:

$$M^{+2} + HD^{-2}(blue) \rightleftharpoons H^+ + MD^-(red)$$

These compounds are discussed in detail by Schwarzenbach.[59]

3. *Fluorescence Analysis.* Some metal chelates fluoresce and this can be used analytically.[65]

4. *Solvent Extraction Procedures.*[66] At present solvent extraction procedures are widely used to separate metallic cations for two main purposes: (a) analysis and (b) purification (especially of materials produced by nuclear processes). In both cases, coordination compounds are often found to furnish a convenient path for transferring the species from an aqueous to a non-aqueous phase. Historically, the recognition of the solvent extraction methods as useful separation techniques for metals can be traced back seventy years. It is primarily in the last thirty years that these methods have been extended to most of the elements, and their great popularity is an even more recent phenomenon.

The principle governing the distribution of a species between two imiscible phases is the distribution law. This may be considered to be a variant of the law of mass action applied to the transfer of a species from one phase to another. For a simple species we can write:

$$MX \text{ (water)} \rightleftharpoons MX \text{ (organic)}$$

and the distribution coefficient (or equilibrium constant) will be:

$$K_D = \frac{[MX] \text{ organic}}{[MX] \text{ water}}$$

For *each* of the species present in a two phase system there will be a corresponding distribution coefficient. It will usually be possible to ignore this complicating factor for one or more of the species and safely assume that

[65] H. M. Stevens, *Anal. Chim. Acta* **20**, 389 (1959).

[66] G. H. Morrison and H. Freiser, *Solvent Extraction in Analytical Chemistry*, John Wiley & Sons, Inc., New York (1957).

they will be present (essentially) in only one of the phases. Thus in the distribution of a neutral metal chelate between an aqueous and an organic phase, the metal salt from which the chelate is derived may be assumed to be present entirely in the aqueous phase.

The distribution coefficient, like any equilibrium constant, is affected by those properties of the system which affect the activity coefficients. There is every reason to believe in the constancy of the distribution coefficient when the concentration of the distributed species is relatively low (up to about 10^{-3}M).[67] Thus use of these equilibrium "constants" is attended by no more nor no less difficulty than the use of the solubility product, ionization constant, or instability constant. Like these, it can be held constant in many cases by the addition of large amounts of a neutral salt.

When considering examples of this kind of separation process it is well to keep in mind that systems may exhibit large numbers of peculiarities due to the specificity of some of the chemical reactions taking place in them. Some examples are given below to convey some indication of the features which may be encountered.

   a. Dithizone (also Diphenylthiocarbazone) as an Extractant. This com-

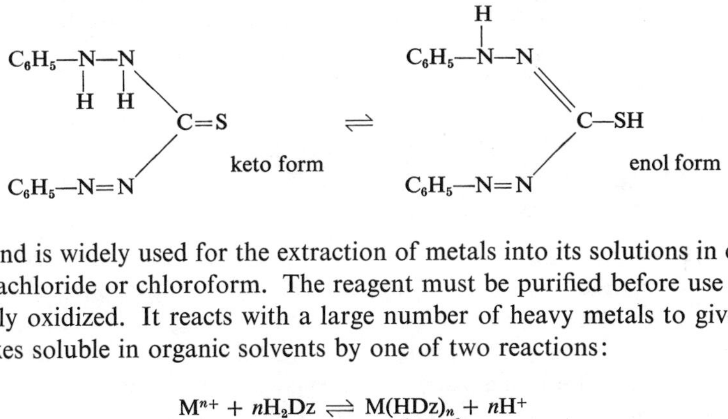

keto form $\rightleftharpoons$ enol form

pound is widely used for the extraction of metals into its solutions in carbon tetrachloride or chloroform. The reagent must be purified before use as it is easily oxidized. It reacts with a large number of heavy metals to give complexes soluble in organic solvents by one of two reactions:

$$M^{n+} + nH_2Dz \rightleftharpoons M(HDz)_n + nH^+$$
$$\text{keto form}$$

$$2M(HDz)_n \rightleftharpoons M_2Dz_n + nH_2Dz$$
$$\text{enol form}$$

The keto forms are the ones usually utilized in analytical work. Since so many metals can be extracted with dithizone, it is common to use masking reagents to increase the selectivity of the extraction process. Ions such as cyanide, thiosulfate, and thiocyanate are often useful for this purpose. The usual order of extractability is (Morrison and Freiser)

[67] D. C. Grahame and G. Seaborg, *J. Amer. Chem. Soc.* **60**, 2524 (1938).

Pd > Ag > Hg(II) > Cu (II) > Bi(III) ⩾ Pt(II) > Tl(III) >
Fe(II) > Sn(II) ⩾ Co(II) ⩾ Ni(II) > Zn ⩾ Pb > Mn(II) > Cd(II)

However, if cyanide is added in sufficient quantity, only Zn(II) and Sn(II) are extractable, the other metallic ions will remain tied up as cyanide complexes in the aqueous solution.

b. The Ferric Chloride-Ether System. Iron(III) can be extracted into ethers when it is present in solutions containing large amounts of free hydrochloric acid. If we write the equilibrium as:

$$\underset{\text{water}}{n\text{FeCl}_4^-} + n\text{H}^+ \rightleftharpoons \underset{\text{water}}{n\text{HFeCl}_4} \rightleftharpoons \underset{\text{ether}}{(\text{HFeCl}_4)_n}$$

we find that we have ignored several other equilibria which are concurrently attained in these solutions. These include formation of FeCl_4^-, solvate formation, formation of the extracted complex, distribution of the hydrochloric acid between the two phases, and dissociation equilibria in the ether. This being the case, it is no surprise that for such a complicated system the equilibria have not yet all been unequivocally disentangled. The species present in the ether is apparently a solvated form of the tetrachloroferrate(III) ion which is polymerized with n values of two to four.[68] The compound $\text{HFeCl}_4 \cdot 2(\text{C}_2\text{H}_5)_2\text{O}$ (or $[((\text{C}_2\text{H}_5)_2\text{O})_2\text{H}^+]\,\text{FeCl}_4^-$?) has been isolated from these solutions.[69] A large number of other metallic chlorides form similar systems with hydrochloric acid and ether. The per cent extraction curve for iron(III) in this system (plotted against the concentration of hydrochloric acid) is roughly sigmoid in shape. A small amount of the iron is extracted when the concentration of hydrochloric acid is 1M or less; this is increased rapidly between 3M and 7M and then levels off at 95% or more for solutions with concentrations of hydrochloric acid in excess of 8M.

c. Uranyl Nitrate Extractions. The uranyl ion is extracted from aqueous solutions by a wide variety of extractants, many of them of unusual structures. Uranyl nitrate can be extracted into the following: diethyl ether, kerosene solutions of tributyl phosphate, esters, kerosene solutions of trioctylamine, and tridecylphosphine oxide in kerosene. In some of these, the type of complex which is present is known with some certainty. In the uranyl nitrate-ether system, the neutral molecule (a nitrato complex) is extracted. The extraction into the ether is greatly favored by the presence of other nitrates (e.g., aluminum nitrate) which furnish large concentrations of nitrate ion and favor the formation of the nitrato complex. The use of the long aromatic chains in conjunction with polar functional groups in some of the extractants allows extraction to proceed through either complexation or ion-pair formation.

[68] H. L. Friedman, *J. Amer. Chem. Soc.* **74**, 5 (1952).
[69] J. Houben and W. Fischer, *J. prakt. Chem.* **123**, 89 (1929).

d. The Sc⁺³—SCN⁻ System. Scandium(III) forms a much smaller tervalent ion than the rare earths which usually accompany it in minerals. One of the results of this is a much greater tendency of Sc(III) to form complexes. A separation method which utilizes this difference is that in which Sc(III) is separated from accompanying rare earths by extraction of a solution containing hydrochloric acid and a large excess of ammonium thiocyanate with diethyl ether.[70] Some 90% of the scandium present in a solution originally $0.1M$ in Sc^{+3}, $0.5M$ in HCl, and $7M$ in NH_4SCN is extracted by an equal volume of diethyl ether. The species extracted is presumably $Sc(SCN)_3$. Thiocyanate complexes of a number of other species are also readily extracted under these circumstances but chemical separations for such elements are easily effected by other methods.

5. *Coordination Compounds and Ion Exchange Processes.*[78-83] There are several aspects of the ion exchange processes which bear directly or indirectly on coordination chemistry. Of these, only two will be described below: (a) ion exchange separation processes which use coordination compounds to enhance the separations obtained and (b) chelating ion exchange resins.

Ion Exchange Separations Using Coordination Compounds. It is possible to use either cationic or anionic ion exchange processes to effect the separation of various metallic species. In both types of methods it has been found advantageous to utilize complexes of metals rather than simple ions for many separations which are difficult when carried out by classical methods. At present the most widely used processes are those involving cation exchange resins. An ion exchange resin is simply a polymeric structure on which reactive (salt-forming) groups are present. They can be made so that the groups are sulfonic acid groups, amino groups, carboxyl groups, quaternary ammonium groups, phosphoric acid groups, and a large number of other salt forming groups. They can be prepared by substitution reactions of a substance which is already polymerized or by the polymerization of a monomer which contains a suitable functional group which is not destroyed in the polymerization process. Dowex 50 is a cation exchanger prepared by the sulfonation of a copolymer of 8% divinylbenzene and 92% styrene:

[70] W. Fischer and R. Bock, *Zeit. anorg. u. allgem. Chem.* **249**, 146 (1942).

[78] A. E. Martell and M. Calvin, *Chemistry of the Metal Chelate Compounds*, Prentice-Hall, Inc., Englewood Cliffs, N.J. (1952), pp. 433–451.

[79] S. Chaberek and A. E. Martell, *Organic Sequestering Agents*, John Wiley & Sons, Inc., New York (1959), pp. 348–354.

[80] R. Kunin, *Ion Exchange Resins*, John Wiley & Sons, Inc., New York, 2nd ed. (1958).

[81] G. H. Osborn, *Synthetic Ion-Exchangers*, The Macmillan Company, New York (1956).

[82] O. Samuelson, *Ion Exchangers in Analytical Chemistry*, John Wiley & Sons, Inc., New York (1953).

[83] *Annual Review of Physical Chemistry*—the yearly volumes of this publication contain several articles on the various aspects of the physical chemistry of the ion exchange process.

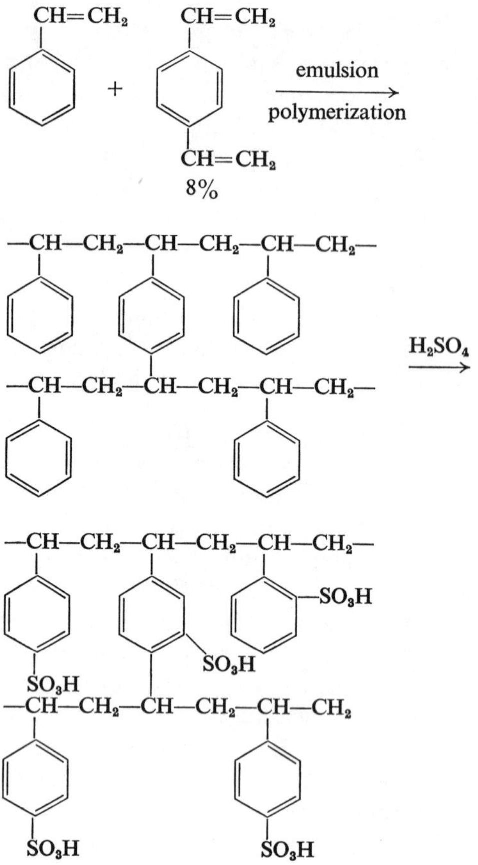

The divinylbenzene is introduced in varying amounts to obtain the degree of mechanical rigidity desired. The sulfonic acid groups are present in various positions on the aromatic rings. They give the resin its ion exchange properties. When they form a salt with a cation it is held in the neighborhood of the group by electrostatic forces and hence bound to the resin. It is the exchange of these bound groups that is referred to as an ion exchange. Anion exchangers such as Dowex 1 or Dowex 2 contain quaternized nitrogens: Resin-N$^+$(CH$_3$)$_3$ as the functional units. The use of different groups allows a degree of flexibility in the choice of exchanger. Commercial resins of most types needed for separations are available and most of the separation work reported utilizes commercial resins. Inorganic types of ion exchangers are now being actively studied in many laboratories.

In using ion exchange resins the sequence of operations usually includes: (1) equilibration of the resin with the solvent (inasmuch as the resins swell when they take up water this step is necessary to prevent the bursting of the packed columns), (2) saturation of the top of the column with the mixture to be separated, and (3) elution of the adsorbed species with a suitable eluting agent. It is in the second and third steps that the separation must be effected and most if not all of the separation is commonly effected by the third step. Ions differ in both the ease with which they are adsorbed on a column and in the ease with which they are eluted by a given eluant solution. By making use of these differences, separations can be effected even for groups of elements whose normal chemical behavior is all but identical (e.g., zirconium and hafnium; the rare earths). Fortunately it is generally possible to select conditions where the adsorption process and the elution process work in the same direction and increase the separation. Thus for the rare earths, the order of adsorbability of the ions on a cation exchange resin decreases from lanthanum to lutetium. The order of the stability of the chelates of these ions increases from lanthanum to lutetium. Thus the use of a chelating agent in the eluting solution will enhance the separation available from their differences in adsorbability. Citric acid, EDTA, or similar chelating agents have been used for this purpose. The ion which forms the most stable complex is the first one to pass into the eluate and this is also the ion which is most weakly adsorbed on the resin.

Complex formation utilizing both the cationic and anionic complexes has been found to be useful with elements such as zirconium, hafnium, niobium, tantalum, and some of the rare earths. From the point of view of convenience, it is usually as convenient to work with one as with the other. For some anionic complexes, such as the fluorides, special working conditions must be employed. The *details* for accomplishing these separations may be found in the journal literature; the processes discussed below are given in outline form only.

RARE EARTH SEPARATIONS. A very considerable number of variations in technique are available for the separations of the rare earths using ion exchangers. The factors which have an effect on the separation include the concentrations of the solutions used, the temperature, the type of resin, the length of the column, the chelating agent used in the eluting solutions, the flow rates, the pH, and the loading of the resin (the amount of material adsorbed on the resin per g). In addition, the equilibrium constants for the adsorption and chelation relations give a measure of the separation which is possible. If the equilibrium constant for the distribution of an ion between the solution and the resin is designated as K_D:

$$K_D = \frac{\text{(Metal/mass of resin)}}{\text{(Metal/volume of soln.)}} = \frac{\text{(Me/mass res.)}}{\text{(Me/vol soln.)}}$$

This is a composite constant made up of the constant for the exchange between the free metal ion and the adsorbed metal and the instability constant of the complexes formed in the eluting solution. Thus for a system in which the metal ion reacts with an ammonium form of the resin and with an eluting solution which contains ammonium citrate we have two equilibria:

$$M^{+3} + 3NH_4R \rightleftharpoons MR_3 + 3NH_4^+$$

$$M^{+3} + nH_xCit^{x-3} \rightleftharpoons M(H_xCit)_n^{3+n(x-3)}$$

If we write

$$K_{exchange} = \frac{[MR_3][NH_4^+]^3}{[M^{+3}][NH_4R]^3}$$

and

$$K_{stability} = \frac{[M(H_xcit)_n^{3+n(x-3)}]}{[M^{+3}][H_xcit^{x-3}]^n} = \frac{1}{K_{instability}}$$

and if

$$[M^{+3}] \ll [M(H_xcit)_n^{3+n(x-3)}]$$

then

$$K_D = \frac{[MR_3]}{[M(H_xcit)_n^{3+n(x-3)}]} = K_{ex} \cdot \frac{[M^{+3}][NH_4R]^3}{[NH_4^+]^3} \cdot K_{instab} \frac{1}{[M^{+3}][H_xcit^{x-3}]^n}$$

if H_2Cit^- is the complexing species and n is 3, the complexing species is formed in the reaction

$$H_3cit \rightleftharpoons H^+ + H_2cit^-$$

$$K_i = \frac{[H_2cit^-][H^+]}{[H_3cit]} \quad \text{or} \quad [H_2cit^-] = \frac{K_i[H_3cit]}{[H^+]}$$

$$K_D = K_{ex} \cdot \frac{[NH_4R]^3}{[NH_4^+]^3} \cdot K_{instability} \frac{[H^+]^3}{[H_3cit]^3 K_i^3}$$

$$K_D = \frac{K_{ex} \cdot K_{instab}}{K_i^3} \frac{[NH_4R]^3}{[NH_4^+]^3} \frac{[H^+]^3}{[H_3cit]^3}$$

The separation factor for two species is designated by a and is defined as:

$$a = \frac{K_{D_1}}{K_{D_2}}$$

When two cations of the same charge type are considered which form complexes of the same types we can write a as:

$$a = \frac{K_{D_1}}{K_{D_2}} = \frac{K_{exchange-1} \cdot K_{instab\ 1}}{K_{exchange-2} \cdot K_{instab\ 2}}$$

Thus both of the factors work in the same direction for the rare earths as both the K_{ex} values and the K_{instab} decrease as we go from lanthanum to lutetium. The result is an enhancement of the separation factor.

Small scale methods have been developed for the separation of the yttrium and cerium groups of the rare earths which require as little as 0.1 mg of each element.[84,85] A Dowex 50 ion exchange resin (270–325 mesh) column, 97 cm long, serves as the separation column. It is kept at 100° C. The rare earth

[84] B. H. Ketelle and G. E. Boyd, *J. Amer. Chem. Soc.* **69**, 2800 (1947); **73**, 1862 (1951).
[85] G. H. Higgins and K. Street, *J. Amer. Chem. Soc.* **72**, 5321 (1950).

mixture which was to be separated was first bombarded with neutrons to induce radioactivity and it was then adsorbed on the column. An eluting solution of ammonium citrate was used. The pH of the initial eluant was 3.25 and a secondary eluant solution was then used which had a pH of 3.3. These passed down the column at a rate of 2 ml/cm²/min. This eluate was put into a counter continuously and the separation could easily be followed by observation of the variation in counts per minute. If the log of the number of counts per minute is plotted vertically and the time is plotted horizontally, a series of peaks are observed, one corresponding to the elution of each given species.

Analogous methods for the large scale separation of the rare earths have been developed by F. H. Spedding and his co-workers.[86] These are now used industrially and are one of the reasons why it is now possible to purchase pound quantities of any of the rare earths (except promethium) in a state of high purity. It is also possible to separate the rare earths on an ion exchange column by the use of the Fe(III)- EDTA chelate as an eluting agent.

SEPARATION OF ZIRCONIUM AND HAFNIUM. In recent years the desire to use zirconium as a structural material in nuclear reactors has prompted a demand for hafnium-free zirconium. The cross section of hafnium for thermal neutrons is much greater than that of zirconium and accordingly its presence is very undesirable. As a result intensive studies have been carried out on the separation of these elements. Previously, these elements had been separated by the fractional crystallization of ammonium hexafluorozirconate, preferential precipitation of the phosphates from solutions in sulfuric acid and related methods. The aqueous chemistry of these elements is complicated by a tendency to hydrolyze which is very difficult to control. This introduces a complicating factor in the ion exchange separations which is generally overcome by working in very strongly acidic media. Both anion and cation exchange methods have been successfully used to separate these elements and they are now available in a state of high purity.

The first successful ion exchange separation of these elements was reported by Street and Seaborg.[87] This method used Dowex 50, a cation exchanger. A mixture of the oxychlorides of zirconium and hafnium was adsorbed on a small amount of the resin which was then placed on the top of a column 30 cm long. Zr^{95} and Hf^{181} were added previously as tracers. Elution was carried out using 6M hydrochloric acid.

An equally satisfactory separation can be effected by the use of an anion exchange resin, such as Amberlite IRA 400.[88,89] In this case fluoro complexes are used and Zr^{95} and Hf^{181} added as tracers to follow the separation.

---

[86] F. H. Spedding *et al.*, *J. Amer. Chem. Soc.* **69**, 2786 (1947); **72**, 2349, 2354 (1950) and later papers from this group.

[87] K. Street, Jr., and G. T. Seaborg, *J. Amer. Chem. Soc.* **70**, 4268 (1948).

[88] K. A. Kraus and G. E. Moore, *J. Amer. Chem. Soc.* **71**, 3263 (1949).

[89] E. H. Huffman and R. C. Lilly, *J. Amer. Chem. Soc.* **73**, 2902 (1951).

Where the activities overlap, a spectrophotometric method may be used for the analysis of the solutions. The fluoro complexes were adsorbed on the Amberlite IRA 400 which was originally present as the chloride salt. The use of a 30 cm column and an eluting solution $0.2M$ in HCl and $0.01M$ in HF with a rate of elution of 6 ml/hr allowed a good separation to be obtained.

A method for separating zirconium and hafnium which uses sulfuric acid as eluant and a Dowex 50 column has been developed by Lister.[90] This allows natural zirconium compounds, which contain from 1.5% to 2.5% hafnium, to be purified to 99.99% zirconium.

An excellent review of the thermodynamics of ion exchange processes involving complexation is given by Kraus and Nelson.[91] A new class of inorganic exchangers has recently been developed which consists of specially prepared hydrous oxides of the elements of Groups IV A, V A, and VI A.[83]

CHELATING ION EXCHANGERS. Ion exchange resins may be prepared with a wide variety of properties. In recent years a number of resins have been prepared in which chelating groups are present. The important requirement is the presence of two or more coordination sites in close proximity. Some of the methods which have been used to obtain resins with these properties are:

1. The condensation of phenolsulfonic acid with formaldehyde in the presence of citric or oxalic acid[92]

2. Condensations of the type listed in 1 carried out in the presence of EDTA, Trilon B, or chromotropic acid[93]

3. Condensation of *m*-phenylenediaminetetraacetic acid with resorcinol and formaldehyde.[94]

4. The coupling of 8-hydroxyquinoline with diazotized polyaminostyrene[95]

5. The crosslinking of polyethyleneimine with ethylene dichloride.[96] This results in a polymer built up of N—C—C—N groups and this material reacts with Cu^{+2} to give doubly charged sites much as would be generated in the reaction of Cu^{+2} with ethylene diamine. The structure of the copper(II) chelate is presumably:

[90] B. A. J. Lister, *J. Chem. Soc.* 3123 (1951).

[91] K. A. Kraus and F. Nelson "Anion Exchange Studies of Metal Complexes" in W. J. Hamer, *The Structure of Electrolytic Solutions*, John Wiley & Sons, Inc. (1959), Ch. 23.

[92] V. N. Lenskaya and M. F. Garaniva, *Zavodskaya Lab.* **21**, 1426 (1955), C.A. 50: 9097.

[93] V. A. Klyachko, *Trudy Komisii Anal. Khim., Akad. Nauk S.S.S.R., Inst. Geokhim. i Anal Khim.* **6**, 296 (1955), C.A. 50: 12732.

[94] E. Blasius and G. Olbrich, *Zeit. anal. Chem.* **151**, 81 (1956); B. Verouvic, *Czech. Pat.* **96**, 465, C.A. 54: 25389.

[95] J. R. Parrish, *Chem. and Ind.*, 137 (1956). This reaction has also been used to prepare poly(ferrocenylstyrene): B. Sansoni and O. Sigmund, *Angew. Chem.* **73**, 299 (1961).

[96] S. Nonogaki, S. Makishima and Y. Yoneda, *J. Phys. Chem.* **62**, 601 (1958).

$$
\begin{array}{c}
\text{H} \\
| \\
-\text{N}-\text{CH}_2-\text{CH}_2 \quad \overset{\text{H}}{\underset{}{|}} \quad \text{CH}_2-\text{CH}_2 \quad \text{CH}_2-\text{CH}_2- \\
\text{N} \qquad\qquad \text{N} \\
\overset{+2}{\text{Cu}} \qquad \text{CH}_2 \\
| \\
\text{CH}_2 \\
\text{N} \qquad\qquad \text{N} \\
-\text{N}-\text{CH}_2-\text{CH}_2 \quad \overset{}{\underset{\text{H}}{|}} \quad \text{CH}_2-\text{CH}_2 \quad \text{CH}_2-\text{CH}_2- \\
| \\
\text{H}
\end{array}
$$

6. By incorporating alpha hydroxy phosphoric acid groups in a polymer[97]

7. By the adsorption of organic chelating anions on a conventional anion exchange resin.[98] Thus adsorption of citrate or tartarate on an anion exchange resin (such as Amberlite IRA 400) leaves functional groups free which can chelate metal ions.

8. By the use of polymerized esters of titanic acid. These result, for example, from the interaction of vinyl acetate and tetrabutyl titanate.[99]

6. *Complexometric Titrations.*[59, 60, 63a] A complexometric titration is one in which the essential reactions involve the very stable complexes which metals form with reagents such as EDTA, nitrilotriacetic acid, 1,2-diaminocyclohexanetetraacetic acid, or diethylenetriaminepentaacetic acid. Schwarzenbach has developed a classification scheme for this kind of reaction and three of these types are: I. Direct Titrations, II. Back Titrations, and III. Substitution Titrations.

I. The direct titrations are based upon reactions of the sort:

$$M^+ + Z^{-y} \rightarrow MZ$$

If the stability constant of MZ is sufficiently large (10^7 or so), the end point in the titration may be detected by the very abrupt decrease in the concentration of the metal (i.e., by the use of an electrode sensitive to the ions of the metal or by some color reaction of the metal).

II. In the back titration, an excess of the complexing agent is added, the metal is completely complexed, and the excess of complexing agent is determined by titration with a metal for which a direct titration is feasible. The back titration procedure is used when a suitable end point indicator is not available for the metal being determined or when the initial reaction is slow, as is the case for nickel(II).

[97] E. S. Lane, *J. Applied Chem.* (London) **8**, 687 (1958).
[98] J. R. Brannan and G. H. Nancollas, *Chem. and Ind.*, 1415 (1959).
[99] E. S. Lane, *J. Applied Chem.* **11**, 1 (1961). Lane has made an extensive study of materials of this sort and the work published previously may be located from this article.

III. In the substitution titrations, the metal solution is allowed to react with a known amount of a second, less stable metal complex. The reaction which occurs is:

$$M^{+x} + NZ \rightarrow MZ + N^{+y}$$

The amount of N liberated is then determined by titration with a standard solution of Z. The metal complex usually used in titrations where Z is EDTA is magnesium. In a typical titration of this sort the presence of the magnesium in solution can usually be detected by the use of a metal indicator such as Eriochrome Black T. When this compound is present in a solution with a pH in the region 7 to 11, it results in a blue solution. The addition of magnesium results in the formation of a red chelate and the color change may be used for endpoint detection in systems in which free magnesium ion is liberated or consumed in the titration reaction.

A typical procedure from Flaschka (*loc. cit.*) illustrates the direct titration. In the determination of magnesium, the unknown solution is adjusted to pH 10 by means of a buffer, Eriochrome Black T is added as an indicator, the solution is warmed to 60° C., and titrated with a standard solution of the dihydrate of the disodium salt of EDTA (i.e., $Na_2H_2C_{10}H_{12}O_8N_2 \cdot 2H_2O$). The endpoint is detected when the last traces of the red tint (of the Mg-Eriochrome Black T complex) disappear. Flaschka gives many examples of the titrations of the other classes and his text may be used as a source of experimental details on these methods.

ELECTROPLATING[71-73]

To a very large extent, successful electroplating practice depends on the use of coordination compounds of various sorts. Most of this practice has been built up in a purely empirical manner and the function of the various additions which are made to the baths is generally specified in terms of the final results rather than in terms of the mechanism through which the additions affect the plating process.

In spite of the enormous growth of the possibilities for plating baths introduced by the large number of commercially available chelating and sequestering agents, the cyanide ion is still the most commonly used coordinating group in these baths. That this should be so in spite of the health and waste disposal problems associated with the use of cyanide is due largely to

[71] R. W. Parry and E. H. Lyons, Jr., in J. C. Bailar, Jr., *The Chemistry of the Coordination Compounds*, Reinhold Publishing Corp., New York (1956), Ch. 19.

[72] S. Chaberek and A. E. Martell, *Organic Sequestering Agents*, John Wiley & Sons, Inc., New York (1959), pp. 354–357.

[73] R. L. Smith, *The Sequestering of Metals*, Chapman & Hall, Ltd., London (1959), pp. 163–168.

the fact that many of the common plating baths are strongly alkaline. Under these strongly alkaline conditions the cyanide ion can compete with the hydroxide ion more successfully than most of the commonly used chelating agents. Chelating agents of various sorts are used as additives to some baths but are more costly than the customary additives. Aside from economic factors there appears to be no reason why sequestering agents cannot be used as the basis for successful plating baths. At present most of the work on this subject is only partly revealed in vaguely worded patents with the result that there are few such new plating procedures published in the open literature.

Plating from complexes very commonly involves the direct reduction of the complex rather than the reduction of the free metal ion in equilibrium with the complex. In many cases (e.g., the silver-cyanide bath) the concentration of the free metal is so low that it appears that an explanation involving reduction of the free metal ion is impossible for explaining the rate at which the metal can be plated out.

Coordination generally serves to reduce the concentration of the free metal ion to such a point that the reduction process which occurs leads to a fine-grained deposit. This can be done by the use of a variety of coordinating agents and those used in practice are generally ones in which the donor atoms have a high specific affinity for the metal ion in the bath though this is not invariably the case by any means. Some examples of the coordination groups used are:

METAL	LIGAND
$Cu(II)$	CN^-
$Ag(I)$	CN^-, thiourea, etc.
$Au(III)$, $Au(I)$	CN^-
Pb	H_2O or oxyacids, etc.
$Fe(II)$	sulfate or chloride baths; no satisfactory plate obtainable from CN^-.
$Cd(II)$	CN^-
$Mn(II)$	sulfate baths

It has been noted by Lyons[74] that, in general, inert complexes give unsatisfactory deposits or none at all. While there are exceptions to this rule, it seems to be a very useful guide in predicting success in plating operations. Those inert complexes for which reduction leads to less stable complexes can be used for electroplating.

In summary it may be said that the use of chelating agents in electroplating is in its infancy. With the great flexibility in structure of these compounds it seems inevitable that they will become more important as time passes, although the replacement of cyanide by such substances may take some time.

[74] E. H. Lyons, Jr., *J. Electrochem. Soc.* **101**, 363, 376 (1954).

SEQUESTERING AGENTS[75-76]

Sequestering refers to the complexing of metal ions in such a manner that one or more of their customary reactions is prevented without actually removing the metallic species from the system.

In practice "sequestration" is used to cover a wide variety of methods by which the effect of metal ions in a system is suppressed. It is customary to exclude sequestration by OH^-, CN^-, or other simple ions, though this seems unreasonable from either a practical or a logical point of view. The chief reason for this exclusion is the rather drastic nature of the changes accompanying sequestration when cyanide or hydroxide ions are used. The use of chelating agents such as EDTA, tartaric acid, etc., as sequestering agents allows the sequestration to be accomplished without large changes in the pH of the system or the introduction of a highly toxic species.

Since sequestration is restricted to complexation in which the metal is not removed from solution, we find that it is used when, for some reason or other, it is desired to reduce the concentration of free metal ions to a low value. Some examples of the use of sequestration are given below. It will be seen that there are many reasons for sequestering ions in addition to the desire to merely reduce their concentration to the lowest possible values.

1. *Regulation of Essential Trace Metal Concentrations in Soils.* Plants need a steady supply of several metals, but this supply need not be large. In many cases where plants exhibit metal deficiencies, these can be remedied by the application of the corresponding EDTA chelate. This releases metal to the plant in amounts sufficient for proper growth but does not give rise to the difficulties which arise when a very soluble salt of that metal is added to the soil. This kind of application is found useful in treating deficiencies of iron, manganese, zinc, copper, and nickel. The amounts of chelate required for such treatment is small in some cases and the use of chelates for this purpose in the future will probably increase.

2. *Water Treatment.* For many purposes it is essential that the iron content of water be as low as possible to avoid discoloration or the formation of scums (as in dyeing processes). EDTA additions are a very effective way of obtaining this result under any but alkaline conditions. It is also a useful reagent in cleaning boilers and similar equipment in which hard water has deposited insoluble salts. The problems which arise from the use of hard water are numerous and the use of sequestering agents is particularly advantageous if the ions exert a catalytic effect (e.g., in catalyzing autoxidations) or have a deleterious effect on the appearance of a product (e.g., discoloration).

[75] S. Chaberek and A. E. Martell, *Organic Sequestering Agents*, John Wiley & Sons, Inc., New York (1959).

[76] R. L. Smith, *The Sequestering of Metals*, Chapman & Hall, Ltd., London (1959).

3. *Pharmacological Applications.* Most pharmacological applications utilize sequestering agents to remove a heavy metal ion from the body fluids or the soft tissues as an antidote to heavy metal poisoning. In using such agents it is usually necessary that side effects be carefully compensated. Thus if EDTA is administered, as such, to counteract the effect of lead poisoning, very considerable decalcification of bones and teeth may result because of the great stability of the calcium complex. To prevent this, EDTA is generally administered as $Na_2CaEDTA$. While *small* amounts of EDTA pass through the body without being changed or having any notable effect (other than decalcification), many other chelating agents which might be useful for the treatment of metal poisoning are themselves too toxic for this use. Thus, aurintricarboxylic acid is a very effective chelating agent for beryllium and can be used to counteract the effect of injected beryllium. It is itself sufficiently toxic, however, that its use leads to death from aurintricarboxylic acid poisoning rather than beryllium poisoning. Beryllium, incidentally, is apparently effective as a poison, in part, because it replaces magnesium in some essential enzymes in the body. It forms stable complexes, unlike magnesium, and stops the enzymatic catalysis.[77]

Some of the chelating agents or sequestering agents and the metals which they tie up, are:

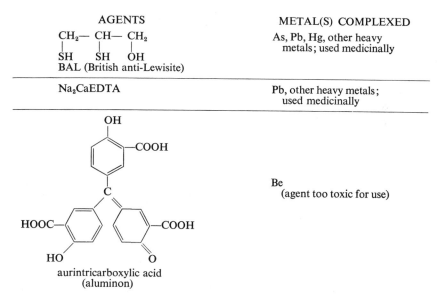

AGENTS	METAL(S) COMPLEXED
CH₂— CH— CH₂ | | | SH SH OH BAL (British anti-Lewisite)	As, Pb, Hg, other heavy metals; used medicinally
Na₂CaEDTA	Pb, other heavy metals; used medicinally
aurintricarboxylic acid (aluminon)	Be (agent too toxic for use)

[77] J. Schubert, M. R. White, and A. Lindenbaum, *J. Biol. Chem.* **196**, 279 (1952); J. Schubert, *Chimia* **11**, 113 (1951) contains an excellent summary of many of the applications of chelates in this general area; *Federation Proceedings* **20**, No. 3, Part II, pp. 1–273 (1961) is a symposium entitled *"Biological Aspects of Metal-Binding"*—this is the most complete compilation covering this field which is presently available.

Ferrous gluconate; gluconic acid is 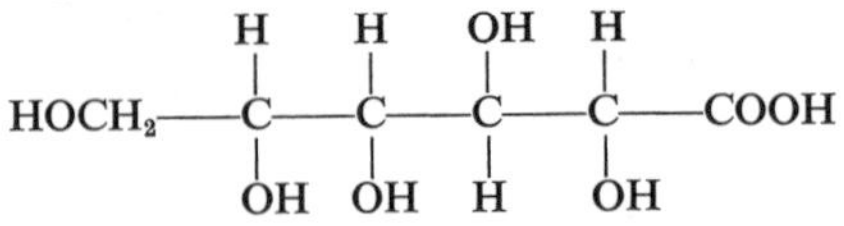	Treatment of anemia, used medicinally

$$HOCH_2 \overset{\overset{\displaystyle H}{|}}{\underset{\underset{\displaystyle OH}{|}}{C}} \overset{\overset{\displaystyle H}{|}}{\underset{\underset{\displaystyle OH}{|}}{C}} \overset{\overset{\displaystyle OH}{|}}{\underset{\underset{\displaystyle H}{|}}{C}} \overset{\overset{\displaystyle H}{|}}{\underset{\underset{\displaystyle OH}{|}}{C}} COOH$$

$H_2CaEDTA$	In vivo regulation of serum calcium levels

4. *Providing Trace Elements in Nutrient Media.* (Smith, *loc. cit.*, p. 138). For the growth of some microorganisms, the presence of trace quantities of certain metals is necessary. If the concentration is too high the organisms will be poisoned; if too low they will be unable to grow. Such trace elements are usually present as impurities in the reagents used to make up the media. When specially purified reagents are used for this purpose, the lack of trace elements will often be revealed by poor growth. The metal-buffer properties of sequestering agents can be used to provide a constant small concentration of essential metals such as copper, zinc, iron, or cobalt in the medium.

EXERCISES

1. Using catalytic processes based upon coordination compounds, suggest syntheses of the following compounds:

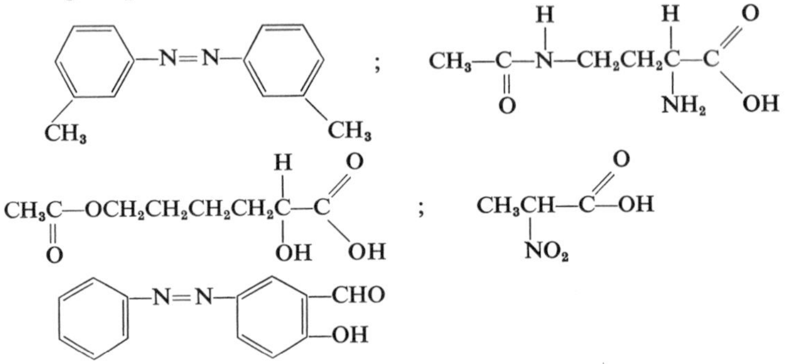

2. Eriochrome Black T is used as a metal indicator in complexometric titrations because it forms chelates which have a characteristic color with several metals. Suggest other chelates which you think might also be suitable for such a use. Suggest some properties of chelates which are important if the material is to be used as a metal indicator.

3. Tell how you would synthesize a chelating resin in which the coordinating groups were —SH groups. What elements would you expect to be very firmly bound to such a resin?

4. You have both Ba^{+2} and Cu^{+2} adsorbed on a cation exchange column. Suggest suitable eluants which will allow their rapid separation.

5. Suggest other metal ions which should be effective in the catalytic deaminations involving pyridoxal and alpha amino acids. What would you predict to be the relative effectiveness of Cu^{+2} and Mg^{+2}?

CHAPTER

11

Some Metal Complexes of Biological Significance

Life hangs suspended by a few slender threads in the primeval inorganic chaos which surrounds it; of these threads, one of the most important is the coordinate bond. Surely none of the others show more directly its connection to that primeval inorganic chaos.

Of the coordination compounds concerned with life processes, many simply cannot be adequately appreciated in such a brief treatment as is given here. Among these we must include hemoglobin, chlorophyll, numerous hematin enzymes such as catalase and cytochrome oxidase, metal activated enzymes, vitamin B_{12}, and those vital, but poorly understood complexes which play such an important role in the metabolism of the metallic ions. The literature cited provides an entry into the very extensive publications on these topics.[1]

METALLOPORPHYRINS. The metalloporphyrins are complexes in which a metal ion is held in the center of a ring of four nitrogen atoms which are themselves constituents of a larger, complex organic structure called a

[1] The literature on this topic is probably equal in volume to that found in all the other fields of coordination chemistry combined. Many of the important fields are covered in summary in the proceedings of a symposium in *Federation Proceedings*, Vol. 20, No. 3, Part II(1961) entitled "Biological Aspects of Metal Binding." This actually may be more accurately described as a symposium on the *zoological* aspects of metal binding. The botanical aspects are just as multifarious, but the literature, except for that on chlorophyll or on trace elements in plant nutrition, is more dispersed. The present chapter is concerned almost exclusively with zoological aspects. An extensive review is given by G. Eichhorn in J. C. Bailar, Jr., *The Chemistry of the Coordination Compounds*, Reinhold Publishing Corp., New York (1956), pp. 698–742.

porphyrin group. These peculiar structures are inseparably linked with the fundamental biological processes of both green plants and animals. The metalloporphyrin, chlorophyll, plays a central role in photosynthesis. It contains magnesium as the central atom. The hemoglobin molecule which allows vertebrates to remove oxygen from the air contains a similarly coordinated ferrous ion in a related structure which, although much more complex than chlorophyll, still relies on the presence of porphyrin groups containing coordinated iron(II) as the central atom for the functional group used in the transport of oxygen. In addition to these compounds, very similar structures are used in life processes for a variety of purposes, most of which are catalytic in nature. These molecules are capable of aiding the transfer of both electrons and simple molecules from one chemical species to another.

HEMOGLOBIN.[2-7] In hemoglobin, as in numerous other iron complexes of this type, the prosthetic group is derived from the porphin molecule. On reaction with a ferrous salt one may obtain an iron(II) porphin complex such as is shown on page 95. Hemoglobin possesses a very complicated structure which contains four such iron(II) coordination centers and a protein (globin). Hemoglobin can be reversibly split into smaller molecules, containing both iron and protein, which can also combine with oxygen. Hemoglobin has a molecular weight of 67,000 and contains 0.335% iron. The closely related molecule, myoglobin, contains only one such iron atom and has a molecular weight one-fourth that of hemoglobin; it is found in muscle tissue as an oxygen carrier. The groups which complete the coordination sphere of the iron include one rather firmly bound imidazole group derived from the globin or protein portion of the molecule and another group more loosely held which may be water or another imidazole group of the globin. While there is no necessity for the iron to have six groups coordinated to it at all times, it is generally accepted that the sixth coordination position contains a labile group, and this is commonly thought to be an imidazole group.[8] In studies

[2] "Conference on Hemoglobin," National Academy of Sciences National Research Council, Publication 557, Washington, D.C. (1958).

[3] A. Vannotti, *Porphyrins, Their Biological and Chemical Importance*, Hilger and Watts, Ltd., London (1954); J. E. Falk, *Porphyrins and Metalloporphyrins*, Elsevier Pub. Co., Amsterdam, 1964.

[4] R. Lemberg and J. W. Legge, *Hematin Compounds and Bile Pigments*, Interscience Publishers, Inc., New York (1949).

[5] J. C. Kendrew, *Science* **139**, 1259 (1962); M. F. Perutz, *ibid.*, **140**, 863 (1963).

[6] F. J. W. Roughton and J. C. Kendrew, editors, *Haemoglobin*, Butterworth's Scientific Publications, London (1949).

[7] J. H. Wang, "Hemoglobin and Myoglobin" in O. Hayaishi, editor, *Oxygenases*, Academic Press, Inc., New York (1962), Ch. 11.

[8] H. Theorell, *Advances in Enzymology VII*, 265 (1947) contains the literature up to the time of its publication. The problem has been of continuing interest. Some of the more recent work may be traced back from A. Kajita, F. Uchimura, H. Mizutani, G. Kikuchi, and K. Kajiro, *J. Biochem.* (Tokyo) **46**, 593 (1959) and ref. 7.

of the complexes of heme, an iron(II) metalloporphin derived from hemoglobin, it has been shown that a complex is formed in which two molecules of histidine (which contains the imidazole group) are united with one mole of heme.[8] Histidine and imidazole are:

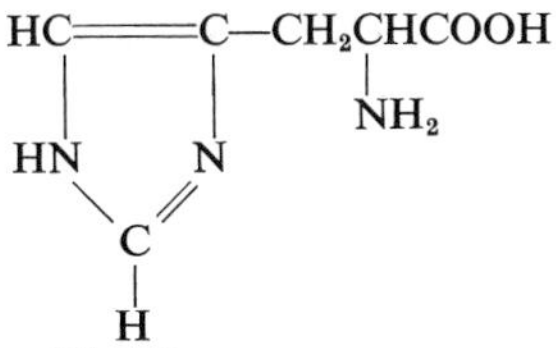

Histidine

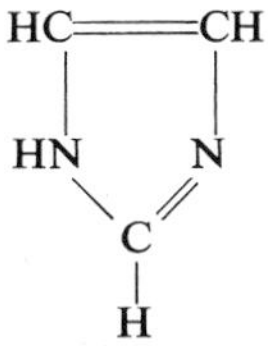

Imidazole

The iron(II) in hemoglobin can form coordinate bonds with a number of ligands including O_2, CO, and NO (cyanide ion forms only a very weak complex), presumably because of the ability of these species to form double bonds. The iron(II) in hemoglobin has four unpaired electrons before coordination and none after bonding to these ligands so they all behave as "strong field" ligands. Since there are four iron porphin coordination centers per hemoglobin molecule, the oxygenation goes via the step-wise reactions:

$$Hb + O_2 \rightleftharpoons Hb(O_2) \qquad (K_1)$$

$$Hb(O_2) + O_2 \rightleftharpoons Hb(O_2)_2 \qquad (K_2)$$

$$Hb(O_2)_2 + O_2 \rightleftharpoons Hb(O_2)_3 \qquad (K_3)$$

$$Hb(O_2)_3 + O_2 \rightleftharpoons Hb(O_2)_4 \qquad (K_4)$$

Adair[9] first derived equations to relate the oxygen content of hemoglobin to the partial pressure of the oxygen and the equilibrium constants for the successive steps in the reaction. These are quite similar in outline to the treatments later used by Bjerrum and Leden. The oxygen saturation, y, is related to the successive equilibrium constants and the partial pressure of the oxygen (p) by the equations:

$$y = \frac{\sum(O_2 \text{ present in all species})}{\sum(O_2 \text{ capacity of all species})}$$

$$y = \frac{K_1 p + 2K_1 K_2 p^2 + 3K_1 K_2 K_3 p^3 + 4K_1 K_2 K_3 K_4 p^4}{4(1 + K_1 p + K_1 K_2 p^2 + K_1 K_2 K_3 p^3 + K_1 K_2 K_3 K_4 p^4)}$$

The successive constants for the oxygenation equilibrium have been determined by Roughton and his co-workers[10] using a precision manometric method. It was found that the successive constants *increase* in magnitude, a situation quite unlike the usual trend in successive complexity constants.

[9] G. A. Adair, *Proc. Roy. Soc.* **109A**, 292 (1925); *J. Biol. Chem.* **63**, 529 (1925).

[10] Q. H. Gibson and F. J. W. Roughton, "Discussions of the Faraday Society" **20**, 195 (1955).

This indicates an interaction which makes it easier for the other heme groups to take up oxygen after one of the four has reacted. Normal hemoglobin is about 95% saturated by an oxygen pressure of 120 mm. In the atmosphere the partial pressure of oxygen is about 155 mm so the equilibrium conditions are quite favorable for the near saturation of hemoglobin with oxygen in the lungs. The dissociation curve of hemoglobin also favors the ready release of almost this entire amount of oxygen when the partial pressure of oxygen is 10 mm or less. The formation and dissociation rates of the oxygen complexes of hemoglobin are very high so these are both rapid reactions.[7] These are pH dependent, an effect called the Bohr effect after its discoverer the Danish physiologist, C. Bohr. In the range of physiological pH this effect shows itself as a decreased ability of hemoglobin to bind oxygen as the partial pressure of carbon dioxide increases. This means that hemoglobin has an especially low affinity for oxygen in those tissues containing the most carbon dioxide. Another aspect of this effect is the established role of hemoglobin in removing carbon dioxide from the body by the formation of carbamic acid derivatives with the amino groups of the globin. In alkaline solution, in the presence of calcium ion, the reaction has been postulated as:

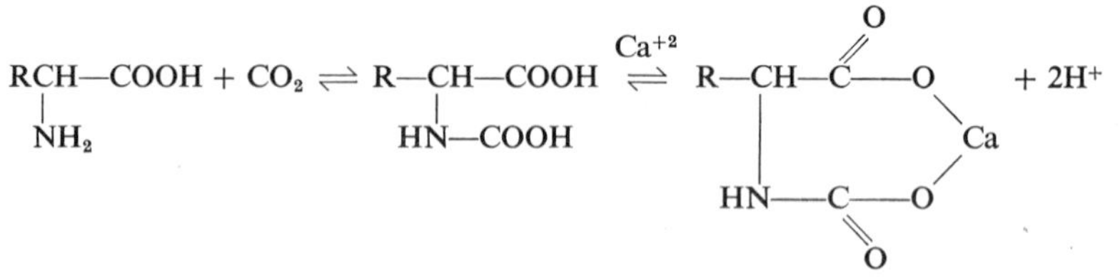

$$
\begin{array}{c}
RCH-COOH + CO_2 \rightleftharpoons R-CH-COOH \overset{Ca^{+2}}{\rightleftharpoons} R-CH-C \\
\end{array}
$$

These two roles of hemoglobin thus seem to compliment each other in a rather unexpected fashion.

There are an enormous number of studies of the aspects of hemoglobin related to its coordination chemistry. The references cited (1–8) provide summaries of this from several different viewpoints.

CHLOROPHYLL. The green pigment in leaves is a magnesium metalloporphyrin called chlorophyll, which is intimately involved in the photosynthetic apparatus of plants. Its structure was given by H. Fischer and is shown on page 70. This structure has been verified by direct synthesis.[11,12] The photosynthetic process is one of considerable complexity; the literature on the subject is enormous and not always in complete harmony. The over-all reaction may be summarized as one in which carbon dioxide and water are transformed into carbohydrates and water:

$$CO_2 + H_2O + h\nu \rightarrow 1/n(CH_2O)_n + O_2$$

[11] R. B. Woodward *et al.*, *J. Amer. Chem. Soc.* **82**, 3800 (1960).

[12] M. Strell, A. Kalojanoff and H. Koller, *Angew. Chem.* **72**, 169 (1960).

Discussions of this process from various viewpoints and with various degrees of completeness in the literature cited are available.[13-25]

In contrast to its behavior in almost all of its other complexes, the magnesium of chlorophyll does not undergo rapid exchange with radioactive magnesium,[26] though it can be removed by treatment with dilute acid. It is generally considered that the chlorophyll molecule acts as an agent for the transfer of radiant energy from the sun to the metabolic processes of the green leaves. Its absorption spectrum includes peaks at 680 mμ and one at 430 mμ which allow the formation of energy rich, excited states. The absorption of light by the chlorophyll molecule thus allows it to attain an excited state from which it can return by transferring the energy to another molecule or system of molecules or by luminescence. In order to transform a molecule of carbon dioxide into a hexose (carbohydrate) one must furnish about 120 Kcals/mole. At 680 mμ, one photon corresponds to 41 Kcals, and experimentally approximately 10 photons must be absorbed per molecule of CO_2 fixed. Photosynthesis is then a reasonably efficient process when it is realized that the fixation of a single molecule of carbon dioxide must be a cooperative act involving a relatively large number of chlorophyll molecules. All of the intermediate steps are not known, but the first product in which the carbon dioxide appears is glycerophosphoric acid which is formed after ribulose diphosphate takes up a molecule of carbon dioxide:

[13] *Encyclopedia of Plant Physiology*, Springer-Verlag, Berlin; Göttingen Heidelberg (1960), Vol. V.

[14] R. C. Fuller, editor, *The Photochemical Apparatus, Its Structure and Function*, Brookhaven National Laboratory, New York (1959).

[15] M. B. Allen, editor, *Comparative Biochemistry of Photoreactive Systems*, Academic Press, Inc., New York (1960).

[16] A. A. Krasnovsky, *Ann. Rev. Plant Physiology* **11**, 363 (1960).

[17] J. A. Bassham and M. Calvin, *The Path of Carbon in Photosynthesis*, Prentice-Hall, Inc., Englewood Cliffs, N.J. (1957).

[18] M. Calvin and J. A. Bassham, *The Photosynthesis of Carbon Compounds*, W. A. Benjamin, Inc., New York (1962).

[19] W. Bladergroen, *Problems in Photosynthesis*, Charles C. Thomas, Publisher, Springfield, Ill. (1960).

[20] H. Gaffron in F. C. Steward, editor, *Plant Physiology*, Academic Press, Inc., New York (1960), Vol. **1B**, p. 3.

[21] *Encyclopedic Dictionary of Physics*, Pergamon Press, New York (1962), Vol. 5, p. 491 ff.

[22] E. Rabinowitch, *J. Phys. Chem.* **61**, 870 (1962).

[23] E. Rabinowitch, editor, *Photosynthesis and Related Processes*, Interscience, Inc., New York, Vol. I, IIa, IIb (1945, 1951, and 1956, resp.).

[24] R. Hill and C. P. Whittingham, *Photosynthesis*, Methuen & Co., Ltd., London (1952).

[25] J. L. Oncley, *Biophysical Science—A Study Program*, J. Wiley & Sons, Inc., New York (1959); W. Stiles, *Science Progress* L, 450 (1962).

[26] S. Ruben, A. W. Fraenkel, and M. D. Kamen, *J. Phys. Chem.* **46**, 710 (1942).

$$
\begin{array}{l}
CH_2OPO(OH)_2 \\
\,|\, \\
C=O \\
\,|\, \\
HC{-}OH \\
\,|\, \\
HC{-}OH \\
\,|\, \\
CH_2OPO(OH)_2
\end{array}
\quad + CO_2 + H_2O \rightarrow \quad
\begin{array}{l}
COOH \\
\,|\, \\
2HC{-}OH \\
\,|\, \\
CH_2OPO(OH)_2
\end{array}
$$

The ribulose diphosphate is then regenerated. The specificity of the magnesium complex, chlorophyll, seems to be absolute for photosynthesis. Related complexes of zinc, iron, copper, or nickel exhibit few or none of the peculiarities of the magnesium complex. The luminescence of the chlorophyll molecule is well established but such behavior is missing in most of the corresponding complexes of other cations. The magnesium in chlorophyll is coordinatively unsaturated and can add amines, water, and other donor molecules containing nitrogen and oxygen as well as fluoride.[27] The functioning of chlorophyll in plants is less completely understood than the role of hemoglobin in mammalian blood.

It is necessary to note that other species than chlorophyll are also necessary for photosynthesis, in particular manganese and hematin compounds. These last are possibly of critical importance in the transfer of energy from the chlorophyll to a more directly useable form[28], as the oxidation of the ferric ion in heme groups to a ferryl group (FeO^{++}) via charge transfer to an excited chlorophyll molecule would provide a systematic basis for the photochemical reactions which occur in photosynthesis.

CATALASE AND RELATED SUBSTANCES. Metalloporphyrins are used by biological systems for the catalysis of a large number of important reactions. Catalase is an enzyme found in an enormous number of types of cell. It consists of an iron metalloporphyrin prosthetic group linked to a protein. It is an extremely powerful catalyst for the decomposition of hydrogen peroxide. The relative activities of ionic iron, hematin, and catalase in liters/mole-second at O° C are 10^{-5}, 10^{-2}, and 10^5 according to Haldane.[29] The enzyme can also catalyze "coupled oxidations" using hydrogen peroxide to oxidize other species such as ethanol. It was originally thought that the function of catalase was the destruction of hydrogen peroxide which accumulated in cells in the course of respiration and would otherwise have a destructive action. This is not presently thought to be the only or the chief function of catalase in cells.

In addition to the role which iron metalloporphyrins play in picking up oxygen from the air, they also play a vital role in the catalysis of processes in the body. Iron compounds generally are effective in the catalysis of many

[27] J. N. Phillips, *Reviews Pure Applied Chem.* **10**, 35 (1960).
[28] M. D. Kamen, ref. 15, p. 332.
[29] J. B. Haldane, *Proc. Roy. Soc.* **108B**, 559 (1931).

oxidation processes because of the ease with which iron can pass from the ferrous to the ferric state and vice versa. One of the most thoroughly characterized of these "respiratory ferments" is cytochrome C. This is a rather stable molecule with a molecular weight of 16,500. It contains one iron metalloporphyrin (hematin) group per molecule. This and the related catalysts of the cytochrome system provide the major pathways for respiration in most cells. The investigation of this process is presently one of the most active fields of biochemistry. The function of these complexes is to activate the oxygen for reaction rather than to merely carry it as hemoglobin does. Much of the chemistry of these complexes is discussed in the book of Lemberg and Legge cited above.

COPPER AND VANADIUM METALLOPORPHYRINS. Copper metalloporphyrins are very probably precursors in the synthesis of hemoglobin and related iron metalloporphyrins. Hemocyanin, a copper-protein complex, *not* a metalloporphyrin is used by many invertebrates for the transport of oxygen.[30] A vanadium complex is found in some invertebrates and vanadium metalloporphyrins are found in many petroleum stocks. Vanadium(IV) complexes may exhibit variable coordination numbers even in relatively simple chelates.[31]

METALLOFLAVOPROTEINS.[32,33] Numerous enzymes contain both a metal and a riboflavin derivative, in addition to a protein constituent. Examples include xanthine oxidase, succinic dehydrogenase, nitrate reductases, and liver aldehyde oxidase. The metals which may be present are molybdenum, iron, copper, and manganese. This is coupled with flavin adenine dinucleotide and a protein containing sulfhydryl groups. Many of these enzymes contain *two* different metals, e.g., xanthine oxidase contains both molybdenum and iron. As an example of the type of reaction involved in the action of such enzymes one may cite the oxidation of hypoxanthine to uric acid by xanthine oxidase:

hypoxanthine → (xanthine oxidase, two steps) → uric acid

In these enzymes the metals are important for several reasons including the facilitation of electron exchange and the linking of the different parts of the

[30] C. R. Dawson and M. F. Mallette, *Advances Protein Chem.*, II, 179 (1945).
[31] H. J. Bielig and E. Bayer, *Ann.* **580**, 135 (1953); **584**, 96 (1953).
[32] H. R. Mahler, *Advances in Enzymology*, XVII, 233 (1956).
[33] E. C. DeRenzo, *Advances in Enzymology*, XVII, 293 (1956).

enzyme. It is of interest to note that tungstate, which can presumably replace the easily lost molybdenum of xanthine oxidase, has a definite inhibitory effect on the activity of this enzyme.[2]

METALS AND ENZYME ACTIVITY: GENERAL ASPECTS.[34] Metals in enzymes are found to be coordinated in two ways corresponding to the two ways in which they are found in inorganic systems. Thus one has metal enzymes in which the metal does not leave the enzyme very rapidly even in the presence of large amounts of a very good coordinating agent. These are inert or robust complexes, though the term "inert" seems quite inappropriate for such active catalysts. One also finds metal enzymes from which the metal can be very readily removed and these are labile complexes. Vallee[34a] designates the stable complexes as *metalloenzymes* and most of the labile ones as *metal-enzyme complexes*. This classification is useful since the rate of exchange of the metal ion of many of the biologically important metal chelates is determined by the structure of the chelating agent rather than the characteristics of the central metal ion (e.g., chlorophyll). Vallee considers that in metalloenzymes the metal and protein are combined in such a firm manner that the combination can be considered to be a single naturally occurring species. The combination involves a *specific* metal and analogous complexes with different central metal ions which do not behave catalytically in the same fashion. In metal-enzyme complexes the metal requirement is usually of a more general nature and may be satisfied by a range of ions of similar charge and size. Thus magnesium and divalent manganese are often *both* effective as activators of many enzymes systems.[35]

This second type of enzyme shows a variation in effectiveness as the stability of the complex between the metal and enzyme increases and there is usually a *maximum* in catalytic effectiveness at some intermediate value of the stability constant. This has its origin in the dynamic nature of the processes which are catalyzed. If the complexes are too stable they can *decrease* the rate of release of the products of the reaction.[36]

The metals which have been found in various enzyme systems include Fe, Cu, Mo, Mn, Zn, and Mg. They are characteristically required in stoichiometric amounts for full activity of the enzyme but with the relatively labile systems the activity of the enzyme usually (but not always) varies in a

---

[34] An enormous fund of information on this item and related topics may be found in P. D. Boyer, H. Lardy and K. Myrback, editors, *The Enzymes*, Academic Press, Inc., New York (1959–), 7 Vols.

[34a] B. L. Vallee, *Advances in Protein Chemistry*, X, 320 (1955).

[34b] A very extensive review of the metal complexes of amino acids and their derivatives may be found in F. R. N. Gurd and P. E. Wilcox, *Advances in Protein Chemistry*, XI, 311 (1956).

[35] G. C. Cotzias, *Federation Proceedings* 20, No. 3, Part II, 98 (1961): A review.

[36] J. Schubert, *Chimia* 11, 113 (1957).

manner consistent with the law of mass action for complexation between the protein part of the enzyme (the apoenzyme) and the metal ion to form the active enzyme:

(a) $$E + M = EM$$

The active enzyme is then capable of reacting with the substrate to give an intermediate which subsequently decomposes into products (derived from the substrate) and the active enzyme:

$$EM + S = EMS, \quad EMS \rightarrow EM + P$$

The proof that an enzyme *requires* a metal ion for full activity may be obtained in many ways but is generally furnished by kinetic studies on the activity of the enzyme in the presence of added metal ions or by very exacting analyses of carefully prepared samples of the enzyme. The difficulties which may be encountered are discussed in a very lucid fashion by Malmstrom and Rosenberg.[37]

Although the reaction sequence given above is the one which seems to be followed by most of the metal-enzyme complex systems, there are two other possible mechanisms which are difficult to distinguish from each other and from the above mechanism by purely kinetic methods. These are the two sequences:

(b) $\quad M + S \rightleftharpoons MS$ (metal-substrate complex)

$\quad E + MS \rightleftharpoons EMS$ (enzyme-metal-substrate complex)

$\quad EMS \rightarrow P + E + M$

(c) $\quad E + S \rightleftharpoons ES$ (enzyme-substrate complex)

$\quad ES + M \rightleftharpoons ESM$ (enzyme-substrate-metal complex)

$\quad ESM \rightarrow P + E + M$ (*P* is the product molecule)

The evidence which is used to support the first mechanism for a given enzyme includes the following items:

(a) It is frequently necessary to incubate the apoenzyme (metal-free enzyme) with the metal for several hours to obtain an enzyme of maximum activity. Incubation with the substrate in these cases is ineffective in promoting the catalytic activity in these systems. This indicates that the active enzyme is formed by a slow reaction between the apoenzyme and the coenzyme (metal).

(b) In many cases where sufficient information is available it is found that the equilibrium constants for the reaction between the apoenzyme and the metal determined by strictly equilibrium methods are the same as those derived from kinetic measurements on the systems. In those cases where metal-substrate complexes are formed, the equilibrium constants are some-

---

[37] B. G. Malmstrom and A. Rosenberg, *Advances in Enzymology* **21**, 131 (1959).

times too small to allow the development of a kinetic mechanism involving them as an essential part other than as a source of inhibition of the enzyme activity. Kinetic studies on the enzyme activities have furnished unambiguous support for the mechanism designated "b" for some enzyme systems.

(c) In some cases the third mechanism may be eliminated by evidence that the enzyme and substrate do not form a complex in the absence of the metal ion or by evidence that the complex which they do form is not sufficiently stable to account for the kinetic results.

Although it is less commonly reported, there are cases where the metal-substrate complex is the actual entity upon which the enzyme acts. These include inorganic pyrophosphatase, hexokinase, and creatine phosphokinase.[38,39,40,41] The first acts on a pyrophosphate complex, and the third on a complex with ATP (adenosine triphosphate).

Some examples of metal activated enzymes, the metals which they can use, and the reactions which they catalyze are listed below.[41] In many cases these reactions are part of important metabolic pathways. When the enzyme contains loosely held cations it is often very difficult to determine the specific cation which is responsible for the in vivo operation of the enzyme.

Enzyme	Activating Ions	Reaction Catalyzed
Prolidase (a metal enzyme)	Mn^{+2}	hydrolysis of —CO—NH— groups in glycyl L-proline:
Enolase (a metal enzyme)	$Mg^{+2}, Mn^{+2}, Zn^{+2}$	2-Phosphoglyceric acid $\rightleftharpoons$ phospho(enol)pyruvic acid + H_2O:

$$\begin{array}{c}
NH_2 \\
| \\
CH_2\text{—}C\text{——}N \\
\overset{\|}{O}\;\;\nearrow \\
\text{split here}
\end{array}
\quad
\begin{array}{c}
CH_2\text{—}CH_2 \\
\diagup \qquad | \\
\qquad CH\text{—}CH_2 \\
\qquad | \\
\qquad COOH
\end{array}$$

$$\begin{array}{c}
CH_2OH \\
| \\
HC\text{—}OPO_3H_2 \\
| \\
COOH
\end{array}
\rightleftharpoons
\begin{array}{c}
CH_2 \\
\| \\
C\text{—}OPO_3H_2 \\
| \\
COOH
\end{array}
+ H_2O$$

[38] L. A. Heppel and R. J. Hilmol, *J. Biol. Chem.* **192**, 87 (1951).

[39] The role of the metal-substrate complex was first propounded extensively by V. Najjar in W. D. McElroy and B. Glass, editors, *Phosphorus Metabolism*, The Johns Hopkins Press, Baltimore, Md. (1951), pp, 500–520.

[40] S. A. Kuby, L. Nody, and H. A. Lardy, *J. Biol. Chem.* **210**, 65 (1954); G. G. Hammes and D. Kochavi, *J. Amer. Chem. Soc.* **84**, 2069, 2073, 2076 (1962) (hexokinase, a very thorough study).

[41] M. Dixon and E. C. Webb, *Enzymes*, Longmans, Green & Company, Ltd., London (1958), p. 88, p. 456 ff. This volume contains a most comprehensive summary of these systems and a very lucid description of the use of kinetic and thermodynamic data for the elucidation of the mechanisms of action of metal-activated enzymes.

Leucine Amino-
peptidase
(a metal enzyme) Mn^{+2}, Mg^{+2} R_1CHNH_2 —$CONH_2 \rightarrow R_1CHNH_2COOH + NH_3$
for certain R_1

Ascorbic acid
Oxidase
(a metalloenzyme) Cu^{+2} oxidation of ascorbic acid:

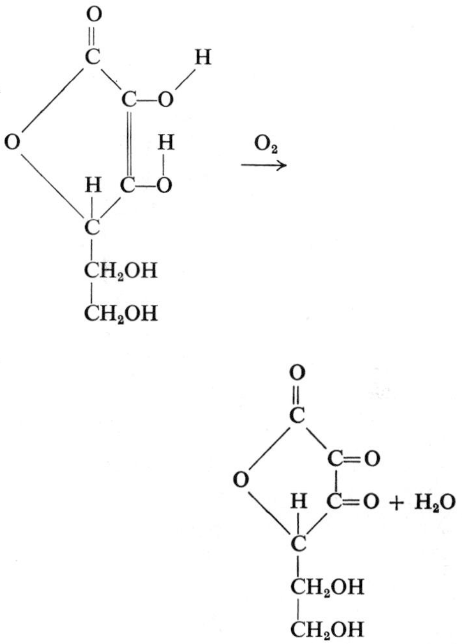

Laccase
(a metalloenzyme) Cu^{+2} oxidation of polyphenols such as catechol and
hydroquinone

Tyrosinase
(a metalloenzyme) Cu^{+2} oxidation of mono- and poly-phenols

Arginase
(a metal enzyme) Co^{+2}, Mn^{+2}, Ni^{+2} Arginine $\rightarrow$ ornithine + urea

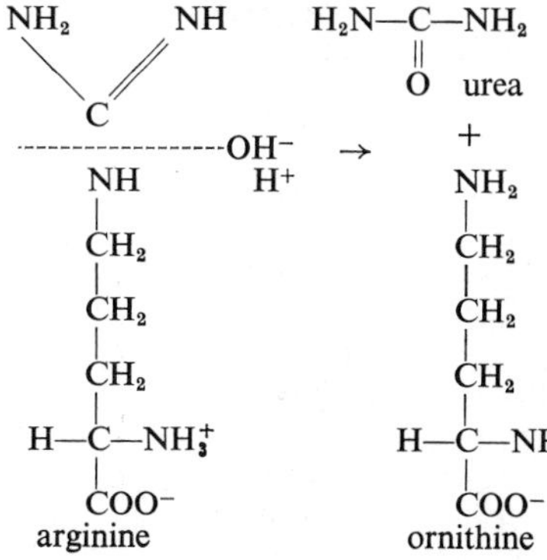

Carboxypeptidase Zn^{+2}
(a metalloenzyme)

$$RC\underset{O}{\overset{\parallel}{-}}\!\!-\!\!N\overset{H}{\underset{\underset{\text{split}}{\underset{\text{here}}{\uparrow}}}{\overset{|}{|}}}\!\!-\!\!C\overset{R}{\underset{H}{\overset{|}{\underset{|}{}}}}\!\!-\!\!COOH$$

Alcohol Zn^{+2} Ethyl alcohol + Diphosphopyridine nucleotide →
Dehydrogenase   Acetaldehyde + reduced Diphosphopyridine
(a metal enzyme)   nucleotide

With the probable exception of enolase, it is quite possible that the detailed mechanism (in terms of the equilibrium and kinetic processes involved) is not known for these enzymes. Aside from these considerations, there is the very real and difficult problem of the elucidation of the chemical mechanism by which these enzymes catalyze reactions. The most commonly used theory for providing a detailed mechanism in these cases is the polyaffinity theory of Bergmann.[42,43] This can be summed up as "enzymes interact with multiple sites on the substrate." The function of the metal may vary but it serves principally for one of two purposes: (a) as a source or sink for electrons in the catalysis of redox reactions and (b) to insure the proper stereospecific orientation of the substrate molecule vis à vis the metal enzyme complex. The especial suitability of the coordination process for furnishing this second kind of action has been emphasized by Calvin.[44] It is well known from studies of the complexes of Co(III) with optically active ligands, that the complexation process for central ions which already contain asymmetric ligands is *stereospecific*. This stereospecificity is well illustrated in the reaction of Co(III) with a racemic mixture of the antipodes of a bidentate ligand. This was first shown by Hürlimann[45] who found that not all of the twenty-one possible isomeric forms could be isolated when the dinitrobis-(propylenediamine) cobalt(III) ion was prepared. He found only the L-*cis-ll*, D-*cis-ll*, D-*cis-ld*, and L-*cis-ld* forms. Jaeger and Blumendahl[46] found an even more striking case of stereospecificity in the complexes of Co(III) and Rh(III) with *trans*-1, 2-diaminocyclopentane, a species which exists in enantiomorphic forms. When complexes containing three ligands per metal atom were prepared, only two of the eight possible isomers could be prepared. With cobalt the D-Co (*lll*) and the L-Co (*ddd*) were found and with rhodium the D-Rh (*lll*)

[42] M. Bergmann, *Harvey Lectures* **31**, 37 (1935–6).

[43] M. Bergmann, L. Zervas, J. S. Fruton, F. Schneider, and H. Schlech, *J. Biol. Chem.* **109**, 325 (1935).

[44] M. Calvin in W. D. McElroy and B. Glass, editors, *The Mechanism of Enzyme Action*, The Johns Hopkins Press, Baltimore, Md. (1954), p. 314.

[45] Hurlimann, Thesis, Zurich (1918), cited in A. E. Martell and M. Calvin, *The Chemistry of the Metal Chelate Compounds*, Prentice Hall, Inc., Englewood Cliffs, N.J. (1952), p. 309.

[46] F. M. Jaeger and H. B. Blumendahl, *Zeit. anorg. Chem.* **175**, 161 (1928). The older literature is collected in F. M. Jaeger, *Optical Activity and High Temperature Measurements*, McGraw-Hill, Inc., New York (1930), Ch. IX, X, XI.

and L-Rh (*ddd*) resulted. These workers also reported several other reactions of this type in which definite stereospecific requirements result in the formation of only a few of the many possible isomers in complexes with asymmetric ligands. A large number of similar reactions have been studied by J. C. Bailar, Jr., and his students,[47] Dwyer and his co-workers,[48] and Irving[49] and his students, all of whom have investigated inert complexes. The coordination act is also stereospecific for labile complexes.[50]

Hellermann pointed out the involvement of metal complexes in enzymatic reactions involving amino acids (arginase) in the 1930's[51,52] and this notion was subsequently developed in greater detail by other investigators.

Smith postulated the formation of mixed complexes as intermediates in metal activated enzymatic reactions involving leucine aminopeptidase and specified these in some detail.[53] One example is that involving glycyl L-leucinamide and the manganous activated enzyme leucine aminopeptidase which is given as:

$$H_2C\!-\!NH_2$$
$$O\!=\!C$$
$$H\!-\!N \longrightarrow Mn \quad | \quad Apoenzyme$$
$$R\!-\!CH$$
$$O\!=\!C\!-\!NH_2$$

Smith also investigated the stereospecificity of leucine aminopeptidase. By examining the action of the enzyme on a large number of compounds of the type:

$$R_1\!-\!\underset{\underset{H}{|}}{\overset{\overset{NH_2}{|}}{C}}\!-\!\underset{\underset{O}{\|}}{C}\!-\!\underset{H}{\overset{H}{N}}\!-\!\underset{\underset{R_2}{|}}{\overset{\overset{H}{|}}{C}}\!-\!CH\!-\!COOH$$
$$\underset{NH_2}{|}$$

[47] J. C. Bailar, Jr., *Chemistry of the Coordination Compounds*, Reinhold Publishing Corp., New York (1956).

[48] F. P. Dwyer, in S. Kirschner, editor, *Advances in the Chemistry of the Coordination Compounds*, The Macmillan Company, New York (1961), p. 21; F. P. Dwyer and A. M. Sargeson, *J. Amer. Chem. Soc.* **81**, 5269, 5272 (1959); F. P. Dwyer and F. L. Garvan, *J. Amer. Chem. Soc.* **83**, 2610 (1961).

[49] H. Irving and R. D. Gillard, *J. Chem. Soc.*, 5266 (1960); 2249 (1961).

[50] W. E. Bennett, *J. Amer. Chem. Soc.* **81**, 246 (1959).

[51] L. Hellerman and M. E. Perkins, *J. Biol. Chem.* **112**, 175 (1935).

[52] L. Hellerman and C. C. Stock, *J. Biol. Chem.* **125**, 771 (1938); L. Hellerman, *Physiol. Revs.* **17**, 454 (1937).

[53] E. Smith in W. D. McElroy and B. Glass, editors, *The Mechanism of Enzyme Action*, The Johns Hopkins Press, Baltimore, Md. (1954), p. 309. Metal ion changes can also vary the reactions catalyzed by a given metal enzyme: F. Kupieki and M. J. Coon, *J. Biol. Chem.* **235**, 1944 (1960); M. J. Schlesinger and M. J. Coon, *Biochim. Biophys. Acta* **41**, 30 (1960).

he found that R_1, *must* be of the L-configuration for any reaction to occur. When this residue is of the D-configuration the enzyme is unable to act upon the compound. As an example, L-leucylglycine and L-leucyl-L-tyrosine are split by the enzyme but D-leucylglycine and D-leucyl-L-tyrosine are *not*. This is exactly the kind of stereospecificity that the results of Jaeger and Blumendahl would lead one to expect as the enzyme which is already coordinated to the metal ion is *asymmetric*.

Another good example of the way in which the knowledge of these systems grows may be seen in the case of enolase. This is an enzyme which may be isolated from brewer's yeast and several other sources. It catalyzes the reaction:

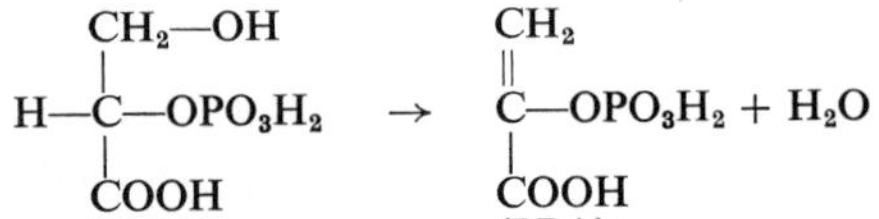

$$
\begin{array}{ccc}
CH_2-OH & & CH_2 \\
| & & \| \\
H-C-OPO_3H_2 & \rightarrow & C-OPO_3H_2 + H_2O \\
| & & | \\
COOH & & COOH \\
(PGA) & & (PPA)
\end{array}
$$

and requires a metal such as magnesium or manganese for full activity, magnesium being the metal probably used in vivo. The investigation of this enzyme by Warburg and Christian[54] included a study of the kinetics of the enzymatic reaction as well as a tentative explanation of the mode of action of the metal. The phosphopyruvic acid (PPA) absorbs light of wave length 240 mμ strongly ($CH_2{=}\overset{\displaystyle O}{\overset{|}{C}}{-}$) while the 2-phosphoglyceric acid (PGA) does not absorb at this wave length. The reaction can thus be followed spectrophotometrically.

The reaction sequence given by Warburg and Christian is:

$$PGA + ME \rightarrow MEPGA \rightleftharpoons MEPPA \rightarrow ME + PPA$$

For the rate of this reaction they gave the equation:

$$\frac{dc}{dt} = k_1 F\left(\frac{C-c}{C}\right) - k_2 F\frac{c}{C}$$

where c is the concentration of PPA

C is the total concentration of acids, PPA plus PGA

F is the enzyme concentration

k_1 and k_2 are rate constants

$(C-c)/C$ is the ratio of the enzyme combined with PGA to that present (saturation of the enzyme is assumed)

c/C is the ratio of the enzyme combined with PPA to that present, and equal binding constants are assumed for the binding of the substrate and the product

[54] O. Warburg and W. Christian, *Biochem. Zeit.* **310**, 385 (1942).

An important step taken by Warburg and Christian was their work on the relationship between the activity of the enzyme and the magnesium ion concentration. They were able to show to a good approximation that the activity of the enzyme was related to the magnesium ion concentration by an expression expected if the active enzyme were a weak complex. For such a reaction:

$$E + Mg^{+2} \rightleftharpoons EMg^{+2}$$

$$K = (EMg^{+2}) / (E)(Mg^{+2})$$

(E) is the concentration of the apoenzyme which contains no metal

(EMg^{+2}) is the concentration of the active enzyme

(Mg^{+2}) is the concentration of the magnesium ion

Since $(EMg^{+2}) + E$ is a constant, and $(EMg^{+2}) / \{(E) + (EMg^{+2})\}$ is the relative activity of the mixture $(= Q/Q_m = b)$, these equations may be combined in the following way.

$$\frac{(EMg^{+2})}{(EMg^{+2}) + (E)} = b; \quad (EMg^{+2}) = K(E)(Mg^{+2})$$

so

$$b = \frac{K(E)(Mg^{+2})}{(E) + K(E)(Mg^{+2})} = \frac{K(Mg^{+2})}{1 + K(Mg^{+2})}$$

or

$$\frac{1}{b} = 1 + \frac{1}{K(Mg^{+2})}$$

so a plot $1/b$ vs. $1/(Mg^{+2})$ should be a straight line of slope $1/K$ if the approximations introduced in the treatment given above are reasonably close to the truth. For certain ranges of pH, enzyme, substrate, and metal ion concentrations these approximations are not too bad and K is found, from such a plot, to be $4 \times 10^{2,[55]}$.

A more complete analysis of the metal ion activation of enolase has been carried out by Malmstrom.[55,56] Malmstrom first developed an expression for the activity of the enzyme based upon a mechanism in which the following reactions occurred:

$$ME + S \overset{K_1}{\rightleftharpoons} MES$$

$$MES \overset{k_1}{\underset{k_2}{\rightleftharpoons}} EP$$

$$MEP \overset{K_1}{\rightleftharpoons} ME + P$$

[55] The references bearing on recent work are collected in B. G. Malmstrom, T. Vanngard, and M. Larsson, *Archives des Sciences* 11, 156 (1958). Special Issue.

[56] B. G. Malmstrom, *The Mechanism of Metal-Ion Activation of Enzymes*, Almqvist and Wiksells, Uppsala (1956); B. G. Malmstrom, *Arch. Biochem. Biophys* **46**, 345 (1953), **49**, 335 (1954).

This introduces the assumption of equal binding of substrate and product to enzyme:

$$ME + S \underset{}{\overset{K_2}{\rightleftharpoons}} MES' \text{ (inactive)}$$

$$ME + P \underset{}{\overset{K_2}{\rightleftharpoons}} MEP' \text{ (inactive)}$$

here ME represents the metal activated enzyme, S is PGA and P is PPA. The apoenzyme is assumed to contain two sites which can bind metal (and hence substrate also) but only one of these sites (e.g., site 1) is enzymatically active and when site 2 is covered, site 1 is inactive also. The fraction of the sites covered at a given metal ion concentration M, are $(M)/\{K_1' + (M)\}$ and $(M)/\{K_2' + (M)\}$, resp., where K_1' and K_2' are constants. The concentration of the active enzyme ME, is then:

$$(ME) = k' \frac{(M)}{K_1' + (M)} \left(1 - \frac{(M)}{K_2' + (M)}\right) = \frac{k'K_2'(M)}{\{K_1' + (M)\}\ \{K_2' + (M)\}}$$

The activity of the enzyme is given by (when S is very large and essentially constant):

$$a = \frac{K_2(ME)(k_1 + k_2)}{(K_1 + S)(K_2 + S)}$$

or with the expression for (ME) given above

$$a = \frac{k'(k_1 + k_2)K_2K_2'(M)}{(K_1 + S)(K_2 + S)\ \{K_1' + (M)\}\ \{K_2' + (M)\}}$$

Since the measurements are customarily carried out at constant substrate concentration, this may be written as:

$$a = \frac{kM}{(K_1' + M)(K_2' + M)}$$

where

$$k = \frac{k'(k_1 + k_2)\ K_2\ K_2'}{(K_1 + S)(K_2 + S)}$$

Experimental values of "a" are then used to evaluate K_1' and K_2'. Values obtained by Malmstrom for Mn^{+2} were $K_1' = 3.8 \times 10^{-5}$ and $K_2' = 1.2 \times 10^{-3}$. For zinc the corresponding values are $K_1' = 5.0 \times 10^{-6}$ and $K_2' = 2.0 \times 10^{-4}$. These equations should also describe the inhibition of the enzyme by nonactivating metals as well as the activation by such metals as Mn^{+2} and Zn^{+2}.

The development of the kinetic equations for describing enzymes which require one atom of metal per molecule of apoenzyme to provide an active site can be seen in the papers of Malmstrom and others.[57,58] There are a

[57] K. J. Laidler and J. P. Hoare, *J. Amer. Chem. Soc.* **71**, 2699 (1949).
[58] G. B. Kistiakowsky and A. J. Rosenberg, *J. Amer. Chem. Soc.* **74**, 5020 (1952).

large number of metal-activated enzymes in addition to those mentioned above; information on these is available in reviews.[34,41]

MODEL SYSTEMS

Because of the great complexity and ease of denaturation of most metal activated enzymes, there has been a great deal of interest in the possibility of studying simpler complexes which catalyze the same or similar reactions, albeit, less effectively. These model systems should be capable of furnishing considerable information on the nature of the enzymatic processes if they are suitably chosen. The study of these systems to date has not been attended with unqualified success, chiefly because of the difficulty in obtaining suitable model complexes. Many of the model systems studied exhibit behavior which is different in some important ways from the behavior of the enzymes which they are supposed to resemble.

The complex between triethylenetetramine and iron(III) was first reported to be catalytically active in the decomposition of hydrogen peroxide (like catalase) by Wang,[59] who subsequently[60] studied this as a model for catalase, an iron metalloporphyrin with a very pronounced ability to catalyze the decomposition of H_2O_2.[61,62] Catalase is by far the most effective catalyst for this reaction. Studies by Wang showed that this model compound was about 10^{-3} as effective as catalase, while many other comparable compounds are far less effective. Hemoglobin is only 10^{-3} times as effective as catalase in catalyzing this decomposition. It was shown[63] by a mass spectrographic analysis of the reaction involving $H_2O_2^{18}$ that all of the oxygen evolved comes from the hydrogen peroxide used and that this is all evolved. This allowed the first of the following two mechanisms to be eliminated.

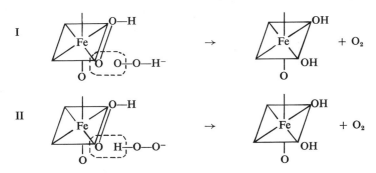

[59] J. H. Wang, *J. Amer. Chem. Soc.* **77**, 822 (1955).

[60] J. H. Wang, *J. Amer. Chem. Soc.* **77**, 4715 (1955).

[61] J. H. Baxendale, *Advances in Catalysis*, IV, 31 (1951) presents a review of the catalysis of this reaction.

[62] P. George, *Advances in Catalysis*, IV, 393 (1951) summarizes work on catalase itself.

[63] R. C. Jarnagin and J. H. Wang, *J. Amer. Chem. Soc.* **80**, 786 (1958).

A more detailed kinetic investigation of this reaction by Beck and Gorog[64] revealed that the mechanism of this "model system" was more complicated than had previously been realized. This ligand is oxidized by the hydrogen peroxide and this reaction was found to be catalyzed by the ferric-triethyl-enetetramine complex. Several other features of this process were also found to be sufficiently complex that the use of the chelate as a model for catalase seems much less promising than was concluded from the initial studies. The exceptional catalytic activity of the complex is accompanied by so many other peculiarities that it is quite possible that the mechanism by which cata-lase and the ferric chelate function are quite different.

Another model system may be seen in the pyridoxal-metal ion catalyzed transamination reactions which have been studied as models of enzymatic transaminations. In 1952, Snell and Metzler reported that metal ions cata-lyzed both the transaminations[65] and the deaminations[66] involving pyridoxal. The first type of process is represented by:

pyridoxal + glutamate → pyridoxamine + ketoglutarate, and the second type by:

$$
\underset{\substack{| \\ OH}}{\overset{\substack{H \\ |}}{CH_2}}\!\!-\!\!\underset{\substack{| \\ NH_2}}{\overset{\substack{O \\ //}}{C}}\!\!-\!\!C\!\!\diagdown_{OH} \quad \xrightarrow[100°\ C]{pyridoxal,\ Al^{+3}} \quad CH_3\!\!-\!\!\underset{\substack{|| \\ O}}{C}\!\!-\!\!\overset{\substack{O \\ //}}{C}\!\!\diagdown_{OH} + NH_3
$$

Since pyridoxal is structurally very closely related to Vitamin B_6, these re-actions have been the subject of considerable interest and have been further investigated by Snell and Metzler both jointly and independently. Pyridoxal and various metal salts (e.g., those of copper, iron, or aluminum) catalyze the racemization of alanine in a reaction reminiscent of the racemization of amino acid esters through Schiff base complexes reported by Pfeiffer and his co-workers.[67,68] The same combination of pyridoxal and metal salt effects a reversible catalytic cleavage of hydroxyamino acids:[69]

$$
\underset{\substack{\ \ |\ \ \ \ | \\ \ \ OH\ \ NH_2 \\ threonine}}{CH_3\!\!-\!\!CH\!\!-\!\!CH\!\!-\!\!COOH} \ \underset{Al^{+3},\ Fe^{+3},\ or\ Cu^{+2}}{\overset{pyridoxal}{\rightleftharpoons}} \ CH_3-\overset{\substack{H \\ |}}{C}=O + \underset{\substack{| \\ NH_2}}{\overset{\substack{H \\ |}}{HC}}\!\!-\!\!\overset{\substack{O \\ //}}{C}\!\!\diagdown_{OH}
$$

The position of the equilibria vary with the amino acid and this may be exploited in biochemical systems. Thus, glycine does not react very readily

[64] M. T. Beck and S. Gorog, *Acta Chim. Acad. Sci. Hung.* **20**, 57 (1959).

[65] D. E. Metzler and E. E. Snell, *J. Amer. Chem. Soc.* **74**, 979 (1952).

[66] D. E. Metzler and E. E. Snell, *J. Biol. Chem.* **198**, 353 (1952).

[67] J. Olivard, D. E. Metzler, and E. E. Snell, *J. Biol. Chem.* **199**, 669 (1952).

[68] P. Pfeiffer, W. Offermann, and H. Werner, *J. prakt. Chem.* **159**, 313 (1941).

[69] D. E. Metzler, J. B. Longenecker, and E. E. Snell, *J. Amer. Chem. Soc.* **75**, 2786 (1953); **76**, 639 (1954).

with pyridoxal but glyoxalate *does* react with pyridoxamine, a reaction which is catalyzed by various metal ions. Glyoxalate, in fact, undergoes direct transamination reactions with many alpha amino acids and this direct reaction is also subject to metal ion catalyses.[70]

A rather general mechanism has been proposed for these reactions[71] which is capable of explaining the observed reactions:

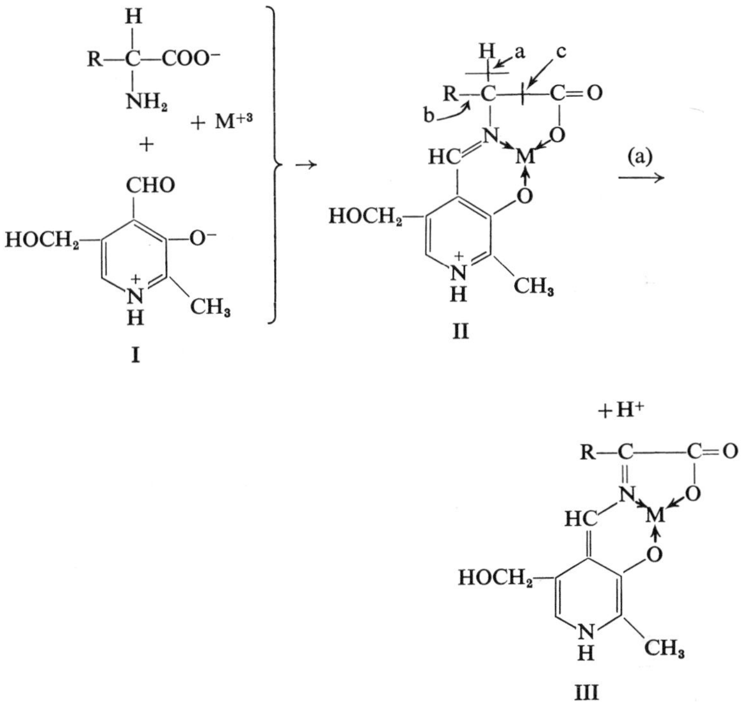

The complex II creates very favorable conditions for the lowering of the electron density on the alpha carbon atom of the amino acid. This will then facilitate the loss of: (a) a proton, (b) an R^+, or (c) a $COOH^+$. Case (a) is illustrated by III; subsequent hydrolysis at the $C=N$ linkage will lead to a transamination. Hydrolysis at the $C—N$ linkage will lead to racemization. The occurrence of cases (b) and (c) is also found with the compounds. The prime requirement of the metal chelate II is that it facilitates electron withdrawal from the alpha carbon atom. Proof of usefulness of the mechanism is

[70] D. E. Metzler, J. Olivard, and E. E. Snell, *J. Amer. Chem. Soc.* **76**, 644 (1954).

[71] D. E. Metzler, M. Ikawa, and E. E. Snell, *J. Amer. Chem. Soc.* **76**, 648 (1954). Cf. C. Cennamo, *Boll. Soc. Ital. Biol. Sper.* **37**, 183 (1961), C.A. 56: 1725; H. Mix, *Zeit. physiol. Chem.* **323**, 173 (1961).

its ability to explain the catalytic activity of 4-nitrosalicylaldehyde for several similar reactions.[72] The reactions of this class possess a certain degree of stereospecificity as in the reaction of L-alanine and α-ketoglutaric acid which forms L-glutamic acid in greater amounts than D-glutamic acid.[73] This actually implies that the metal chelate be asymmetric itself, a condition which is satisfied if an excess of L-alanine is present and coordinated with the metal also to give a Cu^{+2}-L-alanine-Schiff's base complex. It should also be noted that the transamination reactions as well as related pyridoxal-metal ion catalyzed processes can utilize a wide variety of metal cations.[74] Furthermore other reactions are also catalyzed by the pyridoxal-metal ion catalyst; examples include the degradation of esters of serine and threonine:

$$R-\underset{\underset{NH_2}{|}}{\overset{\overset{OX}{|}}{CH}}-CH-COOH + H_2O \xrightarrow[\text{metal ion}]{\text{pyridoxal}} XOH + NH_3 + RCH_2-\underset{\overset{\|}{O}}{C}-COOH$$

$$X = -\underset{\overset{\|}{O}}{C}-NH_2, \quad -\underset{\overset{\|}{O}}{C}-CH_2N_2, \quad H_2PO_3^-, \quad [75]$$

and the cleavage of alpha methyl serine and alpha methylolserine.[76] The whole question of the relation of these model transamination reactions to the enzymatic ones has been discussed in recent reviews.[77–81] It should be noted that pyridoxal can effect transaminations in the absence of metal ions.[71]

BINDING OF SMALL IONS TO PROTEINS AND OTHER LARGE MOLECULES. The binding of small ions to very large molecules which may have dozens of binding sites is an important phenomenon in biological systems. There are numerous types of complications which may arise and in many of these cases the mathematical theory required has been developed in some degree of com-

[72] M. Ikawa and E. E. Snell, *J. Amer. Chem. Soc.* **76**, 653 (1954).

[73] J. B. Longenecker and E. E. Snell, *Proc. Natl. Acad. Sci.* **42**, 221 (1956).

[74] J. B. Longenecker and E. E. Snell, *J. Amer. Chem. Soc.* **79**, 142 (1957).

[75] J. B. Longenecker and E. E. Snell, *J. Biol. Chem.* **225**, 409 (1957).

[76] J. B. Longenecker, M. Ikawa, and E. E. Snell, *J. Biol. Chem.* **226**, 663 (1957).

[77] D. S. Hoare and E. E. Snell, *Proceedings of the International Symposium on Enzyme Chemistry, Tokyo and Kyoto 1957*, Maruzen, Tokyo (1958), pp. 142–147. The discussion on pp. 147–148 brings out some of the problems which are yet unsolved.

[78] E. E. Snell and W. T. Jenkins, *J. Cellular Comp. Physiol.* **54**, Supplement, 161 (1959); G. D. Kalyankar and E. E. Snell, *Biochemistry* **1**, 594 (1962).

[79] E. E. Snell, *Federation Proceedings* **20**, No. 3, Part II, 81 (1961).

[80] D. E. Metzler, *Federation Proceedings* **20**, No. 3, Part II, 234 (1961).

[81] The general aspects of the use of metal complexes as models for enzyme systems have been extensively treated by R. J. P. Williams in *Special Lectures in Biochemistry*, University College, London, (1954–1955), p. 43 ff.; B. R. James, J. R. Lyons, and R. J. P. Williams, *Biochemistry* **1**, 379 (1962).

pleteness. Two situations which have been studied are the binding of a small ion to various classes of sites on a large molecule and the study of linked functions (differing chemical functions on neighboring, identical, or interacting sites).

In the study of binding to complex molecules or cell surfaces it is usual to ignore any statistical considerations insofar as successive equilibrium constants are concerned. The data can usually be fitted by assuming a limited number of sites of a fixed number of types. Where the binding by a few types of sites is sufficiently different in strength, equilibrium constants can be obtained for interaction with the different types of sites by rather straightforward methods. Rothstein and Hayes[82] used a graphical method to study the binding of cations to cell surfaces. Where two sites of sufficiently different binding strength are present this method is quite suitable. Beckett, Dar, and Robinson[83] used this method to study the binding of iron(II) and cobalt(II) to bacterial surfaces in the presence of oxine. Presumably the bacteriostatic action of oxine is related to its ability to prevent the bacterial cells from taking up essential trace metals from the medium in which it is present. A more sophisticated treatment of this kind of problem has been given by several workers and much of the pertinent literature has been summarized.[84]

The study of linked functions is of considerable importance in determining how the various equilibria in which a protein may participate are interdependent. Thus the effect of acid-base equilibria on the oxygen uptake of hemoglobin may be considered to be an example of a linked function. Similarly some of the other reactions of proteins show a structure determined interdependence which is exhibited in the relationship of the equilibrium constants of the reactions involved. The theory of these systems has been studied in some detail.[84,85] The binding of metal ions to large polymeric chelating agents is also an area of study for which special techniques have been developed.[86]

CHEMOTHERAPEUTIC APPLICATIONS. The application of the fundamental theories of the coordination process to reactions of pharmacological significance has been carried out sporadically for many years but it is in the last decade that these attempts have become concerted and widespread. The relations

[82] A. Rothstein and A. D. Hayes, *Arch. Biochem. Biophysics* **63**, 87 (1956).

[83] A. H. Beckett, R. N. Dar, and A. E. Robinson, *J. Pharm. and Pharmacol.*, XI, Supplement 195T (1959).

[84] J. T. Edsall and J. Wyman, *Biophysical Chemistry*, Academic Press, Inc., New York (1959), Vol. I, Ch. 11; C. Tanford, *Advances in Protein Chemistry* **17**, 70 (1962); C. Tanford, *Physical Chemistry of Macromolecules*, John Wiley & Sons, Inc., New York (1963), Ch. 8.

[85] J. Wyman, *Advances in Protein Chem.* **4**, 407 (1948).

[86] D. H. Gold and H. P. Gregory, *J. Phys. Chem.* **66**, 246 (1962) is an example of a study of this kind on the copper(II) complex with poly-N-ethyleneglycine. Earlier literature is cited.

between coordination and drug activity have been a special focal point for many of these studies.

The fact that a living organism is a much more complex system than any that we devise for *in vitro* testing has been forcibly demonstrated in examples where "the experiment was a success but the experimental subject did not survive". The usual basis for the testing of coordination agents has been a desire to tie up certain metal ions and to thus effectively remove their influence from the biological system. The successes have been limited to cases where: (a) the coordinating agent itself has little or no effect on any normal biological process, (b) the degree of specificity in coordination which was required by the metal ion under consideration could be achieved without disturbing any of the vital metal complexing equilibria on which the living organism is so dependent for its proper functioning, and (c) instances where the formation of an extremely insoluble chelate allows a toxic metal to be effectively removed from circulation, though the chelate may be immobilized in the body.[87]

One point which is important in estimating the form in which any chelate will be present in body fluids is the relative stability of its calcium complex. With a ligand such as EDTA, the high calcium content of body fluids insures that a very high proportion will be present as the calcium complex. Schubert has presented equations which allow an estimation of the relative amounts of a metal chelated under such conditions.[88] Where hydroxy species such as MOH can be ignored, the equilibrium governing the distribution is:

$$CaV + M \rightleftharpoons MV + Ca$$

where V is a chelating agent. Then,

$$\frac{[MV]}{[M]} = \frac{K_{MV}}{K_{CaV}} \cdot \frac{(V_t)}{[Ca]}$$

where the K's are the formation constants, V_t is the amount of V remaining after CaV is formed. This shows that unless K_{MV} is much much greater than K_{CaV} the treatment with V will not tie up M in a pharmacologically significant manner. A material such as BAL (British anti-Lewisite, or 1,2-dithiopropanol-3) is effective in removing traces of heavy metals such as lead, mercury, arsenic, or antimony because its complexes with these metals are enormously more stable than its calcium complex. For useful chelating agents a very considerable specificity is desirable even though this is difficult to achieve.

[87] This notion is due to J. Schubert, *Chimia* **11**, 113 (1957).

[88] J. Schubert, *Federation Proceedings* **20**, No. 3, Part II, 219 (1961) presents a more generalized form of the equations originally presented in *Ann. Rev. Nuclear Sci.* **5**, 369 (1955).

The kind of difficulty which may be encountered may be seen in the comprehensive studies carried out by J. Schubert and his collaborators on beryllium poisoning.[89] Schubert studied the inhibition of alkaline phosphatase by beryllium salts. This enzyme normally requires magnesium for its activity but beryllium complexes very firmly with the enzyme and stops its action. Since it was supposed that much of the toxicity of beryllium was due to its substitution for magnesium in vital enzyme systems it seemed reasonable that a chelating agent which could tie up the beryllium should be an effective antidote in cases of poisoning by this metal. It was found that the inhibition of the enzyme could be prevented by the addition of several chelating agents such as salicylates, catechol, oxine, sulfosalicylates, and best of all aurin tricarboxylic acid. The toxic effects of beryllium in mice were definitely reduced when these compounds were administered but unfortunately, the amount of aurin required to counteract the effect of the beryllium was itself capable of killing the mice.

In an analogous manner when EDTA (which is not toxic) is used to counteract lead poisoning by complexing the lead in tissues, it removes sufficient calcium from the body fluids to result in some decalcification of the bones and teeth. Fortunately, the solution to this problem has been found in the administration of $Na_2CaEDTA$.[90] Here the calcium can be replaced by lead present in the body but the complex does not remove calcium from the body. Incidentally, EDTA, when used in small amounts apparently passes through the body without suffering any change. When administered in large or continuous doses, EDTA and its derivatives can cause severe kidney damage[91] which can be fatal.

Chelates have been the most direct treatment for metal poisoning of all sorts. In addition to the examples cited earlier one may list cysteineamine, $H_2NCH_2CH_2SH$ which has been used for thallium poisoning.[92] N-acetyl-*d-l*-penicillamine which has been used to afford protection against mercuric chloride poisoning[93] and sodium diethyldithiocarbamate which has been used to counteract the effects of nickel tetracarbonyl in experimental animals.[94]

A series of studies extending over many years has been carried out by

[89] J. Schubert, "Interaction of Metals with Small Molecules in Relation to Metal Protein Complexes" in F. R. N. Gurd, *Chemical Specificity and Biological Interactions*, Academic Press, Inc., New York (1954).

[90] F. Reiders in M. J. Seven and L. A. Johnson, editors, *Metal-Binding in Medicine*, J. B. Lippincott Co., Philadelphia, Pa. (1960), p. 143.

[91] H. Foreman, "The Pharmacology of Some Useful Chelating Agents" in M. J. Seven and L. A. Johnson, editors, *Metal-Binding in Medicine*, J. B. Lippincott Co., Philadelphia (1960), pp. 88–92.

[92] A. Hendryckx, *Acta Pharmacol. Toxicol.* **14**, 20 (1957), C.A. 53: 18284.

[93] H. V. Aposhian and M. M. Aposhian, *J. Pharm. Exptl. Ther.* **126**, 131 (1959).

[94] B. West and F. W. Sunderman, *Amer. J. Med. Sci.* **236**, 15 (1958); F. W. Sunderman and F. W. Sunderman, Jr., *ibid.*, **236**, 26 (1958).

Albert[95] and his co-workers. Of these, that dealing with the antibacterial activity of 8-hydroxyquinoline is perhaps the most extensive. The data indicate that this material is effective because it is a chelating agent, though the mechanism may be quite complex. Of the seven possible hydroxyquinolines, the six which cannot chelate have no antibacterial action. The penetration of the bacterial wall is easily accomplished by neutral chelates, a fact which is used to explain why the 2:1 8-hydroxyquinoline:Fe^{+2} complex has a maximum toxicity. This feature is also responsible for the decrease of bacteriostatic activity found with derivatives such as 8-hydroxyquinoline-5-sulfonic acid which form water soluble chelates. A number of related examples have been studied by Weinberg, who has also summarized much of the literature.[96] The interference of the chelating agents with metal activated enzyme systems offers a possible route to antibacterial compounds which can be fully exploited only when the specificity of the coordination act can be controlled. The mammalian host of the bacteria *also* requires trace metals and the continued administration of a powerful chelating agent can destroy the functioning of the metal activated enzyme systems of the host.[97]

The use of chelates to introduce metals into the body is also possible. Thus ferrous gluconate is used in the treatment of anemia. This would seem to indicate that the introduction of other required trace metals may also conveniently be effected by the use of readily metabolized chelating agents.

There are an enormous number of metal complexes which are normally present in mammals and the regulation of the amounts of trace metals is usually achieved by a complex and delicately balanced system of metal complexes. Two examples of this may be seen in the utilization of zinc and iron, both of which are toxic when present to excess.

Zinc is required for the activation of some enzyme systems. It is present in trace amounts in many foods and is presumably absorbed from them. Zinc forms stable complexes with nitrogen, oxygen, and sulfur donors, all of which also complex with copper. In at least one example, the effects of an excess of zinc in an animal diet have been relieved by the administration of copper.[98] A summary of the zinc metalloenzymes has been presented by Vallee (*loc. cit.*).

The behavior of iron has been studied more extensively and has been found to exhibit a number of points of interest. The human body contains a relatively small amount of iron, most of which is very firmly complexed. The way in which the body uses iron is quite exceptional and involves some

[95] Much of this is summarized in A. Albert, *Federation Proceedings* **20**, No. 3, Part II, 137 (1961); earlier work may be found in A. Albert, *Selective Toxicity* Methuen & Co., Ltd., London (1951), Ch. V.

[96] E. D. Weinberg, *Bacteriological Reviews* **21**, 46 (1957).

[97] G. L. Curran, *Federation Proceedings* **20**, No. 3, Part II, 118 (1961).

[98] Ref. 95, p. 119.

very unusual complexes. Absorption of iron is confined almost exclusively to ferrous ion absorbed by the stomach and intestines. If ferric ion is present it is reduced in the stomach prior to absorption although some ferric complexes, such as that with citric acid appear to be absorbed as such. Iron present in heme or analogous compounds in food is *not* absorbed. Granick[99] has given a detailed scheme for the regulation of iron absorption. The absorbed iron is transformed to ferritin which is an iron protein compound consisting of a protein portion (apoferritin) of molecular weight 460,000 and iron which is present in micelles of approximate composition $[(FeOOH)_8 \cdot FeOPO_3H_2]$. The ferritin usually contains 17% to 23% iron. It breaks down by reduction when iron is to be transported (e.g. for hemoglobin synthesis) and the *ferrous* ion which is formed can be released to the blood stream. Here the iron is also bound to a protein, siderophilin, from which it can be removed by bone marrow to form ferritin once more, which is then used in the synthesis of hemoglobin. Siderophilin is a compound which chelates the iron, so it is an iron compound quite different in character from ferritin. The literature on these compounds is very extensive but recent work may be found in several reviews.[100,101]

In a short sketch such as this it is impossible to give an accurate indication of the activity presently under way in the study of biological aspects of coordination chemistry. The number of papers published each year in this area is roughly equal to that published on all other phases of coordination chemistry.

EXERCISES

1. Suggest methods by which you might elucidate the ligand groups in a complex biological substance containing: (a) coordinated copper, (b) coordinated iron, (c) coordinated calcium.

2. Try to rationalize the fact that manganous and magnesium ions are often equally effective in the activation of an enzyme which requires a metal.

3. If you were asked to explain why chromium is so rarely found in biological catalysts while iron is so common, what sort of reasons would you give?

4. List chelating agents which you would suggest for the treatment of poisoning by the following metals: (a) molybdenum, (b) palladium, (c) nickel, and (d) cobalt. Check your suggestions against work reported in Chemical Abstracts.

5. If the pyridoxal-metal ion catalyzed transaminations are stereospecific (in part) what restrictions must the metal ion meet? Would you expect the use of the copper(II) and the zinc(II) ions to be equivalent in this reaction?

[99] S. Granick, *Physiol. Revs.* **31**, 489 (1951); S. Granick, *Chem. Revs.* **38**, 379 (1945); S. Granick, *Bull. N.Y. Acad. Med.* **25**, 403 (1949).

[100] G. Eichhorn, *Federation Proceedings* **20**, No. 3, Part II, 40 (1961).

[101] W. W. Westerfeld, *Federation Proceedings* **20**, No. 3, Part II, 158 (1961).

CHAPTER

12

Thermochemistry of Coordination Compounds*

INTRODUCTION. Strictly speaking, the thermochemistry of coordination compounds includes any and all aspects of the equilibrium behavior of these compounds. For convenience, those studies involving direct or indirect measurements of enthalpy changes will be considered here. The measurement of equilibrium constants is discussed separately because it is *not* customary for such measurements to be carried out with the view of providing reasonably complete thermodynamic data on the entire coordination process. Ultimately thermochemical studies should be expected to provide detailed information on bond energies, entropy changes, and thermochemical cycles involving complexation which are completely defined *experimentally*. When an attempt is made to obtain that type of information on coordination compounds which is readily available on most organic compounds (e.g., bond energies, absolute entropies, and relationships between structure and thermodynamic constants) the paucity of experimental data is immediately evident. While current activity in this field promises to remedy this defect, the time required may be rather considerable. A difficulty, which is not present in organic thermochemistry, is the wide variety of behavior which may be exhibited and the corresponding requirement for much more experimental data before any coherent scheme of correlation becomes apparent.

The reasons for desiring such data are quite numerous and of fundamental importance. These include:

* The criticisms and suggestions of Dr. Loren G. Hepler of the Carnegie Institute of Technology have been very helpful in the preparation of this chapter and they are gratefully acknowledged.

1. At present few coordinate bond energies are known and it is not possible to state at present whether bonds of a specific type (e.g., Ir:N) may be considered to have an effectively constant value which can be used in computing heats of formation or not. There is a distinct possibility that the fluctuations in such bond energies may be large in proportion to the total bond energy. If this is the case, a priori calculations of heats of formation will not be feasible until the details of correcting an average bond energy for environmental factors are worked out.

2. Until the energy changes involved in typical changes in bonding are known with reasonable accuracy, the prediction of the relative ease of alternative paths for these reactions cannot be estimated. The thermodynamic data necessary for the interpretation of a large number of thoroughly studied kinetic processes are as yet unavailable.

3. The discovery of some aspects of the behavior of coordination compounds must await experimental determinations of their absolute entropies from heat capacity curves. Thus types of behavior analogous to the transitions from restricted to free rotation in the solid state are most securely established from such data, though they may often be surmised from less direct evidence.

THERMODYNAMIC FUNCTIONS OF INTEREST. Most work on the thermochemistry of complexes has been restricted to work at constant pressure and the thermodynamic functions used are:

1. *Gibb's Free Energy.* This is the maximum work which a system undergoing the specified transformation can perform at constant pressure. The symbol used to designate this is F in most of the American literature; G in European, Japanese and some American work; and Z in the Russian literature. The chemical importance of this is due to two features: (a) at equilibrium $\Delta F = 0$ for the transformation of reactants into products and (b) the standard free energy change is related to the equilibrium constant for the reaction under consideration:

$$\Delta F^\circ = -RT\ln K$$

2. *Enthalpy or Heat Content.* The change in enthalpy which occurs when a reaction occurs at constant pressure is equal to the heat evolved or absorbed in this process.

3. *Entropy.* The entropy content of a system is that part of the enthalpy which cannot be turned into useful work at constant pressure. The absolute entropy is also a measure of the order of a system. Thus in a process which has a net positive gain in entropy the products will possess less order than the reactants. Entropy is most directly interpreted in statistical terms. Thus for a

system of N molecules of one species which may be distributed over i energy levels, the entropy will be

$$S = k \ln W$$

where W is the mathematical probability of the particular distribution of the molecules over the energy levels (i.e., the number of distinguishable ways of obtaining the system). For systems involving large numbers of molecules, W reaches a sharp maximum in the region of a particular distribution and this, the most probable distribution, has the largest entropy and represents the stable state of the system. In reactions in which an entropy increase occurs, the products possess less order or are more numerous than the reactants, or have more accessible energy levels.

Whether a given process is spontaneous or not can be determined from either the change in free energy or the change in entropy which accompanies it. The rules for determining whether a process is spontaneous or not are:

ΔF: A spontaneous process is one in which the system undergoes a decrease of free energy

ΔS: A spontaneous process is one in which the entropy of the system plus its surroundings undergoes an increase

The relations between these parameters and others which are used include the following (at constant temperature):

$$\Delta F = \Delta H - T\Delta S$$
$$\Delta F^\circ = - RT \ln K$$
$$\Delta H = Q_p$$

$$\frac{(\partial \Delta F)}{(\partial T)_p} = -\Delta S$$

$$S_T = \int_{T=0}^{T} \frac{C_p}{T}\, dT$$

The additional terms introduced here are K, the equilibrium constant for the reaction under study and Q_p, the heat absorbed when the reaction is carried out (in a calorimeter) at constant pressure. The experimental methods rely on: (a) measurement of K at various temperatures, (b) measurement of the heat evolved or absorbed when the reaction is carried out in a calorimeter, (c) measurement of heat capacities, and (d) a variety of miscellaneous methods useful in special cases.

EXPERIMENTAL METHODS

Calorimetry. Calorimetric studies are of two principal types: Those involving combustion processes which are carried out in a bomb calorimeter and those involving reactions in solution which are generally carried out in a calorimeter built around a Dewar flask.

Although combustion calorimetry is quite capable of measuring heat effects to $\pm 0.05\%$[1] it is not commonly used in studies on coordination compounds for two reasons. Firstly, the products of combustion of such compounds are often poorly defined compounds such as nonstoichiometric oxides. Secondly, the heat of combustion is very large in comparison to the heat of formation of the complexes from their constituent ions and ligand species. As a result a relatively small error in the heat of combustion may lead to a large error in the heat of formation or heat of complexation. In a few very favorable circumstances (see below) heat of combustion data has proven very useful.

Solution calorimetry has generally proven to be far more useful than combustion calorimetry. The heat of formation of a complex, for example, can be determined by a series of heat of solution measurements if the solution process is one in which the final state of the solute species is the same for simple salt and complex. Thus if a solution contains a strong acid, precipitating agent, or other substance capable of destroying the complex, the heat of formation can be obtained from a relation of the sort used by Heiber in studying ammine complexes.

Consider the following reactions:

1. $CoCl_2(s) \xrightarrow{\text{aq. HCl}} CoCl_2 \text{ (aq. HCl)}$ $\Delta H = \Delta H_s$

2. $en(l) \xrightarrow{\text{aq. HCl}} en(\text{aq. HCl})$ $\Delta H = \Delta H_a$

3. $Co(en)_3Cl_2(s) \xrightarrow{\text{aq. HCl}} CoCl_2 \text{ (aq. HCl)} + 3en(\text{aq. HCl})$ $\Delta H = \Delta H_c$

4. $CoCl_2(s) + 3en(l) \longrightarrow Co(en)_3Cl_2(s)$ $\Delta H = \Delta H_f$

then,

Reaction 4 = (Reaction 1) + 3 (Reaction 2) − Reaction 3

and

$$\Delta H_f = \Delta H_s + 3\Delta H_a - \Delta H_c$$

where ΔH_f = heat of formation of the ammine

ΔH_s = heat of solution of the salt in dil HCl (e.g., $CoCl_2$)

ΔH_a = heat of solution of the amine in dil HCl (e.g., en)

ΔH_c = heat of solution of the complex in dil HCl (e.g., $Co(en)_3Cl_2$)

Since these heat effects are all comparable in magnitude to the heat of formation, one is not faced with the same problems as in the measurements of the heat of formation from the heats of combustion. As a result, heats of formation, good to $\pm 1\%$, are relatively easy to obtain for most labile complexes and for some inert ones.

A far more common procedure used to obtain thermodynamic functions

[1] R. S. Jessup, *Precise Measurement of Heat of Combustion with a Bomb Calorimeter*, NBS Monograph 7, Washington, D.C. (1960).

for reactions involving complexes is to measure the equilibrium constants for their formation over a range of temperature. Unfortunately, this results in data for reactions in which the ligand competes with water for the coordination sites. Thus additional data on heats of hydration is required if these measurements are to be related to processes which do not take place in water. Further complication results when the equilibrium constants are not determined with sufficient precision. In this case $\Delta F°$ values of only fair accuracy can be obtained from the relation $\Delta F° = -RT \ln K$ and $\Delta H°$ values can be obtained via:

$$\frac{d \ln K}{dT} = \frac{\Delta H°}{RT^2}$$

Unfortunately the subsequent determination of $\Delta S°$ from $\Delta F° = \Delta H° - T\Delta S°$ leads to a result of a *low* order of accuracy. An alternative procedure, much less commonly used would be the evaluation of $\Delta S°$ from:

$$\left(\frac{\partial \Delta F°}{\partial T} \right)_p = -\Delta S°$$

Any of the following measurements can be used to obtain information on some type of coordination process: concentration, pressure, optical density, solubility, transference number, magnetic susceptibility, etc. The equilibrium constants obtained by these methods can be determined at various temperatures to obtain the data required for the determination of $\Delta F°$, $\Delta H°$, and $\Delta S°$.

TYPICAL DATA

1. *Combustion Calorimetry.* The heats of combustion of several carbonyls were determined by Fischer, Cotton, and Wilkinson.[2] In the first paper, accurate values for the heats of combustion of $Cr(CO)_6$, $Mo(CO)_6$, and $W(CO)_6$ were obtained using a bomb calorimeter and a platinum resistance thermometer to measure the temperature changes. In these cases it is necessary to correct the results for the incomplete combustion of the metal as some free element is produced. This first paper is of importance as it gives some detailed information on the handling of these sublimable (and volatile) solids. Some typical results are listed below:

		COMBUSTION OF $Cr(CO)_6$		
Run	Vacuum wt. sample	Corr. temp. change	Uncorrected heat of comb.	Corrections for incomplete combustion
1	3.07790	2.6150°	−437.69 Kcals/mole	− 6.88 Kcals/mole
2	2.74739	2.3227°	−435.56 ,, ,,	−11.07 ,, ,,
Run	Washburn corrections	ΔE^{298} comb.		
1	0.74	−443.83		
2	0.76	−445.87		

[2] A. K. Fischer, F. A. Cotton, and G. Wilkinson, *J. Amer. Chem. Soc.* **78**, 5168 (1956); **79**, 2044 (1957).

The Washburn corrections are required for precise work.[3,4,5] From the data they obtained themselves, plus other data obtained from the literature, these authors obtained the following thermodynamic data:

Compound	ΔH°_{298} Combustion	ΔH°_{298} Formation	ΔH°_{298} Vapor- ization	ΔF°_{298} Vapor- ization	ΔS°_{298} Vapor- ization
$Cr(CO)_6$	-443.09 ± 0.51	-257.6	$+17.18$	$+4.98$	$+40.94$
$Mo(CO)_6$	-507.52 ± 0.27	-234.8	$+16.29$	$+4.99$	$+37.92$
$W(CO)_6$	-537.81 ± 0.29	-227.3	$+17.71$	$+5.93$	$+39.52$
$Ni(CO)_4$	-282.2 ± 0.5	-145.1	$+6.5$	0	$+21.8$

In the second paper, nickel carbonyl was examined with the results given above. In this case the manipulation of the liquid sample was attended by some serious problems which were solved satisfactorily.

2. *Heats of Reaction in Solution via Calorimetry.* When the required auxiliary data are available, calorimetric studies on solutions are often a very convenient route to heats of formation of complexes. In general, standard calorimetric procedures have been used in these studies though some have been carried out using an ice calorimeter. Perhaps the chief problem in this work is to obtain reaction products of a well defined nature and with thoroughly specified thermodynamic constants. This requirement is perhaps part of the reason why so little data is available on inert complexes. Their reactions are so slow that the resultant slow evolution of heat is very difficult to measure precisely and must ordinarily be followed using a rather elaborate microcalorimeter. Where the reaction is complete in a time substantially less than an hour or where its kinetics is thoroughly known, a less elaborate experimental setup will suffice.[6] In the last decade a notable increase has occurred in the number of calorimetric studies and it is likely that this will be a field of continuing interest. Much of the earlier experimental work (up to 1950) has been collected by Yatsimirsky.[7]

In an early study, Lamb and Simons[8] studied the reactions of some pentammine complexes of cobalt(III) with solutions of sodium sulfide. This allowed the enthalpies of transformations involving some of these compounds to be evaluated. One example is the following:

[3] E. W. Washburn, *J. Res. Bur. Standards* **10**, 525 (1933).

[4] W. N. Hubbard, D. W. Scott, and G. Waddington, *J. Phys. Chem.* **58**, 152 (1954).

[5] F. D. Rossini, editor, *Experimental Thermochemistry*, Interscience Publishers, Inc., New York (1956) has a great deal of information on both static and rotating bomb calorimetry as well as the precautions required for results of high accuracy.

[6] J. M. Sturtevant in A. Weissberger's, *Physical Methods of Organic Chemistry*, Interscience Publishers, Inc., New York, 2nd ed. (1950), Part I, Vol. I, Ch. XIV.

[7] K. B. Yatsimirsky, *Thermochemie von Komplexverbindungen*, Akademie-Verlag, Berlin (1956). This is a translation of the Russian edition of 1951.

[8] A. B. Lamb and J. P. Simons, *J. Amer. Chem. Soc.* **43**, 2188 (1921).

$2[Co(NH_3)_5Cl]Cl_2 + 3Na_2S = Co_2S_3 + 10NH_3 + 6NaCl \quad \Delta H = 2\,\Delta H_1$

$2[Co(NH_3)_5(H_2O)]Cl_3 + 3Na_2S = Co_2S_3 + 10NH_3 + 6NaCl + 2H_2O \quad \Delta H = 2\,\Delta H_2$

These reactions were studied in the calorimeter. Subtraction of the second reaction from the first followed by division by two gives:

$$[Co(NH_3)_5Cl]Cl_2 + H_2O = [Co(NH_3)_5(H_2O)]Cl_3; \quad \Delta H = \Delta H_1 - \Delta H_2$$

The reaction of these complexes is sufficiently rapid that it can be studied in a calorimeter if enough of the complex is present. Unfortunately, this condition could be satisfied only by working with a suspension of the complexes and carrying out independent studies of the heats of solution of each of the complexes. Some of the data collected by these workers are summarized below:

Ammine	ΔH of reaction with Na_2S
Chloropentammine chloride	− 15070 cals./mole
Aquopentammine chloride	− 12930 ,, ,,
Bromopentammine bromide	− 13290 ,, ,,
Aquopentammine bromide	− 11600 ,, ,,
Nitratopentammine nitrate	− 12340 ,, ,,
Aquopentammine nitrate	− 11860 ,, ,,

A rather similar arrangement was used by Ovenston and Terry[9] to determine the heats of formation and solution of some isomeric cobaltammines. The reactions of *cis-* and *trans*-dichlorotetramminecobalt(III) chloride with sodium sulfide were examined in a calorimeter. Using the standard heats of formation of the products (as obtained from the International Critical Tables) it was possible to use the heats of solution and the heats of reaction with sodium sulfide solution to calculate the heats of formation at ~20°. These results are summarized below (cals./mole):

Salt	Heat of formation (solid)	Heat of soln.	Heat of formation in soln.
trans-[Co(NH$_3$)$_4$Cl$_2$]Cl	− 214,800	+ 8290	− 206,510
cis-[Co(NH$_3$)$_4$Cl$_2$]Cl	− 214,170	+ 9510	− 204,660
trans-[Co(en)$_2$Cl$_2$]Cl	− 171,920	+ 5340	− 166,580
cis-[Co(en)$_2$Cl$_2$]Cl	− 172,830	+ 8019	− 164,820

A somewhat different approach to the use of heats of solution in obtaining heats of formation may be seen in the work of W. Hieber and his co-workers.[10] In the first paper an ice calorimeter was used to measure the heats of reaction with hydrochloric acid solutions of: (a) labile complexes, (b) the amine present in the labile complex, and (c) the parent salt of the complex. From these quantities, the heat of formation, ΔH_f, was determined from the equation:

$$\Delta H_f = \Delta H_s + \Delta H_a - \Delta H_c$$

[9] T. C. J. Ovenston and H. Terrey, *J. Chem. Soc.*, 1660 (1936).

[10] W. Hieber and F. Muhlbauer, *Zeit. anorg. u. allgem. Chem.* **186**, 97–118 (1929).

where the terms have the same meaning as in the previous discussion of this method.

This ΔH_f is the heat of formation of the complex from the constituent ionic and molecular species and *not* from the elements in their standard states. The more important results are summarized below:

Complex	ΔH_f Kcals./mole	Complex	ΔH_f Kcals./mole
$CoCl_2 \cdot 2$Aniline	-17.87	$CoCl_2 \cdot$ en	-32.23
$CoBr_2 \cdot 2$Aniline	-19.43	$CoBr_2 \cdot 1.5$en	-44.20
$CoI_2 \cdot 2$Aniline	-21.46	$CoCl_2 \cdot 3$en	-64.31
$CoCl_2 \cdot 2$Pyridine	-24.72	$CoBr_2 \cdot 3$en	-71.71
$CoBr_2 \cdot 2$Pyridine	-25.67	$CoI_2 \cdot 3$en	-73.38
$CoI_2 \cdot 2$Pyridine	-26.63	$CoCl_2 \cdot 1$ o-phenyl-enediamine	-10.65
$CoCl_2 \cdot 4$Pyridine	-34.93	$CoCl_2 \cdot 4$ o-phenyl-enediamine	-21.23
$CoI_2 \cdot 6$Pyridine	-51.08	$CoI_2 \cdot 4$ o-phenyl-enediamine	-25.75
$CoCl_2 \cdot 2N_2H_4$	-40.30	$CoCl_2 \cdot 6$ o-phenyl-enediamine	-19.47
$CoBr_2 \cdot 2N_2H_4$	-42.41	$CoBr_2 \cdot 4$ o-phenyl-enediamine	-24.33

In this paper is to be found one of the first discussions of coordinate bond energies of metal complexes. Unfortunately, the discussion was based upon the assumption that there were no coordinate bonds in the simple salts. These authors also calculated the heats of formation of some of these complexes from the *gaseous* amines. These results are (in Kcals./mole of amine).

Complex	ΔH Kcals./Mole	Complex	ΔH Kcals./Mole
$CoCl_2 \cdot$ Pyridine	-20.3	$CoBr_2 \cdot 2$Pyridine	-20.8
$CoCl_2 \cdot 2$Aniline	-19.1	$CoBr_2 \cdot 2$Aniline	-19.9
$CoCl_2 \cdot 2NH_3$	-19.9	$CoBr_2 \cdot 2NH_3$	-20.6

Complex	ΔH Kcals./Mole
$CoI_2 \cdot 2$Pyridine	-21.3
$CoI_2 \cdot 2$Aniline	-20.9
$CoI_2 \cdot 2NH_3$	-19.9
$CoI_2 \cdot 6$Pyridine	-16.5
$CoI_2 \cdot 6NH_3$	-16.4

In subsequent papers, Hieber and his co-workers extended these studies to several other central metal ion complexes and also examined the theoretical interpretation of the results in some detail. In particular, they examined the use of thermochemical cycles to obtain values for the heats of formation of the complex from solid salt and gaseous amine, and the estimation of the lattice energies via a Born-Haber cycle. The first step involved the determination of the heats of vaporization of some common ligands with nitrogen and oxygen donors[11] which was done via vapor pressure measurements. The second step involved a careful calorimetric study of the heats of solution as

---

[11] W. Hieber and A. Woerner, *Zeit. Elektrochem.* **40**, 252 (1934).

was done earlier. In this case the heat of solution of the salt or amine was measured using hydrochloric acid containing added amine or salt so that the final solution had the same composition as that obtained from solution of the complex. This added refinement was found to make a small but measurable difference in the heats of solution.[12] Some of the data reported here show the difference between the two isomeric forms of $CoCl_2 \cdot 2Pyridine$.

Complex	ΔH°_{293} from salt and gaseous amine	Complex	ΔH°_{293} from salt and gaseous amine
$CoCl_2 \cdot 2Pyridine$, violet	-22.47 Kcals/mole	$CoCl_2 \cdot 3en$	-16.21
$CoCl_2 \cdot 2Pyridine$, blue	-21.60 Kcals./mole	$CoBr_2 \cdot 3en$	-17.37
$CoCl_2 \cdot 4Pyridine$	-18.54 Kcals./mole		
$CoCl_2 \cdot 2Hydrazine$	-15.34 Kcals./mole		

Also studied were some of the complexes of Co(II) salts with alcohols and glycols. These results are for the reactions at $0°$ C:

Complex	ΔH°_{273} from salt and alcohol
$CoBr_2 \cdot 2CH_3OH$	-13.51
$CoBr_2 \cdot 2C_2H_5OH$	-11.26
$CoCl_2 \cdot 2C_2H_5OH$	-11.02
$CoBr_2 \cdot C_2H_4(OH)_2$	$-17 \cdot 07$
$CoBr_2 \cdot 3C_2H_4(OH)_2$	-19.84
$CoCl_2 \cdot 3C_2H_4(OH)_2$	-17.80

In a continuation of this work, Hieber, Appel, and Woerner,[13] determined heats of formation of a number of Fe(II) complexes including some carbonyl halides. These results were obtained at various temperatures:

Complex	Heat of formation, salt and liq. or solid amine	$T°C$
$FeCl_2 \cdot 2Pyr.$	-24.72	$0°$
$FeBr_2 \cdot 2Pyr.$	-26.34	$0°$
$FeCl_2 \cdot 4Pyr.$	-35.95	$0°$
$FeBr_2 \cdot 4Pyr.$	-38.74	$0°$
$FeBr_2 \cdot 6Pyr.$	-46.00	$0°$
$FeCl_2 \cdot 3en$	-39.72	$0°$
$FeBr_2 \cdot 3en$	-47.19	$0°$
$FeI_2 \cdot 2Pyr.$	-27.35	$20°$
$FeI_2 \cdot 4Pyr.$	-39.82	$20°$
$FeI_2 \cdot 6Pyr.$	-52.23	$20°$
$FeI_2 \cdot 3en$	-64.96	$20°$
$Fe(CO)_4Cl_2$	-17.86	$0°$ from solid salt and gaseous CO
$Fe(CO)_4Br_2$	-28.30	$20°$
$Fe(CO)_4I_2$	-38.94	$20°$

The thermochemistry of the reaction of iron pentacarbonyl with the free halogens was also studied.[14] This work is of some importance as it allows the

[12] W. Hieber and A. Woerner, *Zeit. Elektrochem.* **40**, 256 (1934).

[13] W. Hieber, H. Appel, and A. Woerner, *Zeit. Elektrochem.* **40**, 262 (1934).

[14] W. Hieber and A. Woerner, *Zeit. Elektrochem.* **40**, 287 (1934).

estimation of some bond energies of interest (see below). For the direct formation of the iron carbonyl bromide and iodide the reactions are as follows:

$$Fe(CO)_5 + Br_2 \rightarrow Fe(CO)_4Br_2 + CO \qquad \varDelta H = -34.32 \text{ Kcals}$$
$$Fe(CO)_5 + I_2 \rightarrow Fe(CO)_4I_2 + CO \qquad \varDelta H = -17.14 \text{ Kcals.}$$
$$Fe(CO)_5 + Cl_2 \rightarrow Fe(CO)_4Cl_2 + CO \qquad \varDelta H = -45.84 \text{ Kcals.}$$

Hieber and his co-workers studied other systems also, including numerous zinc complexes with nitrogen donors,[15] and copper(II) and mercury(II) halide complexes with amines.[16]

A somewhat different approach to the problem of obtaining thermodynamic data on complexes may be seen in the work of Mori and Tsuchiya and their co-workers on ionic cobalt complexes. Since a major part of the work was done in solution it was necessary to obtain information on activity coefficients. This was done using two procedures. In the first[17] a cell was set up as follows:

$$Pt(Co) \mid [Co(NH_3)_6]Cl_3 \rightleftharpoons CoCl_3 + 6NH_3 \mid KCl \mid KCl \text{ satd.} \mid Hg_2Cl_2 \mid Hg,$$

and the activity coefficient of the hexamminecobalt(III) chloride determined from measurements of the e.m.f. These are

Concn.: Satd. Soln	.1M	.01M	.001M
$\gamma_\pm$.1143	0.1911	0.5017	0.8024

Alternatively the activity coefficients can be determined by one of the methods listed by Kieliand.[18]

In the second study[19], the heats of solution of the chloride, bromide, nitrate and perchlorate of the hexamminecobalt(III) ion were determined from: (a) solubility measurements over the range 10–35° C, (b) activity coefficients, and (c) the equilibrium constants for the solution process determined from these. From the known standard free energies of the hexamminecobalt(III) ion, the standard free energies of the solid salts could then be determined. These are summarized below:

Complex	Heat of solution	$\varDelta F°$ soln.	$\varDelta F°$ formation
$[Co(NH_3)_6]Cl_3$	8.567 Kcals	6.003 Kcals.	−154.55 Kcals.
$[Co(NH_3)_6]Br_3$	10.026 ,,	7.772 ,,	−136.12 ,,
$[Co(NH_3)_6](NO_3)_3$	15.558 ,,	7.918 ,,	−141.68 ,,
$[Co(NH_3)_6](ClO_4)_3$	18.533 ,,	9.080 ,,	−71.40 ,,

[15] W. Hieber and H. Appel, *Zeit. anorg. u. allgem. Chem.* **196**, 193 (1931).

[16] W. Hieber and E. E. Feder, *Zeit. Elektrochem.* **44**, 881 (1938).

[17] M. Mori and R. Tsuchiya, *J. Chem. Soc. Japan* (Pure Chem. Sect.) **79**, 1164 (1958), C.A. 53: 9793.

[18] J. Kieliand, *J. Amer. Chem. Soc.* **59**, 1675 (1937).

[19] M. Mori, R. Tsuchiya, and Y. O. Kano, *Bull. Chem. Soc. Japan* **32**, 462 (1959).

A combination of these results with vapor pressure measurements was then used to extend these studies to related systems.[20-22] In the first of these papers the dissociation pressure for hexamminecobalt(III) chloride was measured over the temperature range 83–173° C. The reaction which occurs is:

$$[Co(NH_3)_6]Cl_3 \rightleftharpoons [Co(NH_3)_5Cl]Cl_2 + NH_3$$

for this process $\Delta H^\circ_{298} = 9.612$ Kcals; $\Delta F^\circ_{298} = 5.672$ Kcals; and $\Delta S^\circ_{298} = 13.22$ e.u. A similar study was carried out on chloropentamminecobalt(III) chloride but here the reaction is the irreversible one:

$$[Co(NH_3)_5Cl]Cl_{2(s)} = CoCl_{2(s)} + 1/6\ N_{2(g)} + NH_4Cl_{(s)} + 11/3\ NH_{3(g)}$$

For this reaction, the assumption that equilibrium dissociation pressures were measured gives $\Delta H^\circ_{298} = 60.78$, which is in surprisingly good agreement with the value 60.84 Kcals. obtained from the heats of formation of the reactant and products (in the literature). In this paper the rate of change of the vapor pressure was used in both cases to follow the kinetics of the reactions. The extension of these methods to aquopentamminecobalt(III) chloride may be seen in the second of these papers. Here the dissociation process is:

$$[Co(NH_3)_5OH_2]Cl_{3(s)} \rightleftharpoons [Co(NH_3)_5Cl]Cl_{2(s)} + H_2O_{(g)}$$

for which $\Delta H^\circ_{298} = 9.908$ Kcals.; $\Delta F^\circ_{298} = 3.488$ Kcals; and $\Delta S^\circ_{298} = 21.54$ e.u. The problem of obtaining activity coefficients for these salts in solution and of testing the validity of the methods of getting them was carried out as follows: for the solution reaction of a 1–3 valence type, salts such as $[Co(NH_3)_5OH_2]Cl_3$ the solubility process may be represented as:

$$[Co(NH_3)_5OH_2]Cl_3(s) \rightleftharpoons [Co(NH_3)_5OH_2]^{+3}(aq.) + 3Cl^-(aq.)$$

and

$$K = \exp(-\Delta F^\circ/RT)$$

for an electrolyte of this type:

$$\gamma_\pm = \sqrt[4]{K/27M}$$

If the solubility is measured in moles/liter and the specific gravity of the solution is d, the molality is given by:

$$M = \frac{1000C}{(1000d - MC)},$$

where M is the formula weight of the complex.

Since these are general equations for salts of this charge type, they may be combined to give:

$$\Delta F^\circ = 2.303\ RT\ (\log 27 + 4 \log M + 4 \log \gamma_\pm)$$

Over the range where $\log \gamma_\pm$ is a linear function of the concentration this can be written as:

[20] M. Mori and R. Tsuchiya, *Bull. Chem. Soc. Japan* **32**, 467 (1959).

[21] M. Mori, R. Tsuchiya, and Y. Okano, *Bull. Chem. Soc. Japan* **32**, 1029 (1959).

[22] M. Mori and R. Tsuchiya, *Bull. Chem. Soc. Japan* **33**, 841 (1960).

$$\Delta F^\circ_{298} = \alpha + \beta \log M = \alpha^1 + \beta^1 \log C$$

Thus if the approximations involved are valid ΔF°_{298} for solution should be a linear function of log C. These workers found this to be the case with the result that it is now possible to use the solubility to estimate the free energy of solution from this last equation using values of α^1 and β^1 established from their data. From their data:

$$\Delta F^\circ_{298}(\text{soln.}) = 4164 - 3435 \log C \text{ (in cals)}$$

One of the difficulties which arises in the use of enthalpy data for highly charged ions is that the heats of dilution of solution of such species are usually very large. This means that the corrections which must be introduced if the data are to be used at other concentrations are quite large.[23,24]

Information on the thermodynamic changes occurring on complexation is most commonly obtained from studies in which the complexation process is carried out in a solution calorimeter operated at room temperature. These are generally constructed of a Dewar flask with a standard taper joint at the top. In this joint are openings for a stirrer, sample introduction, an electric heater, and usually a platinum resistance thermometer. For a fairly detailed description of such apparatus, reference may be made to an article by Schug and King.[25] This paper is also of interest in that it showed that the catalysis of ligand exchange reactions by chromium(II) complexes could be studied calorimetrically. In this case the reaction was:

$$H_2O + \textit{trans-}[CrCl_2(H_2O)_4]^+ \xrightarrow{\text{Cr}^{+2}} [CrCl(H_2O)_5]^{++} + Cl^-$$

For this, $\Delta H = -5.0 \pm 0.2$ Kcals. at an ionic strength of 5.1. A further study of the following six reactions allows the ΔH for the replacement of the second chloride to be obtained:

Reaction	ΔH	$\Delta H(\mu = 5.1)$
$Cr(ClO_3)_3(2.34M) \rightarrow Cr(ClO_3)_3 (0.034M)$ (in acid)	-5.25	-5.47
$Cr(ClO_3)_3(2.34M) \rightarrow$ "chromite" $(0.034M)$ (in base)	-25.92	-25.9_9
Violet $[Cr(H_2O)_6]Cl_{3(s)} \rightarrow Cr(H_2O)_6^{+3} (0.34M) + 3Cl^-$ (in acid)		-10.8_3
Violet $[Cr(H_2O)_6]Cl_{3(s)} \rightarrow$ "chromite" $(.034M) + 3Cl^-$ (in base)		-32.0_3
green *trans*-$[Cr(H_2O)_4Cl_2]Cl \cdot 2H_2O \rightarrow \textit{trans-}[Cr(H_2O)_4Cl_2]^+$ $(0.034M) + Cl$ (in acid)	$+0.70$	$+1.60$
green *trans*-$[Cr(H_2O)_4Cl_2]Cl \cdot 2H_2O \rightarrow$ "chromite" $(0.034M) + 3Cl^-$ (in base)	-31.3	-30.9_2

Combination of these reactions with the one cited above gives:

$$[Cr(H_2O)_5Cl]^{+2} + H_2O = [Cr(H_2O)_6]^{+3} + Cl^-; \quad \Delta H = +6.6 \pm 0.5 \text{ Kcals at } \mu = 5.1$$

[23] E. Lange and W. Miederer, *Zeit. Elektrochem.* **60**, 34 (1956); $K_3Fe(CN)_6$; $K_4Fe(CN)_6$; and $NiSO_4$.

[24] L. G. Hepler, J. R. Sweet, and R. A. Jesser, *J. Amer. Chem. Soc.* **82**, 304 (1960); $K_3Fe(CN)_3$; $K_3Co(CN)_6$; $K_4Fe(CN)_6 \cdot 3H_2O$.

[25] K. Schug and E. L. King, *J. Amer. Chem. Soc.* **80**, 1089 (1958).

While the nature of the "chromite" species is not known other than that it is probably colloidal, its heat of formation was found to be sufficiently reproducible to be used in the above equations.

This same calorimeter was used in a study of the thermodynamics of the complexation of the mercuric ion by chloride, bromide, and iodide.[26] Here solutions of mercuric perchlorate were added to various mixtures of perchloric acid and, say, HCl. Since the ionic strength was held constant at a value (.5) at which the equilibrium constants were known, it was possible to calculate $\Delta H°$ for the various steps in the complexation reaction from a series of calorimetric measurements. A summary of these results is given below:

Reaction	$HgCl_{n-1}^{+3-n} + Cl^- = HgCl_n^{+2-n}$		
n	K	$\Delta H°$, Kcals	$\Delta S°$, e.u.
1	5.5×10^6	-5.9	$+11.1$
2	3.0×10^6	-6.9	$+6.3$
3	8.9	-2.2	-3.0
4	11.2	$+0.1$	$+5.1$

Reaction	$Hg^{++} + 4X^- = Hg\,X_4^=$		
X	K	$\Delta H°$, Kcals	$\Delta S°$, e.u.
Cl^-	1.64×10^{15}	-14.9	$+19.5$
Br^-	8.9×10^{20}	-27.7	$+3.0$
I^-	7.2×10^{29}	-44.3	-13.4

These workers also carried out a thorough examination of the entropy changes occurring in these processes, using an equation proposed earlier, viz.:

$$\Delta S°_{corr} = a - b\Delta Z^2$$

where a and b are constants and ΔZ^2 is the sum of the squares of the charges on the products minus the sum of the squares of the charges on the reactants.[27,28] The connection between $\Delta S°_{corr}$ and $\Delta S°$ is given by:

$$\Delta S°_{corr} = \Delta S° + R\ln \frac{\sigma_p}{\sigma_R}$$

where σ_p and σ_R are the symmetry numbers of the product and reactant species. It was found that the experimental $\Delta S°_{corr}$ values calculated from the second equation for the 3rd and 4th steps of the complexation with Cl^- were abnormal and it was suggested that this is due to a change in the coordination number of the central ion. It is probable that the simple Hg^{+2} species in water is coordinated to six water molecules octahedrally, while the $HgCl_4^-$ complex presumably has a tetrahedral arrangement. The entropy changes for the substitution of one halide for another were found to be in reasonable agreement with the Latimer and Jolly method of estimating such changes.[29]

[26] P. K. Gallagher and E. L. King, *J. Amer. Chem. Soc.* **82**, 3510 (1960).

[27] E. L. King, *J. Phys. Chem.* **63**, 1070 (1959).

[28] E. L. King and P. K. Gallagher, *J. Phys. Chem.* **63**, 1073 (1959).

[29] W. M. Latimer and W. L. Jolly, *J. Amer. Chem. Soc.* **75**, 1548 (1953).

This method involves estimation of the two principal factors governing the entropy change in a complexation: (a) the entropy change which results from the replacement of coordinated water by a coordinated ligand and (b) the effect of a change in the charge of the complex ion on the water sheath of the ion. The first can be estimated using estimates of the entropies available for the literature. Some of these are:

Species	$S°$ cals/deg. mole
H_2O (bound)	9.4
NH_3 (bound)	13.5
F^- (bound)	6 (for binding to Al^{+3})
H_2O (liquid)	16.7
F^- (aq.)	-2.3
NH_3 (aq.)	26.3
Cl^- (bound)	10

Thus the entropy change due to this may be estimated in specific cases as the following:

$$H_2O \text{ (bound)} + F^-\text{(aq.)} \rightarrow H_2O \ (l) + F^- \text{ (bound)}$$
$$\Delta S° = 16.7 + 6.0 + 2.3 - 9.4 = 15.6 \text{ cals/degree/mole.}$$

The entropy changes due to changes in charge of the central complex may be estimated using the treatment of Powell and Latimer[30] but this effect is usually small in comparison with the first effect.

A series of studies in which the heat effects accompanying chelation were determined may be seen in the papers of Staveley and his co-workers who used a precision calorimeter[31-33] (described in the first paper), to determine the enthalpies of chelation with ethylenediamine and EDTA. For this they used measured heats of mixing together with calculations of the relative amounts of ions present using stability constants reported in the literature. While this procedure might seem to detract from a purely calorimetric determination of ΔH for a given complexation process, it is almost unavoidable. Some of the results obtained are given below [*J. Chem. Soc.*, 2310 (1954)] (in calories).

Ion	ΔH	ΔF	ΔS	$(\Delta S + S$ aq.$)$
$Ni(en)_2^{+2}$	$-17,250$	$-18,250$	$+ 3.4$	$-25.9 \ (21.5)$
$Ni(en)_3^{+2}$	$-28,010$	$-23,840$	-14.0	$-43.3 \ (-38.9)$
$Zn(en)_2^{+2}$	$-11,450$	$-13,710$	$+ 7.6$	-17.9
$Zn(en)_3^{+2}$	$-18,460$	$-15,550$	$- 9.8$	-35.3
$Cd(en)_2^{+2}$	$-13,330$	$-12,820$	$- 1.7$	-16.3
$Cd(en)_3^{+2}$	$-19,700$	$-15,140$	-15.3	-29.9
$Cu(en)_2^{+2}$	$-25,160$	$-27,280$	$+ 7.1$	-16.5

[30] R. E. Powell and W. M. Latimer, *J. Chem. Phys.* **19**, 1139 (1951).

[31] T. Davies, S. S. Singer and L. A. K. Staveley, *J. Chem. Soc.*, 2304 (1954).

[32] R. A. Care and L. A. K. Staveley, *J. Chem. Soc.*, 4571 (1956).

[33] L. A. K. Staveley and T. Randall, "Discussions of the Faraday Society" **26**, 157 (1958).

Here $(\Delta S + S\,\text{aq})$ is the standard entropy of the complex ion, and S aq is the standard entropy of the cation from which it is derived. It is of considerable interest to compare these with calorimetric data obtained for the ammines.[34]

Ion	No. of ligands	ΔH(Kcals)	ΔF(Kcals)	ΔS(e.u.)
H^+	1	-12.4	-12.6	$+\ 0.5$
Ag^+	2	-13.5	$-\ 9.96$	-12.4
Cu^{++}	4	-21.1	-16.4	-16.2
Ni^{+2}	6	-18.9	-10.6	-27.7
Zn^{+2}	4	-15.9	-11.8	-13.7
Cd^{+2}	6	-15.2	$-\ 7.1$	-27.0
Hg^{+2}	4(2)	-28.5	-26.2	$-\ 7.7$
Li^+	(3)	$-\ 0.5$	$-\ 3.26$	-12.6
Mg^{+2}	(6)	$-\ 0.1$	$-\ 4.48$	-19.0

In addition to the methods presented above, most of the experimental techniques used to obtain data on simpler systems can be modified to obtain data on complexes. In many of these it is necessary to take the step-wise nature of the complexation reactions into account either explicitly or implicitly when labile complexes are studied. The procedure utilized here involves the use of the known stability constants to calculate the concentration of each complex species in the product solution obtained in the calorimeter. Once this is done for N solutions the enthalpy changes occurring in the formation of N complexes can be determined. When but a single ligand is taken up, as with EDTA, the corrections are quite easily made.[35] Some of the systems which have been studied by this method are listed in Table 12.1.

TABLE 12.1

SOME CALORIMETRIC STUDIES OF THE ENTHALPIES OF THE FORMATION OF
SUCCESSIVE COMPLEXES

System	Reference
Ni^{+2} and Cu^{+2} complexes with ethylenediamine and trimethylenediamine	36
Hg^{+2} halide 1:1 complexes	37
$Ag^+ - NH_3$	38
Transition metals and ethylenediamine	39
$Cu(II) - $ pyridine	40

[34] W. S. Fyfe, *J. Chem. Soc.*, 2023 (1952).

[35] R. G. Charles, *J. Amer. Chem. Soc.* **76**, 5854 (1954).

[36] I. Poulsen and J. Bjerrum, *Acta Chem. Scand.* **9**, 1407 (1955).

[37] G. N. Malcolm, H. N. Parton, and I. D. Watson, *J. Phys. Chem.* **65**, 1900 (1961).

[38] W. V. Smith, O. L. I. Brown, and K. S. Pitzer, *J. Amer. Chem. Soc.* **59**, 1213 (1937).

[39] M. Ciampolini, P. Paoletti, and L. Sacconi, *Nature* **186**, 880 (1960): *idem, J. Chem. Soc.*, 4553 (1960).

[40] D. L. Leussing and P. K. Gallagher, *J. Phys. Chem.* **64**, 1631 (1960).

TABLE 12.1 (continued)

System	Reference
CdI^+ and ZnI^+	41
Transition metals and triethylenetetramine	42
Cu^{+2} and Ni^{+2} and ethylenediamine	43
Transition ions and ethylenediamine	31
$Cu^{+2} + NH_3$	44
$Al^{+3} - F^-$	28, 29
Zn^{+2}, NH_3	45
Transition metals and 2, 2', 2'' triaminotriethylamine	46

THE BORN-HABER CYCLE FOR COMPLEX COMPOUNDS

The application of the principles of the Born-Haber cycle to complex compounds has a long history. The first such study was apparently that of Biltz and Grimm.[47] Subsequently there have been numerous investigations of the use of such cycles with the primary goal of obtaining coordinate bond energies.[48-51a] The cycle of Biltz and Grimm is given in Figure 43.

Here the symbols have the following meanings:

Q_1^1 to Q_m^1 are the heats of formation of the solid ammines from solid salt and gaseous ammonia

U is the lattice energy of the salt MR

U_1^1 to U_m^1 are the lattice energies of the solid ammines formed from the gaseous simple ions and gaseous ammonia

A_1 to A_m is the energy evolved when the first, ... mth ammonia is added to the gaseous cation $M^+ \ldots M(NH_3)_{m-1}^+$

A_1^1 to A_m^1 is the energy evolved when the 1st to the mth molecules of ammonia are added to an expanded lattice of MR which has been expanded just enough to accommodate the ammonias in the stable lattice found in the final ammine

[41] D. W. Anderson, G. N. Malcolm, and H. N. Parton, *J. Phys. Chem.* **64**, 494 (1960).

[42] L. Sacconi, P. Paoletti, and M. Ciampolini, *Ricerca Sci.* **30**, 1610 (1960), C.A. 55 : 10040.

[43] F. Basolo and R. K. Murmann *J. Amer. Chem. Soc.* **76**, 211 (1954).

[44] K. B. Yatsimirsky and P. M. Milyukov, *Zhur. Fiz. Khim.* **31**, 842 (1957).

[45] T. Takahashi and K. Sasaki, *Denki Kagaku* **25**, 118 (1957), C.A. 55: 20571; 51: 7195; 52: 2607.

[46] P. Paoletti, M. Ciampolini and L. Sacconi, *Ricerca Sci.* **30**, 1791 (1960), C.A. 55: 12020.

[47] W. Biltz and H. G. Grimm, *Zeit. anorg. u. allgem. Chem.* **145**, 63 (1925).

[48] W. Hieber and E. Levy, *Zeit. Elektrochem.* **39**, 26 (1933); *idem, ibid.* **40**, 291, 608 (1934).

[49] K. B. Yatsimirsky and L. L. Pankova, *Zhur. Obschei Khim.* **19**, 617 (1949), C.A. 43:7805; I. I. Chernyaev and V. A. Palkin, *Izvest. Sekt. plat.* IONKh, AN, SSSR **30**, 92 (1955); *idem, Zhur. Neorg. Khim.* **1**, 890 (1956).

[50] F. A. Cotton, *Acta Chem. Scand.* **10**, 1520–6 (1956).

[51] D. H. Busch, *J. Chem. Ed.* **33**, 376, 498 (1956).

[51a] M. H. Dilke and D. D. Eley, *J. Chem. Soc.* 2613 (1949).

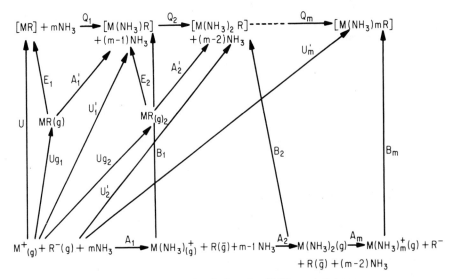

Fig. 43. The thermochemical cycle of Biltz and Grimm.

E_1 to E_m is the work of expanding the lattice from its normal size in MR to the volume of the expanded salt $[MR]_{g_1}$ to $[MR]_{gm}$

U_{g_1} to U_{gm} are the lattice energies of the expanded lattices

Some relations of importance in this diagram are:

$$U_m^1 = \sum A_i + B_m \text{ or } B_m = U_m^1 - \sum A_i$$
$$Q_1^1 = U_1^1 - U$$
$$Q_1^1 = A_1 + B_1 - U$$

Biltz had previously obtained a very large number of Q_m^1 values.[52] Although the quantities $A_1, A_2 \ldots, A_m$ were desired, there was not sufficient experimental evidence (especially structural evidence) to allow the B's which were required, to be estimated with any degree of accuracy. For this reason, Biltz and Grimm utilized the quantities $A_1^1, A_2^1 \ldots, A_m^1$ which could be estimated. The quantities $U_{g_1}, U_{g_2}, \ldots, U_{gm}$ were calculated in the same way as U's but an allowance was made for the expansion of the lattice to accommodate the ammonia molecules. Some values of A^1 obtained are:

Salt	$CaI_2.6NH_3$	$SrI_2.6NH_3$	$BaI_2.6NH_3$	$KI.6NH_3$
A^1 Kcals/mole	182	172	158	85
A^1 per NH_3, Kcals	30	29	26	14

[52] Much of this work is summarized in W. Biltz, *Zeit. anorg. u. allgem. Chem.* **130**, 93 (1923).

Hieber and Levy[48] examined the circumstances governing the order of stability of the complex ammines of a given cation with the various halide anions. The Biltz-Ephraim rule states that the stability of such solids decreases as the size of the halide increases. This rule is found to be of limited validity as a *general* rule because of the effects of polarization which results in a reversed order. It is actually more typical for the heat of formation of such complexes (from the solid salt and the amine) to *increase* in the order chloride < bromide < iodide. This is found in many cases, several of which are cited in the first article. The polarization effects were *not* taken into account adequately in these early calculations of lattice energy. In the second paper the application of these ideas to the iron carbonyl halides is presented and the conclusion is reached that the polarization of the halogen is greater in the carbonyl halides than in the simple halides.

An approach to the more difficult problem of applying such a cycle to the cobalt(III) complexes may be seen in the work of Yatsimirsky and Pankova.[49] By measurement of the heat evolved when a large number of cobalt(III) complexes reacted with solutions of sodium sulfide it was possible to obtain the heats of formation of the solid salts in the standard state. Some of these are:

Compound	$\Delta H°$ Kcals/mole
$[Co(NH_3)_6]Cl_3$	-274.1
$[Co(NH_3)_6]Br_3$	-244.5
$[Co(NH_3)_6]I_3$	-201.6
$[Co(NH_3)_6](NO_3)_3$	-311.5
$[Co(NH_3)_5(H_2O)]Cl_3$	-312.7
$[Co(NH_3)_5(H_2O)]I_3$	-240.9
$[Co(NH_3)_4(H_2O)_2]Cl_3$	-360.6
$[Co(en)_3]I_3$	-133.2
$[Co(en)_3](NO_3)_3$	-243.9

From this information, the heats of solution of the solid salts and the known heats of formation of the anions, the heats of formation of the complex cations in aqueous solutions were determined to be:

cation:	$[Co(NH_3)_6]^{+3}$	$[Co(NH_3)_5(H_2O)]^{+3}$	$[Co(NH_3)_4(H_2O)_2]^{+3}$	$[Co(en)_3]^{+3}$
ΔHKcals:	-146.0	-188.1	-235.7	-81.2

Heats of the formation of the gaseous complex cations were obtained from the relation:

$$-\Delta H_c = -\Delta H_a + \Delta H_s - U$$

where ΔH_a is the heat of formation of the gaseous anion

ΔH_s is the heat of formation of the crystalline complex

U is the lattice energy of the crystalline complex

U was determined by the use of an equation due to Kapustinskii[53]

[53] A. F. Kapustinskii, *Acta Physico-Chem. U.R.S.S.* **18**, 370 (1943), C.A. 38: 5705; *Quarterly Reviews* **10**, 283 (1956).

$$U = 287.2 \ \sum_n \left[\frac{N_1 N_2}{(r_1 + r_2)} \left\{ 1 - [(0.345) / (r_1 + r_2)] \right\} \right]$$

here $\sum_n$ is the number of ions in the molecule, (e.g., 5 for $Al_2(SO_4)_3$), N_1 and N_2 are their valencies and r_1 and r_2 their radii. The radius of the ions other than $Co(en)_3^{+3}$ was taken as 2.40 and that of $Co(en)_3^{+3}$ taken as 2.50. For the four ions listed above the heats of formation of the gaseous ions were found to be:

Ion	ΔH_c(gas) Kcals
$[Co(NH_3)_6]^{+3}$	-658
$[Co(NH_3)_5(H_2O)]^{+3}$	-619
$[Co(en)_3]^{+3}$	-712
$[Co(NH_3)_4(H_2O)_2]^{+3}$	-572

Unfortunately, the heat of formation of $Co^{+3}(g)$ as well as $Co(H_2O)_6^{+3}(g)$, which are needed to complete the thermochemical cycle are not known. While this prevents the calculation of actual bond energies it does not prevent an assessment of their relative values via ΔH_c(gas). This was done in the second paper which contains further experimental data on other ions. One of the results of this study was that the energy evolved when an NO_2^- group replaced a NH_3 group in $Co(NH_3)_6^{+3}$ was found to decrease successively through the series until the replacement of the $2NH_3$'s in $[Co(NH_3)_2(NO_2)_4]^-$ by two more NO_2^- groups takes place with the *absorption* of heat. This illustrates the difference in bonding of neutral and negative groups which can arise as a result of electrostatic effects.

A somewhat different form of the Born-Haber cycle may be seen in the work of Cotton.[50] This is as follows:

$$
\begin{array}{cccc}
 & & & \Delta H_1 \\
2X^-(g) & + M^{+2}(g) & + & 6NH_{3(g)} \longrightarrow M(NH_3)_6^{+2}(g) + 2X^-(g) \\
\uparrow 2A_x & \uparrow I_1 + I_2 & 6\Delta H^\circ{}_{fNH_3} & \quad \uparrow E_L \\
2X_{(g)} & M_{(g)} & & \\
\uparrow D_{x_2} & \uparrow \Delta H_v^m & & \\
X_{2(g)} & + M_{(s)} & +3N_{2(g)} + 9H_{2(g)} \xrightarrow{\ \Delta H_f^\circ\ } M(NH_3)_6 X_{2(s)} \\
\uparrow \Delta H_v^{x_2} & & & \\
X_2(s\ or\ l) & & &
\end{array}
$$

$$- \Delta H_1 = - \Delta H_f^\circ + 6\Delta H^\circ_{fNH_3} + D_{x_2} + 2A_x + \Delta H_v^{x_2} + (I_1 + I_2) + \Delta H_v^m - E_L$$

Of the quantities on the right hand side, all can be evaluated with reasonable accuracy but E_L, which is designated the "pseudo-lattice energy" by Cotton. He proposed that this could be calculated by assuming that the hexammine ion, $M(NH_3)_6^{+2}$, could be regarded as a large spherical cation whose interactions with the other ions in the lattice is essentially coulombic. An important result of this work is the fact that the ΔH_1's can be obtained with a fair precision and from these the bond energies for the coordination of the neutral ammonia molecules to the M^{+2} gaseous ion. This information is of considerable theoretical importance as this gives the heat effect accompanying coordination when it occurs in the absence of other complicating features such as solvation effects. The ΔH_1 for the formation of the $M(NH_3)_6^{+2}$ ions and the bond energies are summarized below:

Ion	Halides used	ΔH_1,Kcals/mole	$D(M^{+2}-N)$Kcals
Ca	Br$^-$, I$^-$	-282	47
Mn	Cl, Br, I	-357	59
Fe	Cl, Br, I	-376	63
Co	Cl, Br, I	-406	68
Ni	Cl, Br, I	-415	69
Zn	Br, I	-401	67

For complexes which are volatile, it is possible to set up thermochemical cycles analogous to those used in the thermochemistry of organic compounds to obtain bond energies. These can then be used to obtain coordinate bond energies via a strictly empirical route. This has been of use in obtaining coordinate bond energies in carbonyls[54] and in inner complex salts.[55]

COMBINATION OF THERMODYNAMIC DATA

One of the most valuable aspects of thermodynamic data is the fact that the *additivity* of free energies (or enthalpies or entropies) allows us to determine the changes in these quantities which occur in any reactions which can be obtained by manipulation of reactions for which these changes have already been obtained.

An example may be seen in the use measurements of the vapor pressure of a number of amine adducts of vanadyl acetylacetonate over a range of temperatures.[56] From these it is possible to determine the thermodynamic changes for reactions of the type:

$$VO(C_5H_7O_2)_2 \cdot M \rightarrow VO(C_5H_7O_2)_2 + M_{(g)}$$

Thus the following data was obtained for the case of ammonia, methylamine, and ethylamine:

Amine	ΔH°_{298}(cals/mole)	ΔF°_{298}(cals/mole)	ΔS°_{298} e.u.
Ammonia	15,100	3,210	40.0
Methylamine	16,800	4,080	42.7
Ethylamine	16,000	3,370	42.4

By combining these equations it is possible to get the changes in ΔH°, ΔF° and ΔS° involved in ligand exchanges:

[54] F. A. Cotton, A. K. Fisher, and G. K. Wilkinson, *J. Amer. Chem. Soc.* **78**, 5168 (1956); **79**, 2044 (1957).

[55] M. M. Jones, B. J. Yow, and W. R. May, *Inorg. Chemistry* **1**, 166 (1962); J. L. Wood and M. M. Jones, *J. Phys. Chem.* **67**, 1049 (1963).

[56] R. T. Claunch, T. W. Martin and M. M. Jones, *J. Amer. Chem. Soc.* **83**, 1073 (1961).

$$VO(C_5H_7O_2)_2 \cdot NH_3 + CH_3NH_2(g) \rightarrow VO(C_5H_7O)_2 \cdot CH_3NH_2 + NH_3(g)$$

for which

$$\Delta H^\circ = \Delta H^\circ_{CH_3NH_2} - \Delta H^\circ_{NH_3} = -16,800 + 15,100 = -1,700 \text{ cals}$$

Similarly,

$$\Delta F^\circ = \Delta F^\circ_{CH_3NH_2} - \Delta F^\circ_{NH_3} = -4,080 + 3,210 = -870 \text{ cals}$$

and

$$\Delta S^\circ = \Delta S^\circ_{CH_3NH_2} - \Delta S^\circ_{NH_3} = -42.7 + 40.0 = -2.7 \text{ e.u.}$$

This type of combination of data may also be seen in earlier work on platinum(II) complexes.[57]

The use of vapor pressure measurements allows ΔF changes to be obtained for systems in which a volatile ligand is evolved, since the equilibrium constant is directly obtained from the pressure. Measurements of this sort have been used with amine complexes in a number of cases[52,56,57,58] and have also been used in systems involving boron compounds in which all of the constituents are volatile.[59,60] Values of the enthalpy and entropy for the coordination process can be obtained from the vapor pressure data over a range of temperatures.

HEAT CAPACITIES OF COORDINATION COMPOUNDS

While the number of studies reporting heat capacities of coordination compounds is not large, the information obtained from such investigations is often of special value.

The design and use of a calorimeter for measuring the heat capacities of complex salts from room temperature to 200° C has been given by Chernyaev and his co-workers.[61] They found that the heat capacities of *cis*- and *trans*-[Pt(NH_3)_2Cl_2] were identical over the range 23° C to 75° C and were comparable to the values found for analogous salts, e.g., for these compounds the C_p values were in the neighborhood of 0.12 cals/g/degree. This is what

[57] C. P. Knop and C. H. Brubaker, *J. Inorg. Nuclear Chem.* **9**, 8 (1959).

[58] A. B. Hart and J. R. Partington, *J. Chem. Soc.*, 104 (1943). This contains a very extensive series of measurements on systems where the ligand is NH_3 or ND_3.

[59] Work up to 1954 is collected by H. C. Brown, D. M. McDaniel, and O. Hafliger in E. A. Braude and F. C. Nachod, editors, *Determination of Organic Structures by Physical Methods*, Academic Press, Inc., New York (1955), Ch. 14. More recent work is included in C. T. Mortimer, *Reaction Heats and Bond Strengths*, Addison-Wesley Publishing Co., Reading, Mass. (1962).

[60] D. E. McLaughlin, M. Tamres, S. Searles, Jr., and F. Block, *J. Inorg. Nuclear Chem.* **18**, 118 (1961) and previous papers by these workers.

[61] I. I. Chernyaev, V. A. Palkin, and R. A. Baranova, *Zhur. Neorgan. Khim.* **3**, No. 7, 1512 (1958) NSF-AEC translation.

one would expect from Kopp's rule: for a solid compound the heat capacity is equal to the sum of the heat capacities of its constituent elements.[62]

Since heat capacity measurements from the neighborhood of 0°K allow the absolute entropy to be obtained via:

$$S_T = \int_{T=0}^{T=T} \frac{C_p}{T} \, dT$$

Such measurements can be used to obtain information on the motion of the units in the solid or on other transitions which result in an increase in the entropy and hence the heat capacity. These have been used in examining the rotation of the ammonium ion in $(NH_4)_2SnCl_6$ and $(NH_4)_2SnBr_6$,[63] low temperature transitions in ferrocene,[64] and the structures of the carbonyls of molybdenum[65] and iron.[66]

In the study of the tin(IV) complex salts mentioned above,[63] a comparison was made of the heat capacities of the isomorphous ammonium and rubidium salts. It was assumed that the difference

$$\Delta C_p = C_p(NH_4 \text{ salt}) - C_p(Rb \text{ salt}) - 2C_p(\text{internal } NH_4^+)$$

should be the contribution from the torsional or rotational movement of the ammonium ion. From the variation of ΔC_p with temperature in $(NH_4)_2SnCl_6$, it was shown that the ammonium ion is prevented from rotating freely by only a slight potential barrier. Ferrocene shows anomalies in its specific heat vs. temperature curve at 163.9° K and 169° K.[64] The interpretation suggested to partially explain this is the occurrence of regions in the crystal where the cyclopentadiene rings are in an eclipsed orientation, rather than the usual staggered one. In the case of $Mo(CO)_6$, the agreement of the absolute entropy obtained calorimetrically with that calculated from various assignments of vibrational frequencies allowed the most likely of the assignments to be confirmed.[65] In the case of $Fe(CO)_5$ an analogous comparison confirmed the trigonal bipyramidal structure and eliminated the square pyramidal one from consideration[66] (when combined with other evidence).

ENTROPY CYCLES

The use of an entropy cycle may be seen in the work of Fyfe[67] who used this method to evaluate the entropy change which occurs when a coordinated

[62] G. N. Lewis and M. Randall, *Thermodynamics* revised by K. S. Pitzer and L. Brewer, McGraw-Hill, Inc., New York, 2nd ed. (1961), p. 57.

[63] R. G. S. Morfee, L. A. K. Staveley, S. T. Walters, and D. L. Wigley, *Phys. and Chem. of Solids* **13**, 132 (1960).

[64] J. W. Edwards, G. L. Kington, and R. Mason, *Trans. Farad. Soc.* **56**, 660 (1960).

[65] R. R. Monchamp and F. A. Cotton, *J. Chem. Soc.*, 1438 (1960).

[66] A. J. Leadbetter and J. E. Spice, *Can. J. Chem.* **37**, 1923 (1959).

[67] W. S. Fyfe, *J. Chem. Soc.*, 2023 (1952).

ammonia is replaced by a coordinated water. Such an entropy cycle is as follows:

$$[M(H_2O)_m]_g^{Z+} + n(NH_3)_g \xrightarrow{\Delta S_2} [M(NH_3)_n]_g^{Z+} + m(H_2O)_g$$

$$(\Delta S_{1a}) \quad \uparrow \Delta S_1(\Delta S_{1b}) \quad (\Delta S_{3a}) \quad \uparrow \Delta S_3(\Delta S_{3b})$$

$$[M(H_2O)_m]_{aq}^{Z+} + n(NH_3)_{aq} \xleftarrow{\Delta S_4} [M(NH_3)_n]_{aq}^{Z+} + m(H_2O)_{aq}$$

Here

$\Delta S_1 = \Delta S$ of hydration of the gaseous ion $+ (-\Delta S)$ of hydration of gaseous ammonia

$\Delta S_2 = $ entropy of ammination in the gaseous phase

$\Delta S_3 = \Delta S$ of hydration of the complex ion plus entropy of condensation of water

$\Delta S_4 = -\Delta S$ of ligand exchange measured in the liquid phase

and

$$\Delta S_1 + \Delta S_2 + \Delta S_3 + \Delta S_4 = 0$$

To get ΔS_4 it was assumed that ΔS_{1a} and ΔS_{3a} were equal and cancelled each other out. ΔS_{1b} was calculated from experimental data and found to be -20 Kcals/mole/deg while ΔS_{3b} is -29 Kcals/mole and ΔS_2 is calculated by assuming that the general translational degrees of freedom of the complex ions remain unchanged and that the entropy changes are restricted to loss of degrees of freedom by the ammonia and a gain of these by water. From the entropies of gaseous and solid water, ΔS_2 may be shown to be equal to $36\,m - 30\,n$. Here it is assumed that the entropies of the coordinated ligands are equal to those of the ligand in the solid state. Thus, for the Cu(II) ion $n = m = 4$

and

$$\Delta S_4 = -\Delta S_1 - \Delta S_2 - \Delta S_3$$
$$\Delta S_4 = -80 - 24 + 116 = 12$$

The measured entropy change is 16 e.u. The original paper should be consulted for further details.

ESTIMATION OF IONIC ENTROPIES IN SOLUTION[68,69,70]

The problem of estimating entropies of ions may be approached in two ways. In the first and most commonly used way an empirical relation of

[68] K. B. Yatsimirsky, *Thermochemie von Komplexverbindungen*, Akademie Verlag, Berlin (1956), Ch. IV.

[69] W. M. Latimer, *The Oxidation States of the Elements and Their Potentials in Aqueous Solution*, Prentice-Hall, Inc., Englewood Cliffs, N.J., 2nd ed. (1952), p. 359 ff.

[70] K. J. Laidler, *Can. J. Chem.* **34**, 1107 (1956).

some sort is established using compounds of known entropies. The second way is to attempt to find the theoretical basis for variations in ionic entropies and this is best illustrated in the work of Laidler.

ENTROPIES OF SOLIDS. Most of the methods for estimating the entropies of solids are descended from an equation proposed by Latimer in 1921.[71] This represented the contribution of each of the species by a term:

$$S^\circ_{298} = 2/3R \ln(\text{atomic weight}) - 0.94$$

Latimer subsequently developed a method of estimating the entropies of solid ionic compounds by assigning constant values to the entropy of each cation and values for each anion which varied with the charge on the cation associated with it.[69]

IONIC ENTROPIES IN SOLUTION. There are a number of systems which have been proposed for the estimation of ionic entropies in solution. Hopefully, these should also apply to complex ions when they are of sufficient generality. Unfortunately the data on complex systems is quite scattered and generally incomplete. An equation proposed for monatomic ions in aqueous solution[72] by Powell and Latimer is:

$$S^\circ_{298} = 3/2R \ln(\text{atomic weight}) - \frac{270Z}{(r + x)^2} + 37.$$

Here Z is the numerical value of the charge on the ion, r is the crystal radius for the ion, and x is 2.00 for positive ions and 1.00 for negative ions. For complex ions there are several suggested equations in the literature. Before looking at these it is worth noting the general features of such expressions. They all must reflect the following empirical information: the entropy of complex ions always: (a) increases with the formula weight other factors being equal, (b) decreases as the ionic charge increases, and (c) increases as the ionic radius increases. Thus, while the method of arriving at such expressions may vary, they are generally of the form:

$$S^\circ_{298} = (3/2) R \ln (\text{formula weight}) - \frac{(\text{ionic charge factor})}{(\text{ionic radius factor})} + \text{constant}$$

An extensive study of the empirical correlations of the entropies of many species of interest in coordination chemistry has been presented by Cobble.[73] For oxyanions, the equation developed is:

$$\bar{S}^\circ - 3/2 \ln M = a - b\left(\frac{Z}{P}\right)$$

$\bar{S}^\circ$ is the partial motal entropy based on $\bar{S}^\circ_{(H+)} = 0$

M is the ionic mass

[71] W. M. Latimer, *J. Amer. Chem. Soc.* **43**, 818 (1921).
[72] R. Powell and W. M. Latimer, *J. Chem. Phys.* **19**, 1139 (1951).
[73] J. W. Cobble, *J. Chem. Phys.* **21**, 1443, 1446, 1451 (1953).

a is a general constant, 66
b is a general constant, 81
Z is the absolute integral charge of the ion
P is an effective ionic radius in angstroms defined as $P = r_{12}/f$ where r_{12} is the interionic distance in the crystal and *f* is a function of the ionic structure for which values corresponding to different structures are tabulated by Cobble.

In correlating the entropies of complex ions in general, Cobble suggests the relation:

$$\bar{S}' = 49 - 99\,(Z/r_{12})$$

where $\bar{S}'$ is a corrected entropy defined by:

$$\bar{S}' = \bar{S} - n\,S^{\circ}_{(H_2O)}$$

where $\bar{S}$ is the normal entropy of the ion and *n* is the number of water molecules replaced by the coordinating agent. For neutral species the equation becomes:

$$\bar{S} = 132 - 354/r_{12}$$

In the last paper in this series Cobble suggests methods for estimating the entropies of complicated organic ligands and species containing chelate rings.

A rather different approach to the correlation and estimation of ionic entropies has been presented by Laidler and his co-workers.[74,75] Taking an electrostatic model due to Born as their starting point, the entropies are shown to vary as Z^2/r rather than Z/r. The empirical equation proposed for simple ions is:

$$\bar{S}^{\circ}_{abs} = 3/2R \ln(\text{atomic weight}) + 10.2 - 11.6\,Z^2/r_u$$

Here *Z* is the charge on the ion and r_u is the univalent radius as defined by Pauling.[76] It is important to note that this equation is based upon a value of -5.5 e.u. for the absolute entropy of the proton rather than the customary value of 0.0 e.u.

In the second paper in this series, it is shown how an analogous equation can be used to estimate the entropies of oxyanions. This equation is:

$$\bar{S}^{\circ}_{abs} = 40.2 + 3/2R \ln M - \frac{27.2\,Z^2}{nr}$$

where *M* is the formula weight of the ion, *Z* is its charge, *n* is the number of charge bearing ligands and $r = r_{12} + 1.40$, where r_{12} is the interatomic distance between the central ion and the oxygen and 1.40 is the van der Waals radius of oxygen.

[74] K. J. Laidler, *Can. J. Chem.* **34**, 1107 (1956).

[75] A. M. Couture and K. J. Laidler, *ibid.*, **35**, 202 (1957).

[76] L. Pauling, *The Nature of the Chemical Bond*, Cornell University Press, Ithaca, New York, 3rd ed. (1960), p. 511 ff.

It is of interest to note that while the heats of solution and the corresponding entropies of solution for monatomic ions in water can be calculated from a reasonable electrostatic model,[77] the same methods give reasonable values for methanol solutions only for the heats of solution.[78] The entropy of solution in non-aqueous solvents apparently includes a reasonable contribution from the reorganization of nonadjacent layers of solvent molecules.

The study of the thermodynamic properties of complex compounds is as yet in its infancy. It is highly probable that many of the correlation methods already in use to estimate the thermodynamic properties of organic compounds[79] can be extended to coordination compounds. In addition to the examples cited above, Table 12.2 contains further work of interest in this field.

[77] D. D. Eley and M. G. Evans, *Trans. Farad. Soc.* **34**, 1093 (1938).
[78] D. D. Eley and D. C. Pepper, *Trans. Farad. Soc.* **37**, 581 (1941).
[79] G. Janz *Estimation of Thermodynamic Properties of Organic Compounds*, Academic Press, Inc., New York (1958).

TABLE 12.2

SOME ADDITIONAL THERMODYNAMIC STUDIES

Nature	Literature
1. Reaction of en complexes of Cd and Ni with HCl	80
2. Heats of solution of uranyl nitrate in water and the calculation of the binding energy of water and other ligands	81
3. The same in diethyl ether and dibutyl ether	82
4. The heat of formation of KBF_4	83
5. $[Co(H_2O)_6]^{+3} + Br^- \rightleftharpoons [Co(H_2O)_5Br]^{+2} + H_2O$	84
6. Heats of combustion of some cobalt(III) ammine azides	85
7. Heats of solvation of some 8-hydroxyquinoline complexes	86
8. Heats of formation of dimesitylenechromium and dipsuedocumenechromium	87
9. Heat of formation of $(NH_4)_2PtCl_6$	88
10. Heats of formation and heat capacities of tetramines and triammines of bivalent platinum	89
11. Magnetic and thermodynamic properties of $K_3Fe(CN)_6$ at low temperatures	90
12. ΔF, ΔH, and ΔS for some Co(III) ammine reactions	91
13. Thermodynamic study of the role of complex formation in the Friedel-Crafts reaction	92
14. Heats of chelation of some copper(II) complexes	93
15. $Ag(NH_3)_2^+$	94
16. Coordinate bond energies for Group III Elements	95
17. Heat of combustion of $Mn_2(CO)_{10}$	96
18. Heats of combustion and bond energies of some inner complexes	55

[80] K. B. Yatsimirsky and A. A. Astasheva, *J. Gen. Chem.* (U.S.S.R.) **20**, 2139 (1950).

[81] L. I. Katzin, D. M. Simon, and R. Ferraro, *J. Amer. Chem. Soc.* **74**, 1191 (1952); L. I. Katsin and J. R. Ferraro, *J. Amer. Chem. Soc.* **74**, 6040 (1952).

[82] V. M. Vdovenko and I. G. Suglobova, *Zhur Neorg. Khim.* **3**, No. 7, 1573 (1958).

[83] J. L. Bills and F. A. Cotton, *J. Phys. Chem.* **64**, 1477 (1960).

[84] J. H. Espenson and E. L. King, *J. Phys. Chem.* **64**, 380 (1960).

[85] T. M. Donovan, C. H. Shomate, and T. B. Joyner, *J. Phys. Chem.* **64**, 378 (1960).

[86] J. H. van Tassel and W. W. Wendlandt, *J. Amer. Chem. Soc.* **81**, 813 (1959); **82**, 4821 (1960).

[87] E. O. Fischer, S. Schreiner, and A. Reckziegel, *Chem. Ber.* **94**, 258 (1961).

[88] A. A. Shidlovskii and K. V. Valkina, *Zhur. Fiz. Khim.* **35**, 294 (1961), C.A. 55: 13033.

[89] I. I. Chernyaev, V. A. Palkin, and R. A. Baranova, *Zhur. Neorg. Khim.* **5**, 821 (1960), C.A. 56: 73.

[90] L. V. Gregor and J. J. Fritz, *J. Amer. Chem. Soc.* **83**, 2832 (1961).

[91] R. G. Yalman and A. B. Lamb, *J. Amer. Chem. Soc.* **75**, 1521 (1953).

[92] H. Campbell and D. D. Eley, *Nature* **154**, 85 (1944).

[93] G. T. Morgan, S. R. Carter, and W. F. Harrison, *J. Chem. Soc.* **127**, 1917 (1925); *ibid.*, 2027 (1926).

[94] R. L. Graham and L. G. Hepler, *J. Amer. Chem. Soc.* **80**, 3538 (1958).

[95] N. N. Greenwood and P. G. Perkins, *Pure and Applied Chem.* **2**, Nos. 1–2, 55 (1961) and the literature cited therein.

[96] W. D. Good and D. W. Scott, *Pure and Applied Chem.* **2**, 77 (1961).

EXERCISES

1. M. Mori and R. Tsuchiya[96] made measurements of the dissociation pressure of hexamminecobalt(III) chloride over the range of temperature from 83° C to 176° C. The reaction which occurs in this system is

$$[Co(NH_3)_6]Cl_{3(s)} \rightarrow [Co(NH_3)_5Cl]Cl_{2(s)} + NH_{3(g)}$$

From the following data determine ΔH, ΔF°_{298}, and ΔS°_{298} for this reaction:

$T°C$	83	102	124	143	153	168
$p(mm, Hg)$	0.70	1.45	2.89	5.33	6.98	10.33

2. Draw up a Born-Haber cycle for $Co(NH_3)_6Br_3$ of the type used by Cotton.[50]

3. Estimate the entropies of the following complex species:

Species	$SnBr_2$	$Co(NH_3)_6^{+3}$	$PdCl_4^=$	$AgCl_2^-$
Radius	2.98			
Charge	0		(To be estimated)	

4. The following heats of solution were measured by Hieber and Muhlbauer.[97] Using them, determine the heat of reaction at 0° for the formation in solution of the complexes $[Co(en)_3]Cl_2$ and $Co(Py)_4Br_2$.

$[Co(en)_3]Cl_2 + .1N\,HCl \rightarrow Co^{+2} + 2Cl^- + 3en \cdot HCl$(all in .1$N$HCl)
  $\Delta H = 39.20$ Kcals/mole

$CoCl_2 + .1N\,HCl$ (containing $\rightarrow Co^{+2} + 2Cl^- + .1N$HCl (containing 3en·HCl per Co)
    3en·HCl per Co) $\Delta H = -16.30$ Kcals/mole

3 en + .1N HCl (containing $\rightarrow$ 3 en·HCl + .1N HCl (containing 1 Co/3 en)
    1 Co/3 en) $\Delta H = -87.32$ Kcals

$Co(pyridine)_4Br_2 + .1N\,HCl \rightarrow Co^{+2} + 2Br^- + 4Pyridine \cdot HCl$ in .1N HCl
  $\Delta H = -12.70$ Kcals/mole

$CoBr_2 + .1N\,HCl$ (containing $\rightarrow Co^{+2} + 2Br^-$ in .1N HCl (containing 4Pyridine per Co)
    4Pyridine per Co) $\Delta H = -17.08$ Kcals/mole

4Pyridine + .1N HCl (containing $\rightarrow$ 4Pyridine·HCl in.1N HCl (containing 1 $CoBr_2$ per
    1 $CoBr_2$ per 4Pyridine)   4Pyridine)
  $\Delta H = -32.37$ Kcals

5. Using Kapustinskii's equation, estimate the lattice energy of $[Rh(en)_3]I_3$ taking 2.50 A as the radius of the $[Rh(en)_3]^{+3}$ ion and that of the iodide ion as 2.17 A.

[96] M. Mori and R. Tsuchiya, *Bull. Chem. Soc. Japan* **32**, 467(1959).
[97] W. Hieber and F. Muhlbauer, *Zeit. anorg. u. allgem. Chem.* **186**, 110 (1929).

Index